COMPANION TO

HUMAN

EVOLUTION

First Edition

Edited by Sally McBrearty
University of Connecticut

cognella®
academic publishing

Bassim Hamadeh, CEO and Publisher
Michael Simpson, Vice President of Acquisitions
Jamie Giganti, Managing Editor
Jess Busch, Graphic Design Supervisor
John Remington, Acquisitions Editor
Brian Fahey, Licensing Associate
Sean Adams, Interior Designer

First published in the United States of America in 2014 by Cognella, Inc.

Printed in the United States of America

ISBN: 978-1-62661-036-1 (pbk)/ 978-1-62661-037-8 (br)

www.cognella.com   800-200-3908

Contents

SECTION III: EARLIEST HOMININS

SECTION IV: *AUSTRALOPITHECUS AFARENSIS*

SECTION V: EVOLUTION OF AUSTRALOPITHECINES

SECTION VI: EARLY HOMO AND HOMO ERECTUS

SECTION VII: NEANDERTHALS

SECTION VIII: EARLY HOMO SAPIENS

SECTION I

INTRODUCTION AND METHODS

The study of human evolution, sometimes called paleoanthropology or human palaeontology, lies at the intersection of the life, physical, and social sciences, notably anthropology, biology, and geology. This section reviews some of the theoretical background to the processes of human evolution, its context, and techniques that enable us to recover evidence for it.

The concept of adaptation, the idea that differential reproduction results in organisms having a good fit to their environment, is central to the understanding of human evolution. The assumption that hominins were well adapted to their environment allows us to infer their diet and habits from their fossil remains. Distinguishing the characters of ancient hominins that reflect their adaptation from those that are the product of their evolutionary history is a major challenge to the study of human evolution.

1. Adaptation

By Richard C. Lewontin

The manifest fit between organisms and their environment is a major outcome of evolution. Yet natural selection does not lead inevitably to adaptation; indeed, it is sometimes hard to define an adaptation

The theory about the history of life that is now generally accepted, the Darwinian theory of evolution by natural selection, is meant to explain two different aspects of the appearance of the living world: diversity and fitness. There are on the order of two million species now living, and since at least 99.9 percent of the species that have ever lived are now extinct, the most conservative guess would be that two billion species have made their appearance on the earth since the beginning of the Cambrian period 600 million years ago. Where did they all come from? By the time Darwin published *On the Origin of Species* in 1859 it was widely (if not universally) held that species had evolved from one another, but no plausible mechanism for such evolution had been proposed. Darwin's solution to the problem was that small heritable variations among individuals within a species become the basis of large differences between species. Different forms survive and reproduce at different rates depending on their environment, and such differential reproduction results in the slow change of a population over a period of time and the eventual replacement of one

Richard C. Lewontin, "Adaptation," *Scientific American*, vol. 239, no. 3, pp. 213–218, 220, 222, 225, 228, 230. Copyright © 1978 by Scientific American. Reprinted with permission.

common form by another. Different populations of the same species then diverge from one another if they occupy different habitats, and eventually they may become distinct species.

Life forms are more than simply multiple and diverse, however. Organisms fit remarkably well into the external world in which they live. They have morphologies, physiologies and behaviors that appear to have been carefully and artfully designed to enable each organism to appropriate the world around it for its own life.

It was the marvelous fit of organisms to the environment, much more than the great diversity of forms, that was the chief evidence of a Supreme Designer. Darwin realized that if a naturalistic theory of evolution was to be successful, it would have to explain the apparent perfection of organisms and not simply their variation. At the very beginning of the *Origin of Species* he wrote: "In considering the Origin of Species, it is quite conceivable that a naturalist … might come to the conclusion that each species … had descended, like varieties, from other species. Nevertheless, such a conclusion, even if well founded, would be unsatisfactory, until it could be shown how the innumerable species inhabiting this world have been modified, so as to acquire that perfection of structure and coadaptation which most justly excites our admiration." Moreover, Darwin knew that "organs of extreme perfection and complication" were a critical test case for his theory, and he took them up in a section of the chapter on "Difficulties of the Theory." He wrote: "To suppose that the eye, with all its inimitable contrivances for adjusting the focus to different distances, for admitting different amounts of light, and for the correction of spherical and chromatic aberration, could have been formed by natural selection, seems, I freely confess, absurd in the highest degree."

These "organs of extreme perfection" were only the most extreme case of a more general phenomenon: adaptation. Darwin's theory of evolution by natural selection was meant to solve both the problem of the origin of diversity and the problem of the origin of adaptation at one stroke. Perfect organs were a difficulty of the theory not in that natural selection could not account for them but rather in that they were its most rigorous test, since on the face of it they seemed the best intuitive demonstration that a divine artificer was at work.

The modern view of adaptation is that the external world sets certain "problems" that organisms need to "solve," and that evolution by means of natural selection is the mechanism for creating these solutions. Adaptation is the process of evolutionary change by which the organism provides a better and better "solution" to the "problem," and the end result is the state of being adapted. In the course of the evolution of birds from reptiles there was a successive alteration of the bones, the muscles and the skin of the forelimb to give rise to a wing; an increase in the size of the breastbone to provide an anchor for the wing muscles; a general restructuring of bones to make them very light but strong, and the development of feathers to provide both aerodynamic elements and lightweight insulation. This wholesale reconstruction of a reptile to make a bird is considered a process of major adaptation by which birds solved the problem of flight. Yet there is no end to adaptation. Having adapted to flight, some birds reversed the process: the penguins adapted to marine life by

Adaptation is exemplified by "industrial melanism" in the peppered moth (*Bistort betularid*). Air pollution kills the lichens that would normally colonize the bark of tree trunks. On the dark, lichenless bark of an oak tree near Liverpool in England the melanic (*black*) form is better adapted: it is better camouflaged against predation by birds than the light, peppered wild type (*top photograph on opposite page*), which it largely replaced through natural selection in industrial areas of England in the late 19th century. Now air quality is improving. On a nearby beech tree colonized by algae and the lichen *Lecanora conizaeoides*, which is itself particularly well adapted to low levels of pollution, the two forms of the moth are equally conspicuous (*middle*). On the lichened bark of an oak tree in rural Wales the wild type is almost invisible (*bottom*), and in such areas it predominates. The photographs were made by J. A. Bishop of the University of Liverpool and Laurence M. Cook of the University of Manchester.

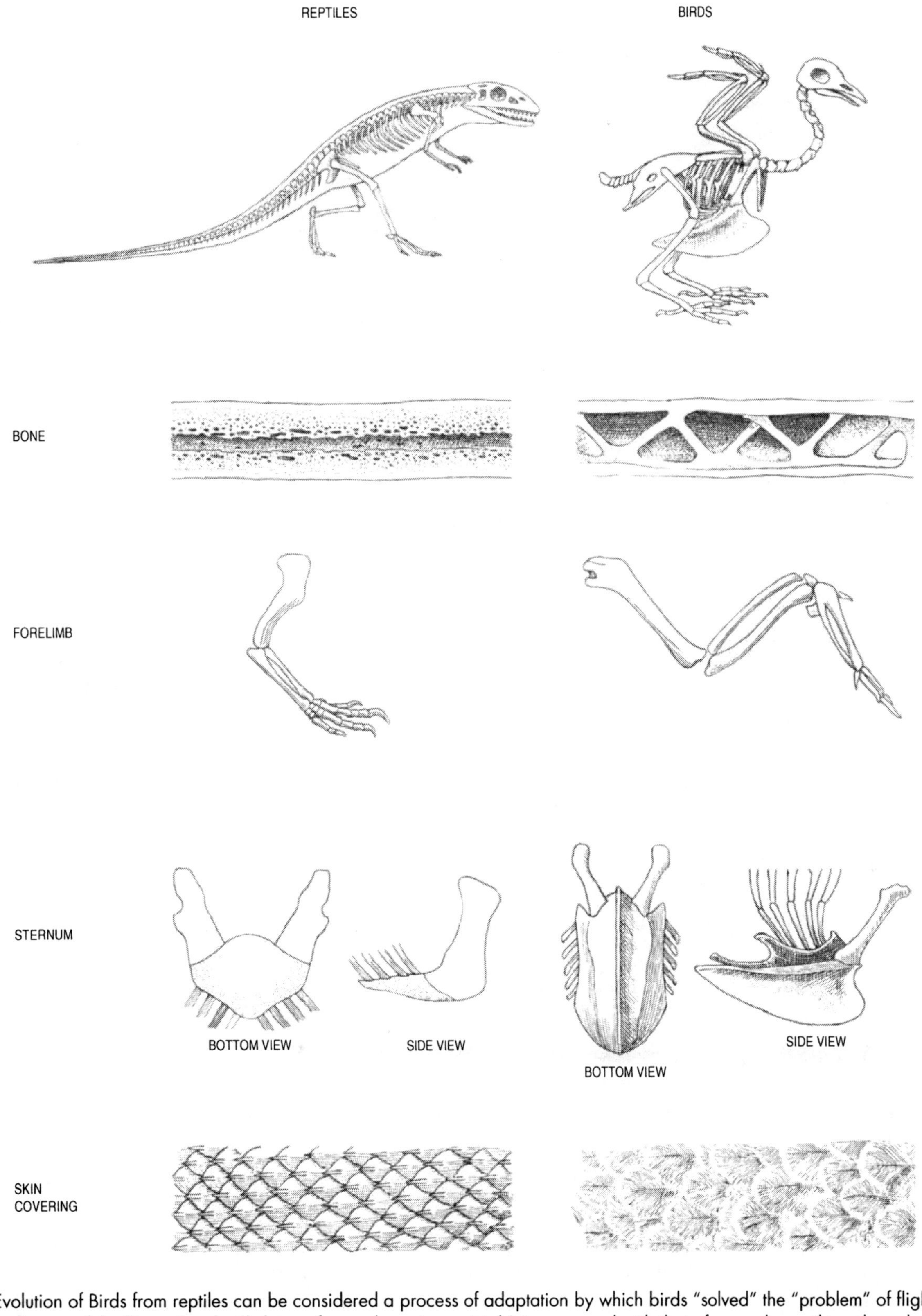

REPTILES   BIRDS

BONE

FORELIMB

STERNUM

BOTTOM VIEW   SIDE VIEW   SIDE VIEW

BOTTOM VIEW

SKIN
COVERING

Evolution of Birds from reptiles can be considered a process of adaptation by which birds "solved" the "problem" of flight. At the top of the illustration the skeleton of a modern pigeon (*right*) *is* compared with that of an early reptile: a thecodont, a Triassic ancestor of dinosaurs and birds. Various reptile features were modified to become structures specialized for flight. Heavy, dense bone was restructured to become lighter but strong; the forelimb was lengthened (and its muscles and skin covering were changed) to become a wing; the reptilian sternum, or breastbone, was enlarged and deepened to anchor the wing muscles (even in *Archaeopteryx,* the Jurassic transition form between reptiles and birds whose sternum *is* pictured here, the sternum was small and shallow); scales developed into feathers.

changing their wings into flippers and their feathers into a waterproof covering. thus solving the problem of aquatic existence.

The concept of adaptation implies a preexisting world that poses a problem to which an adaptation is the solution. A key is adapted to a lock by cutting and filing it; an electrical appliance is adapted to a different voltage by a transformer. Although the physical world certainly predated the biological one, there are certain grave difficulties for evolutionary theory in defining that world for the process of adaptation. It is the difficulty of defining the "ecological niche." The ecological niche is a multidimensional description of the total environment and way of life of an organism.

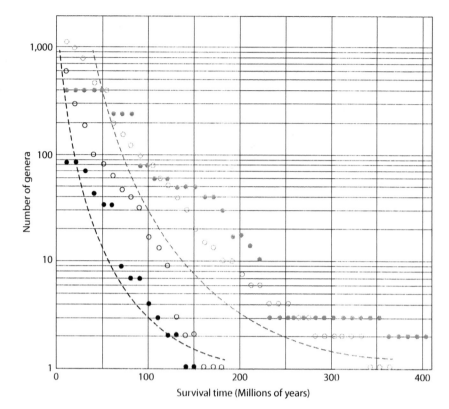

Extinction rates in many evolutionary lines suggest that natural selection does not necessarily improve adaptation. The data, from Leigh Van Valen of the University of Chicago, show the duration of survival of a number of living (*solid dots*) and extinct (*open circles*) genera of Echinoidea (*black*) and Pelecypoda (*color*), two classes of marine invertebrates. If natural selection truly fitted organisms to environments, the points should fall along concave curves (*broken-line curves*) indicating a lower probability of extinction for long-lived genera. Actually, points fall along rather straight lines, indicating constant rate of extinction for each group.

Its description includes physical factors, such as temperature and moisture; biological factors, such as the nature and quantity of food sources and of predators, and factors of the behavior of the organism itself, such as its social organization, its pattern of movement and its daily and seasonal activity cycles.

The first difficulty is that if evolution is described as the process of adaptation of organisms to niches, then the niches must exist before the species that are to fit them. That is, there must be empty niches waiting to be filled by the evolution of new species. In the absence of organisms in actual relation to the environment, however, there is an infinity of ways the world can be broken up into arbitrary niches. It is trivially easy to describe "niches" that are unoccupied. For example, no organism makes a living by laying eggs, crawling along the surface of the ground, eating grass and living for several years. That is, there are no grass-eating snakes, even though snakes live in the grass. Nor are there any warm-blooded, egg-laying animals that eat the mature leaves of trees, even though birds inhabit trees. Given any description of an ecological niche occupied by an actual organism, one can create an infinity of descriptions of unoccupied niches simply by adding another arbitrary specification. Unless there is some preferred or natural way to subdivide the world into niches the concept loses all predictive and explanatory value.

A second difficulty with the specification of empty niches to which organisms adapt is that it leaves out of account the role of the organism itself in creating the niche. Organisms do not experience environments passively; they create and define the environment in which they live. Trees remake the soil in which they grow by dropping leaves and putting down roots. Grazing animals change the species composition of herbs on which they feed by cropping, by dropping manure and by physically disturbing the ground. There is a constant interplay of the organism and the environment, so that although natural selection may be adapting the organism to a particular set of environmental circumstances, the evolution of the organism itself changes those circumstances. Finally, organisms themselves determine which external factors will be part of their niche by their own activities. By building a nest the phoebe makes the availability of dried grass an important part of its niche, at the same time making the nest itself a component of the niche.

If ecological niches can be specified only by the organisms that occupy them. evolution cannot be described as a process of adaptation because all organisms are already adapted. Then what is happening in evolution? One solution to this paradox is the Red Queen hypothesis, named by Leigh Van Valen of the University of Chicago for the character in *Through the Looking Glass* who had to keep running just to stay in the same place. Van Valen's theory is that the environment is constantly decaying with respect to existing organisms, so that natural selection operates essentially to enable the organisms to maintain their state of adaptation rather than to improve it. Evidence for the Red Queen hypothesis comes from an examination of extinction rates in a large number of evolutionary lines. If natural selection were actually improving the fit of organisms to their environments, then we might expect the probability that a species will become extinct in the next time period to be less for species that have already been in existence for a long time, since the long-lived species are presumably the ones that have been improved by natural selection. The data show, however, that the probability of extinction of a species appears to be a constant, characteristic of the group to which it belongs but independent of whether the species has been in existence for a long time or a short one. In other words, natural selection over the long run does not seem to improve a species' chance of survival but simply enables it to "track," or keep up with, the constantly changing environment.

The Red Queen hypothesis also accounts for extinction (and for the occasional dramatic increases in the abundance and range of species). For a species to remain in existence in the face of a constantly changing environment it must have sufficient heritable variation of the right kind to change adaptively. For example, as a region becomes drier because of progressive changes in rainfall patterns, plants may respond by evolving a deeper root system or a thicker cuticle on the leaves, but only if their gene pool contains genetic variation for root length or cuticle thickness, and successfully only if there is enough genetic variation so that the species can change as fast as the environment. If the genetic variation is inadequate, the species will become extinct. The genetic resources of a species are finite, and eventually the environment will change so rapidly that the species is sure to become extinct.

The theory of environmental tracking seems at first to solve the problem of adaptation and the ecological niche. Whereas in a barren world there is no clear way to divide the environment into preexisting niches, in a world already occupied by many organisms the terms of the problem change. Niches are already defined by organisms. Small changes in the environment mean small changes in the conditions of life of those organisms, so that the new niches to which they must evolve are in a sense very close to the old ones in the multidimensional niche space. Moreover, the organisms that will occupy these slightly changed niches must themselves come from the previously existing niches, so that the kinds of species that can evolve are stringently limited to ones that are extremely similar to their immediate ancestors. This in turn guarantees that the changes induced in the environment by the changed organism will also be small and continuous in niche space. The picture of adaptation that emerges is the very slow movement of the niche through niche space, accompanied by a slowly changing species, always slightly behind, slightly ill-adapted, eventually becoming extinct as it fails to keep up with the changing environment because it runs out of genetic variation on which natural selection can operate. In this view species form when two populations of the same species track environments that diverge from each other over a period of time.

The problem with the theory of environmental tracking is that it does not predict or explain what is most dramatic in evolution: the immense diversification of organisms that has accompanied, for example, the occupation of the land from the water or of the air from the land. Why did warm-blooded animals arise at a time when cold-blooded animals were still plentiful and come to coexist with them? The appearance of entirely new life forms, of ways of making a living, is equivalent to the occupation of a previously barren world and brings us back to the preexistent empty niche waiting to be filled. Clearly there have been in the past ways of making a living that were unexploited and were then "discovered" or "created" by existing organisms. There is no way to explain and predict such evolutionary adaptations unless a priori niches can be described on the basis of some physical principles before organisms come to occupy them.

That is not easy to do, as is indicated by an experiment in just such a priori predictions that has been carried out by probes to Mars and Venus designed to detect life. The instruments are designed to detect life by detecting growth in nutrient solutions, and the solutions are prepared in accordance with knowledge of terrestrial microorganisms, so that the probes will detect only organisms whose ecological niches are like those on the earth. If Martian and Venusian life partition the environment in totally unexpected ways, they will remain unrecorded. What the designers of those instruments never dreamed of was that the reverse might happen: that the nature of the physical environment on Mars might be such that when it was provided with a terrestrial ecological niche, inorganic reactions might have a lifelike appearance. Yet that may be exactly what happened. When the Martian soil was dropped into the nutrient broth on the lander, there was a rapid production of carbon dioxide and then—nothing. Either an extraordinary kind of life began to grow much more rapidly than any terrestrial microorganism and then was poisoned by its own activity in a strange environment, or else the Martian soil is such that its contact with nutrient broths results

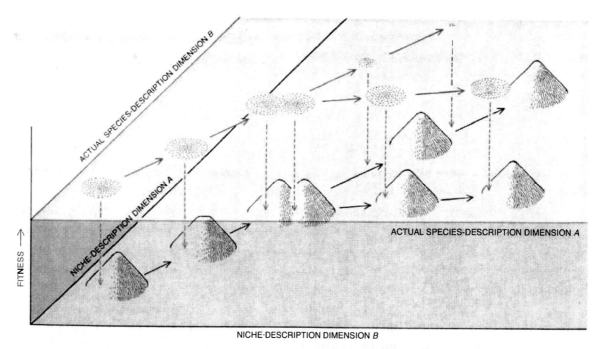

Species track environment through niche space, according to one view of adaptation. The niche, visualized as an "adaptive peak," keeps changing (moving to the right); a slowly changing species population (*colored dots*) just manages to keep up with the niche, always a bit short of the peak. As the environment changes, the single peak becomes two distinct peaks, and two populations diverge to form distinct species. One species cannot keep up with its rapidly changing environment, becomes less fit (lags farther behind changing peak) and extinct. Here niche space and actual-species space have only two dimensions; both of them are actually multidimensional.

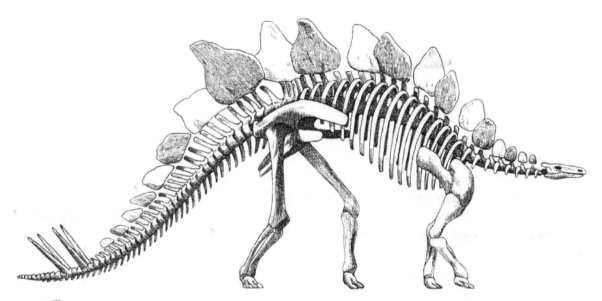

Stegosaurus, a large herbivorous dinosaur of the Jurassic period, had an array of bony plates along its back. Were they solutions to the problem of defense, courtship recognition or heat regulation? An engineering analysis reveals features characteristic of heat regulators: porous structure (suggesting a rich blood supply), particularly large plates over the massive part of the body, staggered arrangement along the midline, a constriction near the base and so on. This skeleton in the American Museum of Natural History is 18 feet long.

in totally unexpected catalytic processes. In either case the Mars life-detection experiment has foundered on the problem of defining ecological niches without organisms.

Much of evolutionary biology is the working out of an adaptationist program. Evolutionary biologists assume that each aspect of an organism's morphology, physiology and behavior has been molded by natural selection as a solution to a problem posed by the environment. The role of the evolutionary biologist is then to construct a plausible argument about how each part functions as an adaptive device. For example, functional anatomists study the structure of animal limbs and analyze their motions by time-lapse photography, comparing the action and the structure of the locomotor apparatus in different animals. Their interest is not, however, merely descriptive. Their work is informed by the adaptationist program, and their aim is to explain particular anatomical features by showing that they are well suited to the function they perform. Evolutionary ethologists and sociobiologists carry the adaptationist program into the realm of animal behavior, providing an adaptive explanation for differences among species in courting pattern, group size, aggressiveness, feeding behavior and so on. In each case they assume, like the functional anatomist, that the behavior is adaptive and that the goal of their analysis is to reveal the particular adaptation.

The dissection of an organism into parts, each of which is regarded as a specific adaptation, requires two sets of a priori decisions. First one must decide on the appropriate way to divide the organism and then one must describe what problem each part solves. This amounts to creating descriptions of the organism and of the environment and then relating the descriptions by functional statements; one can either start with the problems and try to infer which aspect of the organism is the solution or start with the organism and then ascribe adaptive functions to each part.

For example, for individuals of the same species to recognize each other at mating time is a problem, since mistakes about species mean time, energy and gametes wasted in courtship and mating without the production of viable offspring; species traits such as distinctive color markings, special courtship behavior, unique mating calls, odors and restricted time and place of activity can be considered specific adaptations for the proper recognition of potential mates. On the other hand, the large, leaf-shaped bony plates along the back of the dinosaur *Stegosaurus* constitute a specific characteristic for which an adaptive function needs to be inferred. They have been variously explained as solutions to the problem of defense (by making the animal appear to be larger or by interfering directly with the predator's attack), the problem of recognition in courtship and the problem of temperature regulation (by serving as cooling fins).

The same problems that arose in deciding on a proper description of the ecological niche without the organism arise when one tries to describe the organism itself. Is the leg a unit in evolution, so that the adaptive function of the leg can be inferred? If so, what about a part of the leg, say the foot, or a single toe, or one bone of a toe? The evolution of the human chin is an instructive example. Human morphological evolution can be generally described as a "neotenic" progression. That is, human infants and adults resemble the fetal and young forms of apes more than they resemble adult apes; it is as if human beings are born at an earlier stage of physical development than apes and do not mature as far along the apes' development path. For example, the relative proportion of skull size to body size is about the same in newborn apes and human beings, whereas adult apes have much larger bodies in relation to their heads than we do; in effect their bodies "go further."

The exception to the rule of human neoteny is the chin, which grows relatively larger in human beings, whereas both infant and adult apes are chinless. Attempts to explain the human chin as a specific adaptation selected to grow larger failed to be convincing. Finally it was realized that in an evolutionary sense the chin does not exist! There are two growth fields in the lower jaw: the dentary field, which is the bony structure of the jaw, and the alveolar field, in which the teeth are set. Both the dentary and the alveolar fields do show neoteny. They have both become smaller in the human evolutionary line. The alveolar field has shrunk somewhat faster than the dentary one, however, with the result that a "chin" appears as a pure consequence of the relative regression rates of the two growth fields. With the recognition that the chin is a mental construct rather than a unit in evolution the problem of its adaptive explanation disappears. (Of course, we may go on to ask why the dentary and alveolar growth fields have regressed at different rates in evolution, and then provide an adaptive explanation for that phenomenon.)

Sometimes even the correct topology of description is unknown. The brain is divided into anatomical divisions corresponding to certain separable nervous functions that can be localized. but memory is not one of those functions. The memory of specific events seems to be stored diffusely over large regions of the cerebrum rather than being localized microscopically. As one moves from anatomy to behavior the problem of a correct description becomes more acute and the opportunities to introduce arbitrary constructs as if they were evolutionary traits multiply. Animal behavior is described in terms of aggression, division of labor, warfare, dominance, slave-making, cooperation—and yet each of these is a category that is taken directly from human social experience and is transferred to animals.

The decision as to which problem is solved by each trait of an organism is equally difficult. Every trait is involved in a variety of functions. and yet one would not want to say that the character is an adaptation for all of them. The green turtle *Chelonia mydas* is a large marine turtle of the tropical Pacific. Once a year the females drag themselves up the beach with their front flippers to the dry sand above the high-water mark. There they spend many hours laboriously digging a deep hole for their eggs, using their hind flippers as trowels. No one who has watched this painful process would describe the turtles' flippers as adaptations for land locomotion and digging; the animals move on land and dig with their flippers because nothing better is available. Conversely, even if a trait seems clearly adaptive, it cannot be assumed that the species would suffer in its absence. The fur of a polar bear is an adaptation for temperature regulation, and a hairless polar bear would certainly freeze to death. The color of a polar bear's fur is another matter. Although it may be an adaptation for camouflage, it is by no means certain that the polar bear would become extinct or even less numerous if it were brown. Adaptations are not necessary conditions of the existence of the species.

For extinct species the problem of judging the adaptive status of a trait is made more difficult because both the trait and its function must be reconstructed. In principle there is no way to be sure whether the dorsal plates of *Stegosaurus* were heat-regulation devices. a defense mechanism. a sexual recognition sign or all these things. Even in living species where experiments can be carried out a doubt remains. Some modern lizards have a brightly colored dewlap under the jaw. The dewlap may be a warning sign, a sexual attractant or a species-recognition signal. Experiments removing or altering the dewlap could decide, in principle. how

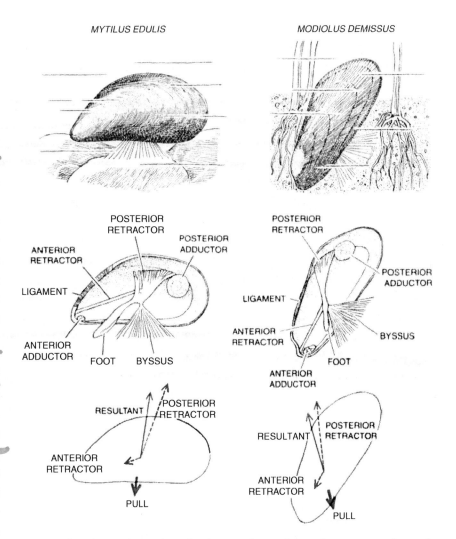

Functional analysis indicates how the shape and musculature of two species of mussels are adapted to their particular environments. Mytilus edulis (left) attaches itself to rocks by means of its byssus, a beardlike group of threads (top). Its ventral, or lower, edge is flattened; the anterior and posterior retractor muscles are positioned (middle) so that their resultant force pulls the bottom of the shell squarely down to the substratum (bottom). Modiolus demissus (right) attaches itself to debris in marshes. Its ventral edge is sharply angled to facilitate penetration of the substratum; its retractor muscles are positioned to pull its anterior end down into the marsh. The analysis was done by Steven M. Stanley of Johns Hopkins University.

it functions. That is a different question from its status as an adaptation, however, since the assertion of adaptation implies a historical argument about natural selection as the cause of its establishment. The large dorsal plates of *Stegosaurus* may have evolved because individuals with slightly larger plates were better able to gather food in the heat of the day than other individuals. If, when the plates reached a certain size. they incidentally frightened off predators, they would be a "preadaptation" for defense. The distinction between the primary adaptation for which a trait evolved and incidental functions it may have come to have cannot be made without the reconstruction of the forces of natural selection during the actual evolution of the species.

The current procedure for judging the adaptation of traits is an engineering analysis of the organism and its environment. The biologist is in the position of an archaeologist who uncovers a machine without any written record and attempts to reconstruct not only its operation but also its purpose. The hypothesis that the dorsal plates of *Stegosaurus* were a heat-regulation device is based on the fact that the plates were porous and probably had a large supply of blood vessels. on their alternate placement to the left and right of the midline (suggesting cooling fins), on their large size over the most massive part of the body and on the constriction near their base, where they are closest to the heat source and would be inefficient heat radiators.

Ideally the engineering analysis can be quantitative as well as qualitative and so provide a more rigorous test of the adaptive hypothesis. Egbert G. Leigh, Jr., of the Smithsonian Tropical Research Institute posed the question of the ideal shape of a sponge on the assumption that feeding efficiency is the problem to be solved. A sponge's food is suspended in water and the organism feeds by passing water along its cell surfaces. Once water is processed by the sponge it should be ejected as far as possible from the organism so that the new water taken in is rich in food particles. By an application of simple hydrodynamic principles Leigh was able to show that the actual shape of sponges is maximally efficient. Of course, sponges differ from one another in the details of their shape, so that a finer adjustment of the argument would be needed to explain the differences among species. Moreover, one cannot be sure that feeding efficiency is the only problem to be solved by shape. If the optimal shape for feeding had turned out to be one with many finely divided branches and protuberances rather than the compact shape observed, it might have been argued that the shape was a compromise between the optimal adaptation for feeding and the greatest resistance to predation by small browsing fishes.

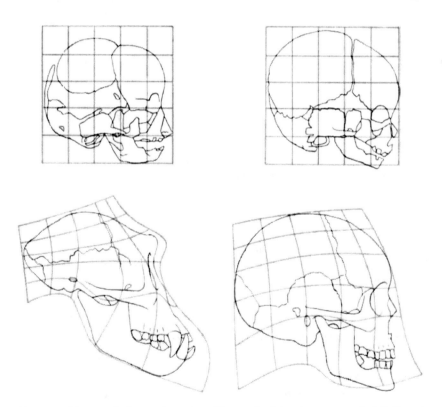

Neoteny of human skull is evident when the growth of the chimpanzee skull (*left*) and of the human skull (*right*) is plotted on transformed coordinates, which show the relative displacement of each part. The chimpanzee and the human skulls are much more similar at the fetal stage (*top*) than they are at the adult stage (*bottom*). The adult human skull also departs less from the fetal form than the adult chimpanzee skull departs from its fetal form, except in the case of the chin, which becomes relatively larger in human beings. The chin is a mental construct, however: the result of allometry, or differential growth, of different parts of human jaw.

Just such a compromise has been suggested for understanding the feeding behavior of some birds. Gordon H. Orians of the University of Washington studied the feeding behavior of birds that fly out from a nest, gather food and bring it back to the nest for consumption ("central-place foraging"). If the bird were to take food items indiscriminately as it came on them, the energy cost of the round trip from the nest and back might be greater than the energy gained from the food. On the other hand, if the bird chose only the largest food items, it might have to search so long that again the energy it consumed would be too great. For any actual distribution of food-particle sizes in nature there is some optimal foraging behavior for the bird that will maximize its net energy gain from feeding. Orians found that birds indeed do not take food particles at random but are biased in the direction of an optimal particle size. They do not, however, choose the optimal solution either. Orians' explanation was that the foraging behavior is a compromise between maximum energy efficiency and not staying away from the nest too long, because the young are exposed to predation when they are unattended.

The example of central-place foraging illustrates a basic assumption of all such engineering analyses, that of ceteris paribus, or all other things being equal. In order to make an argument that a trait is an optimal solution to a particular problem, it must be possible to view the trait and the problem in isolation, all other things being equal. If all other things are not equal, if a change in a trait as a solution to one problem changes the organism's relation to other problems of the environment, it becomes impossible to carry out the analysis part by part, and we are left in the hopeless position of seeing the whole organism as being adapted to the whole environment.

The mechanism by which organisms are said to adapt to the environment is that of natural selection. The theory of evolution by natural selection rests on three necessary principles: Different individuals within a species differ from one another in physiology, morphology and behavior (the principle of variation); the variation is in some way heritable, so that on the average offspring resemble their parents more than they resemble other individuals (the principle of heredity); different variants leave different numbers of offspring either immediately or in remote generations (the principle of natural selection).

These three principles are necessary and sufficient to account for evolutionary change by natural selection. There must be variation to select from; that variation must be heritable, or else there will be no progressive change from generation to generation, since there would be a random distribution of offspring even if some types leave more offspring than others. The three principles say nothing, however, about adaptation. In themselves they simply predict change caused by differential reproductive success without making any prediction about the fit of organisms to an ecological niche or the solution of ecological problems.

Adaptation was introduced by Darwin into evolutionary theory by a fourth principle: Variations that favor an individual's survival in competition with other organisms and in the face of environmental stress tend to increase reproductive success and so tend to be preserved (the principle of the struggle for existence). Darwin made it clear that the struggle for existence, which he derived from Thomas Malthus' *An Essay on the Principle of Population,* included more than the actual competition of two organisms for the same resource in short supply. He wrote: "I should premise that I use the term Struggle for Existence in a large and metaphorical sense.... Two canine animals in a time of dearth, may be truly said to struggle with each other which shall get food and live. But a plant on the edge of the desert is said to struggle for life against the drought."

The diversity that is generated by various mechanisms of reproduction and mutation is in principle random, but the diversity that is observed in the real world is nodal: organisms have a finite number of morphologies, physiologies and behaviors and occupy a finite number of niches. It is natural selection, operating under the pressures of the struggle for existence, that creates the nodes. The nodes are "adaptive peaks," and the species or other form occupying a peak is said to be adapted.

More specifically, the struggle for existence provides a device for predicting which of two organisms will leave more offspring. An engineering analysis can determine which of two forms of zebra can run faster and so can more easily escape predators; that form will leave more offspring. An analysis might predict the eventual evolution of zebra locomotion even in the absence of existing differences among individuals, since a careful engineer might think of small improvements in design that would give a zebra greater speed.

When adaptation is considered to be the result of natural selection under the pressure of the struggle for existence, it is seen to be a relative condition rather than an absolute one. Even though a species may be surviving and numerous, and therefore may be adapted in an absolute sense, a new form may arise that has a greater reproductive rate on the same resources, and it may cause the extinction of the older form. The concept of relative adaptation removes the apparent tautology in the theory of natural selection. Without it the theory of natural selection states that fitter individuals have more offspring and then defines the fitter as being those that leave more offspring; since some individuals will always have more offspring than others by sheer chance, nothing is explained. An analysis in which problems of design are posed and characters are understood as being design solutions breaks through this tautology by predicting in advance which individuals will be fitter.

The relation between adaptation and natural selection does not go both ways. Whereas greater relative adaptation leads to natural selection, natural selection does not necessarily lead to greater adaptation. Let us contrast two evolutionary scenarios. We begin with a resource-limited population of 100 insects of type *A* requiring one unit of food resource per individual. A mutation to a new type *a* arises that doubles the fecundity of its bearers but does absolutely nothing to the efficiency of the utilization of resources. We can calculate what happens to the composition, size and growth rate of the population over a period of time [*see illustration below*]. In a second scenario we again begin with the population of 100 individuals of type *A*, but now there arises a different mutation a, which does nothing to the fecundity of its bearers but doubles their efficiency of resource utilization. Again we can calculate the population history.

In both cases the new type *a* replaces the old type *A*. In the case of the first mutation nothing changes but the fecundity; the adult population size and the growth rate are the same throughout the process and the only effect is that twice as many immature stages are being produced to die before adulthood. In the second

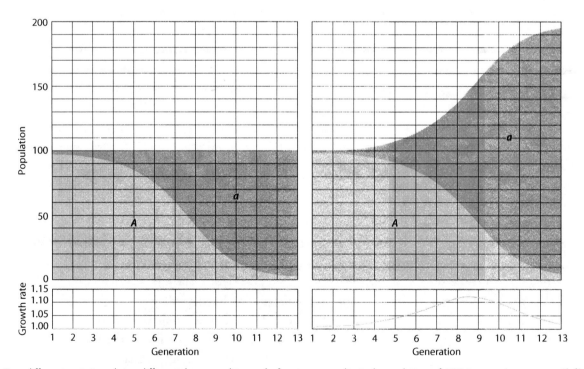

Two different mutations have different demographic results for a resource-limited population of 100 insects. In one case (*left*) a mutation arises that doubles the fecundity of its bearers. The new type (*a*) replaces the old type (*A*), but the total population does not increase: the growth rate (*bottom*) remains 1.00. In the other case

case, on the other hand, the population eventually doubles its adult members as well as its immature members, but not its fecundity. In the course of its evolution the second population has a growth rate greater than 1 for a while but eventually attains a constant size and stops growing.

In which of these populations, if in either, would the individuals be better adapted than those in the old population? Those with higher fecundity would be better buffered against accidents such as sudden changes in temperature since there would be a greater chance that some of their eggs would survive. On the other hand, their offspring would be more susceptible to the epidemic diseases of immature forms and to predators that concentrate on the more numerous immature forms. Individuals in the second population would be better adapted to temporary resource shortages, but also more susceptible to predators or epidemics that attack adults in a density-dependent manner. Hence there is no way we can predict whether a change due to natural selection will increase or decrease the adaptation in general. Nor can we argue that the population as a whole is better off in one case than in another. Neither population continues to grow or is necessarily less subject to extinction, since the larger number of immature or adult stages presents the same risks for the population as a whole as it does for individual families.

Unfortunately the concept of relative adaptation also requires the ceteris paribus assumption, so that in practice it is not easy to predict which of two forms will leave more offspring. A zebra having longer leg bones that enable it to

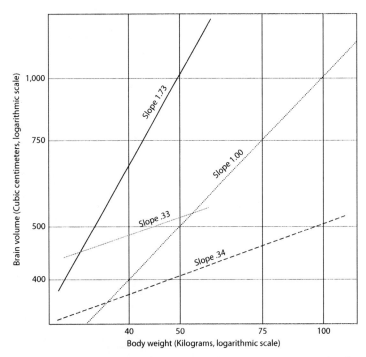

Allometry, or differential growth rates for different parts, is responsible for many evolutionary changes. Allometry is illustrated by this comparison of the ratio of brain size to body weight in a number of species of the pongids, or great apes (*broken black curve*), of *Australopithecus*, an extinct hominid line (*solid black*), and of hominids leading to modern man (*color*). A slope of less than 1.00 means the brain has grown more slowly than the body. The slope of more than 1.00 for the human lineage indicates a clear change in the evolution of brain size.

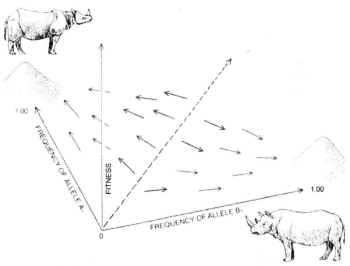

Alternative evolutionary paths may be taken by two species under similar selection pressures. The Indian rhinoceros has one horn and the African rhinoceros has two horns. The horns are adaptations for protection in both cases, but the number of horns does not necessarily constitute a specifically adaptive difference. There are simply two adaptive peaks in a field of gene frequencies, or two solutions to the same problem; some variation in the initial conditions led two rhinoceros populations to respond to similar pressures in different ways. For each of two hypothetical genes there are two alleles: A_1 and A_2, B_1 and B_2. A population of genotype A_1B_2 has one horn and a population of genotype A_2B_1 has two horns.

run faster than other zebras will leave more offspring only if escape from predators is really the problem to be solved, if a slightly greater speed will really decrease the chance of being taken and if longer leg bones do not interfere with some other limiting physiological process. Lions may prey chiefly on old or injured zebras likely in any case to die soon, and it is not even clear that it is speed that limits the ability of lions to catch zebras. Greater speed may cost the zebra something in feeding efficiency, and if food rather than predation is limiting, a net selective disadvantage might result from solving the wrong problem. Finally, a longer bone might break more easily, or require greater developmental resources and metabolic energy to produce and maintain, or change the efficiency of the contraction of the attached muscles. In practice relative-adaptation analysis is a tricky game unless a great deal is known about the total life history of an organism.

Not all evolutionary change can be understood in terms of adaptation. First, some changes will occur directly by natural selection that are not adaptive, as for example the changes in fecundity and feeding efficiency in the hypothetical example I cited above.

Second, many changes occur indirectly as the result of allometry, or differential growth. The rates of growth of different parts of an organism are

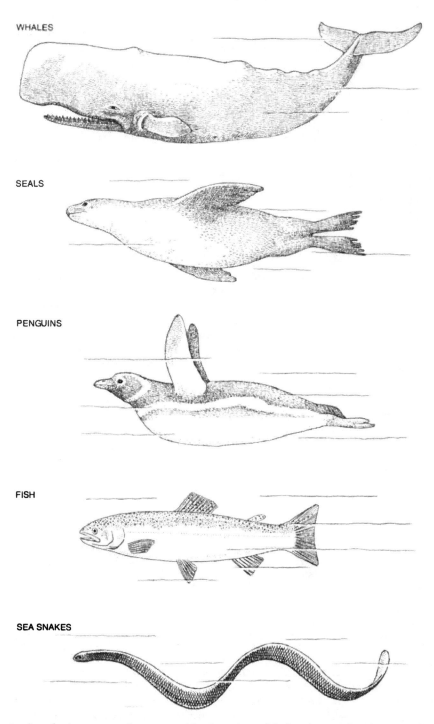

WHALES

SEALS

PENGUINS

FISH

SEA SNAKES

Reality of adaptation is demonstrated by the indisputable fact that unrelated groups of animals do respond to similar selective pressures with similar adaptations. Locomotion in water calls for a particular kind of structure. And the fact is that whales and seals have flippers and flukes, penguins have paddles, fish have fins and sea snakes have a flat cross section.

different, so that large organisms do not have all their parts in the same proportion. This allometry shows up both between individuals of the same species and between species. Among primate species the brain increases in size more slowly than the body; small apes have a proportionately larger brain than large apes. Since the differential growth is constant for all apes, it is useless to seek an adaptive reason for gorillas' having a relatively smaller brain than, say, chimpanzees.

Third, there is the phenomenon of pleiotropy. Changes in a gene have many different effects on the physiology and development of an organism. Natural selection may operate to increase the frequency of the gene because of one of the effects, with pleiotropic, or unrelated, effects being simply carried along. For example, an enzyme that helps to detoxify poisonous substances by converting them into an insoluble pigment will be selected for its detoxification properties. As a result the color of the organism will change, but no adaptive explanation of the color per se is either required or correct.

Fourth, many evolutionary changes may be adaptive and yet the resulting differences among species in the character may not be adaptive; they may simply be alternative solutions to the same problem. The theory of population genetics predicts that if more than one gene influences a character, there may often be several alternative stable equilibriums of genetic composition even when the force of natural selection remains the same. Which of these adaptive peaks in the space of genetic composition is eventually reached by a population depends entirely on chance events at the beginning of the selective process. (An exact analogy is a pinball game. Which hole the ball will fall into under the fixed force of gravitation depends on small variations in the initial conditions as the ball enters the game.) For example, the Indian rhinoceros has one horn and the African rhinoceros has two. Horns are an adaptation for protection against predators, but it is not true that one horn is specifically adaptive under Indian conditions as opposed to two horns on the African plains. Beginning with two somewhat different developmental systems, the two species responded to the same selective forces in slightly different ways.

Finally, many changes in evolution are likely to be purely random. At the present time population geneticists are sharply divided over how much of the evolution of enzymes and other molecules has been in response to natural selection and how much has resulted from the chance accumulation of mutations. It has proved remarkably difficult to get compelling evidence for changes in enzymes brought about by selection, not to speak of evidence for adaptive changes; the weight of evidence at present is that a good deal of amino acid substitution in evolution has been the result of the random fixation of mutations in small populations. Such random fixations may in fact be accelerated by natural selection if the unselected gene is genetically linked with a gene that is undergoing selection. The unselected gene will then be carried to high frequency in the population as a "hitchhiker."

If the adaptationist program is so fraught with difficulties and if there are so many alternative explanations of evolutionary change, why do biologists not abandon the program altogether?

There are two compelling reasons. On the one hand, even if the assertion of universal adaptation is difficult to test because simplifying assumptions and ingenious explanations can almost always result in an ad hoc adaptive explanation, at least in principle some of the assumptions can be tested in some cases. A weaker form of evolutionary explanation that explained some proportion of the cases by adaptation and left the rest to allometry, pleiotropy, random gene fixations, linkage and indirect selection would be utterly impervious to test. It would leave the biologist free to pursue the adaptationist program in the easy cases and leave the difficult ones on the scrap heap of chance. In a sense, then, biologists are forced to the extreme adaptationist program because the alternatives, although they are undoubtedly operative in many cases, are untestable in particular cases.

On the other hand, to abandon the notion of adaptation entirely, to simply observe historical change and describe its mechanisms wholly in terms of the different reproductive success of different types, with no functional explanation, would be to throw out the baby with the bathwater. Adaptation is a real phenomenon. It is no accident that fish have fins, that seals and whales have flippers and flukes, that penguins have paddles and that even sea snakes have become laterally flattened. The problem of locomotion in an aquatic environment is a real problem that has been solved by many totally unrelated evolutionary lines in much the same way. Therefore it must be feasible to make adaptive arguments about swimming appendages. And this in turn means that in nature the ceteris paribus assumption must be workable.

It can only be workable if both the selection between character states and reproductive fitness have two characteristics: continuity and quasi-independence. Continuity means that small changes in a characteristic must result in only small changes in ecological relations; a very slight change in fin shape cannot cause a dramatic change in sexual recognition or make the organism suddenly attractive to new predators. Quasi-independence means that there is a great variety of alternative paths by which a given characteristic may change, so that some of them will allow selection to act on the characteristic without altering other characteristics of the organism in a countervailing fashion; pleiotropic and allometric relations must be changeable. Continuity and quasi-independence are the most fundamental characteristics of the evolutionary process. Without them organisms as we know them could not exist because adaptive evolution would have been impossible.

Knowledge of the order of past events is key to understanding the processes that produced them. Fossils are found preserved in ancient rocks and sediments, and understanding the geology of these rocks and sediments is fundamental to depicting the environmental context of fossils, as well as their age. Methods that rely upon the decay of radioactive isotopes in these rocks and sediments can be used to determine the age of the fossils they contain. For later periods, the study of the decay of the radioactive isotope carbon 14 (^{14}C) in the remains of the animals themselves and in associated organic materials can be used to establish their age.

2. Methods of Dating

By Francis H. Brown

The fossil record of primates begins in the latest Cretaceous period, so primate palaeontologists are interested in techniques of dating applicable over the past 70 million years. Fossil bones themselves are rarely datable with any precision, and these are mainly of late Pleistocene or Holocene age. In general, it is the geological materials with which they are found that are dated. For this reason, dating usually begins with an attempt to order past events, and to relate fossils to rock layers that can themselves be dated. Once this is done, the ages of fossils can be estimated by determining the ages of rocks that lie lower and higher in a stratigraphic section.

During the past 50 years, many techniques for measuring the age of rocks and minerals have been established. These fall into three categories:

- Methods that depend on radioactive decay of one element or another—isotopic methods; for example, radiocarbon, .potassium-argon, fission-track, uranium disequilibrium and thermolurninescence dating
- Methods that depend on slow chemical processes; for example, amino acid racemisation dating

Francis H. Brown, "Methods of Dating," *The Cambridge Encyclopedia of Human Evolution*, ed. Stephen Jones, Robert D. Martin, and David R. Pilbeam, pp. 179–186. Copyright © 1994 by Cambridge University Press. Reprinted with permission.

• Methods that require calibration by radioactive or chemical means, for example, palaeomagnetic polarity stratigraphy, tephrochronology and biochronology

Each technique has its own age range, its own restrictions on materials that are suitable and a need for an event to 'set the clock'—and also an inherent uncertainty in the result.

RADIOCARBON DATING

Radiocarbon or carbon-14 (^{14}C) dating is based on the decay of ^{14}C atoms to nitrogen-14 (^{14}N) by beta-emission. Because the half-life of ^{14}C is only 5730 years, it must be constantly produced or it would no longer be present on earth. This production takes place in the upper atmosphere where ^{14}C is formed from neutron reactions with ^{14}N and other nuclides. Once produced, the ^{14}C is oxidised to carbon dioxide ($^{14}CO_2$), and enters biological systems through various biochemical reactions, and the surface waters of lakes and oceans by diffusion. As a result, living organisms are radioactive, as are the carbonates precipitated from most natural waters. When an organism dies, or when carbonate minerals form, they are removed from this active carbon cycle and the ^{14}C within them begins to decay. By comparing the activity of their ^{14}C with its assumed initial activity, an age can be computed from the ratio of the two numbers.

There are various uncertainties in this estimate, which arise from statistical errors at several stages of the dating process—during the determination of radioactivity, by the contamination of samples by older or younger carbon, and the preferential incorporation by the sample of one isotope over another when carbon is withdrawn from the general environment and enters living material. These sources of error can be dealt with by increasing the period of examination of each sample, dating multiple samples, and measuring the content of the stable carbon isotope ^{13}C to determine the amount of preferential incorporation. Most radiocarbon dates are accompanied by an estimate of the probable error: the plus/minus term (standard deviation) quoted with the date.

Years ago	10^8	10^7	10^6	10^5	10^4	10^3	Datable materials
Fission track							Volcanic minerals, glass, pottery
Potassium-argon ($^{40}K/^{40}Ar$ and $^{39}Ar/^{40}Ar$)							Volcanic minerals and rocks
Rubidium-strontium ($^{87}Rb/^{87}Sr$)							Volcanic minerals and rocks
Uranium disequilibrium ($^{234}U/^{238}U$)							Carbonates (e.g. coral)
Optically stimulated luminescence							Quartz, zircon
Electron spin resonance							Carbonates, silicates, apatite (e.g. tooth enamel)
Uranium disequilibrium ($^{230}Th/^{234}U$)							Inorganic and organic carbonates, volcanic rocks, ?bone, ?tooth dentine
Thermoluminescence							Ceramics, quartz, feldspar, carbonates
Uranium disequilibrium ($^{231}Pa/^{235}U$)							Inorganic and organic carbonates
Radiocarbon (^{14}C)							Organic materials (e.g. bone, shell, charcoal): carbonates

Age ranges over which selected dating methods are applicable, and materials on which they can be used.

Variations in the rate of production of ^{14}C in the past also affect the age estimate, but any uncertainties can be eliminated by calibrating samples against tree rings of known age. Ages are usually expressed in years before present (with the present taken as AD 1950). With careful work, an accuracy of about 2 percent can be achieved.

The use of particle accelerators as sensitive mass spectrometers has made it possible to measure the number of ^{14}C atoms in a sample directly, rather than waiting for their decay. This method has now been applied in radiocarbon dating. Only very small samples (1 mg or less) are needed so the technique can be used to age valuable palaeontological and archaeological material that previously could not be dated by the traditional radiocarbon method. A recent example of this was the dating of the Turin Shroud to the fourteenth century AD. Because such small samples are sufficient for the accelerator mass spectroscopy (AMS) method, a tiny piece of charcoal or a single wheat grain can now be radiocarbon dated.

The AMS technique is proving useful in many other ways. For example, it has done much to refute claims for the presence of humans in the New World 50,000 or 100,000 years ago. Skeletons thought to be very old turn out to date to only a few thousand years ago using this new method.

An application of the radiocarbon method to primate palaeontology has been to date extinct lemurs in Madagascar. Some fossils of extinct species found at Amparihingidro in the

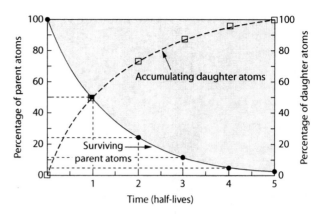

Curves showing the decay of a radioactive parent (P) to a single stable daughter (D). The sum P + D is 100 per cent, whereas the ratio D/P increases from 0 to 1 after one half-life, 3 after two half-lives, and so on.

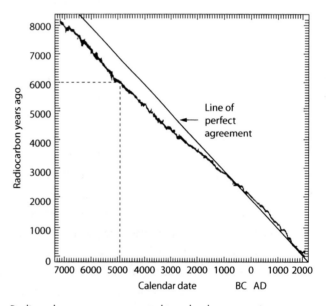

Radiocarbon ages are corrected to calendar ages using a curve established by radiocarbon dating samples of wood that have been given a calendar age by counting tree rings. A radiocarbon age of 6000 years corresponds to a calendar age of 4900 BC.

north-west of the island are only about 3000 years old, and those at Lake Itampola in the south are only about 1000 years old. These forms have therefore disappeared in recent times—since the colonisation of Madagascar by humans.

POTASSIUM-ARGON DATING

The potassium-argon method is used to date volcanic rocks and minerals and is important in primate palaeontology. It depends on the fact that about one part in 10000 of naturally occurring potassium (^{40}K) is radioactive and decays slowly but steadily to the stable isotopes argon (^{40}Ar) and calcium-40 (^{40}Ca).

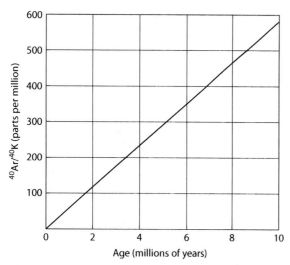

After volcanic material cools, ^{40}Ar accumulates through decay of ^{40}K, changing the ^{40}Ar/^{40}K ratio. Over short times, the change in ratio is nearly linear because of the long half-life of ^{40}K (1250 million years).

In natural samples, the fraction of ^{40}K is constant, but the ^{40}Ar content increases with age. By comparing the amounts of ^{40}K and ^{40}Ar, an age can be computed (the half-life of ^{40}K is 1250 million years). The ^{40}Ar in a sample comes mainly from two sources—the radioactive decay of ^{40}K and the atmosphere. As argon makes up about 0.9 per cent of the earth's atmosphere by volume, a correction must be made for this in order to determine the amount of radiogenic argon in the sample.

Potassium-argon dating is usually applied to minerals separated from hardened volcanic flows (*tuffs*) because they are often interspersed with fossil-bearing sediments, and are formed quickly at temperatures high enough to remove any argon of radioactive origin that was initially present.

The main uncertainties in potassium-argon ages arise from errors of measurement of potassium and radiogenic argon, by contamination of the sample with older materials, from argon contained within the dated material that is not produced by radioactive decay of potassium (excess argon), and from leakage of argon from the samples. The last problem is serious for lava flows that have been altered by weathering or other geochemical processes.

Potassium-argon dates are normally expressed in millions of years, together with a statement of the probable error. With good material the errors are generally about 1 to 3 per cent of the age. Potassium-argon ages can be used only to date stratigraphic levels between which a fossil lies. They hence provide boundary dates only, and a palaeontologist must assess the timing of events between the dated layers. For example, it may be judged that sedimentation was more or less continuous, or that there is a gap in the section, and so on.

This method has been more important in understanding the primate fossil record than any other dating technique. Its use to establish dates for boundaries between geological periods, and between epochs of the Tertiary period, makes it possible to state the approximate age of many primate fossils by studying the fossil remains with which they are associated. In East Africa and elsewhere, where volcanism and sedimentation happened at the same time, it is possible to establish the age of primate fossils precisely by dating tuffs in the fossil-bearing strata. This has been particularly successful for Pliocene and Pleistocene hominid fossils at sites such as Koobi Fora and West Turkana in Kenya and Omo and Hadar in Ethiopia (see Box 1).

An important variant of the K-Ar method is ^{40}Ar/^{39}Ar dating, in which the sample is irradiated to produce ^{39}Ar from ^{39}K. The argon is then extracted in a series of steps at higher and higher temperatures. This method has the advantages that potassium (computed from the ^{39}Ar content) is measured on the same sample as the ^{40}Ar and that an age can be calculated for each fraction of the gas. It is also possible to detect if excess argon is present.

The most elegant variation of the ^{40}Ar/^{39}Ar dating technique is the single-crystal fusion method, which uses a laser to melt previously irradiated crystal fragments to release the argon. Because the heating is so localised, background argon (of atmospheric origin) is reduced so that precise ages can be measured on individual small crystals. The technique greatly reduces the amount of sample needed for an age determination.

Potassium-argon dates could be cross-checked by rubidium-strontium (Rb-Sr) dating of volcanic rock materials, but this is seldom done.

1. CORRELATING THE EAST AFRICAN HOMINID SITES

Once a hardened volcanic ash layer or *tuff* in one stratigraphic section has been dated by the potassium-argon method, its identification in other sections can date those as well. The technique is known as *tephrochronology*.

Nearly all volcanic ashes (*tephras*) from different eruptions can be distinguished from one another by chemical analysis of their contents (glass and various crystals). This is because each ash is the product of a unique mix of processes before and during an eruption, such as partial melting of the source rocks, storage in a magma chamber and crystallisation.

Some volcanic ash layers extend over several thousand kilometres, allowing strata in different depositional basins to be linked. In East Africa, several tephras first known from the Turkana Basin (Omo, Koobi Fora and West Turkana) have been identified from many other areas, including the Awash Valley, some 1100 kilometres to the north-east, and also the deep sea in the Gulf of Aden and the Somali Basin.

The figure shows some of these correlations, which allow us not only to match these widely separated fossil localities stratigraphically but also to apply palaeoclimatic information from the deep-sea cores to the hominid sites on land.

The Koobi Fora Formation contains 58 distinct tuffs. The dispute over the age of the so-called KBS Tuff was eventually resolved by K-Ar and ^{40}Ar/^{39}Ar dating. It was just below the KBS Tuff that the *Homo habilis* skull KNM-ER 1470 was found. For several years, the tuff was thought to be around 2.6 million years old, on the basis of preliminary K-Ar dates and results from fission-track dating. Later, the date was revised, with all the methods confirming an age of 1.88 + 0.02 million years.

Important evidence for the younger age came from correlation of the KBS Tuff with Tuff H-2 of the Shungura Formation in the Omo Valley, which had been dated at about 1.85 million years old. Correlations of pig fossils in Ethiopia and Kenya (see Box 2) also suggested that the deposits just under the KBS Tuff were close to 2 million years old.

Another, even more important result of recent tephrochronological studies in East Africa has been the discovery that several ash layers of—it now turns out—quite different age had all been mapped (erroneously) as the KBS Tuff. *F.H. Brown*

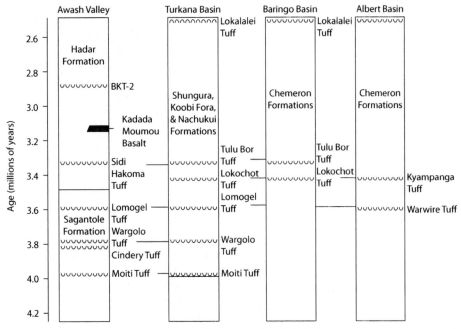

Some volcanic ash layers (tephras) extend over immense areas and connect fossil hominid sites stratigraphically at the localities shown. Many of the hominids known from the Hadar site were found in deposits between the BKT-2 and Sidi Hakoma Tuffs. Their dates were uncertain until these correlations were made. The gracile australopithecine known as 'Lucy' was found above the Kadada Moumou Basalt and below the BKT-2 Tuff.

FISSION-TRACK DATING

Fission-track dating is based on the spontaneous fission of uranium-238 (^{238}U), during which a trail of damage is created near the site of the uranium atom. Its main use in primate palaeontology lies in its application to volcanic rocks and minerals. When these are formed, they contain no fission tracks. The number of tracks increases with time at a rate that depends on the uranium content. By measuring the uranium content and the density of tracks, an age can be computed.

Zircon is the material most commonly used for fission-track dating. It normally contains more uranium than other volcanic minerals, any tracks formed within it are exceptionally stable, and it is very resistant to weathering. In addition, individual zircon grains can sometimes be dated, and volcanic zircons can be identified by their sharp crystal outlines. Other materials that have been dated in this way include apatite, biotite, sphene, and volcanic glasses such as obsidian.

Because fission tracks are only about 10 micrometres long, they must be enlarged so that they can be seen under an optical microscope. An internal surface of the grain to be dated is exposed by grinding and polishing, and the surface is chemically etched. Then the tracks in a fixed area are counted. The concentration of ^{238}U is measured by irradiating the sample with a known number of neutrons, which induce ^{235}U (but not ^{238}U) to undergo fission; the sample is then repolished and re-etched, and the uranium concentration computed from the density of new tracks.

An important application of the fission-track method has been to check potassium-argon dates at East African hominid sites.

URANIUM DISEQUILIBRIUM DATING

Several different elements are formed as naturally occurring radioactive isotopes of uranium—uranium 235 (^{235}U) and uranium-238 (^{238}U) decay by emission of alpha- and beta-particles to stable isotopes of lead.

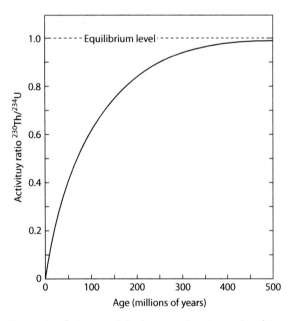

A sample of zircon polished to reveal an internal surface and etched so that the fission tracks can be seen. The number of tracks per unit area increases with the age of the sample at a rate determined by the uranium content.

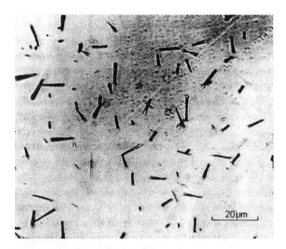

When calcite crystallises it contains uranium but no thorium. As time passes ^{234}U decays to form ^{230}Th, which is itself radioactive. Initially, the activity of ^{230}Th is zero but it increases as ^{230}Th atoms form, until it decays as rapidly as it forms and the activity ratio is 1.00. Although the ^{234}U/^{238}U activity ratio has been set equal to 1.00 to draw this curve, it is usually greater (1.15 in sea water), which alters the shape of the curve. In practice, the shape is corrected by measuring the ^{234}U/^{238}U ratio in the sample.

For example, uranium-234 (^{234}U) is the third daughter isotope and thorium-230 the fourth of the parent isotope ^{238}U, and proctanium-231 (Pa) is the second daughter product of ^{235}U. An uranium-containing mineral will in time contain each one of the elements in the decay series, in a concentration related to each element's half-life. This condition is termed *radioactive equilibrium*.

Under radioactive equilibrium, the radioactivities of each of the decay products in the series are equal. However, these decay products may be separated from each other by processes such as weathering, differential adsorption, crystallisation

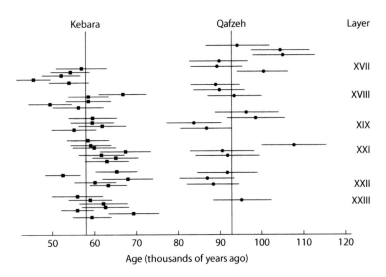

Thermoluminescence ages of burnt flints from Kebara and Qafzeh caves, Israel, for which the external dose was measured by burying dosimeters at the site. Neanderthal fossils were recovered at Kebara (the younger site), whereas early modern human fossils were found at Qafzeh.

of minerals that incorporate one element but exclude another and various biological events to form a system that is out of equilibrium. How much out of equilibrium is a measure of the time when the series was disrupted.

Uranium-disequilibrium dating systems, especially those that depend on the ratio between ^{234}U and ^{238}U, have been applied to non-marine carbonates, such as calcite in caves. The half-life for this process is 248,000 years so that the method has a range of about 1 million years.

The related thorium-230/uranium-234 (^{230}Th/^{234}U) method is also used to date inorganic carbonates. Like other uranium-series methods, it depends on the high solubility of uranium in water. Thus, ground and surface water seeping into limestone caves usually contains uranium but not its daughter isotopes, such as ^{230}Th, which are relatively insoluble. Once crystals of calcite precipitate as stalactites and stalagmites on the cave walls and floors, however, ^{230}Th starts accumulating as the result of the decay of ^{234}U and ^{238}U and this continues until equilibrium is reached. The ratio of ^{230}Th to ^{234}U provides a measure of the time that has elapsed since crystal formation.

The ^{230}Th/^{234}U method is useful for mineral samples younger than 300000 years and has been applied to cave sites in Europe that were once occupied by early *Homo sapiens*, where there are no volcanic rocks suitable for dating by the potassium-argon method. These include Bilzingsleben (Germany), Vértesszöllös (Hungary) and Pontnewydd (Wales), which have ages of 500000 to 200000 years.

Uranium-series dating of archaeological remains in caves can be prone to error because of possible difficulties in working out the order of calcite deposition, especially where fragments of cave wall have broken off and layers have become mixed up. There is also the possibility that the dated calcite was contaminated by uranium from an external source, such as dust particles, or that some of the uranium leached from the carbonate after precipitation. For these reasons, several layers of deposit usually need to be dated and other techniques used to check the results.

THERMOLUMINESCENCE, OPTICALLY STIMULATED LUMINESCENCE AND ELECTRON SPIN RESONANCE

The basis of these methods is the same: they measure the number of electrons caught up in defects in the lattice structure of crystals. The defects are caused by decay of small amounts of radioactive elements such as potassium, thorium and uranium within the crystal. The number of trapped electrons increases with time through exposure to this radiation so that the crystal acts as a dosimeter. Only when the electrons are released from the traps is the clock reset to zero.

In the thermoluminescence (TL) method, the accumulated dose of radiation in the crystal lattice is measured by heating the sample to a high temperature to excite the trapped electrons. As they escape from the lattice they emit light known as *thermoluminescence*. The intensity of thermoluminescence is proportional to the number of trapped electrons. The age of the material is obtained by dividing the accumulated dose by the annual dose. The latter is determined by measuring the amount of uranium, thorium and potassium within the sample and in the soil or rock surrounding it, or by irradiating the sample artificially and remeasuring its thermoluminescence. A companion technique called optically stimulated or photo-stimulated luminescence uses light instead of heat to evict the electrons from the traps.

---

2. FOSSILS AS DATING INDICATORS

Before the days of radiometric dating, the best way of dating a fossil primate site was by comparing fossil mammals from the site with those from a dated sedimentary sequence elsewhere. For some sites without rocks suitable for radiometric dating, such relative dating still provides the main clues to the site's age. Even at those sites that can be radiometrically dated, it is essential to consider evidence from both fossils and rocks before an age is finally accepted.

When fossils are collected from sediments spanning a temporal range whose relative age can be determined because younger rocks lie above older rocks, there are usually changes through time in lineages of both single species and groups of species. For example, the size or complexity of a tooth in a species of pig may increase in successively younger rocks. In such cases, the 'stage of evolution' can be used as a dating tool.

Some sedimentary sequences are rich in fossils throughout and also contain datable volcanic rocks. One such is the Omo Group in Ethiopia and Kenya, which is exposed to the west, north and east of Lake Turkana and ranges from more than 4 million years to under 1 million years old. Many important hominid fossils have come from these rocks. The many animal fossils known from this sequence have been invaluable in clarifying the age of these hominids, particularly those from Koobi Fora, east of Lake Turkana.

When the hominid skull KNM-ER1470 from the Koobi Fora Formation of the Omo Group was found in 1972, the geology of the sedimentary sequence was not fully worked out. A radiometric determination on a volcanic rock just above the hominid suggested an age of 2.6 million years. However, mammalian faunas associated with the cranium suggested that it was younger, close to 2.0 million years.

The pig genus *Mesochoerus* was particularly helpful here. Pig fossils are well known from a long and well-dated sequence in Omo Group rocks in Ethiopia, only 150 kilometres north of Koobi Fora. In two species, *Mesochoerus limnetes* and *M. olduvaiensis*, there was a steady increase in size of the third molar through time. The relevant *Mesochoerus* sample from Koobi Fora matched that from the 2-million-year levels in the Ethiopian part of the sequence.

Subsequent careful redating of the Kenyan rocks showed that their radiometric age was indeed close to 2.0 million years (1.88 + 0.2 million), not 2.6 million years as had previously been believed.

Caves in South Africa are an important source of fossil hominids, but contain no rocks suitable for radiometric dating. In the past 20 years, analysis of the fossil mammals in the cave sequences, especially the bovids (giraffe, pig and cattle family), has made it possible to compare each site with the calibrated East African sequence.

The Pliocene and early Pleistocene faunas of eastern and southern Africa are as dissimilar as are their counterparts today, so exact matches are difficult. Nevertheless, enough is now known to place the principal South African sites in relative order: they run (from oldest to youngest) Makapansgat, Sterkfontein, Kromdraai and Swartkrans.

Progress is also being made towards giving these sites dates. For example, Makapansgat bovids are similar to those found at several sites in East Africa ranging from 3.7 to 2.5 million years ago. If all the evidence is taken into account, the date for the deposition of the Makapansgat cave sediments is probably around 3 million years ago.

These estimates are not as precise as the age determinations for the East African hominid sites, but they do help to clarify the evolutionary patterns of the southern populations of early hominids.

A third example of the use of fossil faunas in dating comes from the later hominid site of Jebel Qafzeh in Israel. From Qafzeh has come an important series of early modern *Homo sapiens*. On the basis of small mammals such as rodents its age was estimated as close to 90,000 years. But evidence from stone tools and the hominids themselves suggested an age of close to 40,000 years. Recent results from thermoluminescence dating suggest that the most probable age is indeed close to 90,000 years (see p. 183).

This is another demonstration of the importance of considering the faunal evidence as well as other kinds of dating evidence before accepting an age for a hominid site.   *David Pilbeam*

See also 'Evolution of australopithecines' (p. 231) and 'Evolution of early humans' (p. 241)

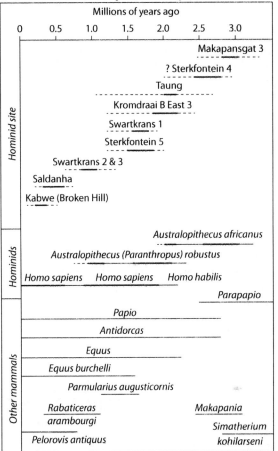

Ages of some southern African hominid sites based on their fossil faunas. Also shown are estimated time ranges of the fossil hominid species known from the sites and of some of the mammalian taxa used to date them. The numbers after the site names are the stratigraphic units (members). *Parapapio* and *Papio* are baboons; *Equus* and *Equus burchelli* are zebras; the remaining species are bovids (buffaloes and antelopes).

In the electron spin resonance (ESR) method, the number of trapped electrons in the sample is determined not by driving them out by hearing but by measuring their absorption of microwave radiation. Traps occupied by a single electron act as paramagnetic centres with a static magnetic field. When placed in a microwave-frequency electromagnetic field the electrons in the traps oscillate between orientation with and against the field. Energy is absorbed from the applied field according to the number of traps occupied by single electrons and correlates to the age of the sample. An advantage of ESR over TL is that a sample can be tested repeatedly by ESR whereas TL dating can be done only once.

TL and ESR measure the time elapsed since the last draining of electron traps—when the sample's clock was reset to zero. For burnt flint artefacts this happens when the material is first heated—for example, in a hearth. Exposure to sunlight does this for sediments while they are being transpoprted and deposited. Burnt flints at Palaeolithic sites, deposits of loess, cave sediments, bone and teeth are among the materials that can be dated by these methods. They are less precise than radiocarbon but have a wider age range and can also be used to date inorganic materials. Careful adjustments have to be made for uptake of radioactive elements from the environment.

The TL method has had an important role in the controversy over the relationship between Neanderthals and anatomically modern people. Dates for burnt flints found at the cave sites of Kebara and Qafzeh in Israel support the idea that Neanderthals were not direct ancestors of modern humans, because they arrived in the Middle East several tens of thousands of years after the first anatomically modern people in the area.

AMINO ACID RACEMISATION

This dating method depends on the slow chemical conversion of left-handed amino acids present in living organisms to their right-handed counterparts. As this is a chemical (rather than nuclear) process, the rate of conversion is very sensitive to the environmental conditions in which it occurs. Not only temperature, but also the composition of the material in contact with the specimen changes the rate of conversion, and this limits the value of the technique.

The best material for this method at present seems to be eggshell of extinct and modern species of ostrich and owl, which is often found at archaeological sites. The technique may be especially useful in Africa at sites with remains of early modern humans that fall between the ranges of the radiocarbon and potassium-argon methods, between about 40000 and 200000 years old. In colder regions, the age range of the method may extend up to a million years.

PALAEOMAGNETIC POLARITY STRATIGRAPHY

This dating method requires prior calibration. The magnetic field of the earth runs from pole to pole. At irregular intervals in geological time the polarity of this field has changed so that the modern pattern (positive in the Northern Hemisphere and negative in the Southern Hemisphere) has been reversed. Processes such as cooling of lava, settling of magnetic particles during sediment deposition and growth of iron-rich minerals within sedimentary rocks can preserve a record of the magnetic field when the rocks were formed. The field direction is measured using a magnetometer. Potassium-argon dating of lavas whose polarity has been measured in this way gives a timescale of the change of polarity for about the past 12 million years. This has been extended to the beginning of the Mesozoic era by study of magnetic anomalies on the ocean floor.

The pattern of ancient changes to the earth's polarity in samples through a stratigraphic section is compared with the known pattern of the palaeomagnetic polarity timescale. Most rock strata are not continuous, so that their approximate age must be established by fossils or by isotopic dating before their magnetic signature can be fitted to the correct time period.

This method gives important information on several primate fossil localities where the chronology is already reasonably well known—for example, at the hominid site of Olduvai Gorge in Tanzania. A most significant contribution has been to give age estimates of the Miocene sediments of the Siwalik region of

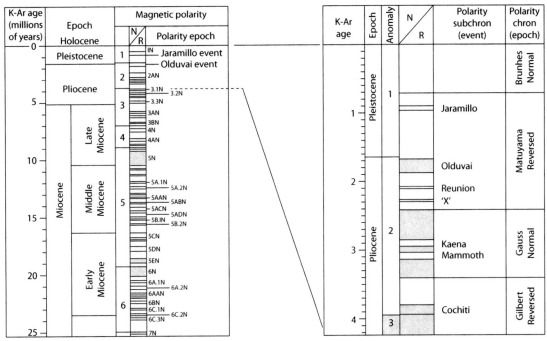

Magnetic polarity intervals for the past 25 million years (left) with the interval from 0–4.2 million years expanded to show details more clearly (right). Normal intervals are shaded; reversed intervals, white.

northern Pakistan, where mammalian fossils, including hominoids, have been found. The faunas of the Nagri and Dhok Pathan Formations in this region are now known to be between 6 and 12 million years old. As 13 palaeomagnetic transitions exist in the sequence between 6.5 and 8.6 million years ago, it is possible to establish an accurate chronology for this portion of the sequence.

F.H. Brown

As we know from our own experience, environments are in a constant state of flux. Climate, driven by astronomical events, varied cyclically over the thousands of years of our evolutionary history, and profoundly influenced its trajectory. Changes in global temperatures caused glaciers at high latitudes to wax and wane, sea levels to rise and fall, and vegetation zones to shift their positions. The ratio of oxygen isotopes (18O and 16O) in seawater reflects water temperature, and the study of ancient marine organisms can reveal the temperature of the ocean when they were alive, and thus to reconstruct ancient climatic conditions.

3. Climatic Change in the Past

By Neil Roberts

In recent geological time the earth has been increasingly restless, not only because of mountain building and other movements of its crust, but also as a result of changes in climate. Climatic oscillations have probably been as violent during the past few million years as they have at any time in earth history, and this has affected primate evolution in many ways. Climatic variability modified such important habitats as river valleys and lake basins, and caused forests, grasslands and deserts to expand and contract across the continents. It also altered the oceans, causing sea levels to rise and fall, which in turn periodically exposed continental shelves as dry land. The climates that provided the backdrop to human evolution were those of the last great Ice Age.

THE ALPINE ICE AGE MODEL

The *Einzeit* or Ice Age theory was first announced in 1837 by Louis Agassiz, a renowned specialist on fossil fishes who was later to found the Harvard Museum of Comparative Zoology. Evidence that glaciers and ice sheets had formerly been more extensive came from the Alps in Agassiz's native Switzerland. Convincing

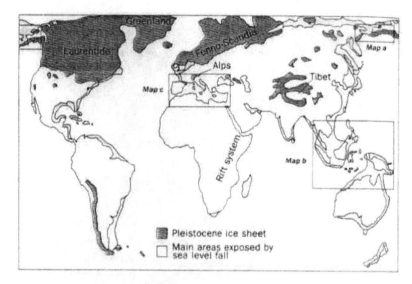

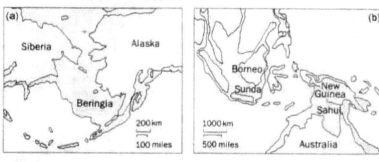

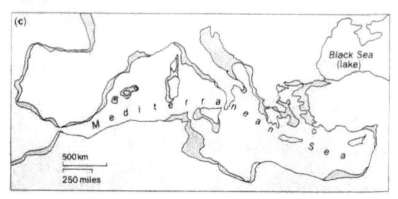

The world during a glacial stage of the last Ice Age. Major ice sheets covered not only Greenland and Antarctica, as they do today, but also North America and northern Eurasia. The ice that was locked up on land caused sea levels to fall by more than 100 metres. Coastlines changed dramatically where there were shallow continental shelves offshore—for example, in the Bering Strait and between Southeast Asia and Australia. Enlargements show the sea-level fall in these two regions and the Mediterranean basin in more detail. While the Mediterranean Sea remained connected to the Atlantic Ocean throughout the Plio-Pleistocene, the Black Sea became isolated as a giant freshwater lake.

as his case was, we can now see—with hindsight—that these mountains were singularly ill-suited to be a model for studying the history of the last great Ice Age. For a start, the Alps have been uplifted during recent geological times. And as the land has risen, the accumulation of snow and ice has increased, making glaciation more likely regardless of any change in global climate. Equally important, formerly glaciated terrain preserves a very incomplete stratigraphic record of earth history. The ice, as it advanced, scoured and bulldozed its way through earlier sedimentary deposits, eroding and overturning them in the process.

Nonetheless, it was to the Alps and other formerly glaciated lands that most scientific attention was drawn during the later nineteenth century. Albrecht Penck and Eduard Bruckner found evidence of more than one past extension of the Alpine ice cap, in the form of a series of fluvioglacial outwash terraces in the valleys draining the German Alps. They recognised four glacial stages within the last Ice Age, and named them after different river valleys: Günz, Mindel, Riss and Würm. This four-stage sequence of cold *glacials* and intervening warmer *interglacials* was to be immensely influential. It provided a template for climatic history not only in other glaciated regions, such as North America and northern Europe, but also in the tropics where four wet phases (or *pluvials* as they were termed) were recognized, matching the four alpine glacial stages. A similar four-stage model for sea-level history was proposed from marine terraces around the Mediterranean, although this region has been as tectonically unstable as the Alps.

Sea levels fluctuate in concert with climate because when there is ice on the northern continents, water is taken out of the hydrological cycle, and when it melts, water returns to the oceans. Some of the most detailed records of sea-level history come from corals that grew near to the former ocean surface. While some corals have been drowned and now lie well below the modern sea level, such as off the coast of Barbados, others, such as on the north coast of New Guinea, are now exposed on land.

When growth of the ice sheets was greatest, sea levels dropped by over 100 metres to

Extent of land ice today and at the peak of a Pleistocene glacial cycle. The biggest of these ice sheets were 5 kilometres thick and their weight depressed the earth's crust by more than 1 kilometre

ICE SHEET	AREA (MILLION SQUARE KILOMETRES)	ICE VOLUME (MILLION CUBIC KILOMETRES)	SEA-LEVEL EQUIVALENT (METRES)
Present day			
Antarctic	12.53	23.45	59
Greenland	1.73	2.60	6
N. America	(negl.)	–	–
Fennoscandia	(negl.)	–	–
Other	0.64	0.20	0.5
Total	14.90	26.25	65
Peak of glacial cycle			
Antarctic	13.81	26.00	66
Greenland	2.30	3.50	11
N. America	15.76	33.01	83
Fennoscandia	6.66	13.32	34
Other	5.20	1.14	3
Total	43.73	76.97	197
Difference	28.83	50.72	132

create land bridges on continental shelves. At these times it was possible to walk from eastern Asia to Alaska across the then dry Bering Strait, from England to the continent of Europe. This certainly aided the spread of plants and animals, and encouraged the migration of early hominids from Africa to Eurasia and thence (late in the Ice Age) to Australia and the America. The inundation that occurred at times of rising sea level may also have stimulated new human adaptations to coastal environments. Certainly the crossing from Southeast Asia to Australia, about 40,000 or possibly 50,000 years ago, had to be accomplished by raft or boat, for there has always been a significant water gap between these two continents.

The four-stage alpine model dominated ice-age research through the first half of the twentieth century, and brought with it a series of wider conclusions, few of which are considered valid today. Among these was the idea that the last Ice Age began abruptly during the Pleistocene epoch about 2 million years ago, following a long period of stable and temperate (albeit gradually deteriorating) climate. The fact that only four Pleistocene glaciations were recognised suggested that the warmer interglacials must have lasted longer than the intervening cold stages.

Despite valiant efforts by the Serbian mathematicians Milutin Milankovitch, it proved impossible to match the alpine model to any known theories of past climatic change, in this case to astronomical variations in the earth's orbit and axial tilt. Finally, the archaeological discoveries that were made during the late nineteenth and early twentieth centuries were fitted into, and often used to help date and hence to prop up, the alpine model of Ice Age history. Indeed, some archaeologists still discuss the Old Stone Age in Europe and the Mediterranean region with reference to a four-stage model of climatic change.

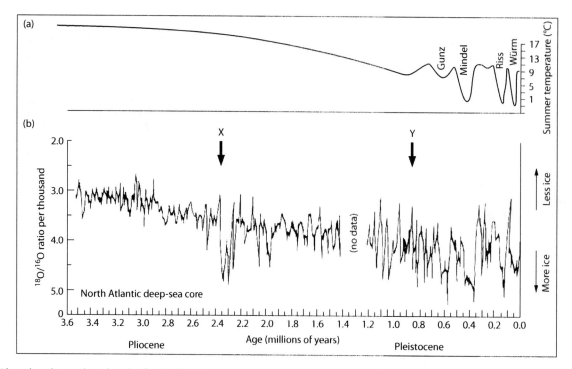

Glacial and interglacial cycles for the Plio-Pleistocene (a) as originally envisaged from the evidence of past glaciation in the Alps and (b) from oxygen-isotope measurements from a North Atlantic deep-sea core. Evidence of glaciation in the Northern Hemisphere goes back much further in time than was once thought (to point X); an important intensification of climatic change occurred about 90,0000 to 80,0000 years ago (point Y).

MODERN SUBDIVISIONS OF THE ICE AGE

A framework that came to replace the alpine model emerged from three independent developments of the late 1940s. The first was the discovery of radiocarbon dating, the earliest of a series of new dating techniques, mostly based on the rate of decay of unstable radioisotopes. The traditional way of dating rocks is through palaeontology (or the study of fossils), but as one moves towards recent geological times this method becomes less and less applicable. Palaeontological dating assumes that the appearance and radiation of new species, and the extinction of old ones, were effectively instantaneous when considered on a geological timescale. While this assumption may be valid for events in the distant past, it is not true for more recent changes, as human evolution itself demonstrates. For this time period a sound chronology was lacking until the advent of radioisotopic methods. One of these new methods (potassium-argon) was to demonstrate the great antiquity of early human evolution in East Africa.

The second of the post-World War II developments was the discovery of *oxygen-isotope analysis*. This technique, based on the ratio between stable rather than unstable isotopes, provided not a dating tool but what was initially thought to be a 'geological thermometer'. Because of the phenomenon known as isotopic fractionation, slightly less of the heavy isotope oxygen-18 (^{18}O) is precipitated at higher temperatures relative to the light isotope oxygen-16 (^{16}O). One of the most important ways that chemical precipitation takes place from sea water is as calcium carbonate in organisms such as corals, molluscs and foraminifera. Further work has shown oxygen isotopes to reflect not only past temperatures but also, and more important, past ice volumes: it gives an index of past glaciations.

The third and final development was the invention of the Kullenberg piston corer for the recovery of deep-sea sediments. From a stratigraphic perspective the deep ocean bed represents the opposite conditions

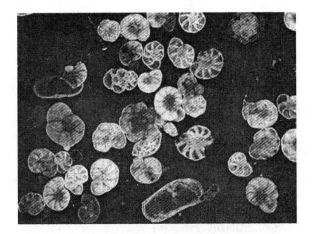

Foraminifera in a deep-sea ooze. These are small marine organisms whose shells (or tests) are made of calcium carbonate. The tests are often well preserved in deep-sea sediments and can be analysed for their oxygen-isotope contents, which provide a measure of past glaciation.

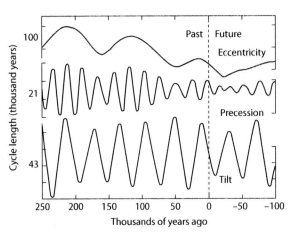

Astronomical variations In the earth's orbit and axial tilt as predicted by Milutin Milankovitch. There are three separate cycles, each with a different wavelength. When superimposed, these cycles match well to the sequence of glacial and interglacial fluctuations reconstructed from deep-sea cores.

to those of glaciated terrain. Here, sedimentation proceeds slowly and steadily, uninterrupted by erosion. But obtaining intact sediment cores from onboard a ship 4 kilometres or more above the ocean floor is not easy. The Kullenberg corer was the first to recover cores that spanned all of the Pleistocene. Cores covering the whole of the late Cenozoic are now available as a result of the advent in 1979 of a hydraulic piston corer as part of the world Ocean Drilling Programme.

Oxygen-isotope analysis has now been applied to calcareous microfossils, notably foraminifera, from deep-sea sediment cores. This has produced a continuous record of ice volume fluctuations and therefore of glacial–interglacial cycles during the past few million years, and is a record very different from that recognised by Penck and Brückner in the Alps. First, many more than four glaciations are recorded in deep-sea sequences. Eight major climatic (that is, glacial–interglacial) cycles have occurred during the past 0.8 million years alone, with many other, less-intense cycles before this. Warmer interglacials represent only around 10 percent of this time, and the climate was almost constantly changing between colder and warmer, or between wetter and drier conditions. According to the oxygen-isotope scheme, warm stages (with low ice volume) are given odd numbers working back from the present day, and colder glacial stages have even numbers; thus the present interglacial—or Holocene—is oxygen-isotope stage 1, the last glacial maximum stage 2, and so forth.

This new stratigraphic framework could be tested against theories of climatic change much more rigorously than was previously possible. In the 1970s, the CLIMAP research group compared the oceanic oxygen-isotope record of glaciation and the input of solar radiation predicted by the Milankovitch astronomical theory. The fit was near perfect, giving strong support to the idea that variations in the earth's orbit acted as a pacemaker for Ice Age climate. These variations result from the superimposition of three separate cycles with wavelengths of 100,000, 43,000 and 21,000 years, and it appears that these cycles—and the middle one in particular—operated throughout the late Cenozoic and not just during the Pleistocene.

CLIMATIC CHANGE DURING THE CENOZOIC

There were important shifts in the tempo of climate, but these did not coincide with the start of the Pleistocene, now estimated at around 1.64 million years ago (but convention-ally often put at 1.83 million years). The last two main shifts were at 0.8 and at 2.4 million years ago (see p. 175), the earlier marking the onset of major glaciation in Greenland and other Northern Hemisphere landmasses. By the Pliocene, about 5 million years ago, the Ice Age in the Southern Hemisphere was already well underway, with Antarctica carrying major ice sheets since at least the middle Miocene. Oxygen isotopes show an abrupt climatic change at about 14 million years, and this may mark the establishment of an ice sheet over East Antarctica similar in size to the one existing today. Glaciation around the South Pole certainly occurred before this, however, and the appearance of iceberg-rafted debris in deep-sea sediments is evidence of glaciers calving into the southern oceans from about 26 million years ago.

An ice cap terminating on land seems to have existed in Antarctica even before this. Seismic records of relative sea level show a major withdrawal of the sea from land (a marine regression) during the Oligocene, probably because of the accumulation of land ice, while subglacially extruded volcanic rocks in West Antarctica date back to 27 million years. Oxygen isotopes suggest glaciation even further back in time, to the Eocene–Oligocene boundary at 35 million years ago, if not earlier.

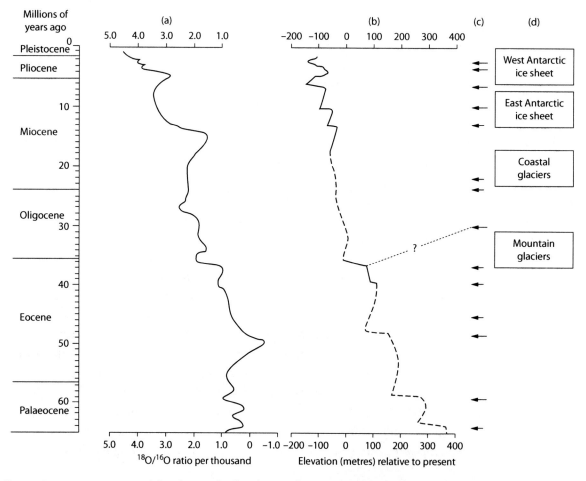

Oxygen-isotope measurements (a) on bottom-dwelling foraminifera in tropical deep-sea cores show a stepped pattern in the build up of land ice during the Cenozoic. Most of this ice accumulated over Antarctica before the Pliocene, initially as mountain glaciers that later expanded to terminate in the sea, and most significantly with the establishment of a true ice sheet over East Antarctica during the middle Miocene (d). The global sea-level curve (b) reflects a progressive decline of about 400 metres during the Cenozoic as a result of sea-floor spreading, which caused the expansion of ocean basins. Superimposed on this gradual decline are more abrupt falls in sea level (c), caused by glaciation on land. These are indicated in the oxygen-isotope record and in seismic profiles of coastal sediments.

These shifts were the result of longer-term changes than those produced by astronomical fluctuations, and were almost certainly related to plate tectonics. The build-up of ice in the Northern Hemisphere may have resulted from the uplift of the Tibetan and Colorado plateaus disturbing global atmospheric circulation (Tibet has risen by some two vertical kilometres during the Plio-Pleistocene). Glaciation in Antarctica was probably initiated by the final break-up of the great southern continent, Gondwanaland. So long as Antarctica was joined to Australia and South America, cold polar ocean currents were deflected northwards towards the Equator and returned as warmer tropical waters. Once the link was broken, however, a circum-Antarctic current developed around the South Pole, isolating it thermally. The opening of Drake Passage between Tierra del Fuego and the Antarctic peninsula from about 22 million years ago may have been critical.

Tectonic changes were also important in determining regional environmental histories. The compression of the zone between the European and African tectonic plates, for example, led to the temporary closure of the Straits of Gibraltar during the Miocene. As a result, Atlantic waters no longer flowed into the Mediterranean Sea, which progressively dried up to become a series of giant salt lakes—the so-called Messinian salinity crisis. Another region where tectonic and climatic histories were intertwined was East Africa. Here the opening of the Rift System during the later Cenozoic led to a diversification of local climates that encouraged adaptation and speciation among the higher apes.

West of the rifts, rainfall was high enough to support tropical moist forest, but to the east, and in the rifts themselves, the climate became drier and more open, savanna vegetation came to dominate. Whether a move down from the trees encouraged bipedalism and other human adaptive traits is hard to know. However, it may be significant that Plio-Pleistocene hominids and modem chimpanzees and gorillas have disjunct distributions in tropical Africa; the apes are found only in moist forests and adjacent wood-lands whereas the hominids lived in the savanna lands within and to the east of the rift system.

To find terrestrial sequences that match the deep-sea record of global climatic change is a major aim of palaeoclimatology. Among the most complete land-based records are those from loess (wind-blown glacial silts), cave deposits, pollen analysis, cores through the ice sheets themselves, and the sedimentary records of long-lived lakes, such as those of the East African rifts. Tropical lake levels, which are a good indicator of wet and dry climatic phases, are now known to have been low at glacial maxima and high during the early part of interglacials (and not the other way round, as the old 'glacial equals pluvial' view envisaged). One of the best-known sequences of lake sediments in East Africa comes from Olduvai Gorge; the source of hominid fossils and stone artefacts that have revolutionised our ideas about human origins. This kind of conjunction has meant that earth scientists and palaeoanthropologists now regularly work together in interdisciplinary teams.

Our understanding of environmental change over the recent geological past is quite different from that which existed a few decades ago. The Pleistocene did not, as was once thought, mark the main break-point in recent earth history. Because the change to a colder and more variable climate began well before this, it is more appropriate to refer to a 'late Cenozoic Ice Age'. Even this label disguises the fact that conditions were not always glacial in character, and that glaciation was just one of a whole series of important changes, such as the expansion and contraction of deserts in low latitudes.

Fluctuations in climate have intensified during the past million years, and have placed increasing pressure on organisms and ecosystems. Adaptability to change has been a key to success for most terrestrial plants and animals during the late Cenozoic. Hominids are no exception. The evolutionary success of our ancestors is testimony to their versatility in the face of a changing environment, first in the savannas of Africa and later in the new and hostile climates encountered in the lands beyond it.   *Neil Roberts*

Evolutionary changes that can be detected in the molecules of DNA in living animals can be used to determine their evolutionary relationships. Some of these changes affect the organisms' phenotypes; others have no discernible effect. In some cases, molecular differences between two organisms can determine the amount of time that has elapsed since they shared a common ancestor.

4. Molecular Anthropology

By Jonathan Marks

S ystematic study of primate taxa using comparative genetic methods. Since evolutionary change involves change in the genes, a study of the genetic systems of primates should reveal the relationships of species. The subfield dates to G. Nuttall's pioneering work in 1902 on the immunological cross-reactions between the bloods of different species. Little progress was made in this area, however, until the studies of M. Goodman in the 1960s.

As immunological distances are a rough measure of protein (and, therefore, genetic) similarity, the first use of these data involved primate phylogeny and established that the African apes (chimpanzee and gorilla) are more closely related to humans than to orangutans. Another method that became available in the 1960s was the direct sequencing of the amino acids composing specific proteins, a more direct reflection of the genetic material. Protein-sequence data not only confirmed the immunological results, but also showed that humans, chimpanzees, and gorillas were genetically more similar to one another than had previously been imagined.

Concurrently, empirical data and theoretical advances pointed to the conclusion that most evolutionary changes in proteins are nonadaptive and not subject to the operation of natural selection. The spread of

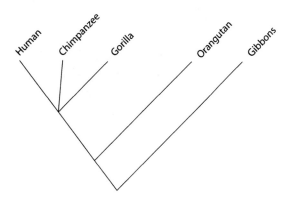

Molecular data show humans, chimpanzees, and gorillas to be approximately equally closely related to one another, but place the orangutan clearly apart from the African apes and humans. Courtesy of Jon Marks.

these *neutral* changes is governed by *genetic drift*, a statistical process. Consequently, any neutral mutation has a (low) probability of spreading through a population over time, and the spread of these mutations is simply a function of how often neutral mutations arise. Natural selection is here relegated to a primarily constraining role, limiting the rate at which a given protein can change but not affecting its evolution in a constructive, directional way.

Thus, although the vast majority of neutral mutations are lost shortly after arising, the laws of probability permit a few to spread through a population. They do so at a rate that fluctuates in the short run but approximates a constant rate in the long run. The amount of genetic difference between two species, therefore, could be taken as a measure of how long two species have been separated from each other.

MOLECULAR CLOCK

The findings that molecular evolution proceeds at a roughly constant rate and that humans, chimpanzees, and gorillas are unexpectedly similar genetically can be reconciled in two ways, which represent the poles of a long-unresolved controversy.

Goodman and coworkers inferred that, since humans and the African apes are so similar genetically, the rate of molecular evolution in these species has been slowing down. Alternatively, A. Wilson, V. Sarich, and coworkers inferred that, since molecular evolution is constant, humans and the African apes must have diverged more recently than 4 Ma.

Sarich and Wilson argued that the prevailing opinion in 1967, that humans and African apes had diverged from each other by 15 Ma because the fossil *Ramapithecus* was a uniquely human ancestor, was flawed. Time has borne out their conclusion, but it also appears that the divergence dates calculated by Sarich and Wilson are somewhat underestimated and that there was, indeed, a slowdown in the rate of molecular evolution among the great apes and humans. These facts are being used to study the microevolutionary history of the human species, and of other primate species, using mitochondrial DNA (deoxyribonucleic acid) as genetic markers.

Recent technological advances have permitted trace amounts of DNA to be amplified into analyzable quantities, via the polymerase chain reaction (PCR). This opens the door to the study of DNA samples from prehistoric (unfossilized) bones, as well as from hair follicles, which can be collected noninvasively.

CYTOGENETIC DATA

Techniques were developed in the 1970s for distinguishing the 23 chromosome pairs in the human karyotype, and, while these techniques have been most useful in clinical applications, they have generated evolutionary data as well.

Chimpanzees and gorillas share several chromosomal inversions, inherited from a recent common ancestor, as well as a unique distribution of C-bands. In humans, these bands, which distinguish areas where the DNA is more tightly condensed than elsewhere, appear only at the centromere of each chromosome; below the centromere of chromosomes 1, 9, and 16; and on the long arm of the Y chromosome. In the African apes, however, they appear at the tips of most chromosomes.

In general, the chromosomes of humans and the African apes appear highly similar when prepared by the common procedure of G-banding. The most significant difference seems to be a recent fusion of two chromosomes in the human lineage, reducing the number of chromosome pairs from 24 (retained in the great apes) to 23 and creating what we now recognize as chromosome 2 in the human karyotype.

Rates of chromosomal change vary widely across primate taxa. We find rapid rates of chromosomal evolution in the gibbons and the most arboreal cercopithecine monkeys, slow chromosomal evolution in the baboons, and a moderate rate in the great apes and humans.

DNA STUDIES

The development of molecular genetics in the late 1970s brought studies of molecular evolution away from phenotypes (even a protein or antibody reaction is, properly speaking, a phenotype) and down directly to the genotype. These studies examine direct aspects of the DNA nucleotide sequence itself or indirect measures of DNA divergence. As phylogenetic data, the results obtained from DNA studies support those obtained from protein analyses. For example, the specific relations among human, chimpanzee, and gorilla are as unclear in their DNA as in their proteins, yet these species all still cluster apart from the orangutan.

Mitochondria are organelles that exist in the cytoplasm of each bodily cell. Although subcellular structures, they contain their own genetic machinery and information encoded in a circular piece of DNA (which is ca. 16,500 nucleotides long in humans). While the evolutionary rules that govern change in mitochondrial DNA are still unclear, in primates their rate of change seems to be about tenfold higher than that of nuclear DNA. Moreover, mitochondria are inherited exclusively through the mother, in contrast to nuclear DNA. These facts have already been used to study the genetic splitting of the human races, using mitochrondrial DNA as genetic markers. It has recently been proposed, based on the rate of change in this DNA, that the principal human groups diverged from one another ca. 200 Ka, a considerably more ancient date than usually thought.

Studies of DNA sequences across species have established that the neutral theory of molecular evolution is more applicable to DNA than to proteins. This is because the genome is now known to be very complex. Although a gene codes for a protein, only a portion of the gene actually consists of coding instructions. These regions (*exons*) are interrupted by DNA segments (*introns*) that do not become translated into part of the protein molecule. Untranslated regions are also found at the beginning and the end of each gene. Further, most of the DNA in the genome consists of *intergenic* DNA (i.e., DNA that

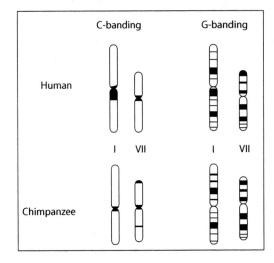

Despite some differences in C-banding (left) humans and chimpanzees share overwhelming similarities in their fine structure, as revealed by G-banding (right). Pictured are two chromosomes (1 and 7) from the human and their counterparts in the chimpanzee. Courtesy of Jon Marks.

lies between genes). It is now clear that, between any two species, intergenic DNA is most different, intron DNA is slightly more similar, and exon DNA is least different. Further, differences in exon DNA fall into two categories: those that direct a different amino acid to become part of the protein *(replacement mutations)* and those that do not change the protein *(silent mutations)*. Silent mutations far outnumber replacement mutations in any gene compared across two species.

What this means is that the neutral theory proposed to explain protein evolution is really only a first approximation, since the mutations that actually are detectable in protein evolution represent the slowest-evolving part of the genome. These replacement mutations are affected by the constraints of natural selection to a greater degree than silent mutations, intron and untranslated mutations, or intergenic mutations.

LEVELS OF EVOLUTION

While evolutionary change is genetic change, and ultimately molecular change, it is impossible at present to associate any adaptive anatomical specialization of humans with any particular DNA change. We may analogize to what is known about phenotypic evolution in other organisms, such as the fruitfly, but we have never located a gene for bipedalism or cranial expansion, and it is likely that there are no genes "for" these traits in the sense that there is a gene "for" cytochrome C or beta-hemoglobin.

Thus, while it is certain that the processes of bone growth and remodeling are under genetic control, as are the processes that govern the development of facultative responses to stresses on bone growth, such genes have not been located. Further, it is difficult to envision at this point how such genes work or what their primary product might be, much less how to isolate such a product.

Consequently, we are not able to explain at present how the primarily nonadaptive changes we find in the DNA account for the primarily adaptive morphological changes we find in the anatomy of the animal. This seems attributable less to any flaws in contemporary evolutionary theory than to our ignorance of how one gets phenotypic expressions out of genotypic information. It is, therefore, useful to conceive of evolution as a multilevel system: first, a level of the genome, where changes are clocklike over the long run and primarily unexpressed and nonadaptive; second, a level of the karyotype, where chromosomal rearrangements are primarily unexpressed and nonadaptive but may generate reproductive incompatibilities that facilitate the process of speciation; and third, a level of morphology, where changes usually track the environment, and individuals with certain anatomical characters outreproduce those with other similar anatomies, on the average.

See also DNA Hybridization; Genetics; Genome; Immunological Distance; Molecular Clock; Non-Darwinian Evolution. [J.M.]

FURTHER READINGS

Buettner-Janusch, J., and Hill, R.L. (1965) Molecules and monkeys. Science 147:836–842.

Devor, E.J., ed. (1992) Molecular Applications in Biological Anthropology. New York: Cambridge University Press.

Gillespie, J. (1986) Variability in evolutionary rates of DNA. Ann. Rev. Ecol. Syst. 17:637–665.

Goodman, M., Tashian, R., and Tashian, J., eds. (1976) Molecular Anthropology. New York: Plenum.

King, M.-C., and Wilson, A.C. (1975) Evolution at two levels in humans and chimpanzees. Science 188:107–116.

Marks, J. (1983) Hominoid cytogenetics and evolution. Yrbk. Phys. Anthropol. 25:125–153.

Marks, J. (1994) Blood will tell (won't it?): A century of molecular discourse in anthropological systematics. Am. J. Phys. Anthropol. 94:59–80.

Wilson, A.C., Cann, R.L., Carr, S.M., George, M., Gyllensten, U.B., Helm-Bychawski, K.M., Higuchi, R., Palumbi, S.R., Prager, F.M., Sage, R.D., and Stoneking, M. (1985) Mitochondrial DNA and two perspectives on evolutionary genetics. Bio. J. Linn. Soc. 26:375–400.

Weiss, M. (1987) Nucleic acid evidence bearing on hominoid relationships. Yrbk. Phys. Anthropol. 30:41–73.

MOLECULAR CLOCK

Comparative studies of protein structure suggested the *molecular-clock hypothesis* to E. Zuckerkandl and L. Pauling in 1962: that proteins evolve at statistically constant rates and that a simple algorithm might, therefore, relate the amount of protein difference between two species and the time since divergence of those species from their last common ancestor. It presents a sharp contrast to anatomical evolution, in which rates of evolution are usually related to environmental exigencies and may fluctuate widely. The concept of a molecular clock was used by V. Sarich and A. Wilson in 1967 to modify earlier assumptions about the remoteness of common ancestry between humans and the African apes.

M. Kimura, a theoretical population geneticist, showed mathematically in the late 1960s that, if most genetic changes had no adaptive effect on the organism, the evolution of these *neutral* mutations would be essentially constant over the long run. While predictions of the neutral theory accord well with the empirical data of protein evolution, it is also possible that models based on natural selection can account for these data.

It is now clear that each protein has its own characteristic rate of change. The most fundamental proteins (e.g., histones, which package cellular DNA) evolve slowly, while globins (which transport oxygen) evolve more rapidly. Further, this rate may fluctuate in the short run, but it averages to a constant rate over the long run. DNA (deoxyribonucleic acid) evolution can be modeled along the same lines as protein evolution. The discovery that most of the genomic DNA is not transcribed or expressed makes it likely that most DNA evolution is more nearly neutral than protein evolution. This makes noncoding DNA a good candidate for the mathematical models of the neutral theory.

See also Immunological Distance; Molecular Anthropology; Non-Darwinian Evolution. [J.M.]

FURTHER READINGS

Avise, J.C. (1994) Molecular Markers, Natural History, and Evolution. New York: Chapman and Hall.

Gillespie, J.H. (1992) The Causes of Molecular Evolution. New York: Oxford University Press.

Kimura, M. (1983) The Neutral Theory of Molecular Evolution. New York: Cambridge University Press.

Li, W.-H., and Graur, D. (1991) Fundamentals of Molecular Evolution. Sunderland, Mass.: Sinauer.

Study Questions

1. What is adaptation?

2. How do you reconstruct the adaptation of an ancient animal from its fossilized remains?

3. What are some of the methods used to determine the age of fossils, or the date of a particular evolutionary event?

4. What is actually analyzed by these methods to arrive at an age estimate?

5. What are the challenges or limits to using each of these methods? In other words, what do they need in order to work well?

SECTION II

LIVING AND FOSSIL PRIMATES

Humans, as members of the Primate Order, share many characteristics with living primates. The study of living primates can aid in understanding earlier phases of human evolution and their impact upon the physiology and adaptations of present-day humans.

Body size is a major factor in understanding an animal's adaptation and life history. It is vitally linked to metabolic rate and nutritional needs. Body size may therefore be used to infer feeding behavior, a key component of an animal's adaptive strategy.

5. A Jarman/Bell Model of Primate Feeding Niches

By Steven J. C. Gaulin[1]

INTRODUCTION

The primates, as a group, exhibit a great range of adaptations. A number of *morphological* definitions of the order have been advanced (Gregory, 1910; Simpson, 1940; Schwartz *et al.*, 1978). The same underlying structural similarities that allow the formulation of such definitions led initially to the classification of *Homo sapiens* as a primate and continue to inform paleoanthropological research into the details of human evolution. But we lack a corresponding set of *ecological and behavioral* characteristics defining the order.

Such diversity poses a problem for the student of ecology and behavior, particularly when the goal is to reconstruct ancestral adaptations. Clearly a reference point should not be chosen on the basis of *post hoc* hypotheses emphasizing the importance of one aspect of adaptation over another. For example, imagine we are concerned with the evolution of human social behavior. Should we base our analysis on an analogy to gibbons, because they form long-term pair-bonds; or chimpanzees, because they make and use tools; or baboons, because they inhabit the savannahs where the genus *Homo* apparently evolved? The answer is "none

[1]Department of Anthropology, University of Pittsburgh, Pittsburgh, Pennsylvania 15260.

Steven J. C. Gaulin, "A Jarman/Bell Model of Primate Feeding Niches," *Human Ecology*, vol. 7, no. 1 , pp. 1–20. Copyright © 1979 by Plenum Publishing Corporation. Reprinted with permission by Springer Science+Business Media.

of the above," because these approaches, already assuming a dominant causal factor, lead to simplistic and self-confirmatory analyses. To the morphologist, the primates comprise a unified group only because their underlying structural similarities are understood. If the basic organizing principles of behavior and ecology could be found, "diversity" would become "pattern"; generalization and prediction would be possible.

On the basis of a growing number of field studies, it became apparent in the early 1960s that there were no easy generalizations to be made about primate behavior and ecology. Subsequently, several investigators have recognized the need for a synthetic approach (Crook and Gartlan, 1966; Crook, 1970; Denham, 1971; Eisenberg et al., 1972). These analyses have been of great value both for their emphasis on ecology as prior in a causal chain leading to other aspects of adaptation, and for their insights into the relationships between ecological and behavioral variables. But they have often been flawed by assuming, either explicitly or implicitly, the efficacy of the mechanism of group selection (cf. Maynard Smith, 1964; Williams, 1966; Williams, 1971). Moreover, they have lacked generality because they do not appeal to a consistent set of explanatory principles.

This paper will attempt to organize some of the diversity found within the order Primates in terms of strictly Darwinian logic, and by reference to some simple models from the fields of theoretical ecology and physiology. It seems reasonable to retain the assumption that the ecological niche will constrain (or at least render more or less efficient) various types of behavior. The focus here is mainly on principles that may explain primate ecological diversity.

FEEDING STRATEGY THEORY

Unlike plants, animals are consumers; they must harvest the resources out of which young are made. It follows that natural selection will tend to favor individuals who maximize the rate of resource-to-offspring conversion (Schoener, 1971). Broadly speaking, this process can be divided into two components: resource *accrual* and resource *conversion*. The set of behavioral, morphological, and physiological characters selected to maximize the rate of resource conversion may be called the animal's *reproductive strategy*. Selection to maximize resource accrual produces a set of adaptations that is referred to as a *feeding strategy* (Schoener, 1971). This paper discusses primate feeding strategies.

If natural selection is to shape feeding strategy it must be the case that: (1) there is some genetic basis to the components of feeding strategy and (2) dietary quantity and quality affect reproductive success such that individuals who feed less efficiently are selected against. It is assumed that the morphological and physiological components of feeding strategy are subject to genetic influence within a broad range of environmental conditions; but what of the behavioral components? The demonstration of such a genetic influence in slowly maturing organisms is difficult because the requisite breeding experiments would require many years. Moreover, we expect natural selection to favor alleles that produce a facultative response, tracking the optimal phenotype (in this case behavior) in different environments (Williams, 1966; Seger, in press). The end product of such gene-environment interactions is difficult to distinguish from "learning." One way to solve this methodological problem would be to short-circuit the facultative response by exceeding the range of environments to which the alleles are adapted. If the animal fails to respond "intelligently," the strong inference is that it has been designed by natural selection with other "expectations" (cf. Garcia and Ervin, 1968; Garcia and Hankins, 1977).

In the case of the primates, a study of mouse lemurs (*Microcebus murinus*) has provided relevant data. The animals were maintained in captivity and offered a fixed proportion of fruits and animal foods over the annual cycle. Consumption of each type was determined by weighing the unconsumed portion of each on a daily basis. Both animals captured in the wild and those born and reared entirely in captivity chose foods in proportion to the seasonal abundance of each in the animal's natural habitat (Andriantsiferana and Rahandraha, 1973). In other words, these animals had "expectations" as to which food types would be more readily available at different times of the annual cycle and they fed accordingly, failing to exploit what was an unprecedented and therefore "incomprehensible" pattern of food abundances.

There are numerous studies in support of the second requisite—an interaction between nutritional status and reproductive success (see reviews by Sadleir, 1969a,b; Schoener, 1971; Gaulin and Konner, 1977). The particular ways in which dietary quantity or quality affect fitness may vary somewhat from species to species, but the known effects can be summarized briefly. For both males and females poor diets delay sexual maturity and result in smaller adult body size. This latter effect reduces fertility or litter size directly in females; in males the consequences are indirect but sometimes very strong, reducing reproductive success primarily by affecting the outcome of male-male competition and female choice. For example, Charles-Dominique (1972) showed that among Demidoff's bushbabies (*Galago demidovii*) only the heaviest 10% of males nest with estrous females. For females, reduced food intake may lower ovulation rates, shorten breeding seasons, and produce higher rates of fetal resorption and lactational failure. Among males its consequences include decreased sperm count, motility, and longevity.

Additional evidence that natural selection can produce animals that are able to make optimal food choices derives from physiological psychology (Halstead and Gallagher, 1962; Rozin, 1967, 1969; Rozin and Kalat, 1971). Although this work has been criticized for its use of laboratory rats as subjects, for our purposes this only renders the results more convincing. For hundreds of generations these animals have been exposed to completely uniform diets and a controlled breeding program, and were thus insulated from the action of natural selection with respect to feeding strategy. However, these rats are still able to make extremely subtle discriminations, choosing, for example, between two diets that are both adequate in all major nutrients except that one of them, although it contains an equivalent amount of protein, is deficient in a single amino acid (Rodgers and Harper, 1970).

Optimization of feeding choice is a considerably more complicated problem in the real world than in any experimental situation. Foods in nature do not come pelletized, purified, and delivered on trays; they must be found, harvested, sometimes subdued, and detoxified. Natural foods thus have associated costs as well as benefits. The theoretical models of autecology have made a major contribution in explicating the interactions among these costs and benefits and their role in shaping diet choice (Emlen, 1966; McArthur and Pianka, 1966; Schoener, 1971). The following equation has been suggested by Schoener (1971) to measure the relative value of food items:

where e_i/t_i represents an index of net energy yield per unit time from items of type i. According to this model an animal can feed optimally by ranking items in order of decreasing e/t and eating just far enough down the list to satisfy its metabolic requirements. If the best food item (highest e/t) is so abundant that the animal can restrict its diet to this type of food and still be assured an adequate intake, the animal should be monophagous. If the density of the best item is lower than this, it will be necessary to include one or

$$\frac{e_i}{t_i} = \frac{\text{potential energy} - \text{pursuit costs} - \text{handling and eating costs}}{\text{pursuit time} + \text{handling and eating time}}$$

more less optimal item types in the diet in order to reach a satisfactory level of food intake. A surprising prediction of the model is that the inclusion or exclusion of an item type should be independent of its density. A good item should always be taken when it is encountered, but it may not be encountered often; poor foods should not be eaten no matter how frequently they are encountered. This prediction has been verified experimentally by Krebs *et al.* (1977). On the other hand, the density of an item is expected to affect the composition of the diet through its effects on the inclusion or exclusion of other item types. For example, if an item type already included in diet becomes more abundant, the increase in food intake which results may allow the animal to delete one or more of its poorest item types (lowest e/t) from the diet. The converse is also true, so that a decrease in the density of a food item will necessitate the inclusion of some new item type(s) to prevent a deficit in food intake. In general then, high overall food density will permit specialization on one or a few food types while low food density forces the animal to exploit a wider range of foods (Schoener, 1971; Wrangham, 1977).

The model presented above can be expanded to more closely approximate reality. For instance, search costs and times are not included. It is assumed that the animal searches for all item types simultaneously and thus any cost (or time) is unassociated with a particular item. This will, of course, not be true whenever items are patchily distributed such that certain subhabitats contain only certain kinds of food items. Both Schoener (1971) and Emlen (1966) have produced models that incorporate search cost and time. Interestingly, these more complicated models yield the same predictions with respect to the effect of food density on diet breadth. A decrease in density results in an increase in the average search time between food items. This in turn reduces the expected profit of skipping an item and continuing to search for a better one. Therefore fewer foods are rejected and the range of foods eaten expands.

Both models assume that natural selection acts to maximize caloric intake. While necessary for maintenance and function in animals, energy is not sufficient; many specific nutrients are needed in large or small quantities. A model incorporating these needs is inherently more complicated not only because the goal (a balanced diet) involves many more variables than does one based on energy maximization, but also because potential foods do not contain uniform proportions of the various required nutrients. Thus one item type may be a good protein source, white another is high in sodium. The necessity of maintaining a balanced diet may more profoundly affect food choice for animals under conditions of high food density. When food density is low, the animal will already be eating a diverse diet; this makes it likely that specific nutrient requirements are satisfied in the course of maintaining an adequate energy supply. Animals under conditions of high food density may, however, be prevented from going all the way to monophagy by their needs for specific substances which cannot be met simply by feeding on the single item type which provides the highest net energy yield per unit time.

The reproductive success of plants may sometimes be favorably affected when they are eaten. For example, animals may disperse seeds, render them more likely to germinate due to the action of certain digestive enzymes on the seed coat, or foster their early survival by depositing them with a supply of organic fertilizer. But such symbioses probably do not represent the general case: predation will usually drastically reduce the reproductive success of prey. To the extent that this is so, prey species will have evolved counterstrategies which decrease the benefit/cost ratio to their predators. One class of such defensive measures among plants involves the synthesis of toxic secondary compounds. Animals may evolve detoxifying mechanisms, but even where they exist, these mechanisms are often rate-limited such that only small quantities of any particular toxin may be processed in a given time period (Freeland and Janzen, 1974). Thus a general model would take account of the necessity to minimize toxin ingestion rates while maintaining an adequate flow of essential nutrients.

Finally, the digestion of foods is generally assumed to be simultaneous with subsequent feeding, but this may be unrealistic. For animals exploiting nutrient-poor foods, nutrient extraction may be the bottleneck in the resource harvesting process. In such cases it may be possible to increase the efficiency of digestion by allocating specific blocks of time to it alone. Some primate species do this, alternating periods of feeding and "resting," for example, Siamangs (Chivers, 1971) and howler monkeys (Richard, 1970; Gaulin, 1977).

Although these ideas are very general, they yield specific predictions regarding diet among the various species of primates when some intrinsic properties of both the potential foods and their consumers are taken into account.

QUALITY AND ABUNDANCE OF POTENTIAL FOODS

Several investigators have studied the nutritional composition of primate diets. Their results are presented in Table I, regrouped by food type. It is apparent that foods differ in the proportions of various nutrients they offer. Fruits and gums are high in sugars; seeds and insects (and to a lesser degree, leaves) are better protein sources. Thus to the extent that animals substitute one food type for another, such substitutions will tend to occur among comparable food types. However, foods also differ in overall quality. Some types contain relatively larger proportions of nutritive substances such as protein, sugars, or lipids; others contain large percentages of water and cellulose (or fiber) and offer little metabolizable material per unit weight.

The food types in Table I are ranked by approximate overall quality, the poorest item at the top. It is interesting that the highest-quality items are also the least abundant. A large fraction of plant biomass is composed of stems, which are structural components with very thick, sturdy cell walls; from the predators' viewpoint, these cell walls obstruct nutrient extraction. Mature leaves, the photosynthetic centers of the plant, are also relatively abundant, and they too have a large percentage of cell mass tied up in indigestible cell wall. Cell wall thickness is positively correlated with the age of a leaf (French, 1957; Campbell and Cassady, 1954). The thinner cell walls of growing leaves render a large proportion of their bulk digestible and their nutrients more easily removed. Most plants produce leaves and fruit seasonally. Hence young leaves, and reproductive structures such as flowers, fruits, and seeds, are not continuously available; over the annual cycle, they are relatively rare. Moreover, since the reproductive success of a plant is tied to the return it gets on energy and matter invested in flowers, fruits, and seeds, plants have in many cases evolved strategies for the defense of these parts (e.g., thorns, shells, toxins). This further reduces the availability of these food types to their predators.

Unlike other plant food sources, gums are not ordinarily made available by the plant; the predator must do something to initiate their availability. Usually, damage to the outer protective layers of the trunk or branches causes some exudate to flow. By gnawing through the bark an animal can create a gum-producing site, but yield per unit time from any one such site is very small, and cannot be effectively increased by the predator. Thus animals that depend heavily on gums for food must develop large numbers of such sites and visit them on a regular basis. Finally, since they themselves are consumers, insects will always comprise a small portion of the biomass relative to plant material and will also have active defense and escape strategies that further reduce their net availability. In summary, quality and availability are negatively correlated characteristics of potential food items. The implications of this relationship for feeding strategy can be made apparent in the light of certain facts of animal physiology.

THE JARMAN/BELL PRINCIPLE

Metabolic requirements are a positive function of body weight over a wide range of animals. The relationship is linear when the data are plotted on log-log coordinates. This indicates an exponential relationship between body weight and metabolic rate; it is important that the exponent is usually near 0.75, and always significantly less than unity (Hemmingsen, 1960; Kleiber, 1961; Schmidt-Nielsen, 1970). This means that

Table I. Composition of the Foods of Feral Primates[a]

FOOD		% H₂O	PRO-TEIN	CARBO-HY-DRATES	RE-DUCING SUGARS	LIPIDS	CELLU-LOSE	FIBER	TOTAL ASH	CA	P
						% OF DRY WEIGHT					
Stems, pith	X̄	91.3	12.1			4.8		20.6	11.6		
	SD	1.6	1.0			2.3		12.8	2.0		
	n	2	3			3		3	3		
Leaves	X̄	78.6	14.0	61.7	11.6	3.7	18.6	15.3	11.4	1.86	.31
	SD	7.4	7.9	11.5	10.3	2.0	8.3	4.8	3.7	1.02	.34
	n	6	14	8	4	14	5	7	9	7	7
Flowers	X̄	78.4	16.7	82.0	10.4	3.4	16.6	5.6	7.5	.20	.41
flower	SD	4.1	5.2		8.1	3.6	1.2	0.8	2.0		
buds	n	5	5	1	3	5	2	2	4	1	1
Fruits	X̄	70.4	6.6	77.7	29.0	15.6	25.2	14.3	4.0	.27	.28
(monocots)	SD	12.9	4.9	17.0	21.2	21.9		12.1	2.0	.16	.34
	n	7	8	3	3	9	1	3	3	4	4
Fruits	X̄	77.2	6.4	84.0	34.0	4.3	10.0	9.3	5.5	.35	.20
(dicots)	SD	10.3	3.4	11.2	15.2	9.7	8.1	6.1	8.1	.37	.11
	n	53	50	23	20	50	20	23	23	34	34
Seeds	X̄	11.6	17.7	67.3		7.7	5.0	5.5	3.8	.19	.22
	SD	4.0	8.5	15.9		8.1	2.0	2.1	1.2	.06	.10
	n	6	6	6		6	4	2	6	2	2
Gums	X̄	14.7		98.5	1.9				1.5		
	SD										
	n	1		1	1				1		
Insects	X̄		54.4		2.0	24.2				.03	.64
	SD		4.6			8.1				.03	.59
	n		2		1	2				2	2

[a]The mean, standard deviation, and sample size are given for each food type and nutrient analysis. Because these results are gleaned from various studies, nutrient categories are not mutually exclusive. (Modified from Gaulin and Konner, 1977.)

metabolic rate increases with increasing body weight, but not as rapidly. Thus, while large animals will have larger total metabolic requirements than small animals, they will actually require less energy intake per unit of body weight: the ratio, energy requirement/body weight, is a decreasing function of body size. Where specific nutrient requirements have been investigated they also scale to about the 3/4 power of body weight [see, for example, Munro's (1969) review of protein use in mammals].

This negative allometric relationship between body weight and nutritional requirements has implications for the coevolution of diet and body size; these implications are referred to collectively as the Jarman/Bell principle (Jarman, 1968, 1974; Bell, 1971; Geist, 1974). The logic is as follows: because of their high daily total food requirements, large animals will usually be unable to base their diets primarily on rare food items. They should eat those items that rank high in e/t (see above) whenever they are encountered, but low abundance relative to the animals' needs will prevent high-quality foods from comprising a large percentage of the diet. On the other hand, due to lower per-unit-weight food requirements, large animals do not need to provide a high rate of nutrient flow to their tissues, and are thus able to subsist on low-quality foods. For small animals the problems are reversed. They do not have large total requirements and can thus make up large fractions of their diet from relatively rare foods. However, they must nourish their tissues at high rates and therefore must concentrate on high-quality foods. This logic is represented graphically in Fig. 1.

It is possible to extrapolate somewhat from this basic model. For example, when other selective factors such as predator pressure or physical constraints of the niche are also shaping body size (e.g., an animal that nests in tree cavities could not be very large) the realized morphology will be a compromise. Under such conditions animals may evolve specializations that allow them to deviate somewhat from their expected diets. In fact, one can predict the kinds of specialization mat might evolve, depending on the direction of the deviation. For a large animal eating rare, high-quality foods (feeding like a small animal), nutrient extraction is less a problem than is total nutrient harvest. Thus these animals should have specializations permitting them to harvest larger numbers of food items and to do so more efficiently. Conversely, a small animal exploiting abundant but low-quality foods could certainly fulfill its total nutrient requirement if it could just remove nutrients from such foods fast enough to allow it to continue foraging. In such cases, specializations in the digestive system leading to more efficient nutrient extraction are expected. In general these specializations—improved harvesting in animals eating rare foods, and improved digestion in animals eating poor-quality foods—will be developed more strongly the farther a species deviates from its expected diet, as predicted by body weight. These feeding adaptations may even evolve, to a lesser degree, among species that fit the predicted pattern, but which represent dietary extremes within their taxonomic subgroup.

PRIMATE DIETS

To test these ideas, data on the feeding habits of 102 primate species have been gathered from the literature (see Tables IIa-d). In the tables, the horizontal axes are divided to create 11 diet types. Based on the data in Table I, diets are arranged from left to right in order of increasing quality and rarity of their constituent foods.

The Jarman-Bell Principle

	total nutrient requirement	$\dfrac{\text{nutrient requirement}}{\text{body weight}}$
large animal	large (abundant foods)	small (poor quality foods)
small animal	small (rare foods)	large (high quality foods)

Fig. 1. Expected characteristics of foods as a function of total and relative nutrient requirement for large and small animals.

(The last category, "omnivorous," is not consistent with this ordering; indeed, because of the diversity of such diets it is not possible to generalize about the characteristics of their constituent foods. Omnivorous diets are therefore discussed separately below.) On the vertical axes genera are arranged in order of decreasing average body weight from top to bottom. The data are presented by taxonomic subgroups on the assumption that comparisons made among closely related species are confounded less by the effects of disparate and independently evolved adaptations than are comparisons made among more divergent taxa.

The tables cannot be construed as regressions because neither axis approximates an interval scale; however, there is a clear trend from upper left to lower right, indicating that heavier species eat low-quality, abundant foods and lighter species eat high-quality, rare foods. Among the prosimians there are two striking exceptions. One of them, the aye-aye (*Daubentionia madagascariensis*) is a fairly large animal for its strongly insectivorous diet. It is highly specialized for harvesting wood-boring insect larvae (Petter, 1965). Large, open-rooted

Table IIa. Body weights of Prosimian Primates According to Diet Types[a]

Genus / Diet type	Leaves, Shoots, pith and bark	Leaves > fruit	Fruit > leaves	Fruit, leaves, and insects	Fruit only	Fruit > Insects	Insects > fruit	Insects, fruit, and gum	Gum > insects	Insects and small vertebrates	Omnivorous
Prosimians											
Indri	6250										
Propithecus		3500									
Daubentonia							2800				
Lemur (5)		1400–3000	1960								
Hapalemur	1300										
Avahi	1300										
Perodicticus						1100					
Lepilemur		600									
Nycticebus							600				
Galago (4)								60–1100			
Cheirogaleus (2)						180–450					
Phaner								440			
Loris										320	
Microcebus (2)								60–385			
Euoticus									270		
Arctocebus							200				
Tarsius										115	
$\bar{X}$	2950	2025	1960			577	1200	366	270	218	

[a]Primate species are assigned to one of 11 diet types. Food types comprising less than 5% of the diet are ignored in making this assignment. Fruit > leaves indicates that both are elements of the diet but that fruit comprises the larger fraction. The mean adult body weight (or range of adult body weights) in grams appears in the appropriate genus/diet cell. Where a number in parentheses follows the genus name, it indicates that data were available on several species within that taxon, and in such cases maximum and minimum species weights appear. Mean body weights for each dietary type are given at the bottom of each table. (After Gaulin and Konner, 1977.)

Table IIb. Body Weights of Ceboid Primates According to Diet Types[a]

Diet type / Genus	Leaves, Shoots, pith and bark	Leaves > fruit	Fruit > leaves	Fruit, leaves and insects	Fruit only	Fruit > Insects	Insects > fruit	Insects, fruit, and gum	Gum > insects	Insects and small vertebrates	Omnivorous
New World monkeys											
Brachyteles	9500										
Ateles (2)		6200–7800									
Alouatta (2)	7200	6700									
Lagothrix					6300						
Cebus (3)						3100–3200					
Chiropotes					2950						
Pithecia					1100						
Saimiri (2)						800–850					
Callicebus						600					
Leontopithecus							520				
Saguinus (6)						340–500					
Callithrix									220		
Cebuella									140		
$\bar{X}$	8100	6900			3450	1427	520		180		

[a]See footnote to Table IIa.

incisors permit it to gnaw through bark, exposing the larval chambers; a highly elongated manual digit allows extraction of the larvae. The aye-aye's large ears may also be a feeding adaptation, helping it to locate larvae by auditory cues (Petter and Petter, 1967; Napier and Napier, 1967). Thus the aye-aye clearly possesses a series of harvesting specializations that make insectivory viable despite the animal's relatively large total nutrient requirements. There may also be some unusual characteristics of the prey which allow their predators to evolve large bodies. In this respect it is interesting that woodpeckers—whose ecology is so similar to that of the aye-aye that they have apparently been unable to colonize its Madagascan homeland (Cartmill, 1974)—are among the largest insectivorous birds.

The sportive lemur (*Lepilemur mustelinus*) represents a deviation in the opposite direction: it is extremely small folivore. *Lepilemur* possesses a unique feeding adaptation: it is coprophagous, that is, it reingests its own fecal material (Hladik and Charles-Dominique, 1974). Coprophagy makes available to the body a larger percentage of the food's potential value, in effect converting nutrient-poor items to nutrient-rich items. Certain small lagomorphs are also highly foli-vorous and have independently evolved coprophagous strategies.

Among the primates, New World monkeys best exemplify the Jarman/Bell principle. Mean body weights follow the predicted trend with no reversals and the extreme species (in size) show some expected specializations. Howler monkeys (*Alouatta sp.*) have evolved an expanded caecum (Hill, 1962; Fooden, 1964; Amerasinghe

Table IIc. Body Weights of Cercopithecoid Primates According to Diet Types[a]

Genus \ Diet type	Leaves, Shoots, pith and bark	Leaves > fruit	Fruit > leaves	Fruit, leaves and insects	Fruit only	Fruit > insects	Insects > fruit	Insects, fruit, and gum	Gum > insects	Insects and small vertebrates	Omnivorous
Old World monkeys											
Papio (3)											16,000–26,000
Mandrillus (2)				20,000							
Nasalis	17,000										
Theropithecus		17,000									
Presbytis (8)		6,000–12,500									
Macaca (9)			12,000	5500–8500		6000					10,000
											8000
Erythrocebus											
Colobus (4)		3700–8000									
Cercocebus (2)			7900								
Cercopithecus (13)			3000–6500	1000–5200	7500						
X̄	17,000	8065	6275	7585	7500	6000					15,800

[a]See footnote to Table IIa.

et al., 1971) for more efficient digestion of their nutrient-poor diet (Hladik et al., 1971). The small marmosets (Callithrix jaccus and Cebuella pygmaea), which eat a large proportion of tree gums (Kinzey et al., 1975; Coimbra-Filho and Mittermeier, 1976, in press) possess rather unusual anterior teeth that may be an adaptation for feeding on gums (since the initial access to this food source requires gnawing through bark).

Few small-bodied forms occur among Old World monkeys and, consistent with the Jarman/Bell principle, diets based primarily on rare, high-quality foods are equally absent. At the low-quality diet extreme, the colobines exhibit specialized digestive systems of a ruminant type involving symbiotic digestion in a separate forestomach. These feeding adaptations have been studied in detail for the genera Presbytis and Colobus (Bauchop and Martucci, 1968; Ohwaki et al., 1974; Amerasinghe et al., 1971). Among the cercopithecoids there are several omnivorous species, such as baboons (Papio sp.), some macaques (Macaca sp.), and the patas monkey (Erythrocebus patas). When the Old World monkeys are grouped by diet type (see Table IIc), these omnivorous species show the second largest mean body size, but their unifying characteristic is that they inhabit open country rather than forest. A possible causal relationship between habitat type and body size is discussed below.

The apes, also large-bodied species, cluster on the left side of the table. However, a trend consistent with the Jarman/Bell principle is obscured by the methodological necessity to limit the number of diet types. The diet of Gorilla gorilla is about 90% leaves, stalks, and other structural components. It is one of the poorest known for any primate (Schaller, 1963; Fossey, 1974). Only 25% of the chimpanzee's (Pan troglodytes) diet is composed of such nutrient-poor items (Rahm, 1967; Suzuki, 1969; Hladik, 1973; Wrangham, 1977).

Table IId. Body Weights of Hominoid Primates According to Diet Types[a]

Genus	Leaves, Shoots, Pith, and bark	Leaves > fruit	Fruit > leaves	Fruit, leaves, and insects	Fruit only	Fruit > Insects	Insects > fruit	Insects, fruit, and gum	Gum > insects	Insects and small vertebrates	Omnivorous
Apes											
Gorilla	125,000										
Pongo			55,000								
Homo											50,000
Pan (2)			35,000–46,000								
Hylobates (4)		10,700	5100–5800		5700						
$\bar{X}$	125,000	10,700	29,380		5700						50,000

[a]See footnote to Table IIa.

The orangutan (*Pongo pygmaeus*), intermediate in body weight between the two other great apes, has a diet of both leaves and fruits (Horr, 1972; Rodman, 1973; MacKinnon, 1974). Although researchers disagree as to which component makes up the larger proportion of the orangutan's diet (quite possibly reflecting real differences between their study populations), their estimates of the percentage of leaf material fall between those for chimpanzees and gorillas. Virtually no information is available on the ecology of the pygmy chimpanzee (*P. paniscus*, see Nishida, 1972) but the Jarman/Bell principle allows the prediction that it will be found to be the most frugivorous of the great apes.

The diets of both the chimpanzee and the orangutan contain a surprisingly large percentage of fruit, given the substantial body weights of these animals. Consequently, they should exhibit adaptations for increasing their harvest of these relatively rare food items. The adaptations seem to be social, or more precisely, asocial. The orangutan has long been something of an embarrassment to those primatologists who expect complex sociality to be exhibited only by the "higher" primates. Since orangutans are, like ourselves, members of the elite Hominoidea, they could at least be decently gregarious. They have, however, refused to exhibit any form of social organization beyond the temporary mother-offspring bond. Solitary habits may be a means of reducing feeding competition among individuals. Animals feeding on foods that are rare, relative to their total nutrient requirements, simply may not be able to afford intraspecific competition. Even among the more social chimpanzee there seem to exist behavioral adaptations that reduce the effects of feeding competition since: (1) party size is highly variable and is proportional to the size of food source being exploited, (2) probability of feeding decreases when party size increases, and (3) when the same season is compared in different years, party size is proportional to food abundance (Wrangham, 1977).

A similar analysis may explain the distribution of sociality among the pro-simians. Many of these species also show strong solitary tendencies and this has generally been attributed to their "primitive" nature; they have evolved neither the morphology nor the behavior of the more "advanced" anthropoids. But many prosimians are predominantly insectivorous. They would suffer both exploitative and interference competition (Miller, 1969) if they fed in groups on such relatively rare and often elusive prey items. Small insectivores are thus expected to avoid conspecifics and to forage alone. However, some larger prosimians, notably *Lemur sp.*, have adopted a rather monkey-like diet of fruits and leaves. It is precisely among these species, where total nutrient supply is presumably not so serious a problem, that "advanced" social grouping tendencies have developed.

HUMAN DIET AS FEEDING STRATEGY

The ideas developed above can be employed to broaden our understanding of human dietary patterns and their emergence. Indeed, much controversy has surrounded the question of the feeding adaptations of our hominid ancestors (Washburn and Lancaster, 1968; Jolly, 1970). But remarkably little attention has been paid to the problem of what human beings presently eat, considering that this information would constitute the logical starting point for any analysis of the evolution of human feeding adaptations. Much has been made of the fact that humans are relatively carnivorous primates, but we are very far from being specialized carnivores. The point is not that we eat meat but that meat is one element, among many, in a typical human diet (see the ecological material in Lee and DeVore, 1968; Gaulin and Konner, 1977). In other words, when viewed in the general context of primate ecology, the most striking feature of human diet is its diversity, its lack of reliance on any particular food type. On behavioral grounds one could conclude that the basic feeding pattern of *Homo sapiens* is omnivory.

This conclusion is sustained by comparative studies of mammalian teeth. Even before Darwin (1859) had published his explanation of the mechanism of evolution, Owen (1840-1845) wrote:

> If we had to judge only by fossil remains we should be warranted in concluding from the human teeth that the species was not intended, under all circumstances and in all places, to subsist upon either animal or vegetable food exclusively. It would be obvious at the first glance that they were intermediate in character between the typical carnivorous and the typical herbivorous dentitions: the presence of canines and the absence of the complex structure arising from the interblending of vertical plates of the different dental tissue in the molars, would prove that the food could not have been the coarse uncooked vegetable substances for which complex molars are adapted; and on the other hand the feeble development of the canines and the absence of molars of the sectorial shape and opposed like scissor-blades, would equally show that the species had been unfitted for obtaining habitual sustenance from the raw quivering fibre of recently killed animals.

All contemporary omnivorous primates exploit savannah or forest-fringe environments. Paleontological evidence suggests that early hominids inhabited these open or ecotonal regions. On the basis of the total faunal assemblages from hominid-bearing strata in south and east Africa, the australopithecines are thought to have lived in savannah habitats (Cooke, 1963; Butzer, 1971). The commitment to open country may be considerably older, however; Shipman's (1977) analysis of material from the *Ramapithecus*-bearing, middle Miocene deposits at Fort Ternan led her to conclude that this early hominid was "primarily a savannah inhabitant" which also exploited the ecotone between forested and open habitats.

The association between omnivory and open habitats can be understood by reference to Schoener's (1971) feeding strategy model. If food abundance is lower in open than in forested habitats, open country animals should exploit a wider range of food types: they should be more omnivorous (unless they evolve specializations for exploiting grasses, as many ungulates and *Theropithecus gelada* have done). Realistic estimates of food availability are difficult to obtain. Biomass, or some fraction or correlate thereof, is often used

(Coelho *et al.*, 1976; Jorde and Spuhler, 1974). However, this approach ignores the fact that seasonality, interspecific competition, varying rates of turnover, and prey counter-strategies may all reduce the proportion of biomass available to the consumer at any time. Nevertheless, in the absence of a better measure, and given the tremendous differences between open and forested habitats, crude biomass will serve as a reasonable estimate of food availability in these two habitat types. Results of the comparison are not ambiguous; biomass in tropical forests is roughly two orders of magnitude greater than that in tropical grasslands. For example, Fittkau and Klinge (1973) estimate biomass in the Amazonian rain forest at 1100 metric tons/ hectare, whereas only the most productive African savannahs produce a standing crop of 20 metric tons/ hectare (Bourliere and Hadley, 1970). Even allowing that some 55% of the biomass in tropical forests may be tied up in such relatively nonnutritive structures as trunks, branches, and larger roots (Odum, 1970), marked differences in the productivity of these two habitat types remain. Lower habitat productivity will force inhabitants of open environments to eat more kinds of foods, thereby including a higher proportion of poor-quality foods in their diets. This in turn may create a selection pressure for larger body size so as to utilize more efficiently these poor-quality items. The large average body size and omnivorous tendencies of open-country cercopithecoids are compatible with this analysis. Moreover, the relatively large body size of extinct hominids (McHenry, 1974) and their apparent adaptation to open habitats suggest that they too had omnivorous diets including a high proportion of low-quality foods.

Although the correlation between body size and feeding niche among contemporary primates is not highly compatible with the idea that Pleistocene hominids were strongly carnivorous, certain elements of feeding strategy theory might support a limited carnivore model. Large animals can exploit rare, high-quality foods if they possess specialized harvesting adaptations. Tools and social hunting could have served this function. Moreover, the relative contribution to the diet of any acceptable food item is proportional to its abundance in the habitat (Schoener, 1971). Because animals comprise a larger proportion of total biomass in open country, they could make up a greater fraction of a savannah-dweller's diet. Of course the constraint on both these arguments is that, given a set of harvesting adaptations, the e/t (or, put more generally, the benefit/cost ratio) of a particular kind of food must be above some threshold value or that food will never be eaten regardless of its abundance. We cannot readily assess the efficiency of hominid foraging techniques, but we do have other reasons for believing that at least for many potential animal prey, e/t was below this threshold. Kay (1975) has systematically investigated the relationship between body weight and surface area of the postcanine teeth in modern primates and found an allometric relationship similar to the one described above. Moreover, there is an interaction with diet, such that folivores have relatively larger teeth than frugivores. Using published estimates of body weight and measurements of fossil teeth Kay concludes:

> the large size of the postcanines of all three [hominid] species compared with the great apes suggests that all *Australopithecus* species may have had diets higher in fiber and grit content.

This is precisely what one would expect if, in the course of shifting to an open-country niche, hominids were forced to expand their diets, becoming more omnivorous and eating a larger proportion of low-quality foods. Thus, taken together, modern human diet, past and present tooth structure and relative size, and hominid body weight and provenance form a coherent pattern which suggests that omnivory was the dominant hominid dietary adaptation, and that selection pressures arising from carnivory have been at most a minor factor in human evolution.

ACKNOWLEDGMENTS

I thank J. A. Kurland, A. Santa Luca, J. H. Schwartz, E. Trinkhaus, R. L. Trivers, and A. C. Walker for directing me to numerous helpful articles, and P. L. Shipman for permission to quote unpublished material. I. DeVore, N. Foltz, J. A. Kurland, J. Seger, and R. W. Wrangham constructively criticized earlier drafts. Kurland introduced me to the work of Geist and suggested the relevance of the Jarman/Bell principle to an analysis of primate feeding adaptations. G. LoAlbo and D. Rawe prepared the manuscript and R. Andrews drew Fig. 1.

REFERENCES

Amerasinghe, F. P., Van Cuylenberg, B. W. B., and Hladik, C. M. (1971). Comparative histology of the alimentary tract of Ceylon primates in correlation with the diet. *Ceylon Journal of Science, Biological Sciences* 9: 75–87.

Andriantsiferana, R., and Rahandraha, T. (1973). Variation saisonnaire du choix alimentaire spontane chez *Microcebus murinus*. *Comptes Rendus Academie des Sciences, Serie D* 277: 2025-2028.

Bauchop, T., and Martucci, R. W. (1968). Ruminant-like digestion of the langur monkey. *Science* 161: 698–700.

Bell, R. H. V. (1971). A grazing ecosystem in the Serengeti. *Scientific American* 225: 86–93.

Bourliere, R., and Hadley, M. (1970). The ecology of tropical savannas. *Annual Review of Ecology and Systematics* 1: 125–152.

Butzer, K. W. (1971). Another look at the Australopithecine cave breccias of the Transvaal. *American Anthropologist* 73: 1197–1201.

Campbell, R. S., and Cassady, J. T. (1954). Moisture and protein in forage on Louisiana forest ranges. *Journal of Range Management* 7: 41–42.

Cartmill, M. (1974). *Daubentonia, Dactylopsila*, Woodpeckers and klinorhynchy. In Martin, R. D., Doyle, G. A., and Walker, A. D. (eds.), *Prosimian Biology*. University of Pittsburgh Press, Pittsburgh.

Charles-Dominique, P. (1972). Ecologie et vie sociale de *Galago demidovii* (Fischer 1808, Prosimii). *Zeitschrift für Tierpsychologie, Suppl.* 9: 7–41.

Chivers, D. J. (1971). The Malayan siamang. *Malayan Nature Journal* 24: 78–86.

Coelho, A. M., Bramblett, C. A., Quick, L. B., and Bramblett, S. A. (1976), Resource availability and population density in primates: A socio-bioenergetic analysis of the energy budgets of Guatemalan howler and spider monkeys. *Primates* 17: 63–80.

Coimbra-Filho, A. F., and Mittermeier, R. A. (1976). Exudate-eating and tree-gouging in marmosets. *Nature (London)* 262: 630.

Coimbra-Filho, A. F., and Mittermeier, R. A. (in press). Tree-gouging, gum-eating and the "short-tusked" condition in *Callithrix* and *Cebuella*. In Kleinman, D. G. (ed.), *Proceedings of the Conference on the Biology and Conservation of the Callitrichidae*.

Cooke, H. B. S. (1963). Pleistocene mammal faunas of Africa, with particular reference to southern Africa. In Howell, F. C., and Bourliere, F. (eds.), *African Ecology and Human Evolution*, Volume 36, Viking Fund Publications in Anthropology, New York, pp. 65–116.

Crook, J. H. (1970). The socio-ecology of primates. In Crook, J. H. (ed.), *Social Behaviour in Birds and Mammals*. Academic Press, New York.

Crook, J. H., and Gartlan, J. S. (1966). Evolution of primate societies. *Nature (London)* 210: 1200-1203.

Darwin, C. (1859). *The Origin of Species*. John Murray, London.

Denham, W. W. (1971). Energy relations and some basic properties of primate social organization. *American Anthropologist* 73: 77-95.

Eisenberg, J. F., Muckenhirn, N. A., and Rudran, R. (1972). The relation between ecology and social structure in primates. *Science* 176: 863-874.

Emlen, J. M. (1966). The role of time and energy in food preference. *American Naturalist* 100: 611-617.

Fittkau, E. J., and Klinge, H. (1973). On biomass and trophic structure of the Central Amazonian rain forest ecosystem. *Biotropica* 5: 2-14.

Fooden, J. (1964). Stomach contents and gastrointestinal proportions of wild-shot Guianan monkeys. *American Journal of Physical Anthropology* 22: 227-231.

Fossey, D. (1974). Observations on home range of one group of mountain gorilla (*Gorilla gorilla beringei*). *Animal Behavior* 22: 568-581.

Freeland, W. J., and Janzen, D. H.: Strategies in herbivory by mammals: The role of plant secondary compounds. *American Naturalist* 108: 269-289.

French, M. H. (1957). Nutritional value of tropical grasses and fodders. *Herbage Abstracts* 27: 1–9.

Garcia, J., and Ervin, F. R. (1968). Gustatory-visceral and telereceptor-cutaneous conditioning—adaptation in internal and external milieus. *Comm. Behav. Biol.* 1 (pt. A): 389–415.

Garcia, J., and Hankins, W. G. (1977). On the orign of food aversion paradigms. In Barker, L. M., Domjan, M., and Best, M. (eds.), *Learning Mechanisms in Food Selection.* Baylor University Press, Waco, Texas.

Gaulin, S. J. C. (1977). The Ecology of *Alouatta seniculus* in Andean Cloud Forest. Ph.D. thesis, Harvard University.

Gaulin, S. J. C., and Konner, M. J. (1977). On the natural diet of primates, including humans. In Wurtman, R., and Wurtman, J. (eds.), *Nutrition and the Brain,* Vol. I. Raven Press, New York.

Geist, V. (1974). On the relationship of social evolution and ecology in ungulates. *American Zoologist* 14(1): 205–220.

Gregory, W. K. (1910). The orders of mammals. *Bulletin of The American Museum of Natural History* 27: 1–524.

Halstead, W. C., and Gallagher, B. B. (1962). Autoregulation of amino acid intake in the albino rat. *Journal of Comparative Physiology and Psychology* 55: 107–111.

Hemmingsen, A. M. (1960). Energy metabolism as related to body size and respiratory surfaces, and its evolution. Copenhagen: *Reports of the Steno Memorial Hospital and the Nordisk Insulinlaboratorium* 9: 1–110.

Hill, W. C. O. (1962). *Primates, Comparative Anatomy and Taxonomy,* Vol. V: Cebidae, Part B. University Press, Edinburgh.

Hladik, C. M. (1973). Alimentation et activité d'un groupe de chimpanzées réintroduits en forêt gabonaise. *Terre et Vie* 27: 343–423.

Hladik, C. M., and Charles-Dominique, P. (1974). The behavior and ecology of the sportive lemur (*Lepilemur mustelinus*) in relation to its dietary peculiarity. In Martin, R. D., Doyle, G. A., and Walker, A. C. (eds.), *Prosimian Biology.* University of Pittsburgh Press, Pittsburgh.

Hladik, C. M., Hladik, A., Bousset, J., Valdebouze, P., Virben, G., and DeLort-Laval, J. (1971). Le régime alimentaire des primates de l'ile de Barro-Colorado (Panama): ré sultats des analyses quantitatives. *Folia Primatologica* 16: 85–122.

Horr, D. A. (1972). The Borneo orang-utan. *Borneo Research Bulletin* 4: 46–50.

Jarman, P. (1968). The effect of the creation of Lake Kariba upon the terrestrial ecology of the middle Zambezi Valley, with particular references to the large mammals. Ph.D. dissertation, Manchester University.

Jarman, P. J. (1974). The social organization of antelope in relation to their ecology. *Behaviour* 58(3,4): 215–267.

Jolly, C. J. (1970). The seed-eaters: a new model of hominid differentiation based on a baboon analogy. *Man* (new series) 5: 5–26.

Jorde, L. B., and Spuhler, J. N. (1974). A statistical analysis of selected aspects of primate demography, ecology and social behavior. *Journal of Anthropological Research* 30: 199–224.

Kay, R. F. (1975). Allometry and early hominids. *Science* 189: 63.

Kinzey, W. G., Rosenberger, A. L., and Ramirez, M. (1975), Vertical clinging and leaping in a neotropical anthropoid. *Nature (London)* 225: 327–328.

Kleiber, M. A. (1961). *The Fire of Life: An Introduction to Animal Energetics.* Wiley, New York.

Krebs, J. R., Erichsen, J. T., Webber, M. T., and Charnov, E. L. (1977). Optimal prey selection in the Great Tit (*Parus major*). *Animal Behavior* 25: 30–38.

Lee, R. B., and DeVore, I. (1968). *Man the Hunter.* Aldine, Chicago.

MacKinnon, J. (1974). The behaviour and ecology of wild orang-utans (*Pongo pygmaeus*). *Animal Behavior* 22: 3–74.

Maynard Smith, J. (1964). Group selection and kin selection. *Nature (London)* 201: 1145–1147.

McArthur, R. H., and Pianka, E. R. (1966). On optimal use of a patchy environment. *American Naturalist* 100: 603–609.

McHenry, H. M. (1974). How large were the australopithecines? *American Journal of Physical Anthropology* 40: 329–340.

Miller, R. S. (1969). Competition and species diversity. *Brookhaven Symposia in Biology* 22: 63–70.

Munro, H. N. (1969). Evolution of protein metabolism in mammals. In Munro, H. N. (ed.), *Mammalian Protein Metabolism,* Vol. 3. Academic Press, New York.

Napier, J. R., and Napier, P. H. (1967). *A Handbook of Living Primates.* Academic Press, New York.

Nishida, T. (1972). Preliminary information on the pygmy chimpanzees (*Pan paniscus*) of the Congo Basin. *Primates* 13: 415–425.

Odum, H. T. (1970). Summary: An emerging view of the ecological system at El Verde. In Odum, H. T. (ed.), *A Tropical Rainforest.* Office of Information Services, Washington D.C.

Ohwaki, K., Hungate, R. E., Lotter, L., Hofmann, R. R., and Maloiy, G. (1974). Stomach fermentation in East African colobus monkeys in their natural state. *Applied Microbiology* 27: 713–723.

Owen, R. (1840–1845). *Odontography.* Hippolyte Bailliere, London.

Petter, J.-J. (1965). The lemurs of Madagascar. In DeVore, I. (ed.), *Primate Behavior: Field Studies of Lemurs, Monkeys and Apes.* Holt, Rinehart and Winston, New York.

Petter, J.-J., and Petter, A. (1967). The aye-aye of Madagascar. In Altman, S. A. (ed.), *Social Communication among Primates.* University of Chicago Press, Chicago.

Rahm, U. (1967). Observations during chimpanzee captures in the Congo. In Starck, D., Schneider, R., and Kuhn, H.-J. (eds.), *Neve Ergebnisse der Primatologie.* Gustav Fischer Verlag, Stuttgart.

Richard, A. (1970). A comparative study of the activity patterns and behavior of *Alouatta villosa* and *Ateles geoffroyi. Folia Primatologica* 12: 241–263.

Rodgers, Q. R., and Harper, A. E. (1970). Selection of a solution containing histidine by rats fed a histidine-imbalanced diet. *Journal of Comparative Physiology and Psychology* 72: 66–71.

Rodman, P. S. (1973). Synecology of Bornean primates. Ph.D. dissertation, Harvard University,

Rozin, P. (1967). Specific aversions as a component of specific hungers, *Journal of Comparative Physiology and Psychology* 64: 237–242.

Rozin, P. (1969). Adaptive food sampling patterns in vitamin deficient rats. *Journal of Comparative Physiology and Psychology* 69: 126–132.

Rozin, P., and Kalat, J. W. (1971). Specific hungers and poison avoidance as adaptive specializations of learning. *Psychological Review* 78: 459–486.

Sadleir, R. M. F. S. (1969a). *The Ecology of Reproduction in Wild and Domestic Mammals.* Methuen, London.

Sadleir, R. M. F. S. (1969b). The role of nutrition in the reproduction of wild mammals. *Journal of Reproduction and Fertility. Supplement* 6: 39–48.

Schaller, G. B. (1963), *The Mountain Gorilla: Ecology and Behavior.* University of Chicago Press, Chicago.

Schmidt-Nielsen, K. (1970). *Animal Physiology,* 3rd ed. Prentice-Hall, Englewood Cliffs, N.J.

Schoener, T. W. (1971). Theory of feeding strategies. *Annual Review of Ecology and Systematics* 2: 369–404.

Schwartz, J. H., Tattersall, I., and Eldredge, N. (1978). Phylogeny and classification of the primates revisited. *Yearbook of Physical Anthropology* 21: 95–133.

Seger, J. (in press). Models of gene action and the problem of behavior. In DeVore, I. (ed,), *Sociobiology and the Social Sciences.* Aldine, Chicago.

Shipman, P. L. (1977). Paleoecology, taphonomic history and population dynamics of the vertebrate fossil assemblage from the middle Miocene deposits exposed at Fort Ternan, Kenya. Ph.D. thesis, New York University.

Simpson, G. G. (1940). Studies on the earliest primates. *Bulletin of the American Museum of Natural History* 77: 185–212.

Suzuki, A. (1969). An ecological study of chimpanzees in a savanna woodland. *Primates* 10: 103–148.

Washburn, S. L., and Lancaster, C. S. (1968). The evolution of hunting. In Lee, R. B., and DeVore, I. (eds.), *Man the Hunter.* Aldine, Chicago.

Williams, G. C. (1966). *Adaptation and Natural Selection.* Princeton University Press, Princeton, N.J.

Williams, G. C. (1971). *Group Selection.* Aldine, Chicago.

Wrangham, R. W. (1977). Feeding behaviour of chimpanzees in Gombe National Park, Tanzania. In Clutton-Brock, T. H. (ed.), *Primate Ecology: Feeding and Ranging Behavior of Lemurs, Monkeys and Apes.* Academic Press, London.

Some specific shared characteristics of living primates reflect the adaptation of the first primates. Nearly all living primates live in trees, and thus modern primate characteristics, such as stereoscopic vision and the opposable thumb, can be interpreted to reflect the early primate arboreal adaptation. Cartmill urges us to consider possible alternative explanations for primate features, such as fruit eating and predation on insects, in the earliest primates.

6. New Views on Primate Origins

By Matt Cartmill

The features that make primates resemble humans are familiar fare in introductory physical anthropology courses. Most of them are apparent to thoughtful zoo-goers. The chief primate peculiarities (Fig. 1) can be grouped under five headings:

Grasping extremities: Primates have soft, moist, pudgy palms and soles covered with fingerprint ridges. The first ("big") toes, and often the thumbs as well, are splayed apart from the adjacent digits and oppose them in grasping tree branches and other objects. (Our own oddly specialized feet no longer fit this description, but our hands do.)

Claw loss. The first toes of primates, and usually the other digits as well, are tipped with flattened, shield-shaped nails instead of the pointed claws seen in more typical mammals.

Optic convergence and orbital approximation: In all primates, the optic axes are convergent–that is, both eyes point in the same direction. The eye sockets, which are encircled by complete bony rings or cups, are drawn together toward the middle of the face. In the skulls of *Loris, Tarsius,* and many small monkeys, the left and right eye sockets are set so close together that they actually touch each other in the midline.

Matt Cartmill, "New Views on Primate Origins," *Evolutionary Anthropology,* vol. 1, no. 3, pp. 105–111. Copyright © 1992 by John Wiley & Sons, Inc. Reprinted with permission.

Enhanced vision: The organs of vision, including the retina and the visual cortex of the brain, are complex and unusually well-developed in primates. However, the organs of smell are smaller and simpler in primates than they are in typical mammals.

Brain enlargement: Primates have bigger brains overall than most other mammals have. This is especially true of "higher," or anthropoid primates (monkeys and apes), and superlatively true of our own species.

The first Darwinian explanations of these primate characteristics were put forward in the early 20th century by two British anatomists, G. Elliot Smith and F. Wood Jones. Both interpreted the distinctive primate traits as adaptations to living in the trees.

Smith, who was an expert on the comparative anatomy of the brain, thought that arboreal life placed a premium on brains in general and on the visual apparatus in particular. A keen nose, he argued, is not much use for a tree-dwelling mammal. However, such animals need sharp eyes in running and leaping from branch to branch and they must have quick wits to plan and follow complex three-dimensional paths through the treetops. Smith concluded that these demands of arboreal life had launched our primate ancestors on an inexorable course of brain enlargement and improvement, leading by successive evolutionary stages from primitive lemurs through tarsiers, monkeys, and apes to *Homo sapiens*.[1]

Wood Jones saw human bipedalism as another product of primate arboreality. In animals that run on the ground, Jones argued, the forelimbs do pretty much the same job as the hind limbs. But the two sets of limbs tend to take on separate functions in tree-climbing animals: the hind limbs typically support and propel the body from below, while the forelimbs explore and reach for new supports above. Jones thought this tendency had worked throughout primate evolution to shift the job of locomotion increasingly to the hind feet, freeing the hands for finer and more delicate work in touching, grasping, and handling objects. As the hands took over these manipulatory functions from the snout, the face shrank, drawing the eyes together in the midline. Like Smith, Jones thought the resulting evolutionary trends had produced a progressively human-like series of primates, from lemurs to tarsiers to man—although he dismissed the monkeys and apes as dead-end side branches from the main line of evolution leading toward the human condition.[2]

The theories of Smith and Jones were worked up into a grand synthesis by another British anatomist, W. E. Le Gros Clark, whose ideas about primate and human evolution dominated textbooks from the late 1920s through the 1960s. Le Gros Clark's studies of tree shrews had convinced him that these animals are primitive primates, closely related to the lemurs of Madagascar. But tree shrews lack the grasping hands and feet, flattened nails, and forward-pointing eyes of lemurs and other primates. Le Gros Clark concluded that these and other typical primate traits had appeared independently in many different lines of primate evolution. It was not a particular suite of traits that distinguished primates from other mammals, Le Gros Clark argued, but tendencies to develop such traits. At first, he regarded these tendencies as predetermined and orthogenetic.[3] In his later writings, he adopted a more orthodox adaptationist view, following Smith and Jones in describing the primate evolutionary trends as the "natural consequence of an arboreal habitat, a mode of life which among other things demands or encourages prehensile functions of the limbs, a high degree of visual acuity, and the accurate control and co-ordination of muscular activity by a well-developed brain."[4]

The "classical primatological synthesis" put together by Le Gros Clark started to fall apart in the late 1960s.[5] As Hennigian phylogenetic systematics began to penetrate primatology, the idea of defining an order by shared parallelisms first became unacceptable and then unintelligible. Taxa now had to be defined in terms of synapomorphies, or shared derived (non-primitive) traits. New fossils of *Plesiadapis* and other so-called archaic primates showed that these animals lacked bony postorbital bars and some other derived traits shared by tree shrews and Madagascar lemurs. But the archaic primates had more primate-like cheek teeth than any tree shrew. Moreover, the bony shell (tympanic bulla) enclosing their middle ear appeared to be formed from the petrosal bone, as in all living primates, rather than from a separate entotympanic bone as it is in tree shrews. By 1970, the resemblances between Malagasy lemurs and tree shrews were generally dismissed as parallelisms (which no longer counted for anything in the new philosophy of systematics). The features of the teeth and ear region shared by archaic and modern primates were accepted as synapomorphies that defined the primate order.

Several new accounts of primate origins have been put forward to fill the vacuum left by the collapse of the classical synthesis. Until recently, the main contenders have been the conflicting stories that F.S. Szalay and M. Cartmill have offered in various versions during the past two decades. Szalay's and Cartmill's[5,6] accounts are now both being challenged by new findings and interpretations.

In Szalay's view, primates evolved from an arboreal

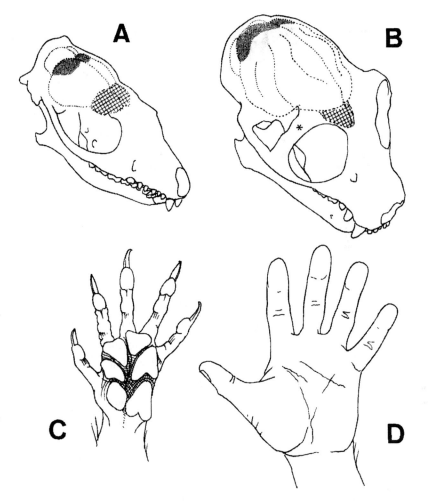

Figure 1. Differences between primates and more primitive mammals. **A:** Skull of the hedgehog *Erinaceus*. The brain (stippled outline) is small, the visual part of the cortex (dark tone) is restricted, and the olfactory bulbs (hachure) are large. The eye sockets face as much sideways as forward and are not encircled in bone. **B:** Skull of the prosimian primate *Otolemur*. The brain is larger, the visual cortex is expanded, and the olfactory bulbs are reduced. The eye sockets, which are larger and face more toward the front of the head than those of *Erinaceus*, are enclosed by complete bony rings (asterisk). **C:** Hand of the treeshrew *Tupaia*. All five digits are about equally divergent and all are tipped with long, pointed claws. The palm bears separate, protruding pads like those on the feet of a dog. **D:** Hand of a primate *(Homo)*. The pads are fused into a broad, soft surface. The first digit (thumb) diverges widely from the other digits, all of which are tipped with flattened, shield-like nails.

"archontan" ancestor (resembling a tree-shrew) through a shift to a more herbivorous diet, which produced the diagnostic features of molar morphology shared by archaic and modern primates.[6] Szalay suspects that *Plesiadapis* and other archaic primates may have had somewhat divergent and thumb-like first toes, but that perfected grasping extremities and flattened nails first appeared in the ancestral "euprimates" (modern or nonarchaic primates) as adaptations for a more acrobatic "grasp-leaping" form of locomotion.[7,8]

Cartmill arrived at a very different account of euprimate origins[9,10] on the basis of his comparative survey of arboreal adaptations in mammals. Most nonprimate tree-dwellers do not look much like euprimates. They typically have sharp, sturdy claws and a well-developed olfactory apparatus, and many of them have laterally directed eyes. Nevertheless, they have no difficulty moving and feeding in trees. On the basis of

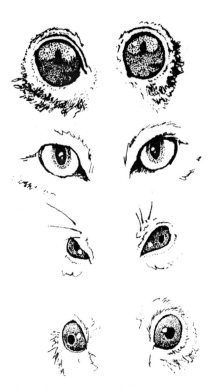

Figure 2. Orientation of the eyes in various mammals From top to bottom: a lorisiform primate (*Nycticebus coucang*), a small Asian cat (*Fells margarita*), a megachiropteran fruit bat (*Nyctimene rabori*), and a phalangeroid marsupial (*Pseudocheirus peregrinus*). In the loris and cat, both eyes point in the same direction; the bat and the phalanger are somewhat wall-eyed.

these facts, Cartmill concluded that something other than arboreal life per se must have been responsible for producing the distinctive euprimate characteristics.

Le Gros Clark had explained the forward-facing eyes of primates as an adaptation for stereoscopic vision, "particularly for the accurate judging of distance and direction in arboreal acrobatics."[11] Cartmill rejected this analysis, arguing that shoving the eyes together in the middle of the face enhances stereoscopy but decreases parallax, thus reducing the distance at which stereoscopic vision can work. Optic convergence, Cartmill insisted, must have evolved in animals that needed a wide field of stereoscopic vision at close range.

Noting that marked optic convergence is also a characteristic of cats and many other predators that rely on vision in tracking and nabbing their prey (Fig. 2), Cartmill sought the adaptive significance of this trait in the predatory habits of small prosimian primates like *Microcebus, Loris,* and *Tarsius,* which track insect prey by sight and seize them in their hands. Grasping extremities and claw loss, he suggested, had also originated as predatory adaptations, facilitating stealthy locomotion among the slender twigs of the forest canopy and undergrowth where insects are most abundant–and where the sharp claws that help many tree-dwellers climb thick trunks are of no use. He saw olfactory reduction as a side effect of the shoving together of the two eye sockets, which necessarily constricts the space available for the organs of smell and their connections to the brain. All these distinctive euprimate traits, Cartmill concluded, could in this way be explained as adaptations for an ancestral habit of "visually directed predation." he urged that *Plesiadapis* and other archaic primates, which showed no signs of such adaptations, be removed from the primate order.

Although R. D. Martin and a few other people have long agreed with this last point,[12] the informed consensus during the 1970s and 1980s favored Szalay's views on the primate affinities of *Plesiadapis* and its relatives. During the past few years, some cracks have started to appear in that consensus. J. R. Wible and H. H. Covert concluded in 1987 that many of the archaic primates have no demonstrable relationship to either *Plesiadapis* or euprimates and that the closest euprimate relatives are probably tree shrews after all.[13] More recently, R. F. Kay and K. C. Beard have both concluded, from different sorts of evidence, that at least some of the archaic primates are probably more closely related to colugos ("flying lemurs") than they are to euprimates.[14,15] If these conclusions hold up in the long run, Szalay's adaptive account of euprimate peculiarities will not be refuted, but the details of his historical account will be confounded.

Those details are important to Szalay, who sees the causes of evolutionary events as highly contingent and case-specific, constrained by the morphological and ecological details of evolving species and the evolutionary baggage that they have carried over from their differently adapted ancestors.[16] Cartmill, on the other hand, has always argued that particular evolutionary events cannot in principle be explained except as instances of some more general regularity. "The only evolutionary changes we can hope to explain," he asserts, "are parallelisms."[17]) For Cartmill, an explanation that applies to only one case–for example, Szalay's description of the prehensile foot of euprimates as an adaptation to a "grasp-leaping" habit unique to

ARCHONTAN PHYLOGENY

Traditional Hypothesis [32, 34, 36]

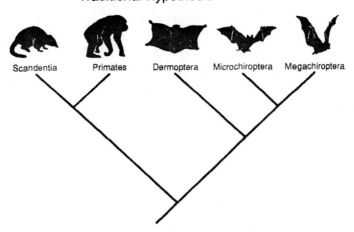

Scandentia   Primates   Dermoptera   Microchiroptera   Megachiroptera

Flying Primate Hypothesis [25, 33, 35]

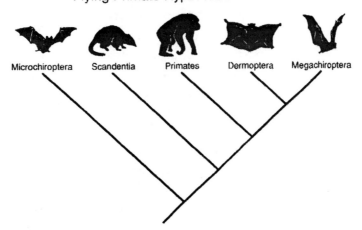

Microchiroptera   Scandentia   Primates   Dermoptera   Megachiroptera

The Archonta

In 1910, William King Gregory[29] proposed that primates (Order **Primates**) tree shrews (**Scandentia**), elephant shrews (**Macroscelidia**), flying lemurs or colugos (**Dermoptera**), and bats (**Chiroptera**) formed a supraordinal grouping that he called Archonta. Although most authorities no longer include the elephant shrews in Archonta, it is now generally believed that the remaining four orders are more closely related to one another than to other groups of mammals.[30,31] However, there is great disagreement and debate about the correct phylogeny among these groups. In advancing the most striking recent hypothesis, Pettigrew and colleagues[25] have argued, on the basis of neuroanatomical similarities, among others, that bats are not a natural group; that Megachiroptera are the sister group of primates; and that megabats and microbats evolved their adaptations for flight independently. Many authors[32] have rebutted Pettigrew's hypothesis, arguing that all aspects of the skeletal and soft tissue anatomy constitute overwhelming evidence that they are a natural group. Nonetheless, the debate continues.[33-36]   JGF

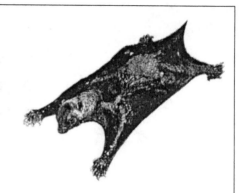

Paromomyids and Flying Lemurs

On the basis of new fossil remains from the early Eocene of Wyoming, several authors have suggested that the paromomyids, normally grouped among the **Plesiadapiformes**, or "archaic primates."[7,37] are actually uniquely related to the flying lemurs or colugos (Order **Dermoptera**). Kay et al.[15] demonstrated unique cranial similarities between *Ignacius graybullianus* (see below) and modern colugos in the inferred path of the blood supply to the brain and the structure of the auditory region.

Beard[14,38] has argued that paromomyids not only shared a unique phylogenetic relationship with dermopterans, but also shared their unusual gliding abilities (above). Beard's reconstruction of the gliding habits of *Ignacius* and *Tinimomys,* another paromomyid, is based on the proportions of the finger bones attributed to these taxa. Krause[39] has questioned some of the proposed associations. Final resolution of the issue awaits more complete, associated skeletal material.

JGF

euprimates—explains nothing.[18,19] Adaptive explanations must be general enough to predict similar adaptations in other cases and they must be rejected if those predictions are not borne out.[10]

Cartmill's own account of primate origins was vulnerable to attack on this ground. Not all visual predators have eyes that point in the same direction. Cats, tarsiers, and owls do; mongooses, tupaiine tree shrews, and robins do not. Therefore, visual predation per se cannot explain optic convergence in ancestral euprimates. Some other factor must be involved.

This flaw in Cartmill's theory was patched up by J. Allman,[20] who suggested that rotating the eyes forward serves not so much to enhance stereoscopy as to allow an animal to see more clearly what lies in front of it. The image projected by a spherical lens is sharpest directly behind the center of the lens. Images that pass through the lens more obliquely are blurred.[21] This means that an animal with eyes facing sideways cannot clearly see things directly in front of it. This does not matter so much in diurnal animals because their pupils constrict in bright light and thus act like pinhole cameras to help focus the blurred image. However, a nocturnal animal with a wide-open iris has problems with spherical aberration. This fact, Allman argued, explains why nocturnal visual predators such as owls and cats have tended, as did early euprimates, to swing their eyes around to the front, while diurnal predators such as mongooses have remained more wall-eyed and retained a more panoramic visual field.

A more serious flaw in Cartmill's theory was his explanation of claw reduction. Garber's fieldwork on Panamanian tamarins, *Saguinus oedipus,*[22] showed that these small anthropoids chiefly feed on insects among the twigs and vines of the forest understory, just as Cartmill's hypothetical euprimate ancestor did. But all their digits except the divergent first toe are tipped with sharp claws, affording them a second mode of feeding in which they cling, squirrel-fashion, to large tree trunks while eating gummy exudates from holes in the bark. Evidently, the claws of tamarins do not hinder movement and foraging on thin branches. They also allow *Saguinus* and its relatives to do things that more typical, clawless primates cannot do. All this makes it hard to argue that adaptation for shrub-layer visual predation would have favored the reduction of claws in ancestral euprimates.

R. W. Sussman criticized Cartmill's theory on other grounds and has advanced alternatives of his own. In 1978, Sussman and the botanist P. H. Raven suggested that early primates might have been adapted for feeding on flowers and nectar, as are glossophagine bats or the Australian marsupial *Tarsipes,* and that this might explain the evolution of flattened nails and grasping feet in the ancestral euprimates. "These adaptations," Sussman and Raven argued, "would have allowed the Eocene prosimians far greater access to fruits and flowers, as well as to many plant-visiting insects, making them much more efficient at locomoting and foraging in the small terminal branches.... It [was] probably this improved ability to feed in terminal branches that was the most important impetus for the major adaptive shift seen in these Eocene primates."[23]

The main difficulty with this first version of Sussman's theory lies in the dental anatomy of early euprimates. Adapid and omomyid dentitions display a wide variety of adaptations for eating insects, fruit, or leaves, but none of them show anything like the dental reduction characteristic of dedicated nectar-eaters like *Tarsipes* or the Glossophaginae. The nectar-feeding theory also affords no explanation of the visual specializations characteristic of euprimates. The ancestral euprimates may occasionally have eaten flowers or nectar, as some Malagasy lemurs do today, but positing such a habit does not seem to help in accounting for their distinctive anatomical characteristics.

Sussman's latest ideas leave nectar largely out of the picture and concentrate on fruit. In a recent article,[24] he argues that most of the small nocturnal prosimians that Cartmill had pointed to as model visual predators eat more fruit than insects and that this was probably true of the ancestral euprimates as well. Sussman sees the grasping extremities of euprimates as an adaptation for fruit-eating, allowing these animals to cling and feed uninterruptedly in terminal branches where fruit grows instead of having to scurry back to perch and eat on larger, safer supports as squirrels do when harvesting nuts. The origin and radiation of the euprimates, Sussman suggests, may have been a side effect of rapid angiosperm diversification in the early Cenozoic, which produced a great radiation of fruit-bearing plants and increased the niche space available for specialized fruit-eaters.

There are problems with this theory, too. Comparative anatomy suggests that in the Cretaceous the ancestral marsupials had grasping feet with divergent, clawless first toes. The Cenozoic diversification of fruit-bearing plants occurred much later, and therefore cannot explain the evolution of primate-like feet in marsupials. Sussman's account also fails to explain the characteristic visual specializations of euprimates. It makes sense that having a wide field of sharp stereoscopic vision directly in front of it would help a visually predatory animal be sure of hitting its prey accurately on the first strike. However, such specializations are hardly needed when the prey is a banana.

Although, on the face of it, Cartmill's theory may seem to do a better job than Sussman's in accounting for the peculiarities of the primate visual apparatus, the distribution of primate-like visual specializations provides some support for both theories.

The forward-facing eyes of nocturnal visual predators such as owls and cats clearly have evolved as predatory adaptations. Yet similar specializations occur among some nonpredatory tree-dwellers. Some of these animals, such as kinkajous (*Potos*) and African palm civets (*Nandinia*), are carnivores that have secondarily turned to a diet of fruit. These creatures probably inherited their forward-facing eyes from visually predatory ancestors. But that explanation does not fit the case of the megachiropteran fruit bats of the Old World tropics. Unlike the small-eyed, sonar-guided, insectivorous microchiropteran bats of the temperate zone, these fruit-eating "flying foxes" have large, moderately convergent eyes (Fig. 2). The neuroanatomist J. D. Pettigrew[25] has recently shown that the megachiropteran bats have an even more strikingly primate-like architecture of the visual parts of the brain. [See box.]

Sussman admits that his theory "does not explain the unique visual adaptations of primates and fruit bats," but the similarities between those two groups demand an explanation of some sort. So far, Pettigrew is the only one who has offered an explanation, arguing that fruit bats are not really bats but primitive primates that have evolved wings. If so, then they might have inherited their primate-like traits from a visually predatory primate ancestor. However, no one has yet urged this possibility, mainly because most sources of evidence still link all the bats within a monophyletic group having no particular ties to primates.[26] The

Figure 3. *Woolly opossum.*

J. Arthur Thomson, from *The Outline of Science*, vol. 1. Copyright in the Public Domain.

importance of such phylogenetic questions about the origin of primate peculiarities underscores the point, made by Szalay and other evolutionary biologists, that the sequence of adaptations through which an evolving lineage has passed must be taken into account in trying to figure out why that lineage has evolved its distinctive traits.

Several people have looked to the primate-like features of marsupials as a key to explaining primate origins. As noted, arboreal marsupials have grasping hind feet with clawless, divergent first toes. Some small Australian marsupials like *Cercartetus* and *Tarsipes* have reduced claws on their other toes and their fingers as well. Most marsupial tree-dwellers have moderately convergent eyes (Fig. 2). The vaguely prosimian appearance of such undergrowth-haunting "pygmy possums" as *Cercartetus* and the South American didelphid *Marmosa* is one of the things that led both Sussman and Cartmill to think that the ancestral primate was also a diminutive shrub-layer forager.

Another South American didelphid, *Caluromys derbianus,* furnishes an important natural experiment bearing on these questions. *Caluromys* (Fig. 3) differs from typical didelphids in that it has many primate-like features, including its relatively large brain and eyes, bony postorbital processes, and short snout. Its orbits are more frontally directed than those of other didelphids (that is, they face more toward the end of its nose and less toward the top of its head).[27] It, like typical primates, gives birth to small litters and has both a long life span and a high basal metabolic rate. More knowledge about the habits of *Caluromys* might therefore shed new light on primate origins.

In 1988, D. T. Rasmussen undertook a field study of *Caluromys*[28] to try to determine the adaptive significance of its primate-like specializations. He concluded that *Caluromys* fits the theories of both Cartmill and Sussman. About half its diet comes from fruit growing in the terminal branches, where its prehensile feet allow it to cling and feed like a primate; the other half consists of insects, which it locates visually and seizes with its hands. On large branches, *Caluromys* stalks its prey deliberately; but when clambering around in thin terminal branches, where it is clumsier and noisier, it just grabs whatever insects its movements stir into flight. On the basis of these observations, Rasmussen argues that early euprimates may have climbed out onto terminal branches in search of fruit (as Sussman thinks) and developed their visual peculiarities to help them catch the insects they encountered there (as Cartmill's theory implies). The available facts thus continue to support Cartmill's contention that "the last common ancestor of the extant primates, like many extant prosimians… subsisted to an important extent on insects and other prey, which were visually located and manually captured in the insect-rich canopy and undergrowth of tropical forests."[10]

More extensive field studies of the adaptations and behavior of other arboreal mammals are now needed to sort out and test the various explanations that have been offered for the evolution of the grasping feet and flattened nails of the first euprimates. We might learn a lot by studying arboreal frugivores having typical mammalian feet (such as *Potos* and *Nandinia*) and comparing them to shrub-layer foragers with primate-like grasping extremities and reduced claws (such as *Tarsipes* and *Cercartetus*).

It would also help if we knew something about the order in which the various primate peculiarities were acquired. If the first euprimates had grasping feet and blunt teeth adapted for eating fruit, but retained small, divergent orbits like those of *Plesiadapis,* Rasmussen's account would gain added plausibility. If they had convergent orbits and the sharp, slicing molar teeth of insect-eaters, that would support Cartmill's ideas. The earliest euprimate fossils we know of at present resembled modern primates in both their foot bones and eye sockets, and so do not help to answer this question. We can only hope that new fossil finds will help us to tease apart the various strands of the primate story, giving us clearer insights into the evolutionary causes behind the origin of the primate order to which we belong.

REFERENCES

1. Smith GE (1924) *The Evolution of Man.* London: Oxford University Press.

2. Jones FW (1916) *Arboreal Man.* London: Arnold.

3. Le Gros Clark, WE (1934) *Early Forerunners of Man,* pp 284–188. Baltimore: William Wood.

4. Le Gros Clark WE (1959) *The Antecedents of Man,* p 43. Edinburgh: Edinburgh University Press.

5. Cartmill M (1982) Basic primatology and prosimian evolution. In Spencer F (ed), *A History of American Physical Anthropology, 1930–1980,* pp 147–186. New York: Academic Press.

6. Szalay FS (1972) Paleobiology of the earliest primates. In Tuttle RH (ed), *The Functional and Evolutionary Biology of Primates,* pp 3–35. Chicago: Aldine-Atherton.

7. Szalay FS, Delson E (1979) *Evolutionary History of the Primates,* p 99. New York: Academic Press.

8. Szalay FS, Rosenberger AL, Dagosto M (1987) Diagnosis and differentiation of the order Primates. Yearbk Phys Anthropol *30*:75–105.

9. Cartmill M (1972) Arboreal adaptations and the origin of the order primates. In Tuttle RH (ed), *The Functional and Evolutionary Biology of Primates,* pp 97–122. Chicago: Aldine-Atherton.

10. Cartmill M (1974) Rethinking primate origins. Science *184*:436–443.

11. Le Gros Clark WE (1959) *History of the Primates: An Introduction to the Study of Fossil Man,* p 48. Chicago: University of Chicago Press.

12. Martin RD (1990) *Primate Origins and Evolution: A Phylogenetic Reconstruction.* Princeton: Princeton University Press.

13. Wible JR, Covert HH (1987) Primates: cladistic diagnosis and relationships. J Hum Evol *16*:1–22.

14. Beard KC (1990) Gliding behaviour and palaeoecology of the alleged primate family *Paromomyidae.* Nature *345*:340–341.

15. Kay RF, Thorington RW Jr, Houde P (1990) Eocene plesiadapiform shows affinities with flying lemurs not primates. Nature *345*:342–344.

16. Szalay FS (1984) Arboreality: is it homologous in metatherian and eutherian mammals? Evol Biol *18*:215–258.

17. Cartmill M (in press) *A View to a Death in the Morning: Hunting and Humanity in Western Thought,* chapt 12. Cambridge: Harvard University Press.

18. Cartmill M (1990) Human uniqueness and theoretical content in paleoanthropology. Int J Primatol *11*:173–192.

19. Cartmill M (1991) Review of *Wonderful Life,* by S J Gould. Am J Phys Anthropol *84*:368–371.

20. Allman J (1977) Evolution of the visual system in the early primates. Prog Psychobiol Physiol Psychol *7*:1–53.

21. Hughes A (1977) The topography of vision in mammals of contrasting lifestyle: Comparative optics and retinal organisation. In Crescitelli F (ed), *The Visual System in Vertebrates,* pp 613–756. Berlin: Springer-Verlag.

22. Garber P (1980) Locomotor behavior and feeding ecology of the Panamanian tamarin (*Saguinus oedipus geoffroyi, Callitrichidae, Primates*). Int J Primatol *1*:185–201.

23. Sussman RW, Raven PH (1978) Pollination by lemurs and marsupials: An archaic coevolutionary system. Science *200*:731–736.

24. Sussman RW (1991) Primate origins and the evolution of angiosperms. Am J Primatol *23*:209–223.

25. Pettigrew JD (1989) Phylogenetic relations between microbats, megabats and primates (*Mammalia: Chiroptera and Primates*). Philos Trans R Soc London *325*:489–559.

26. MacPhee RDE (ed) (in press) *Primates and Their Relatives in Phylogenetic Perspective.* New York: Plenum.

27. Cartmill M (1970) The orbits of arboreal mammals: A reassessment of the arboreal theory of primate evolution. PhD thesis, University of Chicago.

28. Rasmussen DT (1990) Primate origins: Lessons from a neotropical marsupial. Am J Primatol *22*:263–277.

29. Gregory WK (1910) The orders of mammals. Bull Am Mus Nat Hst *42*:95–263.

30. Kenna MC (1975) Toward a phylogenetic classification of the *Mammalia.* In Luckett WP, Szalay FS (eds) *Phylogeny of the Primates: A Multidisciplinary Approach,* pp 21–46. New York: Plenum Press.

31. Luckett WP (1980) *Comparative Biology and Evolutionary Relationships of Tree Shrews.* New York: Plenum Press.

32. Wible JR, Novacek MJ (1988) Cranial evidence for the monophyletic origin of bats. Am Mus Novit *2911*:1–19.

33. Pettigrew JD (1991) Wings or brain? Convergent evolution in the origins of bats. Syst Zoo *40*:199–215.

34. Baker RJ, Novacek MJ, Simmons NB (1991) On the monophyly of bats. Syst Zoo *40*:216–230.

35. Pettigrew JD (1991) A fruitful, wrong hypothesis? Response to Baker, Novacek, and Simmons. Syst Zoo *40*: 231–238.

36. Simmons NB, Novacek MJ, Baker RJ (1991) Approaches, methods, and the future of the Chiropteran monophyly controversy: A reply to J D Pettigrew. Syst Zoo *40*:239–243.

37. Fleagle JG (1988) *Primate Adapatation and Evolution.* New York: Academic Press.

38. Beard KC (in press) Origin and evolution of gliding in early Cenozoic Dermoptera (Mammalia, Primatomorpha). In MacPhee RDE (ed), *Primates and Their Relatives in Phylogenetic Perspective.* New York: Plenum Press.

39. Krause DW (1991) Were paromomyids gliders? Maybe, maybe not. J Hum Evol *21*:177–188.

The behavior of African apes, especially chimpanzees (*Pan*), our closest living relatives, can offer insights into the behavior of our early ancestors. Hunting and tool use have been observed in chimpanzees, and thus may be inferred to have been practiced by the common ancestor of chimps and humans. It can also be argued that collaborative aggression and territoriality are part of the evolutionary legacy shared with *Pan*. We may yet find insight into the evolutionary history of food sharing and human sociality from the study of African apes.

7. Recent Developments in the Study of Wild Chimpanzee Behavior

By John C. Mitani, David P. Watts, and Martin N. Muller

Chimpanzees have always been of special interest to anthropologists. As our closest living relatives,[1-3] they provide the standard against which to assess human uniqueness and information regarding the changes that must have occurred during the course of human evolution. Given these circumstances, it is not surprising that chimpanzees have been studied intensively in the wild. Jane Good-all[4,5] initiated the first long-term field study of chimpanzee behavior at the Gombe National Park, Tanzania. Her observations of tool manufacture and use, hunting, and meat-eating forever changed the way we define humans. Field research on chimpanzee behavior by Toshisada Nishida and colleagues[6] at the nearby Mahale Mountains National Park has had an equally significant impact. It was Nishida[7,8] who first provided a comprehensive picture of the chimpanzee social system, including group structure and dispersal.

Two generations of researchers have followed Goodall and Nishida into the field. As a result, chimpanzees are now one of the best and most widely studied of nonhuman primates. Long-term field research has been conducted at six sites by several researchers spanning 42 years (Fig. 1). Shorter field studies have also been carried out in some areas.[9-11] With this extensive body of research, one might think that we have learned everything about the behavior of these apes in nature. But this is not the case. In fact, we are entering a

John C. Mitani, David P. Watts, and Martin N. Muller, "Recent Developments in the Study of Wild Chimpanzee Behavior," *Evolutionary Anthropology*, vol. 11, no. 1, pp. 9–25. Copyright © 2002 by John Wiley & Sons, Inc. Reprinted with permission.

new and extremely exciting era in the study of wild chimpanzee behavior. The purpose of this review is to highlight some intriguing findings that have emerged through recent study. We focus specifically on results from our own field research conducted in the Kibale National Park, Uganda, giving special emphasis to five areas: social organization, genetics and behavior, hunting and meat-eating, inter-group relationships, and behavioral endocrinology. Our treatment is selective, and we explicitly avoid comment on inter-population variation in behavior as it relates to the question of chimpanzee cultures. Excellent reviews of this topic, of central concern to anthropologists, can be found elsewhere.[12–14]

SOCIAL ORGANIZATION

No single issue in the study of wild chimpanzee behavior has seen more debate than the nature of their social system. We now know that chimpanzees live in a "fission-fusion" society. Individuals form socially and geographically circumscribed "unit-groups" or "communities," within which they associate in temporary subgroups or "parties" that vary in size, composition, and duration. Males are philopatric, whereas females typically disperse. This seemingly clear-cut picture of chimpanzee society did not emerge easily. Giventhe fluid nature of chimpanzee society, it took exceedingly long for field observers to discern regularities in grouping, dispersal, associations, and range use.

Kortlandt[15] was the first to report temporary associations among wild chimpanzees based on early observations in the Belgian Congo. Here he described groups of 1–30 individuals that either contained members of both sexes or consisted of "nursery" groups of females and their young. Kortlandt was prescient in his descriptions of the temporary and fluid nature of chimpanzee aggregations and laid the groundwork for further study. Subsequent reports by Good-all[16] and the Reynolds[17] tended to blur distinctions between communities. After five years of field observations at Gombe, Gooodall[16] wrote: "Since chimpanzee groups in the reserve freely unite from time to time without signs of aggression, they cannot be divided into separate communities. It seems likely that only a geographic barrier would constitute a limiting factor on the size of a community, although individuals living at opposite ends of the range might never come into contact."

Nishida[7] altered this picture by de-fining the social group of wild chimpanzees at Mahale. In contrast to Goodall and the Reynolds, Nishida emphasized the stable nature of chimpanzee communities. Although he never recorded all community members together at a single place and time, his longitudinal observations of association between individuals revealed an unambiguous social net-work and structure (Fig. 2). From these observations, Nishida[7] concluded that, "The chimpanzees live a clear-cut social unit which consists of adult males, adult females, and immature animals." Subsequent field work indicated that chimpanzee communities are not closed. While males typically spend their entire lives in their natal communities, females commonly transfer to neighboring ones during adolescence.[8,18,19]

While effectively laying to rest persistent questions regarding the existence of chimpanzee communities, Nishida[7] simultaneously described sex differences in association. He noted that males associated more frequently with each other than females did with other females. From this he concluded that strong bonds form between males and that males compose the core of chimpanzee society. Subsequent field research at Gombe,[20,21] Mahale,[22,23] and the Kanyawara study area of Kibale National Park, Uganda,[24] validated and expanded Nishida's picture of chimpanzee society. Male chimpanzees in these populations are more gregarious and distribute their activities more widely and evenly over their territories than do females. Goodall[25] aptly summarized the standard picture of chimpanzee society to emerge from these studies: "The most deep-seated principles underlying chimpanzee community structure are those concerned with sex differences in sociability and in the choice of companions. Males are more gregarious than females and prefer each other's company, except when females are in oestrus. Females are less sociable and spend most of their time with their own offspring—except when cycling, at which time they become very sociable."

Consideration of sex differences in reproductive strategies and the costs of feeding competition provide a theoretical rationale to explain observed sex differences in chimpanzee association patterns. Females forage alone because the potential reproductive costs of scramble and contest feeding competition are higher for them

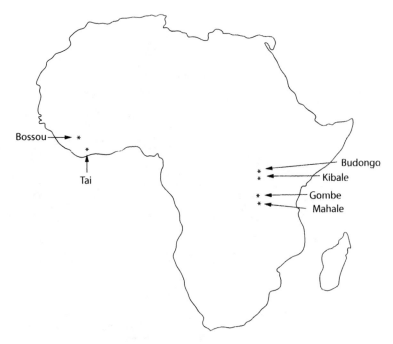

Figure 1. Chimpanzee study sites.

than they are for males.[21,26,27] Males may be more willing to assume the costs of feeding competition to gain mating opportunities and to derive social benefits from associating with other males.[21,26,27] Part of the power of this model lies in its ability to accommodate intraspecific variation in association patterns. The theoretical prediction is that such variation will occur between study sites because for females the costs of grouping are expected to vary with differences in local resource abundance and distribution.[28,29]

In keeping with this model, considerable intraspecific variation exists in chimpanzee association patterns. As far back as 1979, Sugiyama and Koman[30] reported that females were as sociable as males in a small, isolated community at Bossou, Guinea. Ghiglieri[31] found no evidence of sex bias in grouping tendencies in the un-provisioned and largely unhabituated Ngogo community at Kibale. More recently, Boesch[32] and Boesch-Achermann,[33] working in the Taï National Park, Ivory Coast, observed that most parties contained adults of both sexes, while parties consisting of only males or only females were rare. This led them to conclude that members of this population are "bisexually bonded." Given a lack of information regarding feeding behavior and food availability across study sites, we are not presently capable of evaluating whether sex differences in the costs of competition account for these reported intraspecific differences. Temporal variation in association patterns at Taï appears to be consistent with this hypothesis,[34] but again firm conclusions are elusive due to an absence of measures of food availability. Using such measures, our own observations conform to expectation by showing that anestrous and lactating females at Ngogo become more sociable during periods of food abundance.[35]

Problems in recording, measuring, and analyzing associations among chimpanzees, a species with a fluid social system, have plagued field researchers for years. Accordingly, some of the reported intraspecific variation may be more illusory than real. For example, some of the differences may simply reflect differences in how observers record party membership.[36] Other differences can be attributed to the different ways that field researchers have defined age-sex categories.[37] More serious problems ensue from attempts to assay and analyze association patterns to make inferences about social affinities and bonds.[38,39] Standard methods, pioneered by Nishida[7] in his original research, typically involve the use of dyadic association indices.[40] Inferring social affinities from these indices, however, is problematic because they are subject to biases due

Figure 2. Early observations at the Mahale Mountains established the fission-fusion nature of chimpanzee society. Here a temporary subgroup or "party," consisting of individuals of all ages and sexes, is shown.

to variations in individual gregariousness and group demography.[39] For example, high indices between males may indicate genuine social preferences or may simply result from either a tendency to aggregate or a male-biased community sex ratio.

To overcome these problems, we have used recently developed association indices and randomization techniques to analyze associations among chimpanzees living in an unusually large community at Ngogo, Kibale National Park, Uganda. In keeping with past studies, we have found that males at Ngogo are more gregarious than are anestrous females.[39] After controlling for the overall general gregariousness of males, however, we found that males do not associate with other males more often than would be expected by chance.[39] Alternatively, anestrous females associate with each other more frequently than chance expectation after taking their relatively low levels of sociability into account.[39] We note that even these results are vulnerable to methodological criticism. As in other studies, our observations of female behavior were unlikely to compose a random sample. Given their relatively asocial nature, female chimpanzees are elusive and difficult to observe. Our randomization procedures nonetheless provide the kind of unbiased analytical method necessary to determine whether intraspecific variations in association can be attributed to methodological differences and the degree of concordance in patterns across study sites.

While considerable intraspecific variations in associations appear to exist, differences in dispersal patterns have also emerged. Observations from Gombe reveal that female dispersal is the norm there, but that only 60% of females disperse from their natal communities, with 10% doing so only after giving birth for the first time.[19] Although all females have been previously described as dispersing at Mahale,[41] new observations indicate that a few remain and give birth in their natal communities (T. Nishida, personal communication). Recently compiled data from Taï show that only a single female failed to disperse from the main study community during 16 years of observation.[33]

Research at Bossou provides a contrast to the results from Gombe, Mahale, and Taï. Observations over 21 years suggest one successful immigration by an adult male, along with visits by two extra-community males.[42] Moreover, 86% of all adolescent males have disappeared from the Bossou community. Based on these observations, Sugiyama[42] has argued that male dispersal occurs regularly at Bossou because the community has no immediate neighbors and no need for territorial defense. Consequently, selection for male cooperation has been relaxed, and young males disperse to reduce within-group competition for mates. Male transfer between communities is rare or absent at Gombe, Mahale, and Taï. We require more studies across a broader range of habitats to evaluate whether variation in the costs and benefits of territoriality leads to systematic differences in the frequency of male dispersal. Irrespective of resolving this question, dispersal is likely to have important effects on the genetic structure of chimpanzee populations.[43-45]

GENETICS AND BEHAVIOR

Recent advances in extracting, amplifying, and sequencing DNA from hair and fecal samples collected noninvasively in the wild are beginning to revolutionize our understanding of the behavior of animals.[46,47] The study of chimpanzees has contributed to this revolution.[43] Two particularly informative areas of recent investigation have involved the integration of genetic and behavioral data. Recent findings have now produced clearer pictures of the chimpanzee mating system and the role of maternal kinship in structuring aspects of male social behavior.

It took 20 years of field study for the mating habits of wild chimpanzees to come into focus. Working at Gombe, Caroline Tutin[48] was the first to describe the alternative mating tactics employed by male chimpanzees. At Gombe and elsewhere,[33,49,50] the vast majority of observed copulations occur in a group context. Here chimpanzees gather in relatively large parties containing members of both sexes, and estrous females mate repeatedly with multiple males. All adult males present typically share in such opportunistic matings; adolescent males also frequently mate in this context. Males additionally mate in three restrictive situations. In one, high-ranking males attempt to control mating access to females, while mate-guarding them against others in a group setting. This "possessive" pattern differs from consortships, in which male-female pairs move away from other community members and engage in a nearly exclusive mating relationship over the course of a single estrous cycle. Tutin[48] originally described both males and females as equally interested and involved in maintaining consortships. While this clearly is true in some cases, we now know that males often display considerable aggression toward females before "persuading" them to follow.[25,51] Based on our observations of the Ngogo chimpanzees,[50] we can add a third restrictive tactic to the two already described. When the Ngogo chimpanzees form extremely large parties, high-ranking duos and trios begin to mate-guard estrous females. These mating-guarding coalitions appear to form, both successfully and unsuccessfully, when male party sizes become so large that it becomes prohibitive for a single male to mate-guard successfully (Fig. 3).

Early on, Tutin[48] speculated that although the vast majority of all copulations occur opportunistically in a group context, most conceptions actually take place during consortships. Using more recent behavioral observations from Gombe, Wallis[52] has suggested that most conceptions can be attributed to matings that occur in multi-male parties, a finding that concurs with behavioral reports from Mahale.[49,53] In chimpanzees, as with other primates, multiple mating and internal fertilization make it difficult to determine paternity using behavioral observations alone. Recent studies employing genetic markers assayed through noninvasive sampling regimes have permitted more reliable paternity assignments, which, in turn, allow more definitive statements about the payoffs of different male mating tactics.

Perhaps the most startling claim made in recent studies of wild chimpanzees involves paternity determinations among the Taï chimpanzees.[54,55]

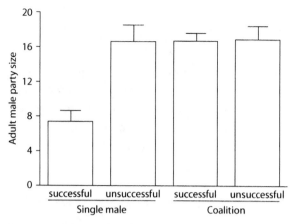

Figure 3. Mate-guarding form and success vary with male party size. Mean (± SE) values are shown for single male and coalitionary mate-guarding episodes at Ngogo, Kibale National Park, Uganda.

Using genetic data derived from 11 microsatellite markers, Gagneux and colleagues assigned the paternity of 13 offspring born into the Taï chimpanzee community between 1990 and 1995. Their surprising results suggested that 7 of the 13 young chimpanzees did not have fathers residing in the community. The clear implication drawn from this analysis was that females actively seek matings with males who live outside their own social group.[33,54,55]

Given the apparently unassailable nature of the genetic data, this astonishing result has been widely reported in major scientific publications,[56] monographs,[33] and textbooks,[57] as well as the popular[58] and news[59] media. As a result, belief that extra-group paternity is a common feature of wild chimpanzee behavior is now widespread both inside and outside the academic community. Reconciling behavioral observations and life history information with the high frequency of extra-group paternity reported at Taï has nevertheless been difficult. We would not be surprised to find that, as in many species of birds and mammals,[60-63] female chimpanzees occasionally conceive offspring with nonresident males. Despite hints that this might be the case,[25,64,65] however, long-term observations in the wild gave no reason to think that extra-group matings and conceptions were so common. The Taï result has also been perplexing because females who engage in such behavior would run the risk of receiving severe aggression from males in their own communities, and if discovered, of having those males kill their infants. Because reproductive opportunities are so rare, with interbirth intervals typically averaging five to six years in the wild,[33,41,52] we expect males to be especially wary, to guard against extra-group matings, and to punish females who engage in them. In principle, the benefits of mate choice might outweigh these risks,[33] but females could gain these same benefits by simply transferring to another group. Alternatively, extra-group paternity may provide insurance against between community infanticide.[33] Any benefits derived here, however, would be offset by increased costs of aggression by males living within communities.

Two recent and independent studies promise to put these questions to rest. Constable and colleagues[66] determined the paternity of 14 infants born into the Kasekela community at Gombe. Their analyses indicate that all 14 infants were sired by resident males. Vigilant and colleagues[67] have reported similar results in a sample of 41 infants from three communities at Taï. Here paternity could be assigned with a probability greater than 99% for 34 of these infants. All 34 infants had probable fathers who resided within the infant's community, although complete sampling of potential fathers was achieved in only 13 cases. Of the seven remaining infants for which fathers could not be ascribed, extra-group paternity was implicated in one for whom all potential fathers were sampled and excluded. Taken together, these new data indicate that extra-group paternity in chimpanzees occurs only rarely in the two populations investigated thus far. Additional research at other sites will be required to evaluate the generality of this finding.

The discrepant results between these two studies and the earlier Taï analysis have been attributed to multiple sources of error.[67] Some samples used in the original Taï paternity study may have been handled improperly, leading to contamination and sample mix-up.[67] Genotyping errors due to amplification artifacts during polymerase chain reaction[68] and allelic dropout[69,70] may have exacerbated these problems. The acknowledgment that imperfect laboratory procedures and analyses led to an erroneous conclusion regarding the importance of extra-group paternity among wild chimpanzees[67] will undoubtedly result in more careful studies in the future. This should also promote critical evaluation of additional claims that are not easily accommodated by theory or empirical observation.

Besides helping to resolve some outstanding questions regarding chimpanzee paternity, Constable and colleagues[66] study is notable for providing additional information regarding the effectiveness of alternative mating tactics employed by male chimpanzees and the relationship between male rank and reproduction. Data regarding the mating tactic employed by fathers was documented for 12 conceptions. Offspring were conceived during opportunistic matings five times (42%), possessive matings four times (33%) and consortships three times (25%). High-ranking males produced half of the infants. The alpha male sired 36% of all offspring (5/14), four times via possessive mating and once through mating the mother opportunistically. Another high-ranking male used opportunistic matings to father two offspring (14%). Interestingly, he conceived one of these infants with his mother. Middle-ranking males were responsible for an additional 36% of all offspring, using opportunistic matings twice and consortships twice; the mating tactic employed by one middle-ranking male to produce another infant was unknown. Finally, two low-ranking males fathered two infants (14%), once during a consortship.

This study may additionally provide an explanation for the higher frequency of consortships that has been reported at Gombe than at other sites. Constable and colleagues[66] note that females tended to consort with low-ranking males when they had high-ranking male relatives in the community. For such females, consortships may be a tactic to avoid inbreeding because male chimpanzees sometimes attempt to force copulations with their unwilling mothers or maternal sisters.[25] Two predictions follow. First, between communities, consortships should be more common in cases where females disperse less often. Second, within communities, natal females should show higher rates of consortship than immigrant females. Additional study will be needed to evaluate these predictions.

While genetic data have furnished novel insights into the chimpanzee mating system, similar information has begun to clarify the effects of maternal kinship on male chimpanzee behavior. Kinship plays a large and important role in the lives of humans as well as other primates,[71] and chimpanzees are frequently used to illustrate the effects of kinship on primate social behavior. Among chimpanzees, enduring and long-lasting bonds form between mothers and their offspring,[5,25] while genetically related males living within the same social group cooperate together in competition with males from other communities.[25,44,72,73]

Male chimpanzees develop strong social bonds with other males in their own community (Fig. 4). These bonds are manifest in several contexts, including association, grooming, proximity, coalitions, meat-sharing, and territorial boundary patrols.[7,21,33,51,73–81] Given the well-known effects of kinship on primate behavior, chimpanzee male bonds have often been assumed to form between close genetic relatives.[25,82] Two independent field studies have recently questioned this assumption. In observations of the Kanyawara community in Kibale, Goldberg and Wrangham[83] showed that male chimpanzees who maintain proximity and frequently groom each other are not necessarily related through the maternal line as assayed by mtDNA haplotype sharing and genetic distances. Our own observations of males at Ngogo support this finding and extend it by revealing that mtDNA genetic relatedness is not significantly correlated with levels of cooperation as measured by participation in coalitions, meat-sharing, and patrols.[84]

These studies raise two important and related questions: Why don't male chimpanzees selectively bias their behavior toward kin? What factors account for the observed patterns of affiliation and cooperation among wild male chimpanzees? Although chimpanzee demography and life history have the potential to provide answers to both of these questions, they have received scant attention. Chimpanzees are an extremely long-lived and slowly reproducing species. With an equal sex ratio at birth and high mortality among infants and juveniles,[25,41,52] the probability is relatively low that a female will give birth successively

Figure 4. Male chimpanzees form strong social bonds with each other. Here one adult male chimpanzee hugs another (a) to seek reassurance (b).

to sons that reach adulthood together. Thus, males will only rarely live with maternal kin who can effectively join them in behaviors that have important fitness consequences. If kin are not generally available, then males might solicit and use others opportunistically.[74,85] Individuals belonging to the same age cohort may be particularly attractive social partners because they grow up together, are generally familiar with each other, and share similar social interests and power throughout their lives. Similar points raise the possibility that males close in dominance rank may also be inclined to form strong affiliative and cooperative relationships.[78]

We have recently examined the effects of age and rank on aspects of male social behavior using observations of male chimpanzees living in the extremely large community at Ngogo.[86] We have found that members of the same age cohort and individuals that are close in rank are more likely to affiliate and cooperate than are males belonging to different age and rank classes. Additional analyses replicate earlier findings and show that males who affiliated and cooperated were not close maternal relatives as assayed by mtDNA haplotype sharing. A role for kinship might still be implicated if reproductive skew is high and male chimpanzees selectively cooperate with age-mates who are paternal siblings.[87] Evaluating this possibility will require additional information regarding nuclear and Y chromosome genetic markers. Until these data are available, we can only conclude that demographic and social factors may constrain patterns of male chimpanzee social behavior to a greater extent than does maternal kinship.

HUNTING, MEAT-EATING, AND MEAT-SHARING

Hunting and meat-eating by wild chimpanzees captures widespread anthropological attention because of its obvious relevance to the study of human origins and evolution.[88–94] Research on chimpanzee hunting and meat-eating also contributes more broadly to our understanding of traditional ecological and ethological problems, such as predator-prey relationships and the evolution of cooperation in animals.[95–98]

Since Goodall's[4] seminal observations, field workers at sites scattered across Africa have documented the regular occurrence of hunting and meat-eating by chimpanzees.[99–104] As a result, we now possess extensive data on chimpanzee prey choice, as well as hunting frequency, success, and participation.[33,98,104,105] With respect to prey choice, we know that chimpanzees selectively hunt red colobus monkeys (*Procolobus badius*) everywhere they live sympatrically (Fig. 5). Hunts of red colobus occur frequently, on an average of 4 to 10 times per month. Chimpanzees are extraordinarily successful in preying on red colobus; hunting success rates average over 50% across study sites. Independent field studies have consistently shown that adult male chimpanzees are responsible for the vast majority of all kills.

Despite this wealth of information about chimpanzee predatory behavior, two fundamental questions have remained unanswered. First, what factors affect decisions to hunt? This question arises because chimpanzees sometimes quickly pursue red colobus on encounter, yet forego hunting attempts at other times.[106,107] Second, why do chimpanzees share meat with conspecifics? Hunts are costly in terms of time and energy, and during predation attempts chimpanzees take considerable risks, given that red colobus males mob them.[108,109] Why, then, do chimpanzees relinquish meat, a scarce and valuable resource, to others?

Five nonmutually exclusive hypotheses have been advanced to provide answers to these two questions. Geza Teleki[110] first made the simplest and most direct proposal. Teleki, who conducted the first systematic investigation of chimpanzee hunting behavior at Gombe, hypothesized that chimpanzees hunt because they are hungry. Chimpanzees are frugivores that rely on sugar-rich fruits that are seasonally available.[111] Teleki proposed that chimpanzees hunt to compensate for the nutritional shortfalls they experience, primarily during the seasonal troughs of fruit availability. Despite the elegant simplicity and intuitive appeal of this

Figure 5. Chimpanzees prey selectively on red colobus monkeys. Here an adult male chimpanzee feeds on a portion of an adult female red colobus.

hypothesis, it has remained untested for more than 25 years. Our recent studies at Ngogo have provided the first direct test.[107,112] Our results show that instead of hunting during fruit-poor times, chimpanzees actually increase the frequency of their hunting attempts when fruit is abundant.

A second hypothesis advanced to explain why chimpanzees hunt and share meat was also developed by Teleki.[110] This hypothesis has recently been revived by Stanford,[92,98,106] who also studied the Gombe chimpanzees. Stanford's work there showed that the single best predictor of a male chimpanzee's decision to hunt was the presence of estrous females. Stanford has used this finding, along with the additional observation that male chimpanzees occasionally exchange meat for matings, to argue for a provocative "meat-for-sex" hypothesis. According to this hypothesis, male chimpanzees hunt in order to obtain meat that they can swap for matings.

The meat-for-sex hypothesis has generated intriguing claims and has received considerable publicity,[113,114] but neither the claims nor the hypothesis appear to stand up well under close scrutiny. Unlike the situation at Gombe, the presence of estrous females does not predict the tendency of the Ngogo males to hunt.[107] Moreover, the predicted behaviors occur infrequently at Ngogo and elsewhere. At Ngogo, estrous females do not reliably obtain meat from their begging efforts nor do matings typically ensue following meat exchanges.[107] Most tellingly, however, our observations indicate that males at Ngogo do not gain any mating advantage by sharing meat with estrous females.[107]

One of the more surprising suggestions stemming from the meat-for-sex hypothesis is that female chimpanzees have a keen interest in acquiring meat because eating meat improves their reproductive performance.[106] Data compiled by McGrew[115] based on observations made from Gombe[25] revealed a positive relationship between the amount of meat a female obtains and her reproduction (Fig. 6). Care needs to be taken when interpreting this result, however, for an important confounding factor related to both of the variables of interest could lead to the posited association. Using long-term observations from Gombe, Pusey and colleagues[116] have shown that female chimpanzee dominance rank is related to lifetime reproductive success. Given that high-ranking females are likely to obtain more meat than low-ranking females do, dominance rank is a probable confounding variable that produces a spurious correlation between female reproduction and meat eating.

If neither hunger nor sex provides the prime motivation to hunt, what does? We suggest that a male chimpanzee's decision to hunt is affected by his assessment of the likelihood of success.[107] Field studies consistently have shown that party size and the number of male hunters are good predictors of hunting success.[101,104,106,117] Male chimpanzees appear to swamp red colobus prey defenses with strength in numbers, so that hunting success increases when chimpanzees form large parties with many male hunters. Ecological constraints limit the formation of large parties, however. During periods of low food availability, when the ecological costs of feeding competition are high, chimpanzees form relatively small parties.[27,35,118] It is only during periods of relative food abundance that chimpanzees regularly gather in large parties. The positive relationship between party size and fruit abundance provides a transparent explanation for our finding that hunting frequency at Ngogo increases during periods of food abundance. We conclude from these considerations that at Ngogo male chimpanzees hunt when they are likely to be successful, which is when they are in large parties with several male hunters. Males forego most hunting attempts when they are in smaller parties because the odds of success are greatly reduced.

Another finding from Ngogo is also consistent with the hypothesis that hunting decisions depend on the likelihood of success and provides quantitative support for the longstanding proposal that chimpanzees preferentially hunt red colobus in situations where the monkeys have few or no escape routes.[119] Hunts that occur in areas where the tree canopy is broken are generally more successful than those where the canopy is continuous and closed.[112] Consequently, chimpanzees are much more likely to hunt red colobus groups that they encounter in forest with a generally low and broken canopy than those they meet in mature forest where the canopy is tall and continuous.[112]

Still open is the question of why male chimpanzees share meat readily with conspecifics. One hypothesis invokes an important role for cooperation. Chimpanzees at Taï appear to hunt cooperatively on a regular basis, both in the sense that individuals coordinate their behavior with each other and that per capita energy gain from hunting increases with the number of active hunters.[97,101] These observations led Boesch[97] to propose that male chimpanzees selectively share meat with others who

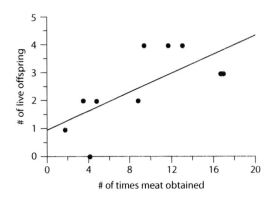

Figure 6. Female chimpanzee reproduction and meat acquisition. Data adapted from Goodall[25] (Table 11.15, p. 310).

have cooperated with them to make kills. According to this hypothesis, selective meat sharing ensures that "bystanders," individuals who are present but fail to participate in hunts, do not obtain meat and thus cannot exploit the hunting efforts of cooperators.

We recognize that distinguishing cooperative hunters from bystanders is theoretically important. We also acknowledge that the cooperative hunting hypothesis may explain meat sharing among the Taï chimpanzees. Evaluating the generality of this hypothesis, however, will be difficult due to conceptual and methodological reasons. As Stanford[98] has noted, the notion of behavioral cooperation in chimpanzee hunting has been hard to operationalize. We lack an objective way to distinguish whether males who pursue prey actually coordinate their efforts to capture the prey or simply pursue their own selfish strategies while taking into account each other's movements and the response of the prey to these movements. Observers at Gombe,[98] Mahale,[117] and Ngogo[112] report that individuals often switch between standing by and pursuing prey during the course of the same hunt. This makes it difficult to differentiate cooperators and cheaters reliably because to do so requires complete information on the activities of all individuals present. Prevailing observation conditions often preclude obtaining complete records; during hunts, multiple chimpanzees frequently pursue red colobus prey high in the tree canopy over areas that sometimes cover several hundred meters.

The use of outcome-based criteria to investigate whether hunting is cooperative in an ecological sense—that is, whether success increases as a function of the number of hunters— also presents problems. Researchers have used various measures, including some that apply to hunting parties as a whole, such as the probability of at least one kill, the total number of kills, and the total amount of meat obtained. Alternatively, others have applied measures that are based on the behavior of individuals, such as the amount of meat obtained per individual or the net energy gained per individual. The results of some studies satisfy some of these criteria,[92,97,112,120] but others do not.[92,96,97,112] As Boesch[33,97] has noted, net energy gain per individual constitutes a theoretically sound measure, and, employing this criterion, cooperation appears to occur at Taï but not Gombe.[97] However, constraints on visibility during hunts and the common occurrence of multiple kills[101,104,112,117,121] make it difficult to monitor the activities and prey intake of all chimpanzee hunters. As a result, field observers have been unable to estimate per capita net energy gain consistently across study sites. Until these data become available, questions about the extent of cooperation will remain open.

A final hypothesis proposed to explain meat sharing implicates the use of meat as a political tool. Using observations of the alpha male of M group at Mahale, Nishida and colleagues[122] suggested that male chimpanzees share meat strategically with others in order to curry their favor and support. These researchers' observations indicated that a particularly shrewd male shared meat nonrandomly and selectively with other males he depended on for support in long-term alliances. Our recent observations at Ngogo are largely consistent with this male social bonding hypothesis.[107] There as elsewhere,[101,122] the vast majority of all sharing events take place between males. Males share nonrandomly and selectively with only certain others and sharing is reciprocated at a group level. In addition, male chimpanzees at Ngogo exchange meat for coalitionary support.

Part of the interest generated by the meat-for-sex hypothesis lies in its claim that male chimpanzees use meat to achieve matings. The male social bonding hypothesis, however, provides a more compelling rationale for how males might use meat in a mating strategy. The great deal of male sexual coercion among chimpanzees[25,51] probably renders female mate choice relatively unimportant in this species. In contrast, levels of male-male competition are high.[25,123,124] Other male chimpanzees are the main obstacle facing individuals who attempt to increase their mating success. Forging long-term alliances with other males via meat-sharing provides an indirect yet effective way to improve mating opportunities. In chimpanzees, alliances are important in the establishment and maintenance of rank,[74,85] and high rank appears to confer mating and reproductive advantages.[48–50,66,73,77]

INTERGROUP AGGRESSION

Chimpanzees are well known for their territorial behavior. They are among the few animals that engage in lethal between-group coalitionary aggression.[80] Encounters between communities are typically hostile and sometimes result in the death of both infants and adults, particularly males.[76,80,99,123–128] Extreme intergroup aggression has led to the extermination of one community at the hands of another at Gombe[76]; a similar process is inferred at Mahale.[72] The functional significance of territoriality and lethal aggression is unclear, but several fitness benefits fall under the imbalance-of-power hypothesis, which holds that attacks on members of neighboring communities result from a motivation to dominate others.[80] This could lead to improved safety, improved access to food, and incorporation of more females into a community.[19,25,80,129]

Assessing the imbalance-of-power hypothesis requires analysis of male patrolling behavior, which is an integral part of chimpanzee territoriality. Male chimpanzees occasionally form parties that move to and along the periphery of their territory, where they search for signs of chimpanzees from other communities. Patrols sometimes make deep incursions into neighboring territories. Behavior during patrols is striking and unusual. Males are silent, tense, and wary. They move in a tight file, often pause to look and listen, sometimes sniff the ground, and show great interest in chimpanzee nests, dung, and feeding remains. Goodall and colleagues[76] were the first to describe patrolling, but this behavior has received little subsequent attention and is still poorly understood. New studies have started to rectify this situation.

Boesch and Boesch-Achermann[33] have described patrolling by chimpanzees in the Taï National Park. Patrols occurred an average of about once a month during 45 months of study, but rates of patrolling varied over time. Much of this variation was a result of changes in the composition of the study community. As the number of adult males declined, the remaining males became more cautious. When male numbers were reduced to four or fewer, they switched from searching for neighbors to avoiding encounters. Although patrols at Taï consisted mostly of males (Fig. 7), females joined to an unusual extent; female participation at other sites is generally rare.[25,73] Patrolling chimpanzees typically made deep incursions, sometimes well over 1 km, into the territories of other groups, but contacted neighbors on only about a quarter of all patrols. Especially intriguing are the complex tactics Taï patrollers used to attack neighbors. These included direct frontal attacks, selective "lateral" attacks on the smallest of several parties nearby, and more complicated assaults supported from the rear by fellow patrollers. Use of these tactics varied with the size and composition of patrols, with large patrols containing many males being those most likely to make direct frontal attacks.[33]

We have also described patrolling by males at Ngogo in the Kibale Na-tional Park.[73] At Ngogo, as elsewhere, males are the primary participants in patrols (Fig. 7). Patrols at Ngogo are larger and contain more males than do those at Taï or Gombe. This is a simple consequence of the fact that the Ngogo community is much larger than the communities at Taï and Gombe and has many more males. The large number of males probably helps to explain the relatively high rate of patrolling at Ngogo, about three times per month.

Patrol participants minimally lose time, expend energy, and face opportunity costs. At worst, patrollers risk injury or even death. These costs could be offset by several benefits, including improved safety, increased access to food, female recruitment, and improved foraging efficiency for resident females.[19,73,129] All patrollers and other members of their communities would benefit from improved safety and increased access to food. If these are the only benefits and males share them equitably, then a collective action problem is likely to ensue.[73] If male mating skew is high, however, males would not share evenly any increases in mating opportunities gained by recruiting females. Males would also obtain unequal shares of increases conferred on the reproductive success of resident females by improved foraging efficiency. Given the potential for unequal benefits, males might be inclined to adjust their participation in patrols to reflect their expected current and future reproductive gains.[73]

Until recently, assessing how individual male chimpanzees weigh these costs and benefits and make decisions to patrol has been difficult. The high frequency of patrols at Ngogo has allowed us to document patrolling effort by individual males to an extent not previously possible.[73] We found significant interindividual variation in patrolling effort. Some males patrol quite frequently, while others do so less often. Some males are especially likely to join patrols whenever the opportunity occurs, whereas others are less inclined to participate. Our observations support the hypothesis that this variation arises partly because males do not derive equal benefits from patrolling. Patrol participation is correlated with mating success. Males who mate frequently and may have the most offspring in the group to protect now and in the future appear to be motivated to patrol often. In addition, males seem to minimize the costs of patrolling by doing so with partners with whom they have strong social bonds and on whom they can rely to take risks. Our observations from Ngogo indicate that joint participation in patrols is positively related to joint participation in grooming bouts and coalitions. Patrolling effort is also positively correlated with frequency of participation in red colobus hunts and with success at capturing prey. Willingness to pursue prey, which involves risk, and hunting skill should give others some indication of a male's willingness and ability to take risks in intergroup aggression.[73]

The ostensible goal of patrols is to seek information or contact with members of other communities. At Ngogo, males encounter members of other communities, either aurally or visually, on 30% to 40% of all patrols.[73] They approach or attack members of the other group in roughly half of all encounters, and either avoid them or flee in the other half. Part of the variation in the tendency to attack or flee can be attributed to the patrollers' assessment of their

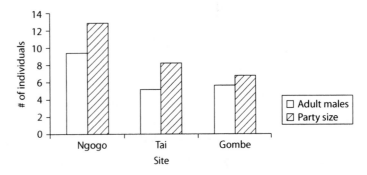

Figure 7. Intercommunity variation in patrol size and composition. The mean number of adult male patrollers and average patrol size are shown for three different communities.

Figure 8. A group of male chimpanzees on patrol.

relative strength. The likelihood of attack increases when patrols are large, whereas small patrol parties are more likely to flee. These data are consistent with the hypothesis that intergroup aggression among chimpanzees occurs whenever the potential costs are low.[130] These observations provide only a weak test of this hypothesis, however, given our lack of data on the respective size of groups with which the Ngogo chimpanzees have interacted.

Stronger support for the low-cost hypothesis comes from experimental play-back studies conducted with the Kanyawara community in Kibale.[131] Here a male's decision to participate in simulated territorial encounters depended primarily on whether a favorable numerical asymmetry existed. When the call of a single extra-group male was played back, parties containing three or more males consistently chorused and approached the speaker. Parties with fewer adult males usually remained silent and approached the speaker less often.

In these simulated encounters, the position that males occupied in parties that approached the speaker varied significantly among individuals. This position was independent of current dominance rank, although two former alpha males had the highest mean approach rates. Willingness to respond to intrusions did not differ among individuals, and all males approached when they overwhelmingly outnumbered the caller.[131]

These results suggest that male chimpanzees obtain mutual benefits from cooperating in intergroup aggression,[131] but further observations of actual territorial encounters are needed to exclude the alternative hypothesis that males participate and benefit unequally because their prospective reproductive gains differ. The play-back experiments did not resolve this issue because most were performed well within the community's territory and all simulated the presence of only one extra-group male. Field observations indicate that intergroup encounters are more likely in border areas, and frequently involve multiple males on both sides.[25,33,73] Under such conditions the potential costs of involvement to individual males may be greater, and individual differences in participation thus more likely to emerge. At Taï, Gombe, and Ngogo, communities neighboring the main study groups have been or are being habituated, which will facilitate recording the details of both sides of actual intergroup encounters.

Fatalities during intergroup aggression are a well-documented aspect of chimpanzee behavior. In some cases, attacks on females and their infants result in infanticide.[25,73,99,126–128] Infanticide has also been documented within communities.[132] Chimpanzees also kill adult members from other groups.[25,76,80,124] Intraspecific killing by chimpanzees is unusual among primates in that the perpetrators also cannibalize their victims.[25,99,123,125–128] Our understanding of the causes of lethal attacks and cannibalism is incomplete. Infanticide among chimpanzees does not obviously satisfy the conditions of the sexual-selection hypothesis[133] because female secondary transfer appears to be rare[19] and males often kill infants in their own communities.[132] Instead of increasing male reproductive opportunities, between-group infanticide may be a male tactic to push females from neighboring communities away from boundary areas, thereby allowing females in their own communities safer and better access to food in these areas.[129] Success in between-group aggression could have this effect in general. In support of this argument, long-term data from the Kasakela community at Gombe show that fe-male reproductive performance was higher when the community's territory was relatively large than it was when pressure from neighbors reduced the size of the territory (A. Pusey, personal communication). Irrespective of the many questions that surround between-group infanticide, within-group infanticides continue to remain a major puzzle in the study of chimpanzee behavior.[132,134]

BEHAVIORAL ENDOCRINOLOGY

Recent developments in sampling and assaying steroid hormones have provided new insights into the physiological mechanisms of primate behavior.[135] Urinary and fecal assays have proven particularly attractive to field workers. Urine and fecal sampling are generally easy and inexpensive to conduct, allow for frequent resampling of individuals, and integrate the short-term fluctuations in hormone production that can confound serum measurements. More importantly, such sampling is noninvasive and does not adversely affect the welfare or behavior of study subjects. There is, consequently, a burgeoning literature on the hormonal correlates of behavior in wild primates,[136–139] to which studies of chimpanzees are contributing.[140]

We have recently completed a set of studies on the behavioral endocrinology of chimpanzees in the Kanyawara community, Kibale National Park. This research has focused on the steroid hormones testosterone and cortisol. Testosterone influences numerous aspects of male reproductive physiology. Cortisol has been widely employed as a marker of both physiological and psychological stress.[141] The stress response is of special interest. Although this response clearly is adaptive in many situations, its chronic activation can lead to increased susceptibility to pathology, including gastric ulcers, atherosclerosis, and suppressed immune function.[141] Thus, there are circumstances in which cortisol measurements can help to assess the costs of particular behavioral strategies.

Sapolsky's[142,143] research on stress physiology in baboons provides the most complete picture available of the interaction between hormones and behavior in a wild primate, and furnishes a context for our findings from the Kanyawara chimpanzees. Sapolsky measured basal cortisol levels in high- and low-ranking baboon males and found that the patterns observed were influenced by the stability of the dominance hierarchy. During a period in which the dominance hierarchy was stable, high-ranking males were less aggressive than low-ranking males and exhibited lower circulating levels of cortisol and testosterone. During a period of extreme dominance instability, however, high-ranking males were more aggressive and had higher levels of cortisol and testosterone than did low-ranking males.

In our studies at Kanyawara, we have observed that across the adult males rates of aggression are positively and significantly correlated with rank, even when the dominance hierarchy appears to be stable; that is, when there are no rank reversals and the rate of reversals in decided agonistic bouts is low.[124] Similar correlations between aggression and rank during periods of relative dominance stability have been reported from Gombe,[144] Mahale,[77] and Taï.[33] At Kanyawara we have also found that dominance rank consistently correlates positively with measures of urinary cortisol.[145] Taken together, these findings suggest that the trials and tribulations of life at the top of the hierarchy are persistently more stressful for male chimpanzees than for male baboons.

What can account for this apparent difference? One possibility is that the fission-fusion nature of chimpanzee social organization introduces an element of unpredictability to male social relationships that is not present in baboon society. Because baboons travel and forage in relatively cohesive groups, it presumably is easy for a male baboon to make accurate assessments of his position in the dominance hierarchy. Furthermore, a high-ranking male can continually monitor developing social relationships between other individuals that might affect the hierarchy in the future. Chimpanzee males, on the other hand, frequently break into small groups that may not come together again for hours, days, or even weeks. Thus, it is more difficult for a high-ranking chimpanzee to monitor the political maneuverings among potential challengers. A dominant male is constantly at risk from opportunistic coalitions formed by lower-ranking individuals and must continually assert his dominance through agonistic display. This idea is supported by the high frequency of aggression that takes place in the context of reunions.[123,124] In sum, even a stable chimpanzee hierarchy may be unstable in comparison to a baboon hierarchy, despite having a low rate of actual reversals.

Of course, as with baboons,[146] dominance rank probably is not the entire story when it comes to chimpanzee stress physiology. The personalities of different individuals may partially mediate the relationship between rank and stress. Ongoing studies at Kanyawara and Gombe will soon allow us to address this issue. In the meantime, it appears that increased stress imposes a general cost on social dominance for male chimpanzees, which must be set against the reproductive benefits described earlier.

An additional cost of social dominance suggests itself in the form of chronically elevated testosterone levels. At Kanyawara, urinary androgen levels also correlate with dominance rank. Although the correlation is not as robust as that with cortisol, there is a clear alpha-male effect,[147] with the highest-ranking male persistently exhibiting the highest levels of testosterone. Additional physiological costs associated with high testosterone include direct energetic costs resulting from increased metabolic rate and immunosuppression.[148]

Testosterone influences multiple aspects of male reproductive physiology, from the development of the male reproductive anatomy to the maintenance of both reproductive function and motivation. It has also classically been associated with aggression. A large body of research, mostly on birds, suggests that variation in circulating testosterone levels is associated primarily with male aggression in reproductive contexts, rather than changes in reproductive physiology.[149] The extent to which this idea, formally known as the challenge hypothesis,[149] applies to mammals is not yet clear.[138,150] Data from Kanyawara permit a preliminary test of this hypothesis in chimpanzees.

In birds, testosterone induces male reproductive aggression at the expense of paternal care.[149] Therefore, cross-species correlations are predicted between basal levels of breed-ing-season testosterone and mating system. Monogamous birds are expected to maintain high testosterone levels during territory formation and breeding, but to decrease testosterone production when providing paternal care. They should also react strongly to challenges from conspecifics with increased testosterone production. Polygynous birds, on the other hand, engage in less paternal care, so they should exhibit high levels of testosterone throughout the breeding season. They are not expected to show a heightened endocrine response to challenges because their testosterone levels are already close to the physiological maximum. These predictions are supported by data from a large number of avian species.[149]

Chimpanzees are not seasonal breeders and do not engage in direct paternal care, so they represent a special case for the challenge hypothesis. Because the availability of cycling females varies temporally and the presence of maximally swollen females is attended by high rates of male aggression, the challenge hypothesis suggests that male testosterone levels should increase during periods of reproductive competition. Our data from Kanyawara support this prediction. Adult males at Kanyawara exhibited significant increases in rates of aggression, particularly escalated aggression such as chases and attacks, on days when maximally swollen parous females were present.[124] Males also exhibited significant increases in mean testosterone levels during these periods of intense competition.[145] Mean cortisol levels also increased significantly, which is consistent with the known role of this hormone in mobilizing energy during periods of crisis.

Estrous females are frequent targets of male aggression, particularly when high-ranking males are attempting to maintain exclusive mating access to them.[25,151] Being mate-guarded is likely to be extremely stressful for females, a proposition that is supported by our preliminary data. We were able to collect multiple samples from one parous female who was intensively mate-guarded during her periovulatory period. During this time the aggression she received from males more than doubled, and she showed dramatic increases in urinary cortisol levels. We also examined multiple samples from a nulliparous female during both swelling and nonswelling periods. Because nulliparous females are not as attractive to males as mothers are, males do not mate-guard them, and they do not appear to receive as much aggression during the late follicular phase.[152] Such was the case with this female, and she did not exhibit the increases in urinary cortisol during maximal swelling that were observed in the parous female. Future work in this area at both Kanyawara and Gombe will help us to document the physiological costs imposed on females by male sexual aggression.

DIRECTIONS FOR FUTURE RESEARCH

This is an especially exciting time for those of us who study chimpanzees in the wild. Years of dedicated field work by numerous researchers at sites scattered throughout Africa have produced a rich body of information regarding the behavior of our closest living relatives. We are now in a unique position to build on previous findings and stand on the threshold of filling several critical gaps in understanding. We conclude by reviewing some topics that warrant more research.

First, what explains intraspecific variations in gregariousness, association patterns, and range use? Ecological factors such as the spatial and temporal distribution of food are frequently invoked as explanatory variables.[153–156] Comparative studies that provide systematic data on food availability and feeding competition promise to provide answers in the case of chimpanzees. Demographic and social factors that affect the description, measurement, and analysis of associations should also be examined to seek clues to intraspecific variations in gregariousness and range use.

Second, we require additional study of the factors that account for differences in dispersal patterns across study sites. Why do female chimpanzees at Gombe frequently remain in their natal group while those at other sites almost always disperse? Feeding competition that ultimately limits fe-male reproduction has been invoked as a causal factor[19,116,129] and here too direct measures of food availability will be necessary to unlock the key to this puzzle. The flip side of female dispersal, male philopatry, constitutes an associated problem seldom addressed in discussions of chimpanzee behavior. We need a new body of theory and empirical research to address the evolutionary causes and proximate determinants of male philopatry, not only in chimpanzees but other animals as well.[157]

Females have taken a back seat to males in the study of chimpanzee behavioral ecology and we require more and better observations of them and their behavior. These data will not only furnish insights into the nature of female competition, reproduction, and social behavior,[158] but also will help to clarify aspects of male-female social relationships and the significance of male coercion in this species.[51] As we have noted, chimpanzee hunting and meat eating take on special significance for anthropologists who seek an understanding of human behavioral evolution. The extent to which male chimpanzees cooperate during hunts remains an empirically challenging area in need of future study. While current evidence suggests that male chimpanzees share meat selectively with others in order to curry their favor and support, alternate hypotheses proposed to explain meat sharing in humans, such as sharing to enhance status and tolerated theft are still to be invoked and tested.[159,160] Technical advances that involve the measurement of genetic relatedness and steroid hormones between and within individuals promise to yield deeper understanding of both the ultimate and proximate factors affecting chimpanzee behavior. Finally, no easy answers regarding the evolutionary factors that contribute to infanticide and cannibalism have emerged, despite decades of study. Understanding here will require more observations of the contexts of these infrequent events.

We would be remiss if we failed to note the critically endangered status of chimpanzees in the wild. It has become depressingly common for field workers to comment on how time is running out to save these animals. This is a regrettable fact. We are fortunate to have been given an opportunity to share in the lives of these animals in the wild. Anyone who has been similarly blessed instantly realizes the extraordinary nature of chimpanzees and recognizes the void that will exist if we do not meet the challenge by doing everything in our power to conserve these remarkable creatures and their habitat in the wild.

ACKNOWLEDGMENTS

We thank John Fleagle for inviting us to prepare this review. Our field work has been sponsored in Tanzania and Uganda by the Makerere University, the Serengeti Wildlife Research Institute, the Tanzanian Commission for Science and Technology, the Tanzanian National Parks, and the Ugandan National Parks. We are grateful to G.I. Basuta, J. Kasenene, E. Massawe, and the staffs of the Makerere University Biological Field Station and Ma-hale Mountains National Park for providing logistical assistance in the field. We thank our Tanzanian and Ugandan field assistants, without whom our research would not have been possible. C. Boesch, J. Fleagle, K. Hunley, S. Olatunde, and R. Wrangham made helpful suggestions on the manuscript, while K. Langergraber provided editorial assistance. Our research on chimpanzees has been generously funded by grants from the Detroit Zoological Institute, the Harry Frank Guggenheim Foundation, the L.S.B. Leakey Foundation, the National Geographic Society, the U.S. National Science Foundation, and the Wenner-Gren Foundation for Anthropological Research. We dedicate this review to Professors Toshisada Nishida and Richard Wrangham, pioneering chimpanzee researchers, mentors, and friends.

REFERENCES

1. Horai S, Hayasaka K, Kondo R, Tsugane K, Takahata N. 1995. Recent African origin of modern humans revealed by complete sequences of hominoid mitochondrial DNAs. Proc Natl Acad Sci 92:532–536.
2. Ruvolo M. 1997. Molecular phylogeny of the hominoids: inferences from multiple independent DNA sequence data sets. Mol Biol Evol 14: 248–265.

3. Chen F, Li W. 2001. Genomic divergences between humans and other hominoids and the effective population size of the common ancestor of humans and chimpanzees. Am J Hum Genet 68:444–456.

4. Goodall J. 1963. Feeding behaviour of wild chimpanzees: a preliminary report. Symp Zool Soc London 10:39–48.

5. Goodall J. 1968. The behaviour of free-living chimpanzees in the Gombe Stream area. Anim Behav Monogr 1:161–311.

6. Nishida T. 1990. The chimpanzees of the Mahale Mountains. Tokyo: University of Tokyo Press.

7. Nishida T. 1968. The social group of wild chimpanzees in the Mahale Mountains. Primates 9:167–224.

8. Nishida T, Kawanaka K. 1972. Inter-unit-group relationships among wild chimpanzees of the Mahale mountains. Kyoto Univ Afr Stud 7:131– 169.

9. Itani J. 1979. Distribution and adaptation of chimpanzees in an arid area. In: Hamburg D, McCown E, editors. The great apes. Menlo Park: Benjamin/Cummings. p 55–71.

10. Tutin C, Fernandez M, Rogers M, Williamson E, McGrew W. 1991. Foraging profiles of sympatric lowland gorillas and chimpanzees in the Lopé Reserve, Gabon. Philos Trans R Soc (London B) 334:179–186.

11. Baldwin P, McGrew W, Tutin C. 1982. Wideranging chimpanzees at Mt. Assirik, Senegal. Int J Primatol 3:367–385.

12. Wrangham R, McGrew W, deWaal F, Heltne P. 1994. Chimpanzee cultures. Cambridge: Harvard University Press.

13. Whiten A, Boesch C. 2001. The cultures of chimpanzees. Sci Am 284:61–67.

14. Whiten A, Goodall J, McGrew W, Nishida T, Reynolds V, Sugiyama Y, Tutin C, Wrangham R, Boesch C. 1999. Cultures in chimpanzees. Nature 399:682–685.

15. Kortlandt A. 1962. Chimpanzees in the wild. Sci Am 206:128–138.

16. Goodall J. 1965. Chimpanzees of the Gombe Stream Reserve. In: DeVore I, editor. Primate behavior. New York: Holt, Rinehart, Winston. p 425–473.

17. Reynolds V, Reynolds F. 1965. Chimpanzees of the Budongo forest. In: DeVore I, editor. Primate behavior. New York: Holt, Rinehart, Winston. p 368–424.

18. Pusey A. 1979. Intercommunity transfer of chimpanzees in Gombe National Park. In: Hamburg D, McCown E, editors. The great apes. Menlo Park: Benjamin/Cummings. p 405–427.

19. Williams J. 1999. Female strategies and the reasons for territoriality in chimpanzees: lessons from three decades of research at Gombe. Ph.D. thesis, University of Minnesota.

20. Halperin S. 1979. Temporary association patterns in free ranging chimpanzees: an assessment of individual grouping preferences. In: Hamburg D, McCown E, editors. The great apes. Menlo Park: Benjamin/Cummings. p 491–499.

21. Wrangham R, Smuts B. 1980. Sex differences in the behavioral ecology of chimpanzees in the Gombe National Park, Tanzania. J Reprod Fertil 28 (suppl):13–31.

22. Kawanaka K. 1984. Association, ranging, and the social unit in chimpanzees of the Mahale Mountains, Tanzania. Int J Primatol 5:411–434.

23. Hasegawa T. 1990. Sex differences in ranging patterns. In: Nishida T, editor. The chimpanzees of the Mahale Mountains. Tokyo: University of Tokyo Press. p 99–114.

24. Wrangham R, Clark A, Isabiryre-Basuta G. 1992. Female social relationships and social organization of Kibale Forest chimpanzees. In: Nishida T, McGrew W, Marler P, Pickford M, deWaal F, editors. Topics in primatology, vol. 1. Human origins. Tokyo: Tokyo University Press. p 81–98.

25. Goodall J. 1986. The chimpanzees of Gombe. Cambridge: Belknap Press.

26. Wrangham R. 1979. On the evolution of ape social systems. Soc Sci Information 18:335–368.

27. Wrangham R. 2000. Why are male chimpanzees more gregarious than mothers? A scramble competition hypothesis. In: Kappeler P, editor. Primate males. Cambridge: Cambridge University Press. p 248–258.

28. Wrangham R. 1986. Ecology and social relationships in two species of chimpanzee. In: Wrangham R, Rubenstein D, editors. Ecological aspects of social evolution: birds and mammals. Princeton: Princeton University Press. p 352–378.

29. Sakura O. 1994. Factors affecting party size and composition of chimpanzees (*Pan troglodytes verus*) at Bossou, Guinea. Int J Primatol 15:167–183.

30. Sugiyama Y, Koman J. 1979. Social structure and dynamics of wild chimpanzees at Bossou, Guinea. Primates 20:323–339.

31. Ghiglieri M. 1984. The chimpanzees of Kibale forest. New York: Columbia University Press.

32. Boesch C. 1996. Social grouping in Taï chimpanzees. In: McGrew W, Marchant L, Nishida T, editors. Great ape societies. Cambridge: Cambridge University Press. p 101–113.

33. Boesch C, Boesch-Achermann H. 2000. The chimpanzees of the Taï forest. Oxford: Oxford University Press.

34. Doran D. 1997. Influence of seasonality on activity patterns, feeding behavior, ranging, and grouping patterns in Taï chimpanzees. Int J Primatol 18:183–206.

35. Mitani J, Watts D, Lwanga J. n.d. Ecological and social correlates of chimpanzee party size *Evolutionary Anthropology 23* and composition. In: Boesch C, Hohmann G, Marchant L, editors. Behavioral diversity in chimpanzees and bonobos. Cambridge: Cambridge University Press. In press.

36. Chapman C, White F, Wrangham R. 1993. Defining subgroup size in fission-fusion societies. Folia Primatol 61:31–34.

37. Matsumoto-Oda A. 1999. Mahale chimpanzees: grouping patterns and cycling females. Am J Primatol 47:197–207.

38. Whitehead H, Dufault S. 1999. Techniques for analyzing vertebrate social structure using identified individuals: review and recommendations. Adv Stud Behav 28:33–74.

39. Pepper J, Mitani J, Watts D. 1999. General gregariousness and specific social preferences among wild chimpanzees. Int J Primatol 20:613–632.

40. Cairns S, Schwager S. 1987. A comparison of association indices. Anim Behav 35:1454–1469.

41. Nishida T, Takasaki H, Takahata Y. 1990. Demography and reproductive profiles. In: Nishida T, editor. The chimpanzees of the Mahale Mountains. Tokyo: University of Tokyo Press. p 63–97.

42. Sugiyama Y. 1999. Socioecological factors of male chimpanzee migration at Bossou, Guinea. Primates 40:61–68.

43. Morin P, Moore J, Chakraborty R, Jin L, Goodall J, Woodruff D. 1994. Kin selection, social structure, gene flow, and the evolution of chimpanzees. Science 265:1193–1201.

44. Goldberg T, Ruvolo M. 1997. The geographic apportionment of mitochondrial genetic diversity in East African chimpanzees, *Pan troglodytes schweinfurthii*. Mol Biol Evol 14:976–984.

45. Gagneux P, Wills C, Gerloff U, Tautz D, Morin P, Boesch C, Fruth B, Hohmann G, Ryder O, Woodruff D. 1999. Mitochondrial sequences show diverse evolutionary histories of African hominoids. Proc Natl Acad Sci 96:5077–5082.

46. Queller D, Strassmann J, Hughes C. 1993. Microsatellites and kinship. Trends Ecol Evol 8:285–288.

47. Kohn M, Wayne R. 1997. Facts from feces revisited. Trends Ecol Evol 12:223–227.

48. Tutin C. 1979. Mating patterns and reproductive strategies in a community of wild chimpanzees (*Pan troglodytes schweinfurthii*). Behav Ecol Sociobiol 6:29–38.

49. Hasegawa T, Hiraiwa-Hasegawa M. 1983. Opportunistic and restrictive matings among wild chimpanzees in Mahale, Tanzania. J Ethol 1:75–85.

50. Watts D. 1998. Coalitionary mate-guarding by male chimpanzees at Ngogo, Kibale National Park, Uganda. Behav Ecol Sociobiol 44:43–55.

51. Smuts B, Smuts R. 1993. Male aggression and sexual coercion of females in nonhuman primates and other mammals: evidence and theoretical implications. Adv Stud Behav 22:1–63.

52. Wallis J. 1997. A survey of reproductive parameters in the free-ranging chimpanzees of Gombe National Park. J Reprod Fertil 109:297– 307.

53. Hasegawa T, Hiraiwa-Hasegawa M. 1990. Sperm competition and mating behavior. In: Nishida T, editor. The chimpanzees of the Mahale Mountains. Tokyo: University of Tokyo Press. p 115–132.

54. Gagneux P, Woodruff D, Boesch C. 1997. Furtive mating in female chimpanzees. Nature 387: 358–359.

55. Gagneux P, Boesch C, Woodruff D. 1999. Female reproductive strategies, paternity and community structure in wild West African chimpanzees. Anim Behav 57:19–32.

56. Wrangham R. 1997. Subtle, secret female chimpanzees. Science 277:774–775.

57. Strier K. 2000. Primate behavioral ecology. Boston: Allyn Bacon.

58. Angier N. 1999. Woman: an intimate geography. Boston: Houghton Mifflin.

59. Hawkes N. 1997. DNA shows chimps' eye for monkey business. The Times May 22, 1997 edition.

60. Westneat D, Sherman P, Morton M. 1990. The ecology and evolution of extra-pair copulation in birds. In: Power D, editor. Current ornithology. New York: Plenum Press. p 331–369.

61. Sillero-Zubiri C, Gotelli D, MacDonald D. 1996. Male philopatry, extra-pack copulations and inbreeding avoidance in Ethiopian wolves (Canis simensis). Behav Ecol Sociobiol 38:331–340.

62. Keane B, Dittus W, Melnick D. 1997. Paternity assessment in wild groups of toque macaques Macaca sinica at Polonnaruwa, Sri Lanka, using molecular markers. Mol Ecol 6:267–282.

63. Petrie M, Kempenaers B. 1998. Extra-pair paternity in birds: explaining variation between species and populations. Trends Ecol Evol 13:52– 58.

64. Sugiyama Y, Kawamoto S, Takenaka O, Kumazaki K, Miwa N. 1993. Paternity discrimination and inter-group relationships of chimpanzees at Bossou. Primates 34:545–552.

65. Morin P, Wallis J, Moore J, Woodruff D. 1994. Paternity exclusion in a community of wild chimpanzees using hypervariable simple sequence repeats. Mol Ecol 3:469–478.

66. Constable J, Ashley M, Goodall J, Pusey A. 2001. Noninvasive paternity assignment in Gombe chimpanzees. Mol Ecol 10:1279–1300.

67. Vigilant L, Hofreiter, Siedel H, Boesch C. 2001. Paternity and relatedness in wild chimpanzee communities. Proc Natl Acad Sci 98:12890– 12895.

68. Edwards A, Civitello A, Hammond H, Caskey C. 1991. DNA typing and genetic mapping with trimeric and tetrameric tandem repeats. Am J Hum Genet 49:746–756.

69. Taberlet P, Waits LP, Luikart G. 1999. Noninvasive genetic sampling: look before you leap. Trends Ecol Evol 14:323–327.

70. Taberlet P, Griffin S, Goosens B, Questiau S, Manceau V, Escaravage N, Waits LP, Bouvet J. 1996. Reliable genotyping of samples with very low DNA quantities using PCR. Nucl Acids Res 24:3189–3194.

71. Silk J. 2001. Ties that bind: the role of kinship in primate societies. In: Stone L, editor. New directions in anthropological kinship. Lanham: Rowman & Littlefield Publishers. p 71–92.

72. Nishida T, Hiraiwa-Hasegawa M, Hasegawa T, Takahata Y. 1985. Group extinction and female transfer in wild chimpanzees in the Mahale Mountains National Park, Tanzania. Z Tierpsychol 67:281–301.

73. Watts D, Mitani J. 2001. Boundary patrols and intergroup encounters among wild chimpanzees. Behaviour 138:299–327.

74. Nishida T. 1983. Alpha status and agonistic alliance in wild chimpanzees (Pan troglodytes schweinfurthii). Primates 24:318–336.

75. Simpson M. 1973. Social grooming of male chimpanzees. In: Crook J, Michael R, editors. Comparative ecology and behaviour of primates. London: Academic Press. p 411–505.

76. Goodall J, Bandora A, Bergmann E, Busse C, Matama H, Mpongo E, Pierce A, Riss D. 1979. Intercommunity interactions in the chimpanzee population of the Gombe National Park. In: Hamburg D, McCown E, editors. The great apes. Menlo Park: Benjamin/Cummings. p 13–54.

77. Nishida T, Hosaka K. 1996. Coalition strategies among adult male chimpanzees of the Mahale Mountains, Tanzania. In: McGrew W, Marchant L, Nishida T, editors. Great ape societies. Cambridge: Cambridge University Press. p 114–134.

78. Watts D. 2000. Grooming between male chimpanzees at Ngogo, Kibale National Park. II. Influence of male rank and possible competition for partners. Int J Primatol 21:211–238.

79. Newton-Fisher N. 1999. Association by male chimpanzees: a social tactic? Behaviour 136:705–730.

80. Wrangham R. 1999. Evolution of coalitionary killing. Yearbook Phys Anthropol 42:1–30.

81. Mitani J, Watts D. 2001. Why do chimpanzees hunt and share meat? Anim Behav 61:915–924.

82. Riss D, Goodall J. 1977. The recent rise to the alpha rank in a population of free-living chimpanzees. Folia Primatol 27:134–151.

83. Goldberg T, Wrangham R. 1997. Genetic correlates of social behaviour in wild chimpanzees: evidence from mitochondrial DNA. Anim Behav 54:559–570.

84. Mitani J, Merriwether DA, Zhang C. 2000. Male affiliation, cooperation, and kinship in wild chimpanzees. Anim Behav 59:885–893.

85. deWaal F. 1982. Chimpanzee politics. New York: Harper and Row.

86. Mitani J, Watts D, Pepper J, Merriwether DA. n.d. Demographic and social constraints on male chimpanzee behaviour. submitted to Anim Behav.

87. Altmann J. 1979. Age cohorts as paternal sibships. Behav Ecol Sociobiol 6:161–164.

88. Ghiglieri M. 1987. Sociobiology of the great apes and the hominid ancestor. J Hum Evol 16: 319–357.

89. Wrangham R. 1987. The significance of African apes for reconstructing human social evolution. In: Kinzey W, editor. The evolution of human behavior: primate models. Albany: State University of New York Press. p 51–71.

90. Boesch H, Boesch C. 1994. Hominization in the rainforest: the chimpanzee's piece of the puzzle. Evol Anthropol 3:171–178.

91. Stanford C. 1995. Chimpanzee hunting behavior and human evolution. Am Sci 83:256–261.

92. Stanford C. 1996. The hunting ecology of wild chimpanzees: implications for the evolutionary ecology of Pliocene hominids. Am Anthropol 98: 96–113.

93. Stanford C. 1999. The hunting apes. Princeton: Princeton University Press.

94. Stanford C. 2001. The ape's gift: meat-eating, meat-sharing, and human evolution. In: deWaal F, editor. The tree of origin. Cambridge: Harvard University Press. p 95–117.

95. Busse C. 1978. Do chimpanzees hunt cooperatively? Am Nat 112:767–770.

96. Boesch C. 1994. Chimpanzees-red colobus monkeys: a predator-prey system. Anim Behav 47:1135–1148.

97. Boesch C. 1994. Cooperative hunting in wild chimpanzees. Anim Behav 48:653–667.

98. Stanford C. 1998. Chimpanzee and red colobus: the ecology of predator and prey. Cambridge: Harvard University Press.

99. Nishida T, Uehara S, Nyundo R. 1979. Predatory behavior among wild chimpanzees of the Mahale Mountains. Primates 20:1–20.

100. Anderson J, Williamson E, Carter J. 1983. Chimpanzees of Sapo Forest, Liberia: density, nests, tools and meat-eating. Primates 24:594–601.

101. Boesch C, Boesch H. 1989. Hunting behavior of wild chimpanzees in the Taï National Park. Am J Phys Anthropol 78:547–573.

102. Alp R. 1993. Meat eating and ant dipping by wild chimpanzees in Sierra Leone. Primates 34: 463–468.

103. Basabose K, Yamagiwa J. 1997. Predation on mammals by the chimpanzees in the montane forest of Kahuzi, Zaire. Primates 38:275–299.

104. Mitani J, Watts D. 1999. Demographic influences on the hunting behavior of chimpanzees. Am J Phys Anthropol 109:439–454.

105. Uehara S. 1997. Predation on mammals by the chimpanzee (*Pan troglodytes*). Primates 38:193–214.

106. Stanford C, Wallis J, Mpongo E, Goodall J. 1994. Hunting decisions in wild chimpanzees. Behaviour 131:1–18.

107. Mitani J, Watts D. 2001. Why do chimpanzees hunt and share meat? Anim Behav 61:915– 924.

108. Busse C. 1977. Chimpanzee predation as a possible factor in the evolution of red colobus monkey social organization. Evolution 31:907–911.

109. Stanford C. 1995. The influence of chimpanzee predation on group size and anti-predator behaviour in red colobus monkeys. Anim Behav 49:577–587.

110. Teleki G. 1973. The predatory behavior of wild chimpanzees. Lewisburg: Bucknell University Press.

111. Wrangham R, Conklin-Brittain NL, Hunt K. 1998. Dietary response of chimpanzees and cercopithecines to seasonal variation in fruit abundance. I. Antifeedants. Int J Primatol 19:949– 970.

112. Watts D, Mitani J. n.d. Hunting behavior of chimpanzees at Ngogo, Kibale National Park, Uganda. Int J Primatol. In press.

113. Gorner P. 1995. Female chimpanzees extract pound of flesh in return for sex. The Chicago Tribune April 1, 1995 edition.

114. Kopytoff V. 1995. Meat viewed as staple of chimp diet and mores. The New York Times June 27, 1995 edition.

115. McGrew W. 1992. Chimpanzee material culture: implications for human evolution. Cambridge: Cambridge University Press.

116. Pusey A, Williams J, Goodall J. 1997. The influence of dominance rank on the reproductive success of female chimpanzees. Science 277:828–831.

117. Hosaka K, Nishida T, Hamai M, Matsumoto- Oda A, Uehara S. 2001. Predation of mammals by the chimpanzees of the Mahale Mountains, Tanzania. In: Galdikas B, Briggs N, Sheeran L, Shapiro G, Goodall J, editors. All apes great and small, vol. 1. Chimpanzees, bonobos, and gorillas. New York: Kluwer Academic Publishers. p 107–130.

118. Chapman C, Wrangham R, Chapman L. 1995. Ecological constraints on group size: an analysis of spider monkey and chimpanzee subgroups. Behav Ecol Sociobiol 36:59–70.

119. Wrangham R. 1975. Behavioural ecology of chimpanzees in Gombe National Park. Ph.D. thesis, University of Cambridge.

120. Packer C, Ruttan L. 1988. The evolution of cooperative hunting. Am Nat 132:159–198.

121. Stanford C, Wallis J, Matama H, Goodall J. 1994. Patterns of predation by chimpanzees on red colobus monkeys in Gombe National Park, 1982–1991. Am J Phys Anthropol 94:213–228.

122. Nishida T, Hasegawa T, Hayaki H, Takahata Y, Uehara S. 1992. Meat-sharing as a coalition strategy by an alpha male chimpanzee? In: Nishida T, McGrew W, Marler P, Pickford M, deWaal F, editors. Topics in primatology. Volume 1. Human origins. Tokyo: Tokyo University Press. p 159–174.

123. Bygott D. 1979. Agonistic behavior and dominance among wild chimpanzees. In: Hamburg D, McCown E, editors. The great apes. Menlo Park: Benjamin/Cummings. p 405–427.

124. Muller M. n.d. Agonistic relations among Kanyawara chimpanzees. In: Boesch C, Hohmann G, Marchant L, editors. Behavioral diversity in chimpanzees and bonobos. Cambridge: Cambridge University Press. In press.

125. Bygott D. 1972. Cannibalism among wild chimpanzees. Nature 238:410–411.

126. Goodall J. 1977. Infant-killing and cannibalism in free-living chimpanzees. Folia Primatol 28:259–282.

127. Newton-Fisher N. 1999. Infant killers of Budongo. Folia Primatol 70:167–169.

128. Watts D, Mitani J. 2000. Infanticide and cannibalism by male chimpanzees at Ngogo, Kibale National Park, Uganda. Primates 41:357–365.

129. Pusey A. 2001. Of genes and apes: chimpanzee social organization and reproduction. In: deWaal F, editor. The tree of origin. Cambridge: Harvard University Press, p 9–37.

130. Manson J, Wrangham R. 1991. Intergroup aggression in chimpanzees and humans. Curr Anthropol 32:369–390.

131. Wilson M, Hauser M, Wrangham R. 2001. Does participation in intergroup conflict depend on numerical assessment, range location, or rank for wild chimpanzees? Anim Behav 61:1203–1216.

132. Arcadi A, Wrangham R. 1999. Infanticide in chimpanzees: review of cases and a new withingroup observation from the Kanyawara study group in Kibale National Park. Primates 40:337–351.

133. van Schaik C. 2000. Infanticide by male primates: the sexual selection hypothesis revisited. In: van Schaik C, Janson C, editors. Infanticide by males and its implications. Cambridge: Cambridge University Press. p 27–71.

134. Hamai M, Nishida T, Takasaki H, Turner L. 1992. New records of within-group infanticide in wild chimpanzees. Primates 33:151–162.

135. Whitten P, Brockman D, Stavisky R. 1998. Recent advances in noninvasive techniques to monitor hormone-behavior interactions. Yearbook Phys Anthropol 41:1–23.

136. Robbins M, Czekala N. 1997. A preliminary investigation of urinary testosterone and cortisol levels in wild male mountain gorillas. Am J Primatol 43:51–64.

137. Strier K, Ziegler T, Wittwer D. 1999. Seasonal and social correlates of fecal testosterone and cortisol levels in wild male muriquis (Brachyteles arachnoides). Horm Behav 35:125–134.

138. Cavigelli S, Pereira ME. 2000. Mating season aggression and fecal testosterone levels in male ring-tailed lemurs (Lemur catta). Horm Behav 37:246–255.

139. Brockman D, Whitten P, Richard A, Benander B. 2001. Birth season testosterone levels in male Verreaux's sifaka, Propithecus verreauxi: insights into socio-demographic factors mediating seasonal testicular function. Behav Ecol Sociobiol 49:117–127.

140. Muller M, Wrangham R. 2001. The reproductive ecology of male hominoids. In: Ellison P, editor. Reproductive ecology and human evolution. New York: Aldine de Gruyter. p 397–427.

141. Sapolsky R. 1992. Cortisol concentrations and the social significance of rank instability among wild baboons. Psychoneuroendocrinology 17:701–709.

142. Sapolsky R. 1982. The endocrine stress response and social status in the wild baboon. Horm Behav 16:279–292.

143. Sapolsky R. 1993. Endocrinology alfresco: psychoendocrine studies of wild baboons. Rec Prog Horm Res 48:437–468.

144. Bygott D. 1974. Agonistic behaviour and dominance in wild chimpanzees. Ph.D. thesis. Cambridge University.

145. Muller M. 2002. Endocrine aspects of aggression and dominance in chimpanzees of the Kibale Forest. Ph.D. thesis. University of Southern California.

146. Sapolsky R. 1991. Testicular function, social rank and personality among wild baboons. Psychoneuroendocrinology 16:281–293.

147. Whitten P. 2000. Evolutionary endocrinology of the cercopithecoids. In: Whitehead P, Jolly C, editors. Old world monkeys. Cambridge: Cambridge University Press. p 269–297.

148. Wingfield J, Jacobs J, Hillgarth N. 1997. Ecological constraints and the evolution of hormonebehavior inter-relationships. Ann NY Acad Sci 807:22–41.

149. Wingfield J, Hegner R, Dufty A, Ball G. 1990. The "challenge hypothesis": theoretical implications for patterns of testosterone secretion, mating systems, and breeding strategies. Am Nat 136:829–846.

150. Creel S, Wildt D, Monfort S. 1993. Aggression, reproduction, and androgens in wild dwarf mongooses—a test of the challenge hypothesis. Am Nat 141:816–825.

151. Matsumoto-Oda A. 1998. Injuries to the sexual skin of female chimpanzees at Mahale and their effect on behaviour. Folia Primatol 69:400–404.

152. Wrangham R. n.d. The cost of sexual attraction: is there a tradeoff in female *Pan* between sex appeal and received coercion? In: Boesch C, Hohmann G, Marchant L, editors. Behavioral diversity in chimpanzees and bonobos. Cambridge: Cambridge University Press. In press.

153. Trivers R. 1972. Parental investment and sexual selection. In: Campell B, editor. Sexual selection and the descent of man. Chicago: Aldine de Gruyter. p 136–179.

154. Bradbury J, Verhencamp S. 1977. Social organization and foraging in emballonurid bats. III. Mating systems. Behav Ecol Sociobiol 2:1–17.

155. Emlen S, Oring L. 1977. Ecology, sexual selection and the evolution of mating systems. Science 197:215–223.

156. Wrangham R. 1980. An ecological model of female-bonded primate groups. Behaviour 75:262–300.

157. Pope T. 2000. The evolution of male philopatry in neotropical monkeys. In: Kappeler P, editor. Primate males. Cambridge: Cambridge University Press. p 219–235.

158. Williams J, Pusey A, Carlis J, Farm B, Goodall J. n.d. Female competition and male territorial behaviour influence female chimpanzees' ranging patterns. Anim Behav. In press.

159. Blurton-Jones N. 1987. Tolerated theft, suggestions about the ecology and evolution of sharing, hoarding and scrounging. Soc Sci Information 26:31–54.

160. Hawkes K. 1991. Showing off—tests of an hypothesis about men's foraging goals. Ethol Sociobiol 12:29–54.

Study Questions

1. What features do primates have that distinguish them from other mammals?

2. What explains the presence of these traits in all primates? In other words, what was the adaptation in the earliest primates?

3. How exactly does an animal's body size influence its diet?

4. What does the study of living chimpanzees tell us about the probable behavior of the common ancestor of humans and chimpanzees?

SECTION III

EARLIEST HOMININS

Humans are bipedal apes, and habitual locomotion on two legs is the primary feature that distinguishes the human evolutionary line from that of the other apes. Bipedalism arose among late Miocene apes about 7 Ma, and the circumstances leading to this development are a topic of intense debate in paleoanthropology.

A great variety of apes existed in the Miocene epoch (23.5 – 5.5 Ma) on all continents of the Old World. The number of ape species in the modern world is greatly impoverished by comparison. Miocene apes varied greatly in body size; most were fruit eating; they practiced a mix quadrupedal and suspensory locomotion. These adaptations left their imprint on early hominins. One of the African Miocene apes no doubt gave rise to the human lineage, but precise identification of the ancestor has so far eluded paleoanthropologists.

8. Evolution of Apes

By Jay Kelley

One of the problems in understanding ape evolution is that there are very few living apes—only four or five genera, depending on whether or not we include the human genus, *Homo*. Only two ape genera, *Pan* (chimpanzees) and *Hylobates* (gibbons), have more than one living species and only *Hylobates* has more than two (around nine altogether). This situation is relatively recent because apes were once much more diverse and widespread.

The inclusion here of humans among the apes emphasises the distinction between a phylogenetic *clade* of relatedness and a *grade* of biological organisation. Humans have as their closest living relatives the other apes, and some apes are more closely related to humans than they are to one another. Therefore, in a phylogenetic sense, humans are apes. We share several features with other apes (such as a broad chest, very mobile arms and the lack of a tail), which indicate that we are derived from a common ancestor not shared with our next closest relatives, the Old World monkeys. In terms of biological organisation, however, humans are fundamentally different from the other apes, which by contrast form a fairly homogeneous group.

With respect to living species, then, the term 'ape' is used here as a grade, and humans are discussed only peripherally. With many fossil species we are confronted with a similar problem: species that appear to be

Jay Kelley, "Evolution of Apes," *The Cambridge Encyclopedia of Human Evolution*, ed. Stephen Jones, Robert D. Martin, and David R. Pilbeam, pp. 223–230. Copyright © 1994 by Cambridge University Press. Reprinted with permission.

phyletic apes are unlike living apes in many anatomical features. It is not always clear just how behaviourally and ecologically like modern apes many of these animals were. As they may not have achieved a modern grade of organisation, we need to broaden our notions of what an ape is.

PHYLOGENETIC RELATIONSHIPS OF LIVING APES

The phylogenetic relationships of living apes can be studied using genetics or morphology. All genetic indicators agree in showing that there is more similarity among great apes and humans than between any member of this clade and gibbons. Likewise, within the great ape and human clade, genetic pointers concur in showing the orang-utan (*Pongo*) to be genetically distant from the African apes—the two chimpanzee species and the gorilla—and humans. However, there is less agreement as to the pattern of genetic similarity among chimpanzees, gorillas and humans. There are inconsistencies in the data and in the ways in which the information is analysed. Interpretation is hindered by uncertainties as to whether genetic change occurs at uniform rates in different lineages.

The two branching events that produced the three lineages probably happened at about the same time, so that chimpanzees, gorillas and humans are genetically quite similar. The present consensus is that the gorilla branched first from a chimpanzee/human clade, and that the split between chimpanzees and humans occurred a little later. However, some studies support an initial chimpanzee/gorilla versus human split.

Inferences about relatedness based on comparative morphology attempt to identify shared, derived features, as opposed to retained, primitive features. Genetic phylogenies most often rely on the degree of overall similarity between lineages, although attempts are now being made to identify derived genetic features. The *cladistic* methods used to identify shared derived features suffer from two difficulties. The first is *character polarity*: identifying which of the *states* of a feature are derived, and in what sequence. The second is spotting any convergence and parallelism among apparently shared characters.

These difficulties are illustrated by the different results obtained in recent analyses of great ape and human morphology. Human–African ape, human–orang-utan and African ape–orang-utan clades have all been proposed, each based on a supposedly rigorous application of cladistics. Although the last two clades have few adherents, even the morphological case for a human–African ape clade is still without unequivocal support. Each of the living apes seems to have acquired a few uniquely derived features superimposed on the rather primitive and generalised body plan of their common ancestor, and certain shared features may have resulted from parallel evolution.

The presence of skeletal features related to knuckle-walking in chimpanzees and gorillas, and their absence in modern humans or their fossil antecedents, suggest to many that there was an initial human/African ape split rather than a human and chimpanzee/gorilla split, and that the two African apes are more closely related than either is to humans. However, this conflicts with much genetical evidence that suggests a closer relationship between humans and chimpanzees, which would imply that hominids were once knuckle-walkers.

If humans do not have an ancestral stage when they knuckle-walked, as many morphologists assert, then this very peculiar locomotor behaviour must have been independently derived in the chimpanzee and gorilla lineages. Although morphologists find this also difficult to accept, it is not yet clear whether skeletal features associated with knuckle-walking in chimpanzees and gorillas are indeed homologous or whether they arose by parallel evolution.

Morphology and genetics thus favour a branching sequence gibbons–orang-utan–African apes/humans, but there is still no agreement on the African ape and human branchings.

Fossil Apes

The fossil record of ape evolution is confined almost entirely to the Miocene epoch, from 23 to 5 million years ago, which probably covers most of the earlier history of the group. The first evidence for a diversification of the apes is in the early Miocene, and an origin of the group in the latest Oligocene or earliest Miocene seems likely. During the middle and late Miocene, apes underwent an extensive phyletic and geographic radiation, extending their range throughout the equatorial and subequatorial regions of the Old World. This was a brief flowering, and well before the end of the Miocene apes had become extinct over much of the area that they had once occupied.

Ape lineages did persist into the Plio-Pleistocene, although some subsequently became extinct. All these surviving lineages were probably more widespread than they are today. However, their record after about 8 million years ago includes only scanty remains of Pleistocene gibbons and orang-utans, dental remains of a recently extinct Pleistocene giant ape (*Gigantopithecus*) and Pliocene fossils of uncertain affinity, all from southeastern Asia. There is no fossil record of chimpanzees or gorillas at all.

The early Miocene record of Old World higher primates is mostly restricted to a small region centered on the East African Rift Valley. The principal sites are Koru, Songhor, Rusinga, Mfwangano and Kalodirr in Kenya, and Napak in Uganda. These all date to between 20 and 17 million years ago. The diverse array of catarrhine species includes several traditionally considered as the earliest apes and

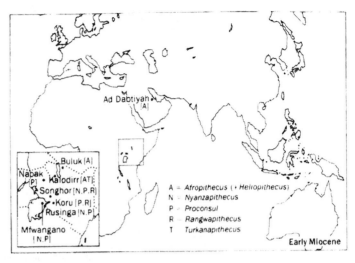

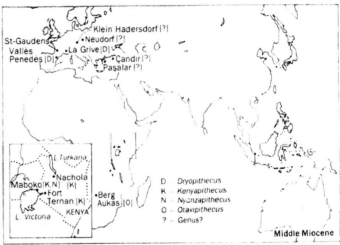

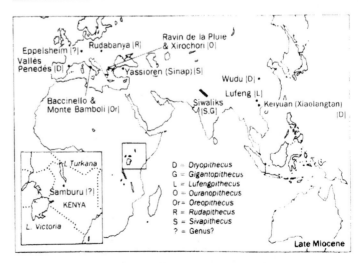

Geographic distributions of fossil hominoids in the early Miocene, 23–16 million years ago, middle Miocene, 16–10 million years ago, and late Miocene, 10–5 million years ago. Only the principal sites are shown.

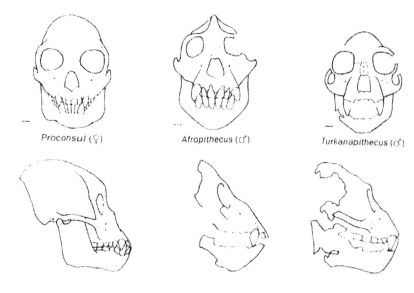

Proconsul (♀)   Afropithecus (♂)   Turkanapithecus (♂)

Representative skulls of late early Miocene apes from Kenya. Notice the width between the orbits and their round to rectangular shape. *Afropithecus* and *Turkanapithecus* have the long snout characteristic of primitive catarrhines from the Oligocene Fayum deposits of Egypt. Males and/or larger specimens of *Proconsul* may have had longer snouts than the female pictured here. Each scale bar = 1 cm.

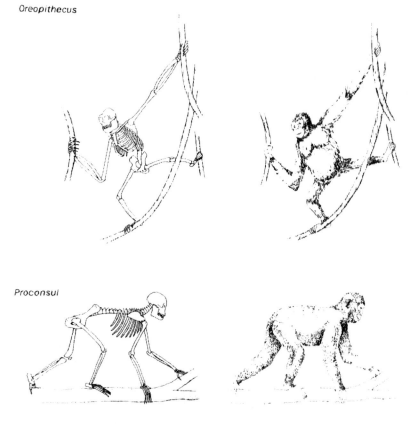

Oreopithecus

Proconsul

Skeletons and reconstructions of early Miocene *Proconsul* (below) and late Miocene *Oreopithecus* (above). Notice in particular the different proportions of the forelimbs and hindlimbs in the two. *Proconsul* may have been mainly a quadrupedal walker and climber along branches, and done relatively little forelimb suspension. *Oreopithecus* is the only fossil ape whose anatomy suggests the frequent use of suspensory locomotion.

classified within the superfamily Hominoidea. These include members of the genera *Proconsul, Rangwapithecus, Nyanzapithecus* and *Limnopithecus*. To this group may now be added the newly discovered *Afropithecus* and *Turkanapithecus* from Kalodirr, and *Heliopithecus* (probably the same as *Afropithecus*) from Saudi Arabia. Whether or not any of these are in fact phyletic apes, or hominoids, is discussed below.

Species of the genera *Aegyptopithecus* and *Propliopithecus* from the middle Oligocene Fayum deposits in Egypt were initially considered to be the earliest apes, but they are now widely thought to be primitive catarrhines that predate the split of apes and Old World monkeys.

The early Miocene African genera varied in size from that of a small monkey to perhaps a large chimpanzee. The many species probably occupied forests of varying types, and the teeth suggest that their diet included both fruit and foliage. Most species were probably markedly sexually dimorphic in canine and in body size. But only one fossil collection, that of *Proconsul* from Rusinga, is complete enough to assess body size dimorphism—which may have been substantial. This sample may, however, include two species of different size. If so, dimorphism in individual species may have been no greater than in chimpanzees. The skeleton of *Proconsul* shows none of the specialisations associated with the locomotion and posture of living apes and Old World monkeys. *Proconsul* species probably used quadrupedal walking with some climbing but little suspension from branches.

Species that are certainly phyletic apes are present by the middle Miocene (16–10 million years ago) and are best represented in Africa. By about 15–14 million years ago, apes had migrated into Eurasia. Here they underwent an extensive adaptive radiation, which was probably already underway in Africa before the migrations began. Fragments of small-bodied catarrhines have been found in deposits in China and Pakistan dating to at least 17 million years ago. These may be early members of the gibbon lineage but this cannot be determined without postcranial remains; they might not even be hominoids.

In Africa, *Kenyapithecus* is found at sites that span most of the middle Miocene, such as Maboko, Fort Ternan and Nachola in northern Kenya. *Kenyapithecus* has derived facial and dental features that differ from those of the early Miocene genera and are more like those of modern apes. It has thick layer of enamel on its molar teeth and very robust jaws (which indicate a shift in food preferences and habitat). The diet of *Kenyapithecus* is still uncertain: its teeth and jaws certainly suggest powerful biting and prolonged chewing, perhaps on very hard and tough foods—a diet unlike that of any living primate. The few postcranial remains are still quite primitive and do not suggest much change in behaviour from the early Miocene. There was substantial sexual dimorphism in the canines and probably in body size. The recently discovered *Otavipithecus* from the late middle Miocene of Namibia represents the first record of Miocene apes from southern Africa.

It is so far known from one specimen, a lower jaw, that, unlike *Kenyapithecus*, appears to have relatively thin-enamelled teeth.

Remains of middle Miocene apes in Europe and Asia are few and not very revealing. They include species known mainly from their teeth from eastern Europe (Neudorf) and Turkey (Paşalar, Çandir) with teeth generally like that of *Kenyapithecus*. The few postcranial remains suggest that their habitat and activity patterns were probably not too different from those of *Proconsul*. Somewhat later than these earliest Eurasian representatives of apes with thick-enamelled teeth is *Dryopithecus*, sporadically known from western and central Europe. *Dryopithecus* has thin-enamelled teeth and probably had a diet different from that of the apes with thick enamel. It has no obvious antecedents in Africa or elsewhere and its origins are unknown.

The late Miocene witnessed the greatest diversity, and probably the greatest geographic expansion, of apes. Major Eurasian sites include the Vallès Penedès in Spain (*Dryopithecus*), Rudabańya in Hungary (*Rudapithecus*, but possibly assignable to *Dryopithecus*), Baccinello and Monte Bamboli in Italy (*Oreopithecus*), Ravin de la Pluie and Xirochori in Greece (*Ouranopithecus*), Yassioren (Mt Sinap) in Turkey (*Sivapithecus*), the Siwaliks in

The Siwalik deposits of northern Pakistan from which have come most of the remains of *Sivapithecus*, a likely member of the orang-utan lineage.

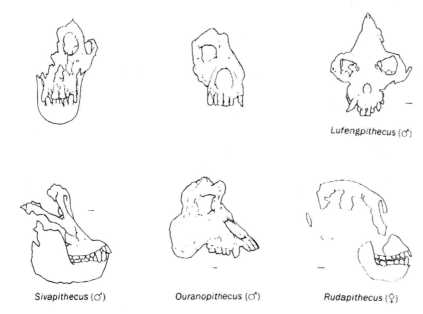

Lufengpithecus (♂)

Sivapithecus (♂)   Ouranopithecus (♂)   Rudapithecus (♀)

Representative skulls of late Miocene apes from Eurasia. Notice the vertically elongate and close-set orbits, and the long, narrow face of *Sivapithecus* compared with *Ouranopithecus* and *Lufengpithecus* and *Rudapithecus*. Each scale bar = 1 cm.

Indo-Pakistan (*Sivapithecus*) and Lufeng (*Lufengpithecus*), Wudu (*Dryopithecus*) and Keiyuan or Xiaolangtan (*Dryopithecus*) in China. Unfortunately, the African late Miocene record consists only of a few teeth and fragmentary jaws. The genus '*Ramapithecus*' (which is historically important in the study of human evolution) was once thought to be present at some of these sites as well as at the middle Miocene sites of Fort Ternan, Maboko and Paşalar, but it is now clear that the only distinguishing feature of specimens attributed to this genus was their small size. These are probably females or small species of the genera at these various sites.

Late Miocene genera shared certain similarities. The animal and plant remains with which they are associated suggest that they occupied forests and dense woods. All were moderately large, ranging in size from large monkeys to chimpanzees, with a few very large species—perhaps as large as orang-utans or female gorillas; and all appear to have been moderately or even highly sexually dimorphic. There is no evidence for the presence of more than one ape species living simultaneously at any of these sites.

The elbows of *Rudapithecus* and *Sivapithecus* were almost like those of modern apes, which might suggest that climbing and suspension were important in their behaviour. However, some other features of the forelimbs of *Sivapithecus* are monkey-like, implying quadrupedal walking and climbing but not suspension. Other parts of the postcranial skeleton of both genera also suggest this type of quadrupedalism, with little of the forelimb-dominated suspensory behaviour thought by most to be the ancestral locomotor pattern of all true apes.

A virtually complete skeleton of *Oreopithecus* has been unearthed. This is similar to modern apes in many features of the trunk and limbs. *Oreopithecus* thus seems to have been more adapted for suspension than was either *Sivapithecus* or *Rudapithecus* (see p. 225).

These three Eurasian lineages hence suggest that there was considerable locomotor diversity among late Miocene apes, and that some were still primitive in features of their postcranial anatomy. Not all of them were as adapted for suspension as are all living apes, including the largely terrestrial gorilla in which vestiges of this heritage are still evident.

All these late Miocene apes were adapted for life in trees, although, given the body sizes of some, they probably came down to the ground occasionally. The disappearance of dense forests and woodlands may have led to their extinction. None shows any sign of the skeletal features associated with the specialised behaviours of living apes. However, none is from Africa, to which the presently more terrestrial chimpanzee and gorilla lines have probably always been confined.

The diets and habitats of late Miocene Eurasian hominoids were probably quite diverse. *Sivapithecus*, *Ouranopithecus* and *Gigantopithecus* had thick-enamelled cheek teeth, and may have had diets similar to that of *Kenyapithecus*, with hard and tough food items. However, they differed in body size and in other features of teeth and jaws, especially in the size and shape of the incisors. *Dryopithecus* species, and probably *Lufengpithecus*, had thinner-enamelled teeth, with *Dryopithecus* also being somewhat smaller. *Oreopithecus* had very unusual teeth and possibly ate leaves more than the others.

By the end of the Miocene, all these Eurasian lineages were extinct in the areas from which they are known as fossils, except in China. Their extinction might have been caused by a cooler, drier and more seasonal world climate, which emerged as the Miocene progressed, and by the resulting decline in evergreen forest and woodland and its partial replacement with deciduous forest, scrub and, perhaps, the first extensive wooded grasslands. Geochemical evidence from fossil soils in the Siwaliks of Pakistan strongly supports this scenario. Soon after the extinction of apes in most of these areas came monkeys that were better adapted to life in more open habitats. The lineages leading to gibbons and the orang-utan persisted, but were confined to the forests of Southeast Asia. The enormous and enigmatic *Gigantopithecus* was probably a ground-dweller in more open habitats before its extinction later in the Pleistocene.

There is no fossil record of gibbons or orang-utans before the Pleistocene, and even these remains tell us only that the Pleistocene species were hardly different from their modern descendants. Although the fossil record of the gorilla and chimpanzees is a complete blank, we can be fairly confident that their ranges did not overlap with those of hominids in East Africa during the past 4 to 5 million years and that they were probably confined to areas west of the Rift Valley.

PHYLOGENETIC RELATIONSHIPS OF FOSSIL APES

Some argue that the 'apes' of the early Miocene (including *Proconsul*) are primitive catarrhine primates from lineages that branched before the Old World monkey lineage split from the apes, and are therefore neither cercopithecoids nor hominoids in the strict sense. It has been thought that one of the more obvious hallmarks of apes is a shift to a posture and locomotion dominated by the forelimb. The joints of living apes are mobile and the shoulder in particular allows the limb to be extended straight upwards. The humerus is also unlike that of monkeys.

As we have seen, species of *Proconsul* have quite primitive skulls and skeletons. Complete elbow and wrist joints, together with a partial shoulder joint, are known. There is nothing particularly ape-like about the wrist. Both elbow and shoulder have features that are somewhat like those of modern apes, but it is not clear whether these are shared, derived hominoid features. Even if they are, and *Proconsul* is a phyletic ape, what they mean in terms of posture is not clear. Humeral shape is otherwise unlike that of living apes. Other parts of the postcranial skeleton, such as the vertebral column, are also unlike those of living apes and suggest quadrupedal walking and running, perhaps in the manner of some New World monkeys.

If *Proconsul* and its relatives are indeed apes, then the earliest apes were not much like their living descendants. The situation is no clearer with other, less well-known early Miocene taxa, such as *Rangwapithecus* and *Afropithecus*; they also have primitive postcranial skeletons and skulls.

Middle Miocene genera such as the African *Kenyapithecus* and the lineage present at Neudorf in eastern Europe are only marginally more like modern apes in forelimb morphology. Even the late Miocene *Sivapithecus*, which is unquestionably an ape and which has elbows like those of modern apes, is otherwise quite primitive in humeral morphology, so that suspension and overhand climbing may not in fact be fundamental attributes of the ape lineage. If these locomotor behaviours are not basic characteristics of apes, then a biological, as opposed to a cladistic, definition of 'ape', becomes difficult.

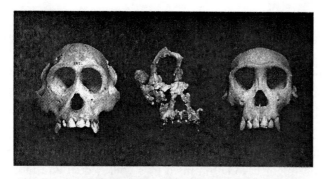

Comparison of a partial 8-million-year-old skull of *Sivapithecus* from the Siwaliks of Pakistan with an orang-utan (left) and chimpanzee (right); front (above) and side (below) views. *Sivapithecus* and the orang-utan share numerous derived facial features relating to the shape and position of the orbits, the morphology of the subnasal area, the embedding of the canine (producing a triangular instead of a squared snout), the profile of the lower face, and the positioning and orientation of the facial skeleton in relation to the braincase.

Where these and other middle and late Miocene apes fit within a living ape phylogeny is mostly unclear. The one exception to this is *Sivapithecus*. *Sivapithecus* shares with the orang-utan several features of the skull and face that are almost certainly derived within the Hominoidea, and some of which are uniquely shared to the exclusion of all other simian primates. These include the absence of a bony sinus in the brow area of the skull, a very narrow bony partition between the eyes, vertically elongated orbits and, most important, a set of features in the *subnasal* area that relates to the way the hard palate joins the premaxillary bone at the base of the nose where the incisors are embedded (the *nasoalveolar clivus*).

The subnasal area is particularly useful because it is often preserved in fossils and consists of several separate characters that associate into three discrete patterns among living apes. Gibbons preserve the primitive simian pattern with a gaping space between the palate and the clivus. In chimpanzees and gorillas, the clivus overlaps the palate to form a large *incisive canal*. The bony opening into this canal is large and there is a precipitous drop from the clivus to the palate. The canal opening in the roof of the mouth is also quite large. In orang-utans, there is also a substantial overlap between the clivus and palate, but in this case the clivus extends well into the nasal cavity. However, both openings into the canal are narrow slits and the canal itself is greatly compressed. The joining of the clivus and palate within the nasal cavity is smooth, without the abrupt drop characteristic of the African apes. *Sivapithecus* uniquely shares this morphological pattern with the orang-utan, which, together with other facial features, implies that there is a phylogenetic relationship between the two.

In most other respects, however, the cranial anatomy of *Sivapithecus* is unlike that of the orang-utan, as is the post-cranial anatomy. Behaviourally and ecologically, *Sivapithecus* was probably not much like an orang-utan, with no evidence of the skeletal adaptations allowing a high degree of limb mobility. Like *Proconsul* and its relatives, these earliest putative members of the orang-utan lineage were not much like their living descendant.

The phyletic relationships of other middle and late Miocene genera are more equivocal. The subnasal area of *Rudapithecus* appears to be similar to that in the African apes. *Kenyapithecus* has been claimed to have a primitive lower face but also seems to share some features with the African apes. *Ouranopithecus* and *Lufengpithecus* certainly do not share the orang-utan facial pattern; the former also seems to resemble African apes.

The position of those genera that appear to be related to the African apes depends on the order of evolution of the lower facial patterns. If the orang-utan pattern is derived from that of the African apes, then these extinct genera may simply be primitive great apes not necessarily on the lineage of any living species. If the two lower facial patterns of extant great apes are independently derived from the primitive form, then the possession of either places the fossil on either the orang-utan or African ape lineage. The association of

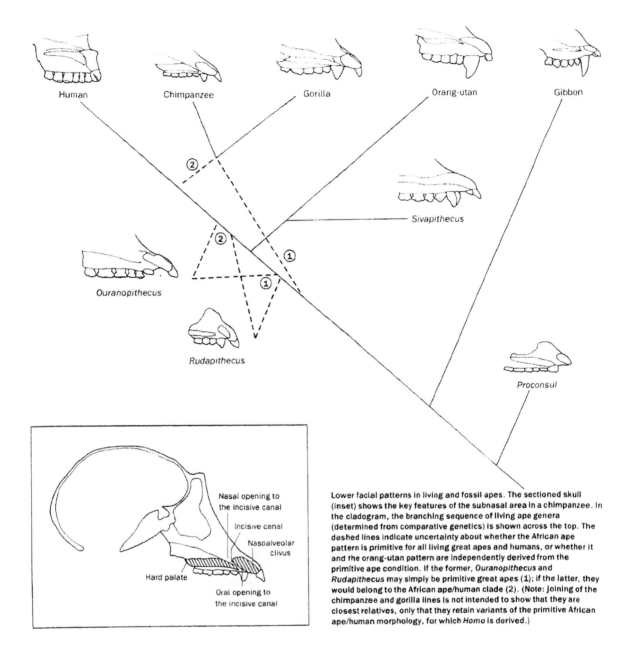

Lower facial patterns in living and fossil apes. The sectioned skull (inset) shows the key features of the subnasal area in a chimpanzee. In the cladogram, the branching sequence of living ape genera (determined from comparative genetics) is shown across the top. The dashed lines indicate uncertainty about whether the African ape pattern is primitive for all living great apes and humans, or whether it and the orang-utan pattern are independently derived from the primitive ape condition. If the former, Ouranopithecus and Rudapithecus may simply be primitive great apes (1); if the latter, they would belong to the African ape/human clade (2). (Note: joining of the chimpanzee and gorilla lines is not intended to show that they are closest relatives, only that they retain variants of the primitive African ape/human morphology, for which Homo is derived.)

a generally African ape subnasal pattern with mostly primitive postcranial characters in *Kenyapithecus* argues for the first alternative, but the latter cannot be dismissed because the remains are still fragmentary, and there is a possibility of convergence.

The orbits and subnasal region are useful because they are so distinctive in the orang-utan. Because the African apes retain a morphology probably closer to that of primitive great apes, features by which fossils could be linked with their clade are not so obvious. One might be the manner in which the face is joined to the braincase, but this requires relatively complete and undistorted skulls.

Complete but badly crushed skulls are known for *Lufengpithecus*, and less-complete crania for Ouranopithecus, *Rudapithecus* and *Kenyapithecus*. The cranium of Ouranopithecus (p. 226) shows a few intriguing similarities to that of African apes, or even to hominids, but whether or not these are phylogenetically relevant is not clear. Although *Lufengpithecus* and *Rudapithecus* have none of the key features of the orang-utan clade possessed by *Sivapithecus*,

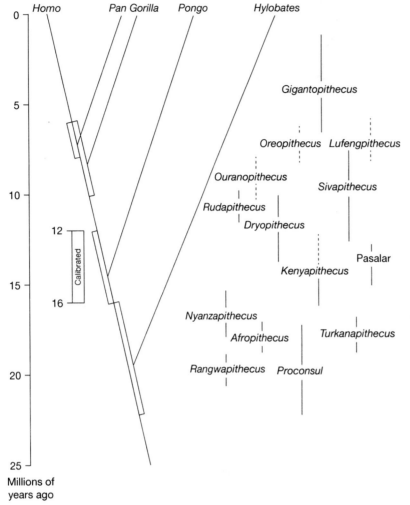

Estimates of the time of branching of living apes, as determined from comparative genetics and based on calibration dates between 12 and 16 million years ago for the origin of the orang-utan lineage. Temporal ranges of fossil ape genera are shown to the right. Solid lines reflect relatively well-known time ranges and dashed lines reflect uncertain temporal positions within a probable interval.

each has other features that may place them as more primitive members of this clade. In most respects, however, all except *Sivapithecus* are variants of a primitive great ape skull. Most may represent lineages that originated before any of the extant great ape branchings. Some fossil apes from the late Miocene of Africa would help clarify the phylogenetic positions of some of these animals.

TEMPO OF APE EVOLUTION

DNA changes at a roughly regular rate within closely related taxa, although there can be considerable differences in rates between more distantly related groups. The genetic distance between lineages can hence be used as a measure of time of divergence. To develop a 'molecular clock' to date divergence times among living animals one must calibrate genetic change with respect to time using the fossil record. It is therefore essential to have a reliable date for the appearance of at least one lineage of living apes. There are two difficulties: recognising early fossil members of a lineage and establishing that there are no earlier members of that lineage. The first issue arises from the problems of fossil phylogeny. The second, which depends to a great extent on an absence of evidence, can be addressed according to the completeness of the appropriate fossil record and the stage of evolution reached by contemporary animals.

The orang-utan lineage has the best potential to calibrate ape evolution. *Sivapithecus* may well be an early member of the orang-utan lineage, despite being very unlike a modern orang-utan in many respects. It has been dated to 12.5 million years ago in the Siwalik sequence of Pakistan. Older sediments give no evidence of *Sivapithecus* or any other large hominoid, and no other Miocene fossil apes can definitely be assigned to the orang-utan lineage. It is unlikely that we would ever find the oldest member of a group, so the date of 12.5 million years ago is a minimum estimate for the origins of the orang-utan lineage.

The divergence times of living apes have been calculated assuming both linear and non-linear rates of change, and even decelerating rates in some lineages. A few have used the orang-utan divergence as the calibration point, with a date ranging between 16 and 12 million years ago. The ranges in branching times (or the other apes utilising these two dates are: apes–Old World monkeys, 33 to 24 million years ago; gibbons–great apes/humans, 22 to 16 million years; gorilla–chimpanzees/humans, 10 to 6 million years; and chimpanzees–humans, 8 to 6 million years. The Siwalik record of *Sivapithecus* favours the more recent of each range and none of these dates conflicts with the fossil evidence.

Defining apes

It is possible to make some general statements about apes throughout their history. They have mostly been moderately to very large. They have always depended on trees, and have been restricted to dense woods or forests. For much of their history, most were generalised quadrupedal walkers and climbers without any marked locomotor specialisations, and were thus unlike any living primate. The very specialised behaviours of all living apes may be relatively recent. Apes have had varied diets but the diet that characterises many middle and late Miocene lineages with thick tooth enamel and heavily buttressed jaws no longer exists. Each of the living apes is in its own way atypical when seen in the context of ape evolutionary history as a whole.

Apes have usually been sexually dimorphic, sometimes extremely so. This is compatible with social systems based on polygyny. Early and middle Miocene apes of Africa formed communities of a few species, while later Miocene habitats in Eurasia contained only one or two species at most—the pattern seen among apes (but not monkeys) today.

What this tells us about ape biology is unclear. Apes differ from monkeys in life-history profile, with a long gestation period, a long period of maternal care, a long interval between births, late achievement of sexual maturity and a long life. Perhaps it is this extended life-history pattern that is the fundamental ape adaptation. In apes, this strategy is correlated with a relatively large brain. But using measures of relative brain size to infer the life history of fossil apes is fraught with problems. Until we have a way of producing precise estimates of body size for fossils, measures of relative brain size will be ambiguous.

It has often been suggested that apes became extinct because they were competitively inferior to monkeys. The fossil record offers no evidence to support this view. Monkeys arrived in late Miocene Eurasia after the demise of apes, probably because of the spread of more open habitats, and in the middle Miocene of Africa diverse groups of monkeys and apes often coexisted. Today's greatly diminished ape fauna reflects the massive loss of suitable habitat during the past 10 million years as the result of climatic change.

Jay Kelly

Research in the last 40 years has produced thousands of early hominin fossils, but until 2004 there was virtually no fossil record for the Africa apes. Fossil *Pan* teeth, dating to more than 500,000 years ago from the Kapthurin Formation in the Rift Valley of Kenya, now comprise the sole known fossil remains of this genus. They were found far outside the geographic range of modern chimpanzees, indicating that African apes were once much more widespread than they are now. While they lived more than 5.5 million years after the origin of hominins, the Kapthurin Formation chimpanzees did not live in the tropical forest, suggesting that the origin of the human line may not have been the result of a split between forest and savannah dwelling apes.

9. First Fossil Chimpanzee

By Sally McBrearty[1] & Nina G. Jablonski[2]

There are thousands of fossils of hominins, but no fossil chimpanzee has yet been reported. The chimpanzee (*Pan*) is the closest living relative to humans[1]. Chimpanzee populations today are confined to wooded West and central Africa, whereas most hominin fossil sites occur in the semi-arid East African Rift Valley. This situation has fuelled speculation regarding causes for the divergence of the human and chimpanzee lineages five to eight million years ago. Some investigators have invoked a shift from wooded to savannah vegetation in East Africa, driven by climate change, to explain the apparent separation between chimpanzee and human ancestral populations and the origin of the unique hominin locomotor adaptation, bipedalism[2–5]. The Rift Valley itself functions as an obstacle to chimpanzee occupation in some scenarios[6]. Here we report the first fossil chimpanzee. These fossils, from the Kapthurin Formation, Kenya, show that representatives of *Pan* were present in the East African Rift Valley during the Middle Pleistocene, where they were contemporary with an extinct species of *Homo*. Habitats suitable for both hominins

[1]Department of Anthropology, University of Connecticut, Box U-2176, Storrs, Connecticut 06269, USA. [2]Department of Anthropology, California Academy of Sciences, 875 Howard Street, San Francisco, California 94103, USA.

Sally McBrearty and Nina G. Jablonski, "First Fossil Chimpanzee," *Nature*, vol. 437, pp. 105–108. Copyright © 2005 by Nature Publishing Group. Reprinted with permission.

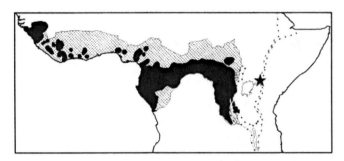

Figure 1 Map showing current (solid black) and historical (stippled) ranges of *Pan* in equatorial Africa relative to major features of the eastern and western Rift Valleys. The Kapthurin Formation, Kenya, in the Eastern Rift Valley is marked by a star.

and chimpanzees were clearly present there during this period, and the Rift Valley did not present an impenetrable barrier to chimpanzee occupation.

The Kapthurin Formation forms the Middle Pleistocene portion of the Tugen Hills sequence west of Lake Baringo (Figs 1 and 2). It consists of a package of fluvial, lacustrine and volcanic sediments ~125 m thick, exposed over ~150 km^2 (refs 7–9) that contains numerous palaeontological and archaeological sites[9–11]. It is divided into five members informally designated K1–K5 (ref. 7), and the sequence is well calibrated by ^{40}Ar/^{39}Ar dating[12].

Hominin fossils attributed to *Homo erectus* or *Homo rhodesiensis* have been found in the fluvial sediments of K3 (refs 11, 13, 14). The new chimpanzee fossils were discovered at Locality (Loc.) 99 in K3', the lacustrine facies of the same geological member. Loc. 99 consists of ~80 m^2 of exposures at an outcrop ~1 km northeast of site Gnjh-19 where hominin mandible KNM-BK (Kenya National Museum-Baringo Kapthurin) 8518 was found[14]. Two chimpanzee fossils, KNM-TH (Kenya National Museum-Tugen Hills) 45519 and KNM-TH 45520, were found in surface context within an area of ~12 m^2 within Loc. 99; additional specimens (KNM-TH 45521 and KNM-TH 45522) were recovered from sieved superficial sediments within the same restricted area. The age of the chimpanzee fossils is constrained by ^{40}Ar/^{39}Ar dates of 545 ± 3 kyr (thousand years) on underlying K2 and 284 ± 12 kyr on overlying K4 (ref. 12). Because they are derived from a position low in this stratigraphic interval, they are probably closer to the maximum age of 545 kyr. *Homo* fossils KNM-BK 63-67 and KNM-BK 8518 from K3 are bracketed by ^{40}Ar/^{39}Ar dates of 543 ± 4 kyr and 509 ± 9 kyr[12] (Fig. 2).

K3' sediments are exposed in an outcrop of ~1 km^2 in the eastern portion of the Kapthurin Formation. They consist of black and red zeolitized clays interbedded with sands and heavily altered volcanics. Sedimentary and geochemical features of the clays indicate that they were laid down in a shallow body of water that alternated between fresh and intensely saline-alkaline, probably as a response to changes in outflow geometry controlled by local volcanism[15]. Additional intermittent sources of fresh water are suggested by localized ephemeral stream channel features and the remains of an extensive fossil spring. Loc. 99 has produced fragmentary fossils representing suids, bovids, rodents, cercopithecoid primates and catfish. Eight additional faunal collecting areas in K3' have also produced elephants, hippopotami, carnivores, crocodiles, turtles, gastropods and additional micromammals. Many K3' taxa, notably hippopotami *(Hippopotamus)*, crocodiles, catfish *(Clarias)*, gastropods and turtles, reflect local aquatic conditions. The bulk of K3' non-aquatic fauna, including a colobine monkey, the elephant, the bovids *Kobus, Tragelaphus* and specimens probably belonging to *Syncerus,* and the suids *Potamochoerus porcus* (bushpig) and the extinct *Kolpo-choerus majus*[16], are consistent with a closed environment. The presence of the cane rat *(Thryonomys)* indicates localized patches of moist, marshy conditions.

Remains of *Homo* (KNM-BK 63-67 and KNM-BK 8518) were recovered at sites GnJh-01 and GnJh-19 by previous workers[11,13,14] from K3 fluvial sediments to the west that represent a system of braided streams, some of which seem to have debouched into the lake. Fluvial K3 deposits and lacustrine K3' deposits are interstrati-fied, indicating a shoreline that shifted in position in response to alterations in lake levels. The similarity in the array of fossils encountered in K3 and K3' sediments suggests that Middle Pleistocene

Pan and *Homo* lived, or at least died, in broadly similar environmental settings. Taken together, the evidence suggests a locally wooded habitat on the shore of an alternately fresh and saline-alkaline lake, fluctuating lake levels, ephemeral nearshore fluvial channels, a nearby freshwater spring, and a semi-arid climatic regime. These conditions are not unlike those found near the shore of Lake Baringo today, although dense human populations have eliminated much of the woodland that formerly supported chimpanzees and the faunal community of which they were a part.

The chimpanzee specimens comprise a minimum of three teeth, probably from the same individual. Two of these are right and left upper central permanent incisors (I^1; KNM-TH 45519 and KNM-TH 45521, respectively). They exhibit broad, spatulate and moderately worn crowns, with thin dental enamel (Fig. 3). The lingual tubercle is large and flanked at the base by deep mesial and distal foveae, characteristic of *Pan*. This feature imparts great thickness to the labiolingual

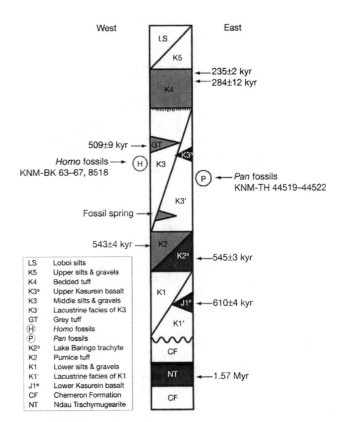

West   East

235±2 kyr
284±12 kyr

509±9 kyr

Homo fossils
KNM-BK 63–67, 8518

Pan fossils
KNM-TH 44519–44522

Fossil spring

543±4 kyr

545±3 kyr

610±4 kyr

1.57 Myr

LS	Loboi silts
K5	Upper silts & gravels
K4	Bedded tuff
K3ᵃ	Upper Kasurein basalt
K3	Middle silts & gravels
K3'	Lacustrine facies of K3
GT	Grey tuff
(H)	*Homo* fossils
(P)	*Pan* fossils
K2ᵃ	Lake Baringo trachyte
K2	Pumice tuff
K1	Lower silts & gravels
K1'	Lacustrine facies of K1
J1ᵉ	Lower Kasurein basalt
CF	Chemeron Formation
NT	Ndau Trachymugearite

Figure 2. Idealized stratigraphic column of the Kapthurin Formation, Kenya.

profiles of the teeth, and clearly distinguishes them from known hominins. The mesial and distal marginal ridges are well formed. The distal corners of the incisal edges are slightly chipped and the labial enamel surfaces exhibit pre-mortem wear as well as slight post-mortem surface weathering. The roots have closed apices and are straight, conical and relatively short. The incisal edges and lingual tubercles exhibit dentinal exposure resulting from wear. Measurements of the specimens, with comparisons to those of extant species of *Pan*, are provided in Table 1. The upper incisors are nearly identical to those of modern *Pan* in all aspects of morphology except their shorter root length. The sub-parallel mesial and distal margins of the incisors bestow a quadrate, rather than triangular, outline to the crowns, a feature that among living chimpanzees is considered to be more common among living *P. troglodytes* than *P. paniscus*[17]. The enamel and cementum coverings are in good condition and the perikymata on the labial surfaces of the crowns and the periradicular striae on the lingual surfaces of the roots can be easily seen. Several of the perikymata near the cervices of the teeth are faintly incised, indicating mild enamel hypoplasia having occurred at about the age of 5 years[18]. The well-matched mesial interproximal wear facets of the Kapthurin Formation *Pan* incisors (KNM-TH 45519 and KNM-TH 45521), the comparable degree of wear on their incisal edges, and the continuity of the enamel hypoplasia on their crowns and the incremental markings on their roots suggest that the two teeth are antimeres.

The third tooth is a lightly worn crown of a left upper permanent molar (KNM-TH 45520) (Fig. 4). It can be problematic to distinguish first from second upper molars in *Pan*, but we identify KNM-TH 45520 as an M^1, judging from the relatively large size of its hypocone, as this cusp is known to decrease in size from M^1 to M^3 (ref. 19). The Kapthurin Formation M^1 is an extremely low molar crown that has lost most of the enamel on its mesial and lingual faces due to breakage after fossilization. The enamel surfaces

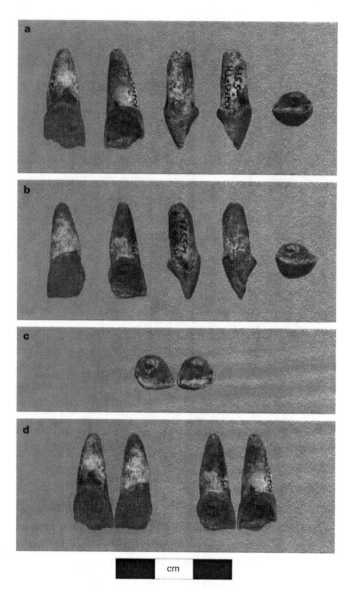

Figure 3. Central upper incisors of Pan from the Kapthurin Formation, Kenya. **a,** KNM-TH 45519. From left to right: labial, lingual, mesial, distal and incisal views. **b,** KNM-TH 45521. Images are in the same sequence as for the previous specimen. **c,** Enlargement of the incisal edge of KNM-TH 45519 (left) and KNM-TH 45521 (right), showing the extreme thinness of the enamel characteristic of modern chimpanzees. **d,** Labial and lingual views of KNM-TH 45519 and KNM-TH 45521.

are pockmarked as a result of chemical and physical weathering. The paracone and metacone are of approximately equal heights and are separated by a sharply incised buccal groove. The hypocone is lower than either of the buccal cusps, but is relatively large and well defined. A shallow trigon basin is delimited by a weak and obliquely oriented post-protocrista (crista obliqua). A deep but short distal fovea lies between the postprotocrista and the low distal marginal ridge. Despite marring of the enamel surface, perikymata are visible on the buccal and distal faces of the paracone, but there is no evidence of enamel hypoplasia. The relative thinness of the enamel can be discerned on the broken mesial and lingual faces of the tooth. The extremely low height of the M^1 crown and the pronounced thinness of the enamel distinguish the tooth from those of known fossil or modern homi-nins. Among living chimpanzees, the presence of a well-expressed hypocone is more common in *P. troglodytes* than in *P. paniscus*[20]. A fourth tooth (KNM-TH 45522), the crown and proximal roots of a tooth that may be plausibly identified as an aberrant right upper third molar (M^3), will be described elsewhere and is not further discussed here.

The state of wear on the incisors and the M^1 conforms to the known sequence of dental emergence in *Pan*[19,21], and it is likely that they come from the same individual. If they do represent the same animal, its age at death can be estimated at approximately 7-8 years based on standards derived from captive animals[22] and known dental maturation schedules for mandibular molars[23]. The presence of linear enamel hypoplasia on the incisors, but not on the molars, is common in modern apes and seems to be related to nutritional stress that is experienced by the animal after weaning[24].

The morphology of the Kapthurin Formation teeth, especially the pronounced lingual tubercle on the incisors, the thickness of the bases of the incisors, the lowness of the molar crown, and the thinness of the enamel on all the teeth clearly supports their attribution to *Pan* rather than *Homo*. Specific diagnosis of isolated teeth within *Pan*, however, must be approached with caution, and for this reason we assign the Kapthurin Formation specimens to *Pan* sp. indet. Non-metric characters that have been suggested as

Table 1. Dimensions of the Kapthurin Formation fossil chimpanzee teeth

SAMPLE	TOOTH	MESIODISTAL DIMENSION (MM)	MESIODISTAL RANGE (MM)	BUCCOLINGUAL DIMENSION (MM)	BUCCOLINGUAL RANGE (MM)
KNM-TH 45519	Right I¹	10.46	–	9.12	–
KNM-TH 45521	Left I¹	10.50	–	9.33	–
P. troglodytes (male)	I¹	12.6 (*n* = 14)	10.5–13.5	10.1 (*n* = 15)	9.0–11.3
P. troglodytes (female)	I¹	11.9 (*n* = 51)	10.0–13.4	9.6 (*n* = 50)	8.3–11.7
P. paniscus (male)	I¹	10.3 (*n* = 15)	8.9–11.9	7.9 (*n* = 15)	7.2–9.2
P. paniscus (female)	I¹	10.4 (*n* = 20)	9.0–11.5	7.6 (*n* = 21)	6.8–8.5
KNM-TH 45520	Left M¹	9.7 (estimate)	–	Damage prevents measurement	–
P. troglodytes (male)	M¹	10.3 (*n* = 19)	9.3–11.2	11.7 (*n* = 19)	10.7–13.2
P. troglodytes (female)	M¹	10.1 (*n* = 51)	9.0–11.9	10.9 (*n* = 50)	7.0–12.8
P. paniscus (male)	M¹	8.5 (*n* = 7)	7.9–9.4	9.5 (*n* = 6)	9.2–10.4
P. paniscus (female)	M¹	8.3 (*n* = 6)	7.6–8.8	9.7 (*n* = 6)	9.3–10.4

Comparative dimensions are given for modern *P. troglodytes* and *P. paniscus* from ref. 19.

diagnostic criteria for *P. troglodytes,* such as a more quadrilateral outline shape to the upper central incisor crowns[17] and a better expressed hypocone on the maxillary molars[19,20], seem to suggest more similarity for the Kapthurin Formation fossils to *P. troglodytes* than to *P. paniscus,* but these features are variably expressed among the living species and subspecies of *Pan*[19, 25]. Although mean tooth size is known to be significantly smaller in *P. paniscus* than in *P. troglodytes*[17,25,26], size ranges overlap (Table 1). Furthermore, apart from the present specimens, we lack a fossil record for the Pliocene and Pleistocene from which to assess past variability within the genus, and it is feasible that the Kapthurin Formation fossils represent members of an extinct lineage within the genus *Pan.*

The Kapthurin Formation fossils represent the first unequivocal evidence of *Pan* in the fossil record, and they demonstrate the presence of chimpanzees in the eastern Rift Valley of Kenya, ~600 km east of the limit of their current range (Fig. 1). The Rift Valley clearly did not pose a physiographical or ecological barrier to chimpanzee occupation. Chimpanzee habitat is now highly fragmented, in part by human activities, but in historic times chimpanzees ranged over a wide belt of equatorial Africa from southern Senegal to western Uganda and Tanzania (Fig. 1). Although much of this region is rainforest, chimpanzees currently also occupy dry forest, woodland and dry savannah, particularly near the eastern edge of their range[27–29].

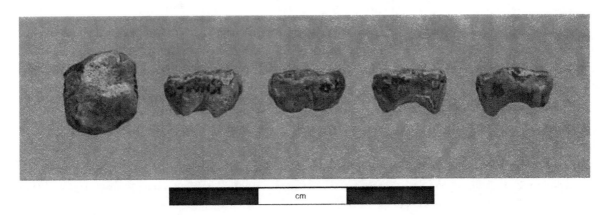

cm

Figure 4. Upper left first molar (KNM-TH 45520). From left to right: occlusal, labial, lingual, mesial and distal views. Note the thinness of the enamel on the broken mesial face of the paracone in the mesial view.

The modern Baringo region ecosystem is a mosaic of semi-arid *Acacia* bushland and riverine woodland, with a significant substratum of perennial and annual grasses[30]. The Tugen Hills palaeosol carbon isotope record indicates that the woodland and grassland components of the vegetation have been present there from 16 Myr[30]. Representatives of both *Homo* and *Pan* are present in the same stratigraphic interval of the Kapthurin Formation at sites only ~1 km apart, and faunal data suggest that they occupied broadly similar environments in the Middle Pleistocene. This evidence shows that in the past chimpanzees occupied regions in which the only hominoid inhabitants were thought to have been members of the human lineage. Now that chimpanzees are known to form a component of the Middle Pleistocene fauna in the Rift Valley, it is quite possible that they remain to be recognized in other portions of the fossil record there, and that chimpanzees and hominins have been sympatric since the time of their divergence.

Received 31 January; accepted 4 July 2005.

1. Ruvolo, M. E. Molecular phylogeny of the hominoids: inferences from multiple independent DNA sequence data sets. *Mol. Biol. Evol.* **14**, 248–265 (1997).
2. Darwin, C. *The Descent of Man and Selection in Relation to Sex* (John Murray, London, 1871).
3. Washburn, S. L. in *Changing Perspectives on Man* (ed. Rothblatt, B.) 193–201 (Univ. Chicago Press, Chicago, 1968).
4. Kortlandt, A. *New Perspectives on Ape and Human Evolution* (Univ. Amsterdam, Amsterdam, 1972).
5. Pilbeam, D. & Young, N. Hominoid evolution: synthesizing disparate data. *C. R. Palevol.* **3**, 305–321 (2004).
6. Coppens, Y. East side story: the origin of mankind. *Sci. Am.* **270**, 88–95 (1994).
7. Martyn, J. *The Geologic History of the Country Between Lake Baringo and the Kerio River, Baringo District, Kenya* (PhD dissertation, Univ. London, 1969).
8. Tallon, P. in *Geological Background to Fossil Man* (ed. Bishop, W. W.) 361-373 (Scottish Academic Press, Edinburgh, 1978).
9. McBrearty, S., Bishop, L. C. & Kingston, J. Variability in traces of Middle Pleistocene hominid behaviour in the Kapthurin Formation, Baringo, Kenya. *J. Hum. Evol.* **30**, 563–580 (1996).
10. McBrearty, S. in *Late Cenozoic Environments and Hominid Evolution: a Tribute to Bill Bishop* (eds Andrews, P. & Banham, P.) 143–156 (Geological Society, London, 1999).
11. McBrearty, S. & Brooks, A. The revolution that wasn't: a new interpretation of the origin of modern human behaviour. *J. Hum. Evol.* **39**, 453–563 (2000).
12. Deino, A. & McBrearty, S. 40Ar/39Ar chronology for the Kapthurin Formation, Baringo, Kenya. *J. Hum. Evol.* **42**,185–210 (2002).
13. Leakey, M., Tobias, P. V., Martyn, J. E. & Leakey, R. E. F. An Acheulian industry with prepared core technique and the discovery of a contemporary hominid at Lake Baringo, Kenya. *Proc. Prehist. Soc.* **35**, 48–76 (1969).
14. Wood, B. A. & Van Noten, F. L. Preliminary observations on the BK 8518 mandible from Baringo, Kenya. *Am. J. Phys. Anthropol.* **69**,117–127 (1986).
15. Renaut, R. W., Tiercelin, J.-J. & Owen, B. in *Lake Basins Through Space and Time* (eds Gierlowski-Kordesch, E. H. & Kelts, K. R.) 561–568 (Am. Assoc. Petrol. Geol., Tulsa, Oklahoma, 2000).
16. Bishop, L. C. Hill, A. P. & Kingston, J. in *Late Cenozoic Environments and Hominid Evolution: a Tribute to Bill Bishop* (eds Andrews, P. & Banham, P.) 99–112 (Geological Society, London, 1999).
17. Johanson, D. C. Some metric aspects of the permanent and deciduous dentition of the pygmy chimpanzee *(Pan paniscus). Am. J. Phys. Anthropol.* **41**, 39–48 (1974).
18. Dean, M. C. & Reid, D. J. Perikymata spacing and distribution on hominid anterior teeth. *Am. J. Phys. Anthropol.* **116**, 209–215 (2001).

19. Swindler, D. R. *Primate Dentition: An Introduction to the Teeth of Non-Human Primates* (CUP, Cambridge, 2002).

20. Kinzey, W. G. in *The Pygmy Chimpanzee* (ed. Susman, R. L.) 65–88 (Plenum, New York, 1984).

21. Smith, B. H., Crummett, T. L. & Brandt, K. L. Ages of eruption of primate teeth: a compendium for aging individuals and comparing life histories. *Yearb. Phys. Anthropol.* **37**, 177–232 (1994).

22. Kuykendall, K. L., Mahoney, C. J. & Conroy, G. C. Probit and survival analysis of tooth emergence ages in a mixed-longitudinal sample of chimpanzees *(Pan troglodytes)*. *Am. J. Phys. Anthropol.* **89**, 379–399 (1992).

23. Anemone, R. L., Watts, E. S. & Swindler, D. R. Dental development of known-age chimpanzees, *Pan troglodytes* (Primates, Pongidae). *Am. J. Phys. Anthropol.* **86**, 229–241 (1991).

24. Skinner, M. F. & Hopwood, D. Hypothesis for the causes and periodicity of repetitive linear enamel hypoplasia in large, wild African *(Pan troglodytes* and *Gorilla gorilla)* and Asian *(Pongo pygmaeus)* apes. *Am. J. Phys. Anthropol.* **123**, 216–235 (2004).

25. Uchida, A. *Craniodental Variation Among the Great Apes* (Harvard Univ. Peabody Mus., Cambridge, Massachusetts, 1996).

26. Johanson, D. C. *An Odontological Study of the Chimpanzee with Some Implications for Hominoid Evolution* (PhD dissertation, Univ. Chicago, 1974).

27. Kormos, R., Boesch, C. Bakarr, M. I. & Butynski, T. M. *West African Chimpanzees: Status Survey and Conservation Action Plan* (IUCN Publication Unit, Cambridge, 2003).

28. McGrew, W. C. Baldwin, P. J. & Tutin, C. E. G. Chimpanzees in a hot, dry and open habitat: Mt. Assirik, Senegal. *J. Hum. Evol.* **10**, 227–244 (1981).

29. McGrew, W. C. Marchant, L. F. & Nishida, T. *Great Ape Societies* (CUP, Cambridge, 1996).

30. Kingston, J. D., Marino, B. & Hill, A. P. Isotopic evidence for Neogene hominid palaeoenvironments in the Kenya Rift Valley. *Science* **264**, 955–959 (1994).

ACKNOWLEDGEMENTS

We wish to thank B. Kimeu, N. Kanyenze and M. Macharwas, who found the chimpanzee fossils reported here. Research in the Kapthurin Formation is carried out with the support of an NSF grant to S.M., and under a research permit from the Government of the Republic of Kenya and a permit to excavate from the Minister for Home Affairs and National Heritage of the Republic of Kenya. Both of these are issued to A. Hill and the Baringo Paleontological Research Project, an expedition conducted jointly with the National Museums of Kenya. We also thank personnel of the Departments of Palaeontology, Ornithology and Mammalogy of the National Museums of Kenya, Nairobi; A. Zihlman; and Y. Hailie-Selassie, L. Jellema and M. Ryan for curation and access to specimens. We express gratitude to A. Hill for his comments on the manuscript. We also thank G. Chaplin for drafting Fig. 1, B. Warren for preparing Figs 3 and 4, and A. Bothell for help with submission of the figures. We are grateful to J. Kelley, J. Kingston, M. Leakey, R. Leakey, C. Tryon, A. Walker and S. Ward for discussions. We thank G. Suwa for his remarks.

AUTHOR INFORMATION

Reprints and permissions information is available at npg.nature.com/reprintsandpermissions. The authors declare no competing financial interests. Correspondence and requests for materials should be addressed to S.M. (mcbrearty@uconn.edu).

Study Questions

1. What kinds of apes were living in the Miocene, and what features are we looking for in order to be able to identify the human ancestor among them?

2. Why are there so few fossils of chimpanzees?

SECTION IV

AUSTRALOPITHECUS AFARENSIS

Australopithecus afarensis is an early bipedal hominin known from hundreds of fossils from the site of Laetoli in Tanzania and the Hadar region of Ethiopia, including the famous 40%-complete skeleton known as Lucy (AL-288-1).

Australopithecus afarensis is the best known early hominin known. It is represented by hundreds of fossils found at the site of Laetoli in Tanzania and in the Hadar region of Ethiopia, including the famous 40% complete skeleton known as Lucy (AL-288-1).

10. Evolution of Human Walking

By C. Owen Lovejoy

Features of her pelvis show that a three-million-year-old hominid, Lucy, was as adept at upright walking as we are. Bipedality could date from the earliest phase of human evolution.

Asked to choose the most distinctive feature of the human species, many people would cite our massive brain. Others might mention our ability to make and use sophisticated tools. A third feature also sets us apart: our upright mode of locomotion, which is found only in human beings and our immediate ancestors. All other primates are basically quadrupedal, and with good reason: walking on two limbs instead of four has many drawbacks. It deprives us of speed and agility and all but eliminates our capacity to climb trees, which yield many important primate foods, such as fruits and nuts.

For most of this century evolutionary theorists have held that human ancestors evolved this strange mode of locomotion because it freed their hands to carry the tools their larger brains enabled them to make. Over the past two decades, however, knowledge of the human fossil record has expanded. Neither a unique brain nor stone tools are in evidence among our earliest known ancestors, the australopithecines of three million years ago and more. Yet these same ancestors do clearly show many of the hallmarks of bipedal walking.

How long had human ancestors been walking upright? Was bipedality fully developed in the hominids of three million years ago, or did they sometimes revert to using all four limbs for running or climbing? The answers can help to solve the puzzle of bipedality's role in early human evolution. If upright walking was well established by the time of *Australopithecus*, its advent could date back as far as the earliest hominids, whose lineage probably diverged from other primates some eight or 10 million years ago. The development of erect walking may have been a crucial initiating event in human evolution.

I have proposed that bipedality accompanied a set of behavioral adaptations that became the key evolutionary innovation of humanity's earliest ancestors. These adaptations included, in effect, the nuclear family lasting monogamy together with care of the offspring by both parents. The male's contribution took the form of providing high-energy food, which expanded the mother's ability to nurture and protect each infant and also enabled her to give birth more often. Bipedality figured in this new reproductive scheme because by freeing the hands it made it possible for the male to carry food gathered far from his mate. These developments must have come long before the current hominid fossil record begins.

Upright walking should therefore have been perfected by the time of an australopithecine female whose fossil has become a test case for early walking. In 1974 the continuing search for human ancestors in the Afar Triangle of Ethiopia, led by Donald C. Johanson of the Institute of Human Origins in Berkeley, Calif, was splendidly rewarded by the recovery of the "Lucy" skeleton, known formally as A.L. 288-1. Although the skeleton is not quite complete, it preserves far more detail than any comparable fossil. In particular, it includes many of the lower-limb bones, one of the innominate bones that, in a mirror-image pair, make up the primate pelvis, and an intact sacrum (the fused vertebrae at the back of the pelvis). Upright walking is so dependent on this structure that an analysis of Lucy's pelvis can reveal how well she and her contemporaries walked.

The distinctive pelvic features of a biped reflect the very different mechanics of two- and four-legged locomotion. In order to propel itself any terrestrial mammal must apply a force against the ground in a direction opposite to the direction of travel. It does so by extending the joints of its legs, which lie between the ground and the animal's center of mass. Lengthening a leg produces a "ground reaction" that propels the torso in a direction determined by the angle between the leg and the ground.

In the quadrupedal posture of most primates the center of mass lies well forward of the hind limbs. Hence extending the hind limbs generates a ground reaction that has a large horizontal component. Because the hip and knee joints of the hind limbs are tightly flexed at the start of each cycle, their extension can be prolonged and powerful.

Our upright posture, in contrast, places our center of mass almost directly over the foot. If we stand erect and lengthen our legs by straightening the knee and rotating the ankle, the ground reaction is directed vertically and we end up on tiptoe. In order to propel our upright trunk we must reposition our center of mass ahead of one leg. The trailing limb is lengthened to produce a ground reaction while the other leg is swung forward to keep the trunk from falling. The strength of the ground reaction is limited, because much of it is still directed vertically and also because the trailing limb is already near its limit of extension owing to our upright posture: the hip joint is fully extended and the knee joint nearly so.

With the new bipedal strategy there came new roles for most of the muscle groups in the lower limb– roles that in turn required changes in the muscles' structure or position and hence in the design of the pelvis. A comparison of the human pelvis with that of our closest living relative, the chimpanzee, highlights these changes in mechanical design.

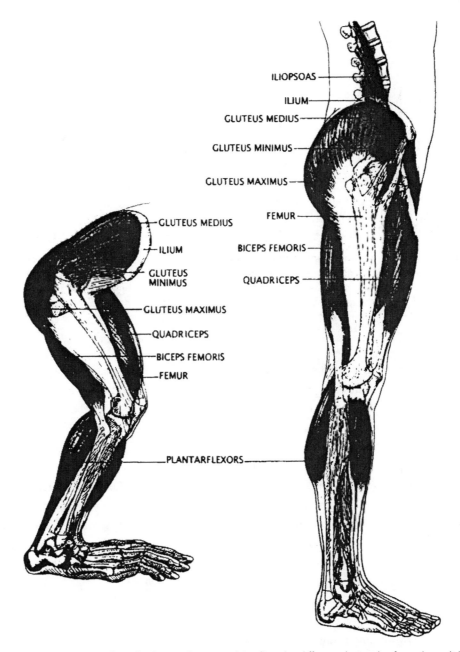

ILIOPSOAS
ILIUM
GLUTEUS MEDIUS
GLUTEUS MINIMUS
GLUTEUS MAXIMUS
FEMUR
BICEPS FEMORIS
QUADRICEPS

GLUTEUS MEDIUS
ILIUM
GLUTEUS MINIMUS
GLUTEUS MAXIMUS
QUADRICEPS
BICEPS FEMORIS
FEMUR
PLANTARFLEXORS

Pelvis and Leg of a chimpanzee (*left*) and a human being (*right*) reflect the differing demands of quadrupedal and bipedal locomotion. The musculature of the chimpanzee pelvis is dominated by the gluteus medius and gluteus minimus, which help to propel the animal by extending its hip joint. They are joined in that task by the hamstrings, which include the biceps femoris. In humans the gluteus maximus dominates the pelvis; it serves the new function of stabilizing the upright trunk. (The shortening of the ilium lowers the trunk's center of mass and makes it easier to control.) Other major muscles, such as the gluteus medius and minimus, the hamstrings and the iliopsoas, also play new auxiliary roles in upright walking. Only two muscle groups—the quadriceps and plantarflexors—are left to provide propulsion.

The need to stabilize an upright torso dictated the most dramatic change in musculature that has come with the adoption of bipedality: the transformation of the gluteus maximus, a relatively minor muscle in the chimpanzee, into the largest muscle in the human body. The gluteus maximus originates over much of the back of the pelvis and is attached to the back and side of the upper femur, or thigh-bone. As such it is defined as a hip extensor, and many classical anatomists believed it serves as the major propulsive muscle in upright walking. By straightening the hip, it was thought, the gluteus maximus contributes to the ground reaction imparted by the trailing leg.

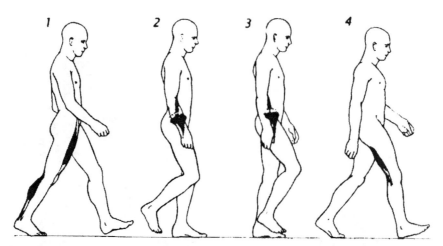

Muscle Activity during human striding is diagrammed. As the weight-bearing leg (here the right leg) becomes angled behind the torso (1), two muscle groups contract to extend it, generating a "ground reaction" that propels the body; they are the plantarflexors, which rotate the foot around the ankle, and the quadriceps, which straighten the knee. The foot then leaves the ground as weight is tranferred to the left leg. Contraction of the iliopsoas begins to tug the right leg forward (2) while the knee flexes passively (3). Near the end of the leg's swing the hamstrings contract to stop it, and the foot is planted (4). The left leg in turn generates ground reaction.

Actually, because the hip is almost completely extended in the first place during erect walking and running, the muscle's contribution to ground reaction is limited. Its hypertrophy in human beings reflects a quite different function. When we run, our upright trunk tends to flex forward at each foot strike owing to momentum. The gluteus maximus has taken on the role of preventing the trunk from pitching forward.

A major modification of the pelvis has made the muscle's stabilizing task considerably easier. Each innominate bone in the pelvis is topped by a blade of bone called an ilium; most of the lower viscera are cradled in the space between the two ilia. In the chimpanzee and other primates the ilia are much longer than they are in humans. The long ilia have the effect of lengthening the torso; when these primates rear up, their center of mass lies well above their hip joints. In the language of engineering, their trunk has a long lever arm. A gluteus maximus working to hold such a trunk upright would tire rapidly. The dramatically shortened human ilium shortens the torso and brings the trunk's center of mass much closer to the hip joints, thereby reducing the muscle's mechanical disadvantage.

The ilium is long in the apes to accommodate a second muscle group that was transformed as our ancestors began walking upright: the anterior gluteals, composed of the gluteus medius and the gluteus minimus. In the chimpanzee these muscles contract between attachment points near the top of the ilium and on the outside of the upper femur. Their position enables them to serve as powerful hip extensors during quadrupedal locomotion, and because the ilium is long, the muscles have a large range of contraction. Human beings can forgo this almost universal skeletal feature of other primates because hip extension contributes very little to bipedal locomotion. Our anterior gluteals have been freed to assume a new role.

This new role is best understood by imagining a head-on view of a person walking. Soon after the heel of the leading foot strikes the ground, the trailing leg leaves the surface and begins to swing forward. While it does so the trunk is supported by only one hip, which lies well to the side of the trunk's center of mass. On their own the pelvis and trunk would tip toward the unsupported side at each step, causing rapid fatigue; they are prevented from doing so by the action of the anterior gluteals, which are also referred to as abductors in human beings.

The transformation of the anterior gluteals from propulsive muscles to stabilizing ones required major changes in their position. A top view of the human and chimpanzee pelvises reveals a radical reorientation of the iliac blades in the human pelvis. In the chimpanzee the blades are flat and lie more or less in a single plane across the back of the torso. In humans each ilium has been rotated forward, carrying with it the upper attachment point of the gluteals. Their lower attachment point falls on the outside of the-upper femur, where the bone forms a neck that angles in to meet the pelvis at the hip joint. The abductors are thus disposed laterally in humans, away from the hip joints, which puts them in position to balance the pelvis against the weight of the trunk.

The reorientation of the ilia required two other changes in pelvic design not dictated directly by the mechanics of bipedality. If the ilia had simply been rotated forward, the space between them would have been sharply narrowed, leaving no room for the lower viscera. In compensation the sacrum, which separates the ilia at the back of the pelvis, has grown wider and the ilia have changed in shape: they are dished, so that the bending that has reoriented the abductors takes place well to the side, leaving ample room within the pelvis.

By increasing the distance between the hip joints, however, this widening of the central pelvis placed the abductors in a position of considerable mechanical disadvantage The force the abductors must exert to offset the weight of the trunk depends in part on how far to the side of the trunk's center of mass each hip joint lies. The greater the separation of the hip joints is, the longer the trunk's lever arm will be and the harder these muscles will have to contract to offset its weight. They will be more likely to tire during walking, and the safety of the hip joint itself may be threatened, since the joint is subjected to both the weight of the torso and the abductors' force of contraction.

A front view of the human pelvis reveals the evolutionary solution. The abductors' own lever arm can be increased, and their work made easier, if their upper and lower attachment points are moved farther out from the hip joint. Two features of the human pelvis serve that purpose. The complex curvature of the human ilium includes an outward flare, which displaces the upper attachment point of the abductors to the side of the hip. In addition the human femoral neck is longer than that of the chimpanzee. The longer femoral neck serves to move the abductors' lower attachment point outward as well, adding to their leverage.

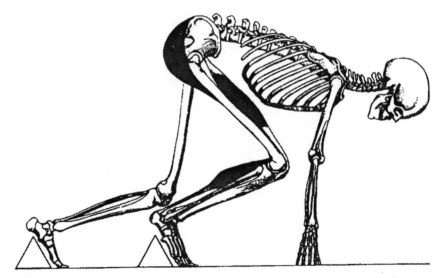

Sprinter on the starting block briefly recovers the advantages of being quadrupedal: the hip and knee joints are tightly flexed, preparing the limbs for prolonged and powerful extension, and the center of mass is positioned well forward of the legs, which gives the ground reaction a strong horizontal component. Ordinary walking or running sacrifices these advantages. An upright posture requires the hip and knee joints to be almost fully extended and places the body's center of mass almost directly over the legs. Both factors tend to limit the strength of the ground reaction.

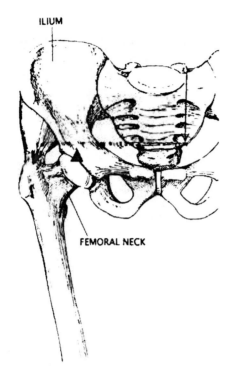

ILIUM

FEMORAL NECK

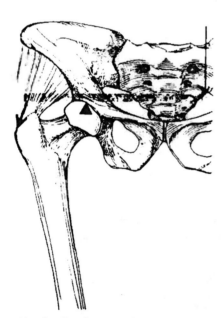

Abductor Muscles (the gluteus medius and minimus) contract to counterbalance the torso when the human pelvis is supported on only one leg. The hip joint acts as a fulcrum, with the weight of the torso and unsupported leg bearing down on one side and the abductors acting on the other (*top*). The abductors are at a mechanical disadvantage: the hip joint lies well to the side of the torso's center of mass, giving the body weight a long lever arm. In the Lucy pelvis (*bottom*) the body-weight lever arm was even longer, but greater lateral flare of the ilium and a longer femoral neck placed the abductors farther from the hip joint, increasing their mechanical advantage.

One set of muscles—the anterior gluteals—that help to propel chimpanzees has thus become co-opted to stabilize the human pelvis. A new role is also evident for another set of propulsive muscles in the chimpanzee: the hamstrings. They connect the lower pelvis to the back of the femur; in quadrupedal locomotion they serve as powerful hip extensors, which contribute even more to ground reaction than the anterior gluteals do. In bipedal walking, in contrast, they serve not to extend the limb but to control it.

A biped must swing each leg forward rapidly when it is not bearing weight. Because the limb is carried almost fully extended in a biped rather than tightly flexed, as it is in a quadruped, its center of mass lies well away from the pelvis. Like a long pendulum, an extended leg has a large moment of inertia, and it takes powerful muscle impulses to start and stop its swing. The iliopsoas, a muscle that originates within the pelvis and extends forward to an attachment point on the femur just below the hip joint, contracts to tug the limb forward. Once the leg has completed its arc, its swing must be checked. The position of the hamstrings, which is largely unchanged from the position in other primates, enables them to contract and decelerate the limb.

In human beings, then, the demands of stabilizing the pelvis and controlling the limb occupy several muscle groups that serve for propulsion in the chimpanzee. Only two muscle groups, the quadriceps and the plantarflexors, are left in positions that enable them to produce a ground reaction. The quadriceps are a mass of four muscles that make up most of the front of the human thigh. They end in a stout tendon, which crosses the patella, or kneecap, and is anchored to the top of the tibia, the main bone of the lower leg.

As the weight-bearing leg becomes angled behind the torso during walking or running, this powerful muscle mass contracts and straightens the knee. The plantarflexors, which originate at the back of the lower leg and are attached to the heel by the Achilles tendon, contract in synchrony with the quadriceps and cause the foot to rotate about the ankle. The extension of the knee and the rotation of the foot together lengthen the trailing leg, producing a strong ground reaction.

How well developed was this set of muscular adaptations by the time of Lucy and her kin, according to the fossil evidence? The discovery included a largely intact sacrum, but the innominate bone that accompanied it had been broken and partially crushed; it consisted of about 40 separate pieces fused into a single mass by the matrix of stone in which it was preserved. Often a fossil in this condition can be reduced to its separate pieces and then reassembled like a jigsaw puzzle. The pieces of Lucy's innominate, however, could not safely be separated. Instead I took a cast of each piece and assembled the casts in proper anatomical juxtaposition; the restored innominate was then mirror-imaged to create its opposite number. The result was a complete pelvis of an almost three-million-year-old human ancestor.

The pelvis bears all the hallmarks of bipedality seen in our own. Its ilia are much shorter than those in the pelvis of an ape. The shortening would have lowered the trunk's center of mass and made it easier to keep upright. The ilia have also become bent around to provide lateral attachment for the abductor muscles that stabilize the bipedal pelvis when it is supported on one leg. The attachment points for the gluteus maximus, abductors and quadriceps can be seen, and they indicate that in Lucy these muscles had attained a size

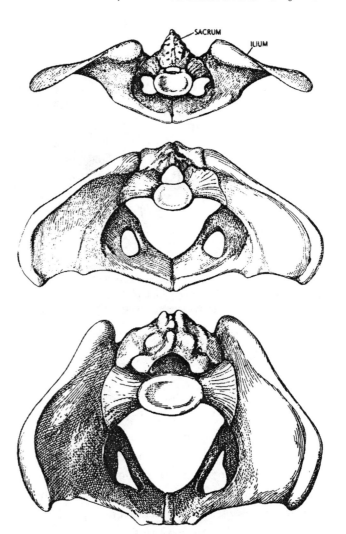

Rotation of the ilia took place as human ancestors began walking upright. In a quadrupedal ape such as a chimpanzee (*top*) the ilia (seen here from above) lie almost flat against the back of the torso. In Lucy (*middle*) they have become bent around, providing lateral attachment points for the abductor muscles, which stabilize the pelvis during walking. The bending takes place well away from the center of the pelvis, leaving room for the viscera; in addition the sacrum, which separates the ilia, has widened. These changes are retained in the modern human pelvis (*bottom*), which has also become longer from front to back to create a more ovoid birth canal.

and disposition remarkably similar to our own arrangement. The same is true for the iliopsoas, the hip flexor that initiates the swing of the leg: a groove on the brim of the pelvis, ahead of the hip joint, matches the groove that indicates the muscle's course in the human pelvis.

In one respect Lucy seems to have been even better designed for bipedality than we are. Her ilia flare outward more sharply than those of a modern pelvis and her femoral necks are longer. Her abductor muscles thus enjoyed a greater mechanical advantage than these muscles do in modern females. Some of the abductors' advantage merely compensated for the slightly wider separation of her hip joints (which gave her trunk a longer lever arm). Yet accurate measurements of both the abductor and the trunk lever arms–possible because the Lucy pelvis is so complete–show that her abductor advantage is still greater than

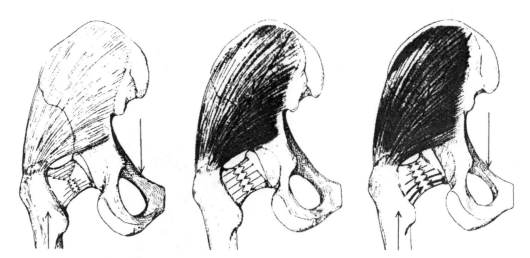

Neck of the Femur (shown from the back) is subjected to stress from two sources during human walking. Body weight imposes bending stress: tension on the top of the neck and compression on the bottom (*left*). At the same time the abductors, acting almost parallel to the femoral neck, subject its entire diameter to compression (*middle*). The sum of the two stress patterns is a gradient of stress running from low stress at the top to high compressive stress at the bottom (*right*).

our own. Her abductors had to exert less force to stabilize the pelvis, which also reduced the pressure on the hip-joint surfaces.

Why should a three-million-year-old hominid have had this mechanical advantage over her descendants? The answer lies in the accelerated growth of the human brain during the past three million years. Lucy's pelvis was almost singularly designed for bipedality. The flaring ilia and long femoral necks increased her abductors' lever arm, but they yielded a pelvis that in top view was markedly elliptical, resulting in a birth canal that was wide but short from front to back. The constriction was tolerable because Lucy predated the dramatic expansion of the brain; her infant's cranium would have been no larger than a baby chimpanzee's. The process of birth in Lucy and her contemporaries would have been slightly more complex than in an ape, but much easier than the modern human birth process [see *illustration on page 125*].

As human ancestors evolved a larger brain, the pelvic opening had to become rounder. The pelvis had to expand from front to back, but at the same time it contracted slightly from side to side. In the process the flare of the ilia was reduced, leaving us with a somewhat shorter abductor lever arm than Lucy's. (These changes are less pronounced in the modern male pelvis, where the abductors retain some of their former mechanical advantage.) Meanwhile the head of the modern femur has become enlarged to withstand increased pressure from the harder-working abductors. The difficulty of accommodating in the same pelvis an effective bipedal hip joint and an adequate passage for a large infant brain remains acute, however, and the human birth process is one of the most difficult in the animal kingdom.

The close resemblance of Lucy's pelvis to that of a modern human and its dramatic contrast to the pelvis of a chimpanzee make it clear that she walked fully upright. But was her bipedal progression truly habitual? Had she forsaken all other kinds of locomotion? The muscular rearrangements that enabled her to walk upright would not have allowed efficient quadrupedal movement on the ground. Perhaps, however, she often took to the trees and climbed, as most primates do, using all four limbs.

Basic evolutionary principles provide one kind of verdict on the possibility. A species cannot develop detailed anatomical modifications for a particular behavior, such as bipedality, unless it consistently employs that behavior. For natural selection to have so thoroughly modified for bipedality the skeleton Lucy inherited, her ancestors must already have spent most of their time on the ground, walking upright. Analysis of the Lucy fossil, however, can yield more direct evidence.

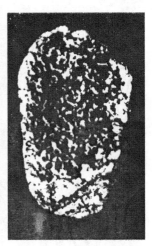

Internal Structure of the femoral neck distinguishes habitual bipeds. Seen in cross section, the femoral neck of the chimpanzee (*left*) has a robust thickness of bone together with a reinforcing ridge (visible in this section as a spike) at the top. These features enable the chimpanzee femoral neck to withstand the high bending stresses imposed by climbing and leaping. The human femoral neck (*middle*) has only a thin layer of bone at the top. It is suited only to the stresses of upright walking and running, when the abductor muscles counteract tension on the top of the neck. A fossil femoral neck from a contemporary of Lucy (*right*) has the same structure as the human one; it was designed exclusively for bipedal walking.

The analysis focuses on the neck of the femur, where much of the stress of locomotion is concentrated. When the leg is bearing weight, the hip joint transmits the weight of the torso to the femoral neck. The neck acts as a cantilevered beam: a beam that is anchored at one end to a supporting structure (the shaft of the femur) and carries a load at the other end. Cantilevering results in high bending stresses at the beam's anchorage–compression along the bottom of the beam and tension along the top–and the stresses increase with the length of the beam. A long femoral neck such as Lucy's reduces pressure on the hip joint by improving the leverage of the abductors, but the neck itself is subject to higher bending stresses.

The femoral neck of the chimpanzee is much shorter than the modern human one; nonetheless, it is robustly engineered to withstand the loads imposed by the animal's terrestrial and arboreal acrobatics. A cross section of the bone reveals a central marrow-filled channel surrounded by a thick layer of dense bone. Dense bone is weaker under tension than it is under compression, and so the upper surface of the structure, which will be subjected to tension when the neck is bent, carries a markedly thicker layer of bone. With this ridge of thick bone (a bone "spike" in cross section), the chimpanzee femoral neck imitates the principle of an I beam: material is placed where it can best resist bending stresses.

Because the human femoral neck is longer than the chimpanzee's and must resist the combined force of body weight and abductor contraction, one would expect it to be even more robustly constructed. A cross section of the human bone reveals a surprise: the outer ring of solid bone is thick only at the bottom, and the rest of the neck is bounded by a thin shell of bone and filled in by a lattice of fine bone plates called trabeculae. Such porous bone, as one might expect, is weaker than solid material. The upper part of the femoral neck, where tensile stresses are presumably the highest, actually contains less bone than any other part of the structure. How can our femoral neck survive the greater stresses imposed by its length and function when it seems so much less sturdy than the femoral neck of the chimpanzee?

The answer lies in the action of muscles that operate only in bipedal locomotion: the abductors. These muscles have lines of action that are not vertical but are sharply inclined, which makes them roughly parallel

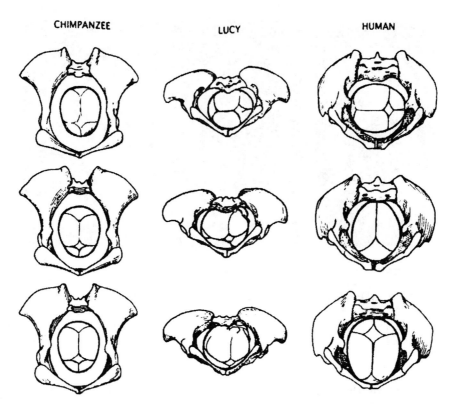

CHIMPANZEE   **LUCY**   **HUMAN**

Birth Process has competed with bipedality in shaping the modern human pelvis. In the chimpanzee pelvis (shown from the back) the head of the fetus descends without difficulty through the inlet (*top*), midplane (*middle*) and outlet (*bottom*) of the birth canal. In Lucy the birth process was somewhat more difficult: her short, flaring ilia were well suited to bipedality but resulted in a birth canal that was broad but constricted from front to back. Her infant's cranium could pass through only if it was first turned sideways and then tilted. The much larger brain in the human infant demands a rounder birth canal The necessary lengthening of the pelvis reduced the flare of the ilia and hence the mechanical advantage of the abductor muscles; even so, the human birth process is complex and traumatic, requiring a second rotation of the fetal cranium within the birth canal. The illustration is based on one by Robert G. Tague of Louisiana State University and Linda Budinoff of Kent State.

to the femoral neck. When they contract, they push the femoral neck into the hip socket, compressing the neck along its length. This compressive stress combines with the stresses that result from bending (tension on the top of the femoral neck and compression on the bottom). The effect is to eliminate tension at the top of the femoral neck and create a gradient of increasing stress running from the top of the femoral neck, where stress is now minimal, to the bottom, where stress is very high but purely compressive. The bottom of the human femoral neck has a robust layer of solid bone, and even the porous bone that fills in the rest of the section is reasonably strong as long as it remains under compression.

Other muscles work with the abductors to keep the femoral neck under compression when it is loaded. The most important of them is the piriformis, which originates on the front of the sacrum and extends to the outer end of the femoral neck. That orientation enables the muscle to increase the femoral neck's level of compression. The synchronized action of all these muscles when body weight is supported on one leg makes it possible for this seemingly fragile bone to cope with its load.

Because of its distribution of bone, however, the femoral neck is indeed vulnerable if the abductors and other muscles do not act in the proper synchrony. The femoral neck is a primary site of fracture in old age, and not just because bone quality is reduced in old people. These "broken hips" are also a product of reduced muscular coordination. Thus the design of the human femoral neck requires the muscular action of bipedal walking. The bone is poorly engineered for climbing and arboreal acrobatics, where it would be frequently subjected to bending stresses without being compressed at the same time by the abductors.

The femoral neck in *Australopithecus*, because it was even longer than that of modern humans, was subject to even greater bending stresses. If these human ancestors had often taken to the trees, stressing their femoral neck without coordinated compression by the abductors, the bone would have had to have been even more robust than it is in the apes. Was it? The same site where Lucy was found also yielded several femurs that had broken during their long burial, affording a view of the neck's internal structure. Each specimen clearly shows the human feature of thin bone on the upper part of the femoral neck. Lucy's femoral neck, then, was suited exclusively for bipedality. She was not just capable of walking upright; it had become her only choice.

I have concentrated on the pelvic anatomy of Lucy because the hallmarks of bipedality are so vivid there. A review of the rest of her skeleton and of other *Australopithecus* skeletons would reveal equally dramatic modifications that favor bipedality and rule out other modes of locomotion. The knee, for example, is adapted for withstanding greater stress during complete extension than the knee of other primates, and its design brings the femur and the tibia together at a slight angle, so that the foot can easily be planted directly under the body's center of mass when body weight is supported on one leg. The ankle is also modified for supporting the entire body weight, and a shock-absorbing arch helps the foot to cope with the added load. The great toe is no longer opposable, as it is in quadrupedal apes, but runs parallel to the other digits. The foot is now a propulsive lever for upright walking rather than a grasping device for arboreal travel. The arms have also become less suited to climbing: both the limb as a whole and the fingers have grown shorter than they are in the apes.

Lucy's ancestors must have left the trees and risen from four limbs onto two well before her time, probably at the very beginning of human evolution. I have suggested an explanation of why bipedality, with its many disadvantages, appeared long before our ancestors could have put their freed hands to use in carrying tools or weapons: it was part of a novel reproductive strategy that included provisioning by the male, a strategy that enabled the first hominids to flourish and diversify. The explanation will continue to be debated, but the evidence is conclusive that this curious form of locomotion was among the first anatomical characteristics to mark the ascent to cognitive life.

FURTHER READING

Human Walking. Verne T. Inman, Henry J. Ralston and Frank Todd. Williams & Wilkins, 1981.
LUCY: THE BEGINNINGS OF HUMANKIND. Donald C. Johanson and Edey Maitland. Simon and Schuster, 1981.
The Origin of Man. C. Owen Lovejoy in *Science*, Vol. 211, No. 4480, pages 341–350; January 23, 1981.
The Obsteric Pelvis of A.L. 288-1 (LUCY). Robert G. Tague and C. Owen Lovejoy in *Journal of Human Evolution*, Vol. 15, No. 4, pages 237–255; May, 1986.

The nature of *Au. afarensis* anatomy and locomotion has been a subject of contention since the discovery of the first fossils in the 1970's. Stern outlines the history of this debate, pointing out the unique nature of *Au. afarensis* bipedalism and the probable retention of climbing abilities in this species and in later hominins.

11. Climbing to the Top

A Personal Memoir of *Australopithecus Afarensis*

By Jack T. Stern, Jr.

Last autumn marked the 25th anniversary of the discovery of "Lucy." While that certainly was a momentous event in paleoanthropology, it had no less profound an effect on my academic life, for it presaged my eventual seduction into the arena of hominid fossil interpretation. My friend John Fleagle, editor of Evolutionary Anthropology, says I may introduce this paper with a history of that experience. He assures me this is appropriate because I have now reached the age when young people in the field have no idea who I am.

DOWN THE GARDEN PATH

Just a few months before the A.L. 288-1 partial skeleton was found, I had seen the first published picture of the A.L. 129 knee.[1] It was obviously valgus, a trait expressed most markedly in bipedal hominids, and the discoverers described the morphology of the distal femur as "tres humaine." The following year yielded a published photograph of Lucy.[2] While it was difficult to discern from the picture what she would tell us

Jack T. Stern Jr., "Climbing to the Top: A Personal Memoir of Australopithecus Afarensis," *Evolutionary Anthropology*, vol. 9, no. 3, pp. 113–133. Copyright © 2000 by John Wiley & Sons, Inc. Reprinted with permission.

about the origins of bipedalism, the authors commented that the pelvis had some similarities to that of Sts 14 (*Australopithecus africanus*), and that the knee bones were virtually identical to the A.L. 129 specimens. Like many other physical anthropologists, I looked forward to what future analyses of the Hadar finds would reveal. In January 1976 there appeared an abstract stating that the high bicondylar angle, deep patellar groove, and elliptical lateral femoral condyle of the A.L. 129 knee indicated mechanical features that characterize the modern human knee, including "the capacity of hyperextension."[3] The following year came the first abstract of potential interest for reconstructing Lucy's locomotor behavior.[4] It reported that "the degree of medial rotation of the tibia on the talus during dorsiflexion was 3 to 4 times greater than that of modern humans."

The 1979 meeting of the American Association of Physical Anthropologists contained a special session devoted to the Hadar finds. Owen Lovejoy[5] presented his reconstruction of the A.L. 288-1 pelvis, concluding that it "exhibits adaptation to full bipedality," and making special note of the broad iliac blade and the mechanically advantageous position of the anterior gluteals. That same year, Leakey and Hay[6] formally presented the discovery of the Laetoli hominid footprints, which they said evinced a "fully upright, bipedal and free striding gait." In 1980 Lovejoy's[7] abstract on the role of reproductive-behavioral adaptations in hominid evolution referred to the "fully developed adaptation to bipedality" of *A. afarensis,* and two analyses of the Laetoli footprints found them to be indicative of a modern human-like form of bipedalism.[8,9]

Meanwhile, other workers were making some rather different observations. While not disputing that the Hadar hominids were bipedal, Senut[10,11] noted traits of the upper limb (the narrow, deep intertubercular sulcus of the humerus, the well-developed lateral margin of the humeral trochlea, the relatively proximal origin of the lateral epicondyle of the humerus, the relatively distal position of the ulnar tuberosity, and the long and narrow neck of the radius) that were so similar to those of apes as to "signify a certain ability and possible propensity on the part of these hominids to climb trees."[11] Tardieu's[12,13] thorough analysis of the knee identified traits of the A.L. 129 and/or A.L. 288-1 specimens that suggested to her a shorter stride, less frequent total extension of the knee, absence of terminal locking rotation of the knee, and freer voluntary rotation of the tibia. These included modest development of the lateral lip of the patellar groove on the femur, an incipiently elliptical lateral femoral condyle, anteroposte-riorly short femoral condyles, the relatively narrow anterior region of the medial femoral condyle, the incipient development of a human-shaped femoral intercondylar notch, narrowness of the tibial intercondylar eminence relative to the width of the femoral intercondylar notch, and the convex articular surface of the lateral tibial condyle. Tardieu concluded that the smaller of the Hadar hominids represented an early stage in the development of hominid bipedality and that it probably maintained a certain aptitude for arboreal locomotion.

This was the state of affairs in December 1980, six years after Lucy's discovery, when my colleague Randy Susman walked into my office to proclaim his opinion that we were as well qualified as anyone to perform a comprehensive functional analysis of the Hadar postcranial material. I immediately realized that Randy was half right. He further suggested that we should visit Ethiopia to look at the fossils. Not being able to find Ethiopia on a map of Long Island, I was reluctant, but eventually agreed. A trip was planned for the summer of 1981. Randy thought it would be wise to prepare for our study of the original fossils by taking a look at casts of the *A. afarensis* material in the Cleveland Museum of Natural History. Bill Jungers asked to come along so he could take some measurements of Lucy's body proportions. In May of 1981, the Stony Brook contingent of three arrived at the Cleveland Museum of Natural History, where Don Johanson graciously gave us complete access to all the casts of the Hadar material and the original specimen of the A.L. 333-115 foot. We collected many measurements, made extensive notes, and took numerous photographs, most of which were overexposed because Randy was not the excellent photographer he had claimed to be. (Randy redeemed himself on a 1992 visit to Addis during which he studied the original fossils and took fairly good pictures.)

We left Cleveland with the tentative conclusion that the portrayals of *A. afarensis* locomotion by Senut and Tardieu were not far off the mark.

Although we did not learn so until several months later, it turned out that some of our observations we thought to be novel had also been made by Russell Tuttle.[14] While we were in Cleveland, he published a paper noting the markedly curved pedal proximal phalanges of Hadar foot specimens, the broad peroneal groove on the fibula, and somewhat laterally oriented iliac blades. Such features caused him to conclude that the Hadar hominids were rather recently derived from arboreal bipeds and may have engaged in a notable degree of tree climbing. Because Tuttle found the shapes of the Laetoli footprints to be indistinguishable from those made by striding humans who habitually go barefoot, he found it difficult to assign their maker to the same species as that represented by the A.L. 333-115 foot.

We arrived in Ethiopia in August of 1981. British Airways lost my luggage. I was not only anxious about being in a country that had street signs preaching the evils of Uncle Sam, but also was not adjusting well to having only one of each clothing item. (I absolutely refused Randy's offer to share his underwear.) To make a long story short, Randy and I were denied permission to look at the Hadar fossils and, while Randy was sleeping, I received a phone call from an Ethiopian government official advising us to leave the country immediately.

Upon our return, we decided to complete our work on reconstructing *A. afarensis* locomotor behavior using casts instead of original material. Don Johanson saw to it that the material we needed was sent to Stony Brook. As we were completing our analysis of the Hadar postcrania, Johanson's and Edey's[15] book *Lucy* was published. Here it was stated that the Hadar hominid was not a climber, despite having slightly long arms for its size, a tendency for the fingers to curl a bit more, some ape-like wrist bones, arched and relatively long pedal phalanges, and metatarsal heads having a shape intermediate between those of apes and humans. Rather, as shown by the pelvis, knee, hallux, and joints of the toes, *A. afarensis* was said to be a fully erect bipedal creature that could walk at least as well as a modern human, a conclusion said to be confirmed by the Laetoli footprints. Lucy's ability to run as fast as a modern human was considered debatable.

The April 1982 the issue of the American Journal of Physical Anthropology was devoted to detailed descriptions of the Hadar hominids, but it contained no functional interpretations of the postcranial material. That summer, Bill Jungers' paper on the proportions of Lucy's limbs was published.[16] He showed that Lucy's humerus, compared to that of a modern human, was not relatively long, but that her femur was relatively short. Bill concluded that Lucy's ability to climb was less than an ape's, and that her relatively short stride length suggested a greater cost and lower maximum speed of bipedal locomotion. In September 1982, Marc Feldesman published a multivariate study of distal humeral dimensions showing that the Hadar specimens are "quite primitive, and may be close to the point where hominids and pongids diverged."[17]

Mine and Randy's paper on the locomotor anatomy of *A. afarensis* was published in March of 1983.[18] One month later, three of us from Stony Brook went west to participate in Don Johanson's symposium on *A. afarensis* locomotion. There began a change in my career that I had not anticipated. Virtually overnight, I was transformed from an obscure electromyographer into someone being quoted in the New York Times and featured in Discover magazine. Over the course of the next few years, four separate television crews visited Stony Brook to tape us (mainly Randy) talking about the origin of bipedalism. I became alienated from Owen Lovejoy, a person whom I have always considered one of the most creative and insightful workers in our field. I became such a staunch advocate for one position that I am no longer certain of my objectivity. Sometimes I hope we will be proven wrong, just so I won't feel aggravated when I see a paper by Owen, Bruce Latimer, or Jim Ohman. But this desire quickly passes, as will soon become evident.

Table 1. Postcranial Traits Identified by Stern and Susman,[18] Jungers and Stern,[21] and Susman and Coworkers[22] As Distinguishing *A. Afarensis* from Modern Humans

Relatively short hindlimb (A*, N**)	Lateral lip of patellar groove weakly developed for degree of valgus at knee (N)
Relatively long foot (N)	Medial femoral condyle wider than lateral condyle (N)
Elongated, rod-shaped pisiform (A)	Distal articular surface of Lucy's tibia angled to face posteriorly (N)
Finger metacarpals with large heads and bases relative to parallel-sided and somewhat curved shafts (A)	Proximal margin of talar facet on fibula is oblique (A)
Finger proximal phalanges slender and markedly curved, with a bilateral expansion of shaft correlated with strong expression of flexor sheath ridges (A)	Peroneal groove on fibula is wide, deep, and has prominent medial lip (A)
Trochleae of finger proximal phalanges subtend large angles and are deeply grooved (A)	Anterior limit of lateral margin of talar trochlea is extended distally (A)
Strong impressions for insertion of flexor digitorum superflcialis on finger middle phalanges (A)	Calcaneus has large peroneal trochlea and small lateral plantar process (N)
Glenoid cavity of scapula faces more superiorly (A)	Hallucal tarsometatarsal joint is curved (A)
Relatively larger moment arm of hamstrings (A, N)	Head of hallucal metatarsal is mediolaterally very curved (A, N)
Relatively wide tuberoacetabular sulcus (N)	Lack of mediolateral widening of dorsal region of metatarsal heads (N)
Hamstring surface of ischial tuberosity makes a sharp angle to adductor magnus surface (N)	Pedal proximal phalanges ll-V are slender, relatively long (N), and markedly curved (A)
Absence of falciform crest on medial aspect of ischial tuberosity (N)	Pedal proximal phalanges ll-V have bilateral expansion in region of well developed flexor sheath attachments (A)
Ventral concavity of sacrum slightly developed (N)	Trochleae of pedal proximal phalanges ll-IV subtend large angles (A)
Sacrum lacks well developed upper lateral angles (N)	Lack of dorsoplantar expansion at base of pedal proximal phalanges ll-V (N)
Acetabular lunate articular surface has a diminutive anterior horn (N)	Proximal phalanx of toe II is shorter than that of toe III (A)
Absence of iliopubic eminence (N)	Pedal middle phalanges are relatively long compared to proximal phalanges (A, N)
lliac blades more coronally oriented (N)	Laetoli footprints have small impression or none for ball of big toe (N)
Superior articular margin of femoral head runs from posterolateral to anteromedial (A)	Laetoli footprints show variable length of impressions for lateral toes (N)

*A = interpreted as being related to an arboreal component of behavior.

**N = interpreted as being related to a novel form of bipedalism

JACK OF TWO TRADES, MASTER OF NEITHER

There is no real dispute that *A. afarensis* progressed bipedally when on the ground (but see Sarmiento[19,20] for the sole contrasting view) nor that this was such an important part of its overall locomotor repertoire as to have engendered anatomic changes promoting its performance. The chief evidence for these conclusions comprises the shortened ilium, the posterior displacement of its auricular surface relative to the acetabulum, the presence of an iliac pillar, and a high bicondylar angle of the femur. However, while acknowledging this, our papers[18,21–25] claimed that:

1. *A. afarensis* also possessed anatomic adaptations for movement intrees (Table 1 and Fig. 1).

2. Certain anatomic traits long thought to be diagnostic of a completely human-like form of bipedalism are not truly diagnostic of such behavior or are not actually present on Hadar specimens. These include an iliopsoas groove on the os coxae, ananterior inferior iliac spine, a femoral intertrochanteric line, an

obturator externus groove on the femoral neck, and thin superior cortical bone coupled with thick inferior cortical bone in the femoral neck.

3. *A. afarensis* possessed anatomic traits suggesting that its bipedalism lacked human-like extension at the hip and knee during stance phase (Table 1 and Fig. 1), and that early in the stance phase of bipedal walking the lesser gluteal muscles controlled side-to-side balance at the hip by acting as medial rotators of the partly flexed thigh.[26] Even if these particular claims are incorrect, the relatively short lower limb and relatively long foot of *A. afarensis* point to an energetically more costly form of bipedalism[16,21] and a kinematically distinctive swing phase.[27]

At the same time or shortly after the publication of our earliest papers on *A. afarensis* locomotion, there appeared a spate of other contributions reporting a mosaic of human-like and ape-like features in its postcranial anatomy. Clearly, these were based on work that had been done simultaneously with or even before our own. Marzke,[28] analyzing bones and joints of the wrist, and McHenry,[29] focusing on the capitate, seemed willing to recognize the possibility of some degree of arboreality in *A. afarensis* locomotor behavior but were reluctant to actually draw this conclusion. Rose,[30] who made many of the same observations on the Hadar feet and hands that we did, showed no such reluctance, nor did Schmid,[31] who focused on the ribs and pelvis. Deloison's[32] study of the Hadar calcanei led her to state explicitly that *A. afarensis* bipedalism must have been distinct from that of modern humans. In contrast, Wolpoff,[33,34] challenging Jungers's[16] claim that Lucy's lower limb was shorter than expected for a diminutive human-like biped, drew a picture of *A. afarensis* as an efficient terrestrial biped that also made extensive use of arboreal resources. Berge[35-37] seemed to have a difficult time deciding on the functional significance of her multivariate osteometric study of the A.L. 288-1 and Sts 14 innominates. She interpreted the lateral orientation of the iliac blade, the proximity of the iliac pillar to the anterior edge of the bone, and the beaked form of the anterior superior iliac spine as pointing to a type of bipedal adaptation differing from that of modern humans. Furthermore, she stated that the smallness of the acetabulum, auricular surface, and the portion of the ilium just above the hip joint indicate a limited adaptation for weight bearing. Yet Berge also stated that gracile australopithecines were "as bipedal as *Homo*," with an equally effective lateral balance mechanism and pelvic proportions that in no way provide evidence for an arboreal adaptation. Finally, the formal publication of Tardieu's[38] thesis contained a new section reporting that the knee of *A. afarensis* was distinctly nonhuman by virtue of having only a single attachment of the lateral meniscus anterior to the external tibial spine. Tardieu[39,40] linked this trait to an enhanced range of lateral tibial rotation and said it would be useful if the foot were used as a prehensile organ.

From 1982 to 1985 there seemed to be a growing consensus that not only favored an adaptively important role for arboreality in the life of the Hadar hominids, but even recognized the possibility that their manner of bipedalism was recognizably different from that practiced by modern humans. Tardieu joined Senut in expressing the belief that both *Homo* and *Australopithecus* were represented at Hadar, and that the anatomy of the Hadar postcranial material indicated two different locomotor profiles, one human-like and one not. (More recently, Tardieu has attributed all the Hadar specimens to *A. afarensis* and makes no mention of a type with human-like locomotion.) In 1984, we expressed our opinion that there was one

Figure 1. Some of the traits identified in Table 1 as indicating that *A. afarensis* either possessed anatomic adaptations for movement in the trees or was not entirely human-like in its manner of terrestrial bipedality. A = *A. afarensis*, B = bonobo, C = chimpanzee, G = gorilla, H = human, O = orangutan. 1. Outline drawings of body shapes illustrating the relatively short lower limb of *A. afarensis*. 2. Side views of manual proximal phalanges from ray IV showing the marked curvature of this bone in *A. afarensis*. 3. Radial views of pisiform bones illustrating the rod-like nature of this bone in *A. afarensis*. 4. Ventral views of scapulae illustrating that the glenoid cavity faces more cranially in *A. afarensis*. 5. Lateral views of hip bones illustrating in the fossil the relatively wide tuberoacetabular sulcus (1), the relatively large distance from the center of the hip joint to the hamstring origin (2), the sharp angle between the area for origin of the hamstrings (2) and the area for origin of the adductor magnus (3), the absence of an iliopubic eminence (4), and the small size of the anterior horn of the acetabular lunate surface (5). 6. On the left, cranial views of sacra illustrating the poorly developed upper lateral angles in *A. afarensis*; on the right, side views of sacra illustrating the slight development of the ventral concavity in *A. afarensis*. 7. Cranial views of iliac crests illustrating the coronal orientation of the iliac blades in *A. afarensis*. 8. Distal views of femoral condyles illustrating that the patellar groove's lateral lip (arrow) is weakly developed in *A. afarensis*. 9. On top, lateral views of distal tibiae (anterior to the left, posterior to the right) illustrating that in Lucy (leftmost specimen, reversed for ease of comparison) the distal articular surface is inclined posteriorly; on bottom, medial views of distal fibulae (anterior to the right, posterior to the left, some specimens reversed for ease of comparison) illustrating the obliquity of the talar facet's proximal margin (arrow) in *A. afarensis*. 10. Dorsal views of hallucal metatarsals illustrating the marked mediolateral curvature of the head in *A. afarensis*. 11. Distal views of metatarsal heads from rays I-V (dorsal toward the top, ventral toward the bottom) illustrating the lack of mediolateral widening of the dorsal regions in *A. afarensis*. 12. Side views of pedal proximal phalanges from ray III illustrating the marked curvature of such bones in *A. afarensis*.

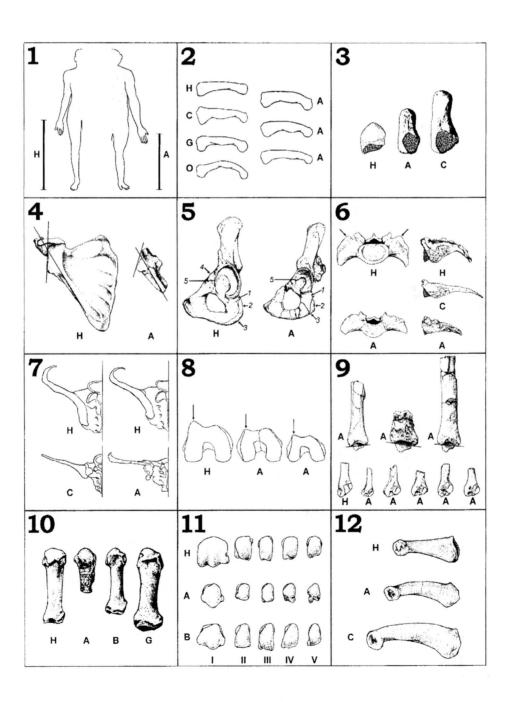

hominid species at Hadar and that all its members were distinctly nonhuman-like in locomotion, but that sexual dimorphism in the degree of arboreality was possible.[22]

During this period only one abstract was published portraying the Hadar hominid as a fully developed biped.[41] It dealt with the foot, reporting that metatarsophalangeal joint conformations provide evidence of the extreme dorsiflexion that occurs during toe-off in a habitual biped. Curved proximal phalanges were dismissed as "an adaptive response to large dorsoplantar bending moments," prehension as exhibited in the modern ape foot not being part of the *A. afarensis* locomotor repertoire. Longitudinal and transverse bony arches were said to exist and to indicate a bipedal foot. The arches were short-lived, however, for analysis of the navicular and cuboid from Hadar published a year later indicated that "*A. afarensis* possessed a more mobile transverse tarsal joint, and probably a wider and flatter tarsus than is characteristic of the normal modern human foot.[42]

THE EMPIRE STRIKES BACK

Of course there really was no consensus that the positional behavior of *A. afarensis* was distinct from that of modern humans. The long-awaited response to such views was presented in a series of papers, largely emanating from Kent State University, between 1986 and 1990.[43-49] Table 2 lists and Figure 2 illustrates traits identified in these papers as proving the adaptive insignificance of arboreality in the life of *A. afarensis* and the human-like nature of its bipedality. Five of the seven papers were restricted to a consideration of the ankle and foot.

Many of the papers summarized in Table 2 contained suggestions to the effect that no significant adaptation to bipedalism can occur unless the commitment to this behavior is total. It was stated directly that hominoid arboreality is not to be viewed as a natural continuum and that arboreal capacity in early hominids should not be discussed in terms of "degrees" of adaptation.[44] A later contribution suggested that no selective advantage could accrue to an arboreal animal from any change that diminished its ability to climb.[50] Consequently, the presence of anatomic alterations for bipedalism that compromise climbing ability make it unlikely that arboreality remained adaptively significant. It was argued that if arboreality was adaptively significant for *A. afarensis*, its upper limb should have maintained, or even shown to a higher degree, all the features we have come to associate with pongid arboreality. In one way or another, the authors of all these papers agreed that "To suggest that *A. afarensis* still employed a significant degree of pongid-like arboreal behavior or that the stride pattern in this species included a 'primitive bent-hipped, bent-knee' gait (as has been recently suggested; see Stern and Sus-man, 1983; Susman et al., 1984) not only contradicts available anatomical evidence from the hip, knee, ankle, and foot but also completely contradicts the basic rudiments of neo-Darwinian theory."[47]

THE VIEW OF A CAST-OUT ANGEL

Can there be a home in neo-Darwin-ian heaven for those who do not believe the significance of derived traits overwhelms that of primitive traits for reconstructing the locomotor behavior of fossils? I have always had a simplistic way of looking at this issue. The whale ancestor *Ambulocetus* shows anatomic adaptations for aquatic locomotion that have clearly diminished its terrestrial expertise.[51] Still, no one has suggested that terrestrial behavior was adaptively insignificant for *Ambulocetus*. Why then conclude that arboreal behavior was adaptively insignificant for *A. afarensis* because its anatomic adaptations for bipedal locomotion diminished its arboreal expertise? Other authors have thought and written more insightfully on this problem as it relates to human evolution. Rose[30,52] envisions the adoption of terrestrial bipedalism by a human ancestor as a process in which the animal moves through a series of compromise morphologies. "For an animal with a compromise morphology each of the component activities of the [locomotor] repertoire is performed less energetically efficiently than it would be given optimal design ... Although it is not maximally efficient, each activity within the repertoire is performed effectively, according to the purposes for which it was used."[52] Duncan and coworkers[53] stated that "Every species is composed of characteristics that reflect both its ancestry as well as its unique evolutionary pathway; understanding the overall functional pattern of the organism requires an equal consideration of all its anatomical features, regardless of whether they are apomorphies, plesiomorphies, or homoplasies. This viewpoint serves to frame the fossil as a once fully functional living organism." I am persuaded by these arguments. If you are not, then without further ado you should accept *A. afarensis* as a fully committed and human-like terrestrial biped. You may proceed directly to the Acknowledgments; do not pass GO, do not collect $200.

JUST THE FACTS, MA'AM

Coffing[54] attributes much of the disagreement about reconstructing *A. afarensis* locomotor behavior to the previously mentioned differences in concepts of natural selection. However, it is also true that the opposing camps have doubted the accuracy, as well as the interpretation, of one another's data.

Possible Errors by Randy and Bill

1. Using an adult intraspecific regression line of scapular bar-glenoid angle (Fig. 1, part 4) versus glenoid length derived from 50 modern human scapulae, we predicted that a modern human of Lucy's size should have a bar-glenoid angle of 140 degrees, much greater than the 130 degrees observed in Lucy's scapula. Mensforth and coworkers[55] found our prediction to be in error. They reported that a similar analysis of 100 modern human scapulae yielded an expected value of ~130 degrees for the bar-glenoid angle of a Lucy-sized modern human scapula. More recently, Inouye and Shea[56] arrived at a value of 136 degrees, but pointed out that low correlations, together with the practice of extrapolating to a size below that found in one's modern sample, make any such estimate worthless. When Inouye and Shea included subadult human scapulae in their sample, the range of bar-glenoid angles encompassed Lucy's value, and the human regression line virtually ran through 130 degrees. (It appears from their graphs that Inouye and Shea used 2.25 cm, the value we reported, for Lucy's glenoid length. However, we did not include the supraglenoid tubercle in our measurement, whereas they reported doing so for all their specimens of extant species. The measurement of Lucy's glenoid length including the supraglenoid tubercle is 2.57 cm. If Inouye and Shea had used this value, they would have predicted a bar-glenoid angle for a Lucy-sized human of 137.5 degrees using the adult human regression line and one of 132 degrees using the ontogenetic human regression line.)

    If the approach used by Inouye and Shea is appropriate for assessing the significance of Lucy's cranially directed glenoid cavity, then this trait no longer belongs on the list of characters suggesting arboreality. In accepting this possibility, I am being far more generous than Bill Jungers, who has conveyed to me his conviction that it is incorrect to apply an ontogenetic allometric trend to answer a question concerning the shape of a small adult. He is now scouring museums for a few adult human scapulae as small as Lucy's.

2. We asserted that the superior border of the articular margin of Lucy's femoral head exhibited a disposition found in apes but not in humans. We said this disposition was compatible with a greater range of abduction than occurs in modern humans. Asfaw,[57] using a much larger sample than ours, found the "ape-like" condition in 9% of human individuals. MacLatchy[58] showed that if the neutral posture of the femur is assumed to occur when the fovea capitis is centered in the acetabular fossa, the neutral position of Lucy's thigh was more adducted than that of modern humans. Furthermore, despite the fact that the lunate surface of Lucy's acetabulum was restricted dorsally and cranially relative to the acetabulum of modern humans, this difference was insufficient to allow greater abduction of the thigh.

These two studies cause me to doubt greatly the significance of our observations on the articular surface of Lucy's femoral head. Nonetheless, I wish to point out that limitation of hip abduction in modern humans is probably due to passive tension in the stretched adductor muscles. Although I am almost totally sedentary, I am able to abduct my extended thigh 40 to 50 degrees and my flexed thigh 50 to 60 degrees. Observations of gymnasts lead me to conclude that people who stretch their adductor muscles can abduct the thigh at least 90 degrees. So the question about the abductibility of the *A afarensis* hindlimb is really a question of the rest-length of its hip adductors, which we will never know.

3. Tuttle described our statements on the Laetoli footprints as an example of "haste making paleontological waste."[59] He claimed that the chimpanzee footprints described by Manter and Elftman[60] and those produced by our own "incarcerated" chimpanzees[18] were atypical by having a somewhat adducted hallux and partially curled lateral toes. He also found that traits we identified as characteristic of modern human footprints are in fact commonly absent. White and Suwa[45] agreed, adding that we had incorrectly interpreted the footprint surface at Laetoli. We did not respond, but Deloison's[61] comparison of Laetoli footprints to those of chimpanzees and modern humans found the fossil pattern to be characterized by, among other things, a narrow impression for the heel, a depression likely to be caused by a large abductor hallucis, a partly abducted big toe, and folded lateral toes. Deloison concluded that the overall form was more similar to that of a chimpanzee than that of a human. The definitive word on the subject has yet to be uttered.

4. We asserted that the relatively long toes of *A. afarensis* were compatible with use of the foot for some kind of prehension in trees, and would also have increased the length of the foot in a way that would have affected the kinematics of bipedal swing phase. White and Suwa[45] reconstructed the length of Lucy's foot, finding the length of her toes relative to the rest of the foot to be halfway between that of a human and a gorilla, and 45% to 50% longer than that of the average human. Nonetheless, the authors claimed that the ratio of total foot length to femur length for Lucy was at the upper end of the modern human range of variation and, therefore, of minimal consequence for her manner of bipedalism. Latimer and Lovejoy[48] compared the length of Lucy's proximal pedal phalanx to four other postcranial measures and, despite its position intermediate between gorilla and human, concluded that the fossil toe was not particularly long. We had previously published two of the same comparisons[18,22] and, with very similar numbers, came to a quite different conclusion. Lucy's toes were probably as long as the fingers of a two-year old human. The lengths of the phalanges in the A.L. 333-115 foot are comparable to those in the hands of children between the ages of nine and ten years.[62] The real question seems to be how long is "particularly" long?

5. Our use of the superior edge of the talar facet on the fibula (Fig. 1, part 9) to judge the range and set of plantar-flexion at the ankle was said to be inaccurate because "talofibular joint congruence cannot be reliably assessed."[44] Latimer and colleagues[44] found no indication of a greater plantarflexion range in Lucy when they manipulated her tibia upon her talus. On the other hand, when applied to chimpanzee

Table 2. Traits said to indicate Human-Like bipedality and adaptive insignificance of arboreality in
A. Afarensis

The head of the first rib articulates with the body of only the Tl vertebra.[43] (I)
The deltoid muscle marking on the clavicle faces anteriorly.[43] (I)
The supratalar joint space is nearly perpendicular to the long axis of the tibia.[44] (I, H)
The flexion-extension axis of the talocrural joint is oriented so that there is little conjunct axial rotation of the tibia during flexion-extension movements at the ankle.[44] (I)
The Laetoli footprints have a fundamentally human-like total morphological pattern.[46] (H)
The ilia of Lucy are bent around to provide lateral attachment for the lesser gluteal muscles.[46] (H)
The attachment points and dispositions of the gluteus maximus and quadriceps are human-like.[46] (H)
An iliopsoas groove is present on the pelvis.[46,68] (H)
The hip abductors have a mechanical advantage surpassing that of the hip abductors in modern humans.[46] (H)
The foot has a shock-absorbing arch.[46] (H)
The upper limbs and fingers are relatively shorter than those of apes.[46] (I)
The inferolateral corner of the calcaneal corpus is expanded and a clearly defined lateral plantar process is present.[47] (H)
The posterior talar facet of the calcaneus is less convex and more vertically oriented than is that in apes.[47] (I, H)
The distal articular surface of the Hadar medial cuneiform faces more directly distally than does that in apes.[48] (I)
The proximal articular surface of the hallucal metatarsal is virtually divided into two separate facets by a slight transverse ridge.[48] (I)
The distal location of the "sub-bursal groove" for the tendon of tibialis anterior on the medial surface of the medial cuneiform is human-like.[48] (I)
The heads of metatarsals are inflated and angled dorsally.[49] (H)
The proximal articular surfaces of the pedal proximal phalanges are more superiorly oriented than are those of apes.[49] (H)
The superior cortical bone of the femoral neck is thin.[46] (I, H)

*I = interpreted as showing insignificance of arboreal behavior.
**H = interpreted as showing human-like bipedalism

bones, their method did not reveal the greater range of plantarflexion that we demonstrated by radiographic images of living animals.[22] My conclusion is that there is something very different about the talar facet of Hadar fibulae, but that we have not proven its functional significance.

6. Our comments on the size of the large peroneal trochlea and its relation to the lateral plantar process were described as inexplicable, inaccurate, and implausible.[47] While I admire the alliteration, I must point out that our assessment of the sizes of these bony bumps is fully concordant with that of Deloison.[32,63]

7. Whereas Wolpoff[33,34] criticized Jungers[16] for concluding that Lucy's lower limb was relatively short, and we responded with further evidence to support this contention,[21] Kramer[64] has recently published a mathematical simulation of Lucy's bipedalism purporting to show that Lucy was not energetically compromised by her short legs: "On a mass specific basis, the configuration developed from the fossil remains of AL 288-1 uses less energy to move than, and has the same cost of transport as, the modern human configuration." The assumptions underlying Kramer's conclusion are that Lucy had the same movement profile as a modern human, that the masses of Lucy's lower limb segments were proportionally the same as in a modern human, and that it is most appropriate to compare energy use of the two species when Lucy is walking at about 80% of the speed of a modern human.

If Lucy really had the same movement profile as a modern human, this alone would cause me, but not my colleagues, to classify her as a human-like biped regardless of energetic cost. Therefore, it is of little moment to me if the calculation of energy-use based on Kramer's assumptions is correct or not. For me, the issue is the implausibility of the assumptions. Furthermore, knowing that mathematical simulations are often highly dependent on the values of input parameters, it is troublesome that Kramer

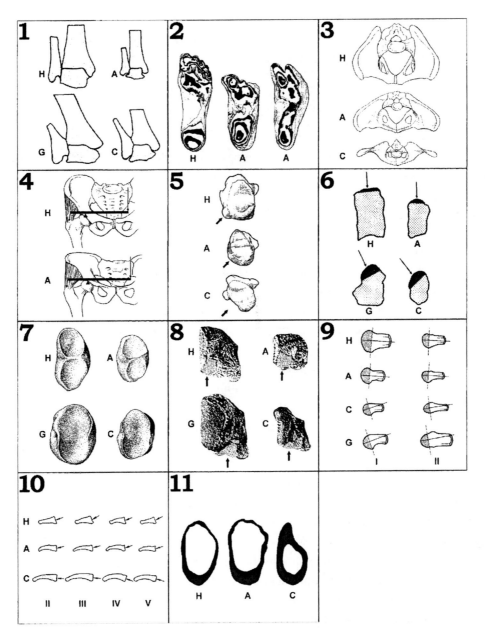

Figure 2. Some of the traits identified in Table 2 as indicating human-like bipedality and the adaptive insignificance of arboreality in *A. afarensis*. A = *A. afarensis*, C = chimpanzee, G = gorilla, H = human. All drawings are modified from originals that appeared in the indicated references. 1. Outline tracings from midcoronally sectioned casts of ankle joints illustrating that the supratalar joint space is nearly perpendicular to the long axis of the tibia in humans and *A. afarensis*.[44] 2. Contour maps of footprints said to illustrate the fundamentally human-like pattern of the Laetoli footprints. 3. Cranial views of pelves said to illustrate that the ilia of Lucy are bent around to provide lateral attachment for the lesser gluteal muscles.[46] 4. Anterior views of hip joints and pelves said to illustrate that the hip abductors of *A. afarensis* have a mechanical advantage surpassing that of the hip abductors in modern humans.[46] 5. Posterior views of left calcanei illustrating that the calcaneal corpus' inferolateral corner (arrow) is expanded and said to possess a clearly defined lateral plantar process.[47] 6. Transverse sections of right medial cuneiforms illustrating that in *A. afarensis* the distal articular surface faces more directly distally than it does in apes.[48] 7. Proximal articular surfaces of left hallucal metatarsals said to illustrate that this surface is virtually divided into two separate facets by a slight transverse ridge in both humans and *A. afarensis*.[48] 8. Medial views of right medial cuneiforms illustrating the human-like distal location of the "sub-bursal groove" (arrow) for the tendon of tibialis anterior.[48] 9. Outline tracings of midsagittally sectioned casts of the first and second metatarsal heads said to illustrate that they are inflated and angled dorsally in both humans and *A. afarensis*.[49] 10. Outline tracings of midsagittally sectioned casts of pedal proximal phalanges said to illustrate that in *A. afarensis* the proximal articular surfaces are more superiorly oriented than in apes[49] 11. Drawings of the femoral neck's cortical bone seen on transverse sections (superior to the top) illustrating that the superior cortical bone of the femoral neck is thin in humans and *A. afarensis*.[46]

uses values for Lucy's segment masses and moments of inertia that are substantially different from the estimates provided by Crompton and coworkers.[65]

Do Unto Others As They Have Done Unto You

Those of you familiar with the history of the dispute about the locomotor behavior of *A. afarensis* know that we did not respond to criticism of our work by turning the other cheek. We, and sometimes other authors, claimed to have found the following flaws in the works of Latimer, Lovejoy, and Ohman.

1. Bill Jungers and I[66] said that Ohman's[43] claim about the uniqueness of the univertebral articulation of the human first rib was untrue. Schmid[67] pointed out that Ohman's description of Lucy's first rib as having only one facet on its head was contradicted by Johanson and coworkers,[68] who said it had a distinct double facet separated by a central ridge. Schmid also noted that the Johanson and coworkers reported Lucy's clavicle as having a rounded superior surface presenting a roughened area for the attachment of the deltoid, whereas Ohman said it had the hominid condition of a deltoid attachment at the anterior edge of the bone. In the disagreements between Ohman and Johanson and coworkers, I do not know who is correct.

2. The calculation by Latimer and coworkers[44] that conjunct rotation of the tibia during flexion or extension movements of the ankle would have been minimal in Lucy directly contradicts the results reported by Christie,[4] which were based on manipulating the specimens.

3. Lovejoy's[46] assertion that the ilia of Lucy are bent around to provide lateral attachment for the lesser gluteal muscles to act as abductors (Fig. 2, part 3) is the opposite of what we[18] and Schmid[67] claim (Fig. 1, part 7).

4. The statement that the attachment points of the gluteus maximus and quadriceps femoris in Lucy indicate that they were as big as our own and similarly disposed[46] is unsupported by evidence.

5. Statements that an iliopsoas groove is present on Lucy's pelvis[46,68] are contrary to our observations.[18]

6. Lovejoy[46] stated that the greater outward flare of Lucy's ilia, coupled with a relatively long femoral neck, gave her abductors such a big moment arm that, despite the slightly greater interacetabular distance, they had a mechanical advantage surpassing our own (Fig. 2, part 4), resulting in reduced hip joint pressure. This was disproved by Jungers[25] and Ruff.[69] Indeed, Ruff's analysis showed that if Lucy had walked as modern humans do, she would be expected to have a relatively larger acetabulocristal buttress, larger femoral head, and greater resistance of the femoral shaft to mediolateral bending than do humans. She does not.

7. We have already published[70] some of our complaints regarding the analysis of the Hadar calcanei conducted by Latimer and Lovejoy.[47] We pointed out temporal inconsistencies in their descriptions of the lateral plantar process (it grew to more human proportions from early to later papers) and their failure to include the ape-like A.L. 333-37 specimen when calculating cross-sectional areas of the calcaneal tuber.

   There may also be a problem regarding their assessments of posterior talar facet curvatures in the fossil calcanei. The authors calculated the included angle of this facet to be 82 degrees for the A.L. 333-8 specimen (the lower the value of included angle, the flatter is the surface). Such a value is close to the mean of 78.5 degrees they report for humans and far from means they found in African apes (gorilla = 100 degrees, chimpanzee = 110 degrees). On the other hand, Deloi-son,[32] who calculated an undefined "index of curvature" of the same facet, found that the value in the fossil fell within the normal range of chimpanzees and outside that of modern humans.

Latimer and Lovejoy[47] stated that damage to the A.L. 333-55 calcaneus precluded reliable measurement of the included angle of its posterior talar facet, but they did offer an estimate of its radius of curvature equal to the value of 24.5 mm for A.L. 333-8 (the higher the value of radius of curvature, the flatter is the surface). Indeed, in A.L. 333-55, the facet is crossed by a longitudinal crack, but Latimer and associates[71] previously assured us that "owing to good apposition it is of no metric consequence." Using a cast of the specimen, I calculated the A.L. 333-55 posterior talar facet radius of curvature to be 16 mm and its included angle to be 96 degrees. Such values are concordant with Deloison's assessment of the better preserved A.L. 333-8 specimen.

8. The identification of the tibialis anterior "facet" on the Hadar medial cuneiform as being human-like in position and orientation[48] (Fig. 2, part 8) has been challenged by Deloison,[72] who found this structure to be so variable in both humans and chimpanzees as to preclude any conclusion about affinities of the fossil.

9. Latimer and Lovejoy[48] described the proximal articular facet of the A.L. 333-54 hallucal metatarsal as having indentations in both its medial and lateral edges (Fig. 2, part 7). They say this conformation was not found in their sample of African apes but is common in humans. Deloison[63] described the facet in chimpanzees as being bilaterally constricted, but that in humans as reniform. She concluded that the similarity is between the fossil and apes. Furthermore, she found both regions of the fossil's proximal articular surface to be concave, with radii of curvatures that match those in chimpanzees.[61]

10. The statement that in *A. afarensis* the proximal articular surfaces of the pedal proximal phalanges have the degree of superior orientation found in modern humans[48] (Fig. 2, part 10) has been shown to be incorrect by Duncan and coworkers,[53] whose quantitative analysis proved that the orientation in the fossils is intermediate between that in humans and African apes.

11. Duncan and colleagues[53] pointed out inaccuracies in the statement that the metatarsal heads of *A. afarensis* are angled dorsally as in humans, but not pongids[48] (Fig. 2, part 9). The same authors could not duplicate Latimer's and Lovejoy's results on metatarso-phalangeal joint excursion and suggested that the method used was unreliable.

12. Susman and I[23] disputed the statement that the thin superior cortical bone of the femoral neck in Hadar femora is a trait aligning them with humans and distinguishing them from arboreal primates[46] (Fig. 2, part 11). I have to admit that of all the traits said to align the fossil with humans and push it away from apes, this was the one that gave me the most concern that we might be wrong. I have always been impressed by Pauwels'[73] explanation of why humans have this trait. Nonetheless, not knowing the condition in apes, Randy and I determined to see what comparable sections through human and nonhuman primate femoral necks would show. We did an extremely cursory job, looking only at one specimen each of *Homo, P. troglodytes, P. paniscus, Gorilla, Symphalangus,* and *Ateles*. All we could say was that most of the nonhuman primates in our sample also had thinner cortical bone on the superior aspect of the femoral neck than on its inferior aspect. We didn't quantify our results, and I expected that had we done so humans would have been at the extreme of the primate range, joined there by the A.L. 128-1 proximal femur and probably some other fossil specimens of the same period. Indeed, my fears were justified, for a few years later Ohman and coworkers[74] seemed to have demonstrated precisely this point in their thorough quantitative comparison of humans and African apes. My only solace was the authors' concession that the trait no longer precluded arboreal behavior, but simply demonstrated that such behavior could only have been an insignificant component of the *A. afarensis* locomotor repertoire. Then along came a paper by Rafferty,[75] who extended the analysis of femoral neck structure to cercopithecoids and strepsirhines. She found the distribution of cortical bone in the femoral necks of these two groups, most species of which are predominantly arboreal, to be similar to that in humans.

It seems that apes and atelines are unusual in having a more even distribution of cortical bone around the femoral neck. Rafferty surmised that this more even distribution was linked to the less stereotyped locomotor behavior of a climber-clamberer. So one conclusion would have to be that *A. afarensis* was not a pongid-like or ate-line-like climber-clamberer. I feel comfortable with that view. I also believe that much is yet to be learned about what determines the distribution of cortical bone in the femoral neck. After all, radiographs of cerebral palsy patients, who walk with limited extension of the hip, appear to illustrate the same general pattern of femoral neck bone distribution as that found in people who walk normally[76] (Fig. 3).

IS THERE HOPE FOR RESOLUTION?

I imagine that the scenario of argument and counterargument has become tiresome to many noncombatants. What hope is there for resolving the debate on *A. afarensis* locomotion? Maybe the answer lies in some truly novel ideas and data that have emerged in the last several years.

New Ideas About Old *Afarensis* Material

Rak,[77] accepting the notion that the sagittal plane excursions of Lucy's limbs were the same as those in modern humans, proposed a difference between Lucy's and modern humans' manners of walking with regard to rotation of the pelvis around a vertical axis. He suggested that Lucy's wide pelvis and long femoral neck enabled her to have a human-like stride length without suffering an increase in vertical excursion of the center of mass that would otherwise occur because of her short lower limbs. According to Rak, an increase in vertical excursion of the center of mass would have brought about both an increased cost of locomotion and increased joint reaction forces.

I am concerned that the relationships among energy cost, vertical excursion of the center of mass, and pelvic rotation are not as simple as Rak suggests. While it is true that for modern humans faster walking speeds are associated with longer strides and greater vertical oscillations of the center of mass,[78] for any speed there is an optimal stride length that minimizes energy cost.[79,80] At shorter stride lengths there will be less vertical oscillation but greater energy expenditure. When walking normally at any speed, we could always force ourselves to rotate the pelvis more in order to decrease the extent of center-of-mass fall, but we do not do so.[78] I presume there is an energy cost associated with pelvic rotation and that adopting more than is customary would offset any savings afforded by a reduced vertical oscillation of the center of mass. Nevertheless, if Rak's idea is correct, it would certainly mean that Lucy's gait would look different from that of a modern human even to a casual observer, though in a way far different than we suggested.

Berge[81-83] attempted to reconstruct the lines of action of muscles about the hip joint in A.L. 288-1, in one case assuming a human-like morphology and in another an ape-like disposition. She concluded that the ape-like disposition would actually have enabled Lucy to be a better biped. However, she stated that because extensors of the thigh in A.L. 288-1 had relatively longer moment arms than do those of humans, these muscles would have been more powerful in their ability to move the hip than to stabilize it. Berge further concluded that stability at the hip and knee in the coronal plane required a sort of waddling gait with large axial rotatory movements of the pelvis and counter-rotations of the shoulders, entailing a greater energy cost. Finally, her estimates of muscle torques led Berge to conclude that *A. afarensis* had a greater ability than humans do to move their lower limbs in different spatial positions, thereby promoting arboreal capability.

I have already mentioned Ruff's[69] demonstration that Lucy lacked certain osteologic traits expected to be present had she walked as do modern humans. Ruff concluded that Lucy may have walked bipedally in a way that allowed her trunk center of gravity to lie closer to a vertical line through the support-side hip joint. He suggested this could be accomplished if she laterally flexed her trunk toward the support side and elevated her pelvis on the nonsupport side. He likened this to the gait of a human with bilaterally painful hip joints because such individuals and Lucy would both have the goal of reducing hip joint reaction force.

Actually, the citation Ruff offered in support of this analogy provides a somewhat erroneous analysis of the gait of patients with a painful hip. It is true that during stance phase on the painful side, lateral lurch of the trunk toward that side is apparent,[84,85] but the majority of such patients exhibit a descent, not an elevation, of the pelvis on the nonsupport side.[84] Contralateral pelvic elevation could only be effective in reducing support-side hip joint force if it were brought about using muscles of the trunk. Use of support-side lesser gluteal muscles to accomplish this elevation would actually cause an increase in the hip joint reaction force. In this regard it is interesting to note that Schmid's[67] interpretation of Lucy's iliac blade orientation emphasizes increase in leverage of lateral flexors of the trunk.

Ruff also says that lateral trunk flexion and contralateral pelvic elevation probably characterize chimpanzee bipedalism, an assertion confirmed by the work of Tardieu.[86] Ruff's conclusion that Lucy's bipedal walking was less energetically efficient than that of modern humans is consistent with the view that although Lucy was a facultative biped, she probably was not a long-distance traveler.

Recently Ruff and colleagues[87] have drawn attention to the fact that Lucy and several other australopithecines have very robust femoral shafts relative to femoral head size. They concluded that overall mechanical loading of the skeleton was increased in these ancient hominids to about the same level as in modern African apes. As I read such statements, I wonder how this analysis of cortical stress would have been affected had Ruff not assumed full extension of the thigh during the support phase. Maybe walking with a less than fully extended hip and knee would necessitate relatively robust femoral shafts, but I am not smart enough to solve this problem.

Speaking of walking with a less than completely extended hip and knee, Crompton and coworkers[65] claim that their mathematical simulations of Lucy's bipedalism, bolstered by preliminary experimental data on humans, show that bent-hip, bent-knee gait is mechanically ineffective and likely to produce a rapid, large rise in core body temperature. My own response[88] to these arguments is that although bent-hip, bent-knee gait is more energetically costly than normal human bipedal walking, the cost is not as large as might be imagined and would not be prohibitive in an animal that used its bipedalism primarily as a feeding adaptation.[30,52,89,90] My reading of the relevant physiological literature has convinced me that such a mode of locomotion would be no more likely to result in an increased body temperature than would any other activity of comparable energetic cost. It is also worth mentioning that Schmitt and colleagues[91,92] have gathered force-plate and accelerometer data showing that the energetic disadvantage of bent-hip, bent-knee walking might be compensated for by an advantage in terms of joint-force reduction.

Some interesting functional analyses relating to vertebral morphology have been published in the last few years. Abitbol[93] argued that if Lucy had walked in the completely upright manner of a modern human, the superior surface of her sacrum would have been inclined only 20° from vertical as compared to an average of 60° in modern humans. Such a near-vertical superior sacral surface would require a truly extraordinary amount of lumbar lordosis to bring the trunk upright, and would place Lucy at great risk of spondylolisthesis. Abitbol suggested that Lucy would have walked either with her pelvis tilted backward or her trunk tilted forward, or a combination of both. Sanders[94] has recently published a functional analysis of two *A. afarensis* lumbar vertebrae (both probably L3) and the superior articular facets of Lucy's sacrum. One of the *A. afarensis* lumbar vertebrae is dorsally wedged, indicating lumbar lordosis; the other is not.

The superior articular facets of the sacrum are relatively widely spaced, as in humans, and are relatively large, even larger than those of humans. Maybe such traits reflect a need to resist a relatively greater tendency toward spondylolisthesis.

Some fascinating new data on bony development in primates are quite relevant to an interpretation of *A. afarensis* locomotion. Responding to the notion that the curved fingers of *A. afarensis* might be primitive retentions that tell us little about actual use of the hand,[95] Paciulli[96] and Richmond[97,98] demonstrated a correlation between ontogenetic changes in phalangeal curvature and those in locomotor behavior for macaques, gibbons, chimpanzees, and gorillas. Richmond[98] concluded that "The sensitivity of phalangeal curvature to functional use in extant primates suggests that it faithfully reflects arboreal use in early hominids."

A second developmental study, this one on the distal femoral epiphysis of humans and apes, was undertaken by Christine Tardieu, no stranger to the debate on *A. afarensis* locomotion. Some of what she discovered runs counter to her own stated views. Tardieu observed that in juvenile humans the opposing surfaces of the distal femoral metaphysis and epiphysis are nearly flat, whereas in young apes these surfaces are characterized by interdigitating grooves and ridges. With respect to both characteristics, the immature Hadar femora match the human condition. Tardieu and Preuschoft[99] have interpreted the pongid state as being necessary for stabilization of the epiphysis during arboreal activities. If this is true, it is potent evidence against the practice of such activities by juvenile *A. afarensis*.

Tardieu[100] has also shown that the bony distal femoral epiphyses of human children between the ages of 10 and 12 years bear remarkable resemblances to the adult distal femora from Hadar in that they are mediolaterally wide, lack a pronounced lateral lip of the patellar groove, and have an almost circular lateral condyle. While Tardieu found no contradiction between these results and her longstanding view that *A. afarensis* was only a facultative biped, I consider the similarity in shape between the distal femur of a juvenile human and that of *A. afarensis* to be profoundly significant. If the shape of a juvenile distal femur is accurately reflected by its bony epiphysis, Tardieu has demonstrated that traits both she and I thought were essential for human-like bipedality are not so; they are absent in young humans, who are quite expert bipeds. This may indeed turn out to be the case, but in a more recent study Tardieu[101] has found that the cartilaginous distal femur of human fetuses is, in some cases, more similar in shape to that of an adult than are the juvenile bony epiphyses on which she previously reported. She recognizes the necessity of acquiring a growth series of cartilaginous epiphyses in order to resolve this issue.

New Fossils

Since our initial publications on *A. afarensis* locomotion, not only has additional postcranial material of this species been described, but there have been discoveries of other species, older, contemporaneous, and younger, that bear on the probability that *A. afarensis* was a partly arboreal, funny-walking biped.

Ardipithecus ramidus

The oldest of the australopithecines is *Ardipithecus ramidus*, dated to ~4.4 Myr. The first description of this species referred to portions of the humerus, radius, and ulna of a single individual.[102] The very preliminary description of these bones mainly served to convince me that the ulna lacked any features associated with knuckle-walking. Many people who are interested in the origins of bipedalism are keenly awaiting a more detailed presentation of the *A. ramidus* material. Meanwhile, we must content ourselves with a statement attributed to Tim White: "Let's just say *ramidus* had a type of locomotion unlike anything living today. If you want to find something that walked like it did, you might try the bar in Star Wars."[103]

Australopithecus anamensis

In 1994, Leakey and coworkers[104] combined ~4.1-Myr-old specimens from Kanapoi and Allia Bay, Kenya, to create the new australopithecine species, *A. anamensis*. The evidence that *A. anamensis* was bipedal is provided by certain features of proximal and distal ends of a tibia that is larger than any found at Hadar: the articular surface of the lateral condyle is concave, the lateral condyle is nearly as large as the medial condyle, and the lateral facet of the distal articular surface faces inferiorly. Leakey and colleagues pointed out that the Kanapoi humerus, known for many years, has often been seen as human-like. They did not mention that Feldesman's multivariate analysis[17] found it to be further removed from that of *Homo* than are the humeri of living apes, or that Hill and Ward[105] had found its morphology to be consonant with the general pattern in *Australopithecus*. A recent multivariate study by Lague and Jungers[106] also concluded that the Kanapoi humerus "is not much more 'human-like' than any of the other australopithecine fossils, despite prior conclusions to the contrary." Indeed, it clustered with the Hadar specimens in a group that was unique among hominoids but was somewhat more chimp-like than human-like.

Another postcranial specimen from Allia Bay is a large radius that was described prior to the naming of *A. anamensis* but now is attributed to it. Heinrich and colleagues[107] portrayed this specimen as a larger version of Lucy's radius. Its ape-like traits, including an eccentrically placed proximal articular fovea associated with a beveled margin of the radial head, a long radial neck, and a well-developed crest for insertion of the brachioradialis, were interpreted as being well-suited to arboreal activity. The specimen also shared some human-like traits with A.L. 288-1: a robust radial neck, a relatively straight shaft, and a dorsally convex and ventrally concave distal shaft. The large lunate facet on the distal articular surface, and curvatures of this surface, are similar to features of the radii of Asian apes and, according to Henrich and coworkers,[107] are also similar to the A.L. 288-1 radius. These characteristics were said to enhance flexibility in climbing.

More recent postcranial finds attributed to *A. anamensis* are a capitate and proximal manual phalanx from Allia Bay.[108] They also come from individuals comparable in size to, or larger than, the biggest Hadar individuals. The capitate is even more ape-like than that of *A. afarensis* in that it has a facet for the second metacarpal that faces directly laterally, as opposed to distolaterally. The proximal phalanx from the hand is said to have the same degree of curvature and strong markings for the fibrous digital flexor sheath as do the manual proximal phalanges from Hadar.

More of *A. afarensis*

In 1993, White and coworkers[109] described a ~3.4-Myr-old humerus from the Maka site in Ethiopia. They ascribed it to an adult *A. afarensis* male.

It is very robust, has a large deltoid tuberosity, an extremely well-developed supracondylar ridge, and human-like retroflexion. White and colleagues inferred that *A. afarensis* "retained a powerful upper limb, but an upper limb that lacked the key arboreal adaptation of great length." Jungers[110] replied with evidence that humans cannot be distinguished from African apes with regard to humerus length relative to body mass. White[111] then said that Jungers should have included orangutans and gibbons in his comparison, and that every other aspect of *A. afarensis* anatomy shows that it was not at home in the trees, so who cares about its humeral length.

Kimbel and coworkers[112] reported on further discoveries at Hadar: a partial upper limb skeleton including a complete left ulna, dated at ~3.0 Myr, and a humeral shaft dated at ~3.4 Myr. Both specimens were considered to be from males. The ulna lacks any trait that could be construed as adaptive for knuckle-walking, and in this regard resembles human ulnae. The humerus is similar in all regards to that from Maka. The authors used these specimens to estimate the ulna-length/humerus-length index for an *A. afarensis* male (~91%) and compared to this index that of Lucy (~92.5%). They noted that the resulting values are distinctly closer to those of chimpanzees ($\bar{x} = 95\%$) than to those of modern humans ($\bar{x} = 80\%$). This seems to provide convincing evidence that the upper limbs of *A. afarensis* were relatively much longer than those of humans.

Ward and coworkers[113] recently described a capitate, hamate, lunate, the distal end of a metacarpal, and the proximal end of a proximal pedal phalanx from a single individual (KNM-WT 22944) found at the ~3.5 Myr old South Turkwel site in Kenya. On the whole, the morphologies of these specimens were said to be very similar, but not identical, to those of *A. afarensis* from Hadar. The authors found no reason to assign them to a different species. Some aspects of the carpal bones are ape-like, others are human-like. The distal metacarpal is said to be most similar to a human third metacarpal. The hamate has a massive hamulus, even larger than that of the Hadar hamate. This feature was said to indicate a large transverse carpal ligament, a deep carpal tunnel, and/or a strong flexor carpi ulnaris. However, because Neandertals also have large hamate hamuli, readers are warned against concluding that powerful forearm musculature is indicative of a climbing adaptation. The distal projection of the hamulus was said to suggest that its flexor carpi ulnaris was functionally more like that of extant apes than that of humans. Ward and associates conclude that there are no obvious indicators in the South Turkwel hand of specialized adaptations for climbing or suspension. They described the proximal part of the South Turkwel pedal phalanx as having an articular surface for the metatarsal that faces somewhat dorsally, making it resemble that of humans more closely than that of great apes. According to Leakey and coworkers,[108] "The dorsally-oriented metacarpal facet on the pedal phalanx of KNM-WT 22944 suggests that this individual was adapted for habitual bipedal locomotion."

South African Australopithecus sp.

From Sterkfontein Member 2 (~3.5 Myr) come the four bones that comprise "Little Foot."[114] Clarke and Tobias described the talus and the tuberosity of the navicular as quite human-like. On the other hand, the navicular facets for the cuneiforms were said to be oriented as in apes, suggesting an abducted forefoot, and the medial cuneiform was said, in most respects, to be like that of an ape, forming a joint with the first metatarsal. That suggests a wide range of movement and a naturally abducted position of the hallux. The authors conclude that "It is becoming clear that *Australopithecus* was likely not an obligate terrestrial biped, but rather a facultative biped and climber." My joy at this discovery and its interpretation has been considerably lessened by, of all people, Randy Susman. He recently saw the original specimen and found the hallucal tarsometatarsal joint to be less ape-like than he had anticipated.

Australopithecus africanus

Berger and Tobias[115] have reported on proximal and distal tibial fragments from Sterkfontein Member 4 (~2.7 Myr). They describe the articular surface of the lateral tibial condyle as being extremely convex, and thus ape-like. A further resemblance to apes, and also to the Hadar proximal tibia, is the indication that the lateral meniscus had a single site of attachment anterior to the external tibial spine. Berger and Tobias also described ape-like attachment areas of the semimembranosus and tibialis posterior. While little of functional significance could be gleaned from the distal tibial fragment, its articular surface appears to have a posterior tilt and thereby is allied to those of living apes and Lucy. In summary, the authors found these specimens to be the most ape-like of any Plio-Pleistocene hominid tibia and, indeed, even more ape-like than the tibia of *A. afarensis*.

McHenry and Berger[116] analyzed new finds from Sterkfontein Member 4 using an approach similar to that used by Oxnard[117] to study previously known material from South Africa. After assigning all the post-cranial specimens to size categories, the authors found that 95% of those representing the upper limb were classified as medium or large, while 90% of those from the lower limb were classified as small. This strong

Figure 4. A depiction of *Australopithecus* making a life for itself on the African savanna. This was the commonly accepted view in the early 1970s.

Wikimedia Commons / Public Domain.

indication that *A. africanus* was characterized by distinctly ape-like interlimb proportions was supported by an analysis of the Stw 431 associated material, which showed that the size of its elbow joint surfaces relative to the SI body or acetabulum were comparable to those of apes and much larger than those of humans. Similar analyses on *A. afarensis* showed its intermediate position between apes and humans. McHenry and Berger also noted that the two associated skeletons attributed to *H. habilis* seem to have the same more ape-like interlimb proportions that characterize *A. africanus*. These authors conclude that because *A. afarensis* is craniodentally primitive as compared to both *A. africanus* and *H. habilis,* whereas its limb proportions are more human-like, the place of all these species in the human lineage is confused by extensive homoplasy. To me, their results also show that previous portrayals of *A. africanus* as having a fully human-like locomotor repertoire[118–120] should be viewed with the scepticism shown by Oxnard.[113,121–123]

Spoor and colleagues[124–126] offered a very different approach to understanding *A. africanus* locomotor behavior. They demonstrated that the posterior and anterior semicircular canals of humans are relatively larger than those of apes, whereas the lateral semicircular canal of humans is relatively smaller. Arguing that large vertical canals are probably an adaptation to human-like obligatory bipedalism, and finding that the three canals of *A. africanus* are of the same relative dimensions as those of apes, they concluded that this early hominid was probably a facultative biped, combining arboreal activities with a form of terrestrial bipedalism that lacked such complex movements as running and jumping.

Bouri Hata Hominids

Craniodental specimens assigned to the new taxon *A. garhi*[127] have been recovered from several different areas of the ~2.5 Myr old Hata beds, Bouri Formation, in the Ethiopian Middle Awash. In the same beds were found shafts of various long bones and a proximal pedal phalanx. Although the postcranial elements could not be conclusively assigned to *A. garhi,* they still are valuable indicators of hominid locomotor anatomy during this period. A number of the limb bone shafts are thought to come from a single individual and to enable calculation of reasonably accurate limb length proportions. Such calculations indicate that Bouri Hata hominids were distinguished from *A. afarensis* by relative femoral elongation resulting in a human-like humerofemoral index. On the other hand, they are said to share with *A. afarensis* a high brachial index. The Bouri Hata proximal pedal phalanx is said to be similar to that of *A. afarensis* in curvature.

Homo (Australopithecus?) Habilis

As the debate about the locomotor anatomy of *A. afarensis* was unfolding, Johanson and coworkers[128] published their discovery of the ~1.8-Myr-old O.H. 62 partial skeleton from Olduvai Gorge, attributing it to *Homo habilis* based on craniodental evidence. The associated bits and pieces of its humerus, radius, ulna, femur, and tibia were said to be very similar to Lucy's, with one notable exception: the humerofemoral index of O.H. 62 was estimated at ≥95 as compared to values of 85 for Lucy, 74 for human pygmies, and 98 for bonobos.[21] Korey[129] pointed out that the error associated with calculating a humerofemoral index from the reconstructed lengths of the O.H. 62 limb bones is so great that one cannot justifiably assert either that it was significantly greater than in Lucy or significantly less than in a common chimpanzee ($\bar{x} = 102$). Asfaw and colleagues[127] claim that any statement that the humerofemoral index is more primitive in O.H. 62 than in Lucy is erroneous because the length of the O.H. 62 femur cannot be accurately estimated. However, Hartwig-Scherer and Martin,[130] using a variety of other measurements on limb bones, confirmed that interlimb proportions of O.H. 62 are far more pongid-like than are those of *A. afarensis*.

Emanating from East Lake Turkana and dated at ~1.9 Myr is the KNM-ER 3735 specimen comprising parts of the skull and of both the upper and lower limbs.[131] The postcranial material is in poor condition, but those measurements that could be taken indicate an upper limb that was much bigger than the lower limb, nearly to the degree found in a chimpanzee. Features of the distal humerus and proximal radius indicate climbing abilities as marked as in *Pan*. Phalangeal fragments were said to belong to a hand capable of extremely powerful flexion. Leakey and colleagues did not definitively assign the specimen to a known species, but considered the possibility that it might be a male *H. habilis*. Clearly, they were uncomfortable with the idea that a creature of this anatomy could evolve into *H. erectus* during the 200 Kyr time span available.

If the O.H. 62 and KNM-ER 3735 partial skeletons are indeed attributable to *Homo,* they present a picture of locomotor anatomy that differs markedly from that of all others members of our genus. This was a major consideration in Wood and Col-lard's[132] decision to transfer *Homo habilis* to *Australopithecus habilis.* One is then tempted to view *A. habilis* as a more craniodentally advanced de-scendent of something like *A. africanus*.

Were the Hominids Predating *A. afarensis* Less Well Adapted to Terrestrial Bipedalism Than Were Lucy and Her Hadar Relatives?

The postcranial material of *A. ramidus* has not been described in sufficient detail for any conclusion to be reached about its locomotion. The tibia of *A. anamensis* seems very much like that of *A. afarensis,* suggesting a no more primitive kind of bipedalism. The upper limb material, while pointing to an arboreal adaptation, also seems to be little different from that of *A. afarensis.*

Do New Finds of A. afarensis or The Contemporaneous Sterkfontein Member 2 Australopithecus Sp. Reveal Anything New About the Locomotion of 3.0-3.5 Myr Old Hominids?

New finds of *A. afarensis,* largely because they show great humeral robusticity and long forearms, add support to any suggestion that it possessed an adaptively significant component of arboreality. The analysis of "Little Foot" by its discoverers led them to claim it came from a creature with a grasping hallux. My colleague Randy Susman doubts it is more apelike than the hallux of *A. afarensis,* which we and others have stated possessed a modicum of mobility.

What Do Younger Australopithecines Tell Us About A. afarensis Locomotion?

Perhaps the most interesting new insights into early hominid locomotion come from discoveries of material that postdate *A. afarensis.* By virtue of having an elongated lower limb, the ~2.5-Myr-old Bouri Hata hominid appears further advanced toward the evolution of human-like bipedalism than was *A. afarensis.* It remains to be determined whether its relatively long forearm is a functionally irrelevant retention of a primitive trait or signifies that adaptively significant arboreal behavior coexisted with relatively advanced bipedalism, as we proposed for *H. habilis.*[133] On the other hand, despite possessing rather obvious osteologic signs of terrestrial bipedalism, *A. africanus* and *A. habilis* seem more arboreally adapted than *A. afarensis.* Implied in the reclassification of *H. habilis* to *Australopithecus,*[127] and in the suggestion that *A. garhi* might be the ancestor of true early *Homo,*[110] is the possibility that among the descendants of *A. afarensis* is one species (*garhi*) that was evolving toward a more human-like locomotor adaptation and another (*africanus* → *habilis*) that was evolving away from one. But what is the likelihood of this scenario if *A. afarensis* itself was a fully terrestrial human-like biped?

CONCLUSION

In 1986, after the first wave of papers on *A. afarensis* locomotion had appeared, Henry McHenry[134] acknowledged that he could no longer hold to his decade-long belief that all the primitive characters of australopithecine postcranial anatomy were simply evolutionary baggage that had little to do with locomotion: "The Hadar postcranial material sample of *A. afarensis* make this hypothesis much less likely." In 1991, after the second wave of analyses appeared, McHenry[135] had not changed his mind: "The host of 'ape-like' traits seen in these early hominids probably implies that their bipedalism was kinematically and energetically different than modern humans and may imply that they were more efficient tree-climbers than are modern humans. This arborealism was different from ape-like tree climbing, however, because the hindlimb was specialized for bipedality...." Now, 25 years after Lucy's discovery, it remains my opinion that nothing has been discovered, no criticism offered, nor any analysis published that should cause rejection of McHenry's conclusions. Indeed, the majority of new information that has come to light points even more firmly to them.

In 1972, Time-Life Books portrayed *Australopithecus* as a human-like biped making a life for itself on the savanna of Africa (Fig. 4). Three years ago, National Geographic portrayed the very same creature feeding high in the trees of the dense forest (Fig. 5). While pictures in the popular press do not constitute evidence, they do reflect the fact that ever-increasing numbers of anthropologists are accepting arboreal behavior as an adaptively significant component of early australopithecine behavior.

I was never as certain about the nature of *A. afarensis* bipedalism as I was about its retained adaptations for movement in the trees. I am no more or less certain now. Whereas we suggested a form of bipedalism with less extension at the hip and knee than is characteristic of modern humans, others have proposed differences concerning axial rotation of the pelvis or lateral flexion of the trunk. Moreover, a significant number of people still hold to the view that early australopithecine bipedalism was fully human-like. I have often felt there is a bias in favor of viewing early hominid bipedalism as characterized by completely extended lower limbs because it is difficult for modern humans to walk with bent knees and hips. It seems inconceivable that such a manner of progression could last for more than the briefest of geologic times before evolving into our superior way of doing things. Returning to my simplistic analogy to cetacean evolution, I think if we were whales we would have great difficulty understanding how an ancestor could survive a million years while being such a poor swimmer. I have tried to overcome this bias. Along with others, I believe the bipedal adaptation first arose to improve access to food sources close to the ground, movement between such sources, or both.[30,52,89,90] Bipedalism probably persisted in this nascent but effective state for a million years, with no indication that it would be anything other than an evolutionary sidelight. Only later did some unknown event impel one of the creatures with this adaptation to abandon the trees more completely than any of its predecessors had done and become a tool-making hunter or tuber-gatherer.

This memoir is at its end. The siren calls of electrodes, strain gauges, and force plates beckon. For out of obscurity was I taken, and unto obscurity shall I return, at least until the *ramidus* material is made generally available and Randy walks into my office to proclaim that we are as well qualified as anyone to perform its comprehensive functional analysis.

ACKNOWLEDGMENTS

I am very grateful to Brigitte Demes, William Jungers, Susan Larson, and Randall Susman for their helpful comments on early versions of this paper. I am equally grateful to Henry McHenry, Bernard Wood, Richard Klein, Clark Howell, and one anonymous reviewer for comments made on the first submitted version of the manuscript. I thank Luci Betti-Nash for preparation of the illustrations. The research I and my Stony Brook colleagues conducted on the origins of hominid bipedalism has been supported by the National Science Foundation, most recently, by NSF Research Grant SBR9806291.

REFERENCES

1. Taieb M, Johanson DC, Coppens Y, Bonne-fille R, Kalb J. 1974. Découverte d'hominidés dans les séries Plio-Pléistocénes d'Hadar (Bassin de l'Awash; Afar, Éthiopie). CR Acad Sci Paris, Sér D, 279:735–738.

2. Taieb M, Johanson DC, Coppens Y. 1975. Expedition internationale de l'Afar, Ethiopie (3ᵉ campagne 1974); Découverte d'hominidés dans les séries Plio-Pléistocénes a Hadar. CR Acad Sci Paris, Sér D, 281:1297–1300.

3. Johanson DC, Lovejoy CO, Burstein AH, Heiple KG. 1976. Functional implications of the Afar knee joint. Am J Phys Anthropol 44:188.

4. Christie PW. 1977. Form and function of the Afar ankle. Am J Phys Anthropol 47:123.

5. Lovejoy CO. 1979. A reconstruction of the pelvis of AL 288 (Hadar Formation, Ethiopia). Am J Phys Anthropol 50:460.

6. Leakey MD, Hay RL. 1979. Pliocene footprints in the Laetoli Beds at Laetoli, northern Tanzania. Nature 278:317–323.

7. Lovejoy CO. 1980. Hominid origins: the role of bipedalism. Am J Phys Anthropol 52:250.

8. White TD. 1980. Evolutionary implications of Pliocene hominid footprints. Science 208:175–176.

9. Day MH, Wickens EH. 1980. Laetoli Pliocene hominid footprints and bipedalism. Nature 286: 385–387.

10. Senut B. 1978. Etude comparative des piliers de la palette humerale. Cahiers d'Anthropol (Paris) n° 3:1-8.

11. Senut B. 1980. New data on the humerus and its joints in Plio-pleistocene hominids. Coll Anthropol 4:87-94.

12. Tardieu C. 1979. Analyse morpho-fonctionelle de l'articulation de genou chez les primates. Application aux hominides fossiles. These, Universite Pierre et Marie Curie, Paris IV.

13. Tardieu C. 1979. Aspects bioméchaniques de l'articulation du genou chez les Primates. Bull Soc Anat Paris n° 4:66–86.

14. Tuttle RH. 1981. Evolution of hominid bipedalism and prehensile capabilities. Proc Trans R Soc Lond B 292:89–94.

15. Johanson DC, Edey MA. 1981. Lucy, the beginnings of humankind. New York: Simon & Schuster.

16. Jungers WL. 1982. Lucy's limbs: skeletal allometry and locomotion in *Australopithecus afarensis*. Nature 297:676-678.

17. Feldesman MR. 1982. Morphometric analysis of the distal humerus of some Cenozoic catarrhines: the Late Divergence hypothesis revisited. Am J Phys Anthropol 59:73–95.

18. Stern JT Jr, Susman RL. 1983. The locomotor anatomy of *Australopithecus afarensis*. Am J Phys Anthropol 60:279–317.

19. Sarmiento EE. 1987. Long bone torsions of the lower limb and its bearing upon the locomotor behavior of australopithecines. Am J Phys Anthropol 72:250.

20. Sarmiento EE. 1996. Quadrupedalism in the hominid lineage: 11 years after. Am J Phys Anthropol Suppl 22:208.

21. Jungers WL, Stern JT Jr. 1983. Body proportions, skeletal allometry and locomotion in the Hadar hominids: a reply to Wolpoff. J Hum Evol 12:673-684.

22. Susman RL, Stern JT Jr, Jungers WL. 1984. Arboreality and bipedality in the Hadar hominids. Folia Primatol 43:113-156.

23. Stern JT Jr, Susman RL. 1991. In: Coppens Y, Senut B, editors. Origine(s) de la bipédie chez les hominidés. Paris: CNRS, p 99–111.

24. Stern JT Jr, Larson SG. 1993. Electromyographic study of the obturator muscles in non-human primates: implications for interpreting the obturator externus groove of the femur. J Hum Evol 24:403–427.

25. Jungers WL. 1991. A pygmy perspective on body size and shape in *Australopithecus afarensis* (AL 288-1, "Lucy"). In: Coppens Y, Senut B, editors. Origine(s) de la bipédie chez les hominidés. Paris: CNRS, p 215–224.

26. Stern JT Jr, Susman RL. 1981. Electromyography of the gluteal muscles in *Hylobates, Pongo,* and *Pan:* implications for the evolution of hominid bipedality. Am J Phys Anthropol 55: 153-166.

27. Susman RL, Demes AB. 1994. Relative foot length in *Australopithecus afarensis* and its implications for bipedality. Am J Phys Anthropol Suppl18:192.

28. Marzke MW. 1983. Joint functions and grips of the *Australopithecus afarensis* hand, with special reference to the region of the capitate. J Hum Evol 12:197–211.

29. McHenry HM. 1983. The capitate of *Australopithecus afarensis* and *A. africanus*. Am J Phys Anthropol 62:187–198.

30. Rose MD. 1984. Food acquisition and the evolution of positional behaviour: the case of bipedalism. In: Chivers DJ, Wood BA, Bilsborough A, editors. Food acquisition and processing in primates. New York: Plenum Press. p 509–524.

31. Schmid P. 1983. Eine Rekonstruktion des Skelettes von A.L. 288-1 (Hadar) und deren Konsequenzen. Folia Primatol 40:283–306.

32. Deloison Y. 1985. Comparative study of calcanei of primates and *Pan-Australopithecus-Homo* relationship. In: Tobias PV, editor. Hominid evolution: past, present and future. New York: Alan R. Liss. p 143–147.

33. Wolpoff MH. 1983. Lucy's lower limbs: long enough for Lucy to be fully bipedal? Nature 304: 59–61.

34. Wolpoff MH. 1983. Lucy's little legs. J Hum Evol 12:443–453.

35. Berge C, Ponge J-F. 1983. Les characteristiques du bassin des australopitheques (*A. robustus, A. africanus* et *A. afarensis*), sont-elles liees a une bipedie de type humain? Bull Mem Soc Anthropol Paris, ser XIII, 10:335–354.

36. Berge C. 1984. Multivariate analysis of the pelvis for hominids and other extant primates: implications for the locomotion and systematics of the different species of australopithecines. J Hum Evol 13:555–562.

37. Berge C, Kazmierczak J-B. 1986. Effects of size and locomotor adaptations on the hominid pelvis: evaluation of australopithecine bipedality with a new multivariate method. Folia Primatol 46:185–204.

38. Tardieu C. 1983. L'articulation du genou, analyse morpho-fonctionelle chez les primates et les hominidés fossiles. Paris: CNRS.

39. Tardieu C. 1986. The knee joint in three primates: application to Plio-pleistocene hominids and evolutionary implications. In: Taub DM, King FA, editors. Current perspectives in primate biology. New York: Van Nostrand. p 182–192.

40. Tardieu C. 1986. Evolution of the knee intraarticular menisci in primates and some fossil hominids. In: Else JG, Lee PC, editors. Primate evolution, vol. 1. Cambridge: Cambridge University Press, p 183–190.

41. Latimer B. 1983. The anterior foot skeleton of *Australopithecus afarensis.* Am J Phys Anthropol 60:217.

42. Gomberg DN, Latimer B. 1984. Observations on the transverse tarsal joint of *A. afarensis,* and some comments on the interpretation of behaviour from morphology. Am J Phys Anthropol 63: 164.

43. Ohman JC. 1986. The first rib of hominoids. Am J Phys Anthropol 70:209–229.

44. Latimer B, Ohman JC, Lovejoy CO. 1987. Talocrural joint in African hominoids: implications for *Australopithecus afarensis.* Am J Phys Anthropol 74:155–175.

45. White TD, Suwa G. 1987. Hominid footprints at Laetoli: facts and interpretations. Am J Phys Anthropol 72:485–514.

46. Lovejoy CO. 1988. Evolution of human walking. Sci Am 259:118–125.

47. Latimer B, Lovejoy CO. 1989. The calcaneus of *Australopithecus afarensis* and its implications for the evolution of bipedality. Am J Phys Anthropol 78:369–386.

48. Latimer B, Lovejoy CO. 1990. Hallucal tarsometatarsal joint in *Australopithecus afarensis.* Am J Phys Anthropol 82:125–133.

49. Latimer B, Lovejoy CO. 1990. Metatarsophalangeal joints of *Australopithecus afarensis.* Am J Phys Anthropol 83:13–23.

50. Latimer B. 1991. Locomotor adaptations in *Australopithecus afarensis:* the issue of arboreality. In: Coppens Y, Senut B, editors. Origine(s) de la bipédie chez les hominidés. Paris: CNRS, p 169–176.

51. Thewissen JGM, Hussain ST, Arif M. 1994. Fossil evidence for the origin of aquatic locomotion in archaeocete whales. Science 263:210–212.

52. Rose MD. 1991. The process of bipedalization in hominids. In: Coppens Y, Senut B, editors. Origine(s) de la bipédie chez les hominidés. Paris: CNRS, p 37–48.

53. Duncan AS, Kappelman J, Shapiro LJ. 1994. Metatarsophalangeal joint function and positional behavior in *Australopithecus afarensis.* Am J Phys Anthropol 93:67–81.

54. Coffing KE. 1999. Paradigms and definitions in early hominid locomotion research. Am J Phys Anthropol Suppl 28: 109–110.

55. Mensforth RP, Latimer B, Senturia S. 1990. A review of the functional significance of the AL-288 axilloglenoid angle. Am J Phys Anthropol 81:267–268.

56. Inouye SE, Shea BT. 1997. What's your angle? size correction and bar-glenoid orientation in "Lucy" (A.L. 288–1). Int J Primatol 18:629–650.

57. Asfaw B. 1985. Proximal femur articulation in Pliocene hominids. Am J Phys Anthropol 68: 535–538.

58. MacLatchy LM. 1996. Another look at the australopithecine hip. J Hum Evol 31:455–476.

59. Tuttle RH. 1985. Ape footprints and Laetoli impressions: a response to the SUNY claims. In: Tobias PV, editor. Hominid evolution: past, present and future. New York: Alan R. Liss. p 129-133.

60. Elftman H, Manter J. 1935. Chimpanzee and human feet in bipedal walking. Am J Phys Anthropol 20:269-279.

61. Deloison Y. 1992. Empreintes de pas à Laetoli (Tanzanie). Leur apport à une meillure connaissance de la locomotion des Hominidés fossiles. CR Acad Sci Paris, Sér II, 315:103-109.

62. Garn SM, Hertzog KP, Poznanski AK, Nagy JM. 1972. Metacarpophalangeal length in the evaluation of skeletal malformation. Radiology 105:375-381.

63. Deloison Y. 1991. Les australopitheques marchaientils comme nous? In: Coppens Y, Senut B, editors. Origine(s) de la bipédie chez les hominidés. Paris: CNRS, p 177-186.

64. Kramer PA. 1999. Modelling the locomotor energetics of extinct hominids. J Exp Biol 202:2807-2818.

65. Crompton RH, Li Y, Wang W, Giinther M, Savage R. 1998. The mechanical effectiveness of erect and "bent-hip, bent knee" bipedal walking in *Australopithecus afarensis.* J Hum Evol 35:55-74.

66. Stern JT Jr, Jungers WL. 1990. The capitular joint of the first rib in primates: a re-evaluation of the proposed link to locomotion. Am J Phys Anthropol 82:431-439.

67. Schmid P. 1991. The trunk of the australopithecines. In: Coppens Y, Senut B, editors. Origine(s) de la bipédie chez les hominidés. Paris: CNRS, p 225-234.

68. Johanson DC, Lovejoy CO, Kimbel WH, White TD, Ward SC, Bush ME, Latimer BM, Coppens Y. 1982. Morphology of the Pliocene partial hominid skeleton (A.L. 288-1) from the Hadar Formation, Ethiopia. Am J Phys Anthropol 57:403-451.

69. Ruff C. 1998. Evolution of the hominid hip. In: Strasser E, Fleagle J, Rosenberger A, McHenry H, editors. Primate locomotion, recent advances. New York: Plenum Press, p 449-469.

70. Susman RL, Stern JT Jr. 1991. Locomotor behavior of early hominids: epistemology and fossil evidence. In: Coppens Y, Senut B, editors. Origine(s) de la bipédie chez les hominidés. Paris: CNRS, p 121-131.

71. Latimer BM, Lovejoy CO, Johanson DC, Coppens Y. 1982. Hominid tarsal, metatarsal, and phalangeal bones recovered from the Hadar Formation: 1974-1977 collections. Am J Phys Anthropol 57:701-719.

72. Deloison Y. 1992. Articulation cunéométa-tarsienne de l'hallux consideree comme un des elements determinants de la forme de locomotion a partir de son anatomie osseuse. Comparison entre l'australopitheque, l'homme et le chim-panze. CR Acad Sci Paris, Ser II, 314:1379-1385.

73. Pauwels F. 1958. Funktionnelle Anpassung durch Langenwachstum des Knochens. Verh Dtsch Orthop Ges, 45. Vers, p 34-56.

74. Ohman JC, Krochta TJ, Lovejoy CO, Mensforth RP, Latimer B. 1997. Cortical bone distribution in the femoral neck of hominoids: implications for the locomotion of *Australopithecus afarensis.* Am J Phys Anthropol 104:117-131.

75. Rafferty KL. 1998. Structural design of the femoral neck in primates. J Hum Evol 34:361-383.

76. Howard CB, Williams LA. 1984. A new radiological sign in the hips of cerebral palsy patients. Clin Radiol 35:317-319.

77. Rak Y. 1991. Lucy's pelvic anatomy: its role in bipedal gait. J Hum Evol 20:283–290.

78. Inman VT, Ralston HJ, Todd F. 1981. Human walking. Baltimore: Williams Wilkins.

79. Zarrugh MY, Radcliffe CW. 1978. Predicting metabolic cost of level walking. Eur J Appl Physiol 38:215–223.

80. Holt KG, Hamill J, Andres RO. 1991. Predicting the minimal energy costs of human walking. Med Sci Sports Exerc 23:491–498.

81. Berge C. 1991. Quelle est la signification fonctionelle du pelvis trés large de *Australopithecus afarensis* (AL 288–1)? In: Coppens Y, Senut B, editors. Origine(s) de la bipédie chez les hominidés. Paris: CNRS, p 113–119.

82. Berge C. 1993. L'évolution de la hanche et du pelvis des hominidés. Paris: CNRS.

83. Berge C. 1994. How did the australopithecines walk? A biomechanical study of the hip and thigh of *Australopithecus afarensis*. J Hum Evol 26:259–273.

84. Murray MP, Gore DR, Clarkson BH. 1971. Walking patterns of patients with unilateral hip pain due to osteo-arthritis and avascular necrosis. J Bone Jt Surg 53A:259–273.

85. Murray MP, Gore DR. 1981. Gait of patients with hip pain or loss of hip joint motion. In: Black J, Dumbleton JH, editors. Clinical biomechanics. A case history approach. New York: Churchill Livingstone, p 173–200.

86. Tardieu C. 1992. Le centre de gravité du corps et sa trajetoire pendant la marche. Évolution de la locomotion des hommes fossiles. Paris: CNRS.

87. Ruff CB, McHenry HM, Thackery JF. 1999. Cross-sectional morphology of the SK 82 and 97 proximal femora. Am J Phys Anthropol 109:509–529.

88. Stern JT Jr. 1999. The cost of bent-knee bent-hip bipedal gait. A reply to Crompton et al. J Hum Evol 36:567–570.

89. Hunt KD. 1994. The evolution of human bipedality: ecology and functional morphology. J Hum Evol 26:183–202.

90. Hunt KD. 1998. Ecological morphology of *Australopithecus afarensis:* traveling terrestrially, eating arboreally. In: Strasser E, Fleagle J, Rosenberger A, McHenry H, editors. Primate locomotion: recent advances. New York: Plenum Press, p 397–418.

91. Schmitt D, Stern JT Jr, Larson SG. 1996. Compliant gait in humans: implications for substrate reaction forces during australopithecine bipedalism. Am J Phys Anthropol Suppl 22:209.

92. Schmitt D, Lemelin P, Trueblood AC. 1999. Shock wave transmission through the human body during normal and compliant walking. Am J Phys Anthropol Suppl 28:243–244.

93. Abitbol MM. 1995. Lateral view of *Australopithecus afarensis:* primitive aspects of bipedal positional behavior in the earliest hominids. J Hum Evol 28:211–229.

94. Sanders WJ. 1998. Comparative morphometric study of the australopithecine vertebral series Stw-H8/H41. J Hum Evol 34:249–302.

95. Gebo DL. 1996. Climbing, brachiation, and terrestrial quadrupedalism: historical precursors of hominid bipedalism. Am J Phys Anthropol 101:55–92.

96. Paciulli LM. 1995. Ontogeny of phalangeal curvature and positional behavior in chimpanzees. Am J Phys Anthropol Suppl 20:165.

97. Richmond BG. 1997. Ontogeny of phalangeal curvature and locomotor behavior in lar gibbons. Am J Phys Anthropol Suppl 24:197.

98. Richmond BG. 1999. Reconstructing locomotor behavior in early hominids: evidence from primate development. J Hum Evol 36:A20.

99. Tardieu C, Preuschoft H. 1996. Ontogeny of the knee joint in humans, great apes and fossil hominids: pelvi-femoral relationships during postnatal growth in humans. Folia Primatol 66:68–81.

100. Tardieu C. 1998. Short adolescence in early hominids: infantile and adolescent growth of the human femur. Am J Phys Anthropol 107:163–178.

101. Tardieu C. 1999. Ontogeny and phylogeny of femoro-tibial characters in humans and hominid fossils: functional influence and genetic determinism. Am J Phys Anthropol 110:365–377.

102. White TD, Suwa G, Asfaw B. 1994. *Australopithecus ramidus,* a new species of early hominid from Aramis, Ethiopia. Nature 371:306–312.

103. Gore R. 1997. The first steps. Natl Geogr 191:72–99.

104. Leakey MG, Feibel CS, McDougall I, Walker A. 1995. New four-million-year-old hominid species from Kanapoi and Allia Bay, Kenya. Nature 376:565–571.

105. Hill A, Ward S. 1988. Origin of the Homini-dae; the record of African large hominoid evolution between 14 My and 4 My. Yearbk Phys Anthropol 31:49–83.

106. Lague MR, Jungers WL. 1996. Morphometric variation in Plio-Pleistocene hominid distal humeri. Am J Phys Anthropol 101:401–427.

107. Heinrich RE, Rose MD, Leakey RE, Walker AC. 1993. Hominid radius from the middle Pliocene of Lake Turkana, Kenya. Am J Phys Anthropol 92:139–148.

108. Leakey MG, Feibel CS, McDougall I, Ward C, Walker A. 1998. New specimens and confirmation of an early age for *Australopithecus anamensis.* Nature 393:62–66.

109. White TD, Suwa G, Hart WK, Walter RC, WoldeGabriel G, de Heinzelin J, Clark JD, Asfaw B, Vrba E. 1993. New discoveries of *Australopithecus* at Maka in Ethiopia. Nature 366:261–265.

110. Jungers WL. 1994. Ape and hominid limb length. Nature 369:194.

111. White TD. 1994. Ape and hominid limb length-White replies. Nature 369:194.

112. KimbelWH, Johanson DC, RakY. 1994. The first skull and other new discoveries of *Australopithecus afarensis* at Hadar, Ethiopia. Nature 368:449–451.

113. Ward CV, Leakey MG, Brown B, Brown F, Harris J, Walker A. 1999. South Turkwel: a new Pliocene site in Kenya. J Hum Evol 36:69–95.

114. Clarke RJ, Tobias PV. 1995. Sterkfontein Member 2 foot bones of the oldest South African hominid. Science 269:521–524.

115. Berger LR, Tobias PV. 1996. A chimpanzee-like tibia from Sterkfontein, South Africa and its implications for the interpretation of bipedalism in *Australopithecus africanus.* J Hum Evol 30: 343–348.

116. McHenry HM, Berger LR. 1998. Body proportions in *Australopithecus afarensis* and *A. africanus* and the origin of the genus *Homo.* J Hum Evol 35:1–22.

117. Oxnard CE. 1975. Uniqueness and diversity in human evolution: morphometric studies of australopithecines. Chicago: University of Chicago.

118. Lovejoy CO, Heiple KG, Burstein AH. 1973. The gait of *Australopithecus.* Am J Phys Anthropol 38:757–780.

119. Lovejoy CO. 1975. Biomechanical perspectives on the lower limb of early hominids. In: Tuttle RH, editor. Primate functional morphology and evolution. The Hague: Mouton, p 291–326.

120. Lovejoy CO. 1978. A biomechanical review of the locomotor diversity of early hominids. In: Jolly CJ, editor. Early hominids of Africa. New York: St. Martin's Press, p 403–429.

121. Lisowski FP, Albrecht GH, Oxnard CE. 1974. The form of the talus in some higher primates. Am J Phys Anthropol 41:191–216.

122. Oxnard CE, Lisowski FP. 1980. Functional articulation of some hominoid foot bones: implications for the Olduvai (Hominid 8) foot. Am J Phys Anthropol 52:107–117.

123. Oxnard CE. 1983. The order of man. A bio-mathematical anatomy of the primates. Hong Kong: Hong Kong University.

124. Spoor F. 1993. The comparative morphology and phylogeny of the human bony labyrinth. Utrecht: F. Spoor.

125. Spoor F, Wood B, Zonneveld F. 1994. Implications of early hominid labyrinthine morphology for evolution of human bipedal locomotion. Nature 369:645–648.

126. Spoor F, Wood B, Zonneveld F. 1996. Evidence for a link between human semicircular canal size and bipedal behaviour. J Hum Evol 30:183–187.

127. Asfaw B, White TD, Lovejoy O, Latimer B, Simpson S, Suwa G. 1999. *Australopithecus garhi*: a new species of early hominid from Ethiopia. Science 284:629–634.

128. Johanson DC, Masao FT, Eck GG, White TD, Walter RC, Kimbel WH, Asfaw B, Manega P, Ndessokia P, Suwa G. 1987. New partial skeleton of *Homo habilis* from Olduvai Gorge, Tanzania. Nature 327:205–209.

129. Korey KA. 1990. Deconstructing reconstruction: The OH 62 humerofemoral index. Am J Phys Anthropol 83:25–33.

130. Hartwig-Scherer S, Martin RD. 1991. Was "Lucy" more human than her "child"? Observations on early hominid postcranial skeletons. J Hum Evol 21:439–449.

131. Leakey RE, Walker AC, Ward CV, Grausz HM. 1989. A partial skeleton of a gracile hominid from the Upper Burgi Member, of the Koobi Fora Formation, East Lake Turkana, Kenya. In: Giacobini G, editor. Hominidae: Proceedings of the 2nd International Congress on Human Paleontology, Turin. Milan: Jaca, p 167–173.

132. Wood B, Collard M. 1999. The human genus. Science 284:65–71.

133. Susman RL, Stern JT Jr. 1982. Functional morphology of *Homo habilis*. Science 217:931–934.

134. McHenry HM. 1986. The first bipeds: a comparison of the *A. afarensis* and *A. africanus* postcranium and implications for the evolution of bipedalism. J Hum Evol 15:177–191.

135. McHenry HM. 1991. First steps? Analyses of the postcranium of early hominids. In: Coppens Y, Senut B, editors. Origine(s) de la bipédie chez les hominidés. Paris: CNRS, p 133–141.

Like other mammals, humans maintain a consistent body temperature. Thus, they are subject to Allen's and Bergmans's rules, and their body form and proportions reflect the latitude and environmental conditions in which they live. This relationship can be seen in both living humans and hominin fossils.

12. Climatic Adaptation and Hominid Evolution

The Thermoregulatory Imperative

By Christopher B. Ruff

S ince classical antiquity, it has been popular to ascribe morphological differences between human populations to climatic causes.[1] Ridgeway, in a 1908 address to the Anthropology Section of the British Association for the Advancement of Science, made what may have been the first systematic attempt to apply general climatic or zoological "laws" to humans.[2] Unfortunately, the text of Ridgeway's speech also illustrates in no uncertain terms how such environmental or geographical "determinism"[3] can be over-applied and misused for political or economic purposes. This same general issue has continued to haunt more recent scientific attempts to relate human body form to climatic factors.

In the early 1950s, an upsurge of interest in climatic adaptation among humans led to the publication of several major studies within just a few years.[4-8] This interest was probably stimulated by the greater world awareness brought about by World War II[9] and the human physiological studies carried out as part of the war effort,[10] as well as the evidence from biogeographical studies of nonhuman animals that had accumulated during preceding decades.[10-13] In any event, these new investigations of living humans set the stage for publication, in 1962, of Carleton Coon's *The Origin of Races*,[9] which still is the most

Christopher B. Ruff, "Climatic Adaptation and Hominid Evolution: The Thermoregulatory Imperative," *Evolutionary Anthropology*, vol. 2, no. 2, pp. 53–60. Copyright © 1993 by John Wiley & Sons, Inc. Reprinted with permission.

ambitious and controversial attempt to apply climatic "rules" to the interpretation of fossil hominids and human evolution. As in Ridgeway's address more than half a century earlier, the scientific validity of this application became confused with Coon's broader, and generally discredited, views of human racial origins and evolution.[14–16] Perhaps because of this negative association, consideration of hominid fossils in terms of climatic adaptation was relatively uncommon over the next two-and-a half decades, with some notable exceptions.[17–19]

During the past several years there has been a resurgence of interest in the effects of climate on hominid morphological variation and evolution.[20–25] This interest has been spurred, at least in part, by the discovery of new hominid fossil remains. For example, discovery of the Laetoli footprints and Hadar fossils during the 1970s confirmed the large time lag between the development of bipedalism and the increase in brain size in hominids and contributed to the development of Falk's thermoregulatory "radiator" theory of brain evolution in *Homo*.[21] The discovery in 1984 of the juvenile *Homo erectus* skeleton, KNM-WT 15000,[26] together with the discovery a decade earlier of the *Australopithecus afarensis.* A.L. 288-1 ("Lucy") skeleton,[27] demonstrated conclusively that general body morphology differed dramatically between early African *H. erectus* and *Australopithecus*. This has prompted exploration of possible thermoregulatory mechanisms that could have led to such variation in body shape and the implications of these mechanisms with regard to the ecology of early hominids.[22,25] The evidence, both theoretical and empirical, suggests that climatic adaptation was and is a pervasive factor in hominid evolution, influencing not only body form, but also other biological and behavioral characteristics, including brain size.

ECOGEOGRAPHICAL RULES

If one drops from the same height a piece of paper and another object having the same weight but a more compact geometry—say, a paperclip—the more compact object hits the ground first. The reason it does so is because its surface area is smaller, so that it offers less air resistance on the way down. The same general kind of principle underlies the so-called climatic, or ecogeographic "rules" relating variations in body form to climatic gradients. Changes in the size or geometry of a body can change markedly its ratio of surface area to mass (weight). This, in turn, affects temperature regulation: a large surface area promotes loss of heat through increased radiation, convection, and evaporation, whereas a small surface area promotes heat retention. (This general observation will be obvious to anyone who has sat down to breakfast and noticed how quickly waffles, with their increased surface area, cool down when compared to pancakes!).

Bergmann's and Allen's rules, named after the nineteenth-century scientists who first clearly formulated them in print,[28,29] define two aspects of the relationship between surface area and body mass. Bergmann's rule states that within a warm-blooded polytypic species (i.e., one that varies in morphology over its range), populations inhabiting colder regions tend to be larger than those in warmer regions. This is because, all else being equal, large body size in itself leads to a lower ratio of surface area to body mass. For example, the surface area of a sphere with a radius r equals $4\pi r^2$, while its volume equals $4/3\pi r^3$. Thus, the ratio of surface area to volume (equivalent to mass) is $1/(3r)$. The fact that r is in the denominator means that as r increases, the ratio of surface area to body mass decreases, just as a function of size increase.

Allen's rule states that under the same general conditions as those pertaining to Bergmann's rule, populations in colder regions are characterized by relatively shorter extremities (limbs, tails, ears, etc.) than those in warmer climates. Extremities, by their nature, are smaller than the body as a whole, as well as more drawn out and cylindrical, or flattened, which increases their surface area relative to their mass (as in the example

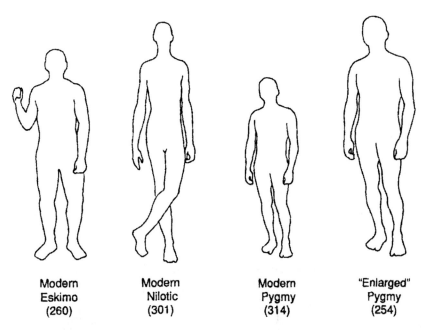

Figure 1. Body outlines of a modern Eskimo, Nilotic, and Pygmy drawn to their natural scale, and on the right, the Pygmy outline enlarged to the same height as the Nilotic. The approximate ratio of body surface area to body mass (cm²/kg) is given below each outline. Larger ratios are adaptive for higher temperatures, smaller ratios for lower temperatures. Surface areas were calculated using Dubois' formula based on body weight and stature.[64] Average body weights and statures for each group were obtained from the literature (see Ruff[22]). The body weight of the hypothetical "enlarged" Pygmy was obtained using prediction formulae based on bi-iliac breadth and stature (scaled up) that give excellent results in modern populations, including Pygmies.[38] Body outlines of the Eskimo and Nilotic were traced from a figure in Howells[32]; that of the Pygmy was traced from a photograph in Coon.[9]

of the paper and paperclip). The literature of the last several decades cites many examples of mammalian and bird species, as well as groups of closely related species, that vary in body size and shape across their ranges in accordance with these rules.[13,30,31] I have recently discussed some of the possible objections to the rules and how they can be reconciled with the available empirical evidence.[22]

BODY SHAPE IN LIVING HUMANS

As I noted earlier, anthropologists and others did not hesitate to apply such ecogeographical rules to humans, particularly by the middle of this century, when considerable metric data had been collected. Since that time, one of the most frequently illustrated comparisons of human body form to appear in biological anthropology texts and other publications is that between an African Nilotic and an arctic Eskimo. The left half of Figure 1 shows a tracing of what is, perhaps, the most well-known of these illustrations.[32] The ratio of approximate surface area to body mass of each body form is shown below its outline.

The body of the Nilotic, which is more linear than that of the Eskimo, clearly has a greater ratio of surface area to body mass. However, as Schreider[33] emphasized, it is misleading to limit the analysis to this particular contrast. The third outline in Figure 1 is that of a living Pygmy, drawn to the same scale as the Nilotic and Eskimo. Pygmies are not long and linear like Nilotics but, as Coon et al.[4] recognized, their small size also gives them a high surface area relative to their by mass.

On the right side of Figure 1 is another outline of the same Pygmy enlarged to the stature of the Nilotic. This makes the nonlinear, bulky build of the Pygmy even more obvious. At this size, his ratio of surface area to body mass falls below even that of the Eskimo. In fact, populations having this general body size and shape are rarely, if ever, found living in the tropics. Instead, as I have shown elsewhere,[22] taller tropical populations are also relatively more linear, because body breadth remains almost constant regardless of stature. For example, male Nuer, the tallest living Africans, average 48 cm taller, but less than 3 cm wider in body breadth than female Eastern Pygmies, the smallest living Africans. In these and other comparisons, the dimension I have used for body breadth is bi-iliac breadth, the maximum width across the iliac blades of the pelvis. This dimension has several advantages as a general measure of body breadth, including comparability between living and skeletal samples.[22]

Taking the analysis one step further, if the body is modeled as a cylinder, it can be shown theoretically that as long as the breadth of the cylinder (body) is held constant, stature can vary freely while still maintaining the same ratio of surface area to body mass.[22] Conversely, increasing the absolute breadth of the cylinder will always reduce the ratio of surface area to body mass, regardless of stature. Geographic variation among modern human populations fits the theoretical model well: not only do populations living in the same climatic zone have similar body breadths, regardless of stature, but populations living

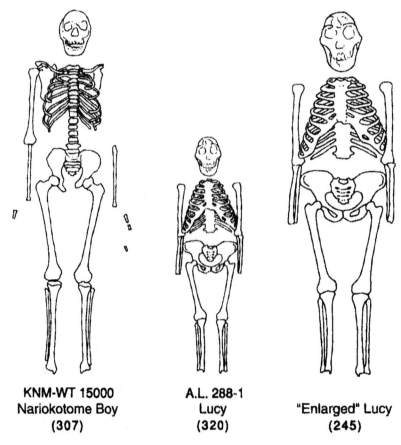

KNM-WT 15000
Nariokotome Boy
(307)

A.L. 288-1
Lucy
(320)

"Enlarged" Lucy
(245)

Figure 2. Tracings of the skeletons of KNM-WT 15000, an 11- to 12-year-old male *Homo erectus*, and A.L. 288-1 ("Lucy"), an adult female *Australopithecus afarensis*. The outline on the right is the hypothetical form of A.L. 288-1 if it were enlarged to the same height as KNM-WT 15000. Approximate ratios of surface area to body mass are given below each outline. Surface area was calculated from stature and body weight as described in the legend for Figure 1. The stature and body weight of KNM-WT 15000 were taken from Ruff and Walker.[38] The stature of A.L. 288-1 was taken from Jungers[65] and the body weight from McHenry.[66] Body weight of the hypothetical "enlarged" A.L. 288-1 was obtained by scaling up bi-iliac breadth and stature and using the prediction equations given in Ruff and Walker[38] corrected for greater ellipticity of the pelvis in A.L. 288-1. Both outlines were traced from photographs in Simons.[67] The reconstruction of A.L. 288-1 was originally done by Schmid.[68] The tracing of KNM-WT 15000 is of the actual skeletal elements recovered, without major reconstruction, whereas about half of the A.L. 288-1 skeleton shown was reconstructed using mirror imaging.

in cold climates have, on average, absolutely wider bodies than do those in the tropics, regardless of variation in stature. In fact, the correlation between latitude and absolute body breadth in a large number of modern populations is better than 0.90. The partial correlation between absolute body breadth and latitude, holding stature constant, is about the same.[22] Nutritional factors are unlikely to explain this geographic variation (see box).

BODY SHAPE IN EARLIER HOMINIDS

Because it is so rare in paleoanthropology that enough of a single skeleton is recovered to allow any certainty in the reconstruction of the individual's body size and shape, such reconstructions can vary widely. For example, robust australopithecines were previously thought to weigh about 70 to 90 kg.[34] Now, based on new skeletal material and new methods of analysis,[35] they are believed to have been only about half as large.

Over the past two decades, though, two extraordinary partial skeletons of earlier (pre-sapiens) hominids have been discovered that allow fairly confident assessment of their body sizes and proportions. A.L. 288-1 ("Lucy"), an adult female *Australopithecus afarensis* from Hadar, Ethiopia has been dated to about 3 million

---

Dietary Factors

It is well known that nutritional differences can have profound effects on body size and shape. Indeed, it has been suggested that these differences could explain in large or small measure, the ecogeographic trends in body morphology observed among humans.[57,58] However, this explanation seems unlikely, at least regarding the major differences in body shape examined here. Although good nutrition leads to increases in height, it does not lead to increases in body breadth or, at least, breadth of the skeleton. Studies of secular trends among Japanese living in Hawaii[59] and graduates of Harvard University[60] showed significant gains in stature, but no change or even a slight decrease in bi-iliac (maximum pelvic) breadth. The same trends can be inferred for Japanese living in Japan[61] and Israeli immigrants.[62] Thus, the strong ecogeographic clines in absolute bi-iliac breadth observed among modern humans, as well as earlier hominids,[22] are not likely to be the result of nutritional variation.

In contrast, some relative proportions of limb to trunk length may be influenced by nutrition. The secular trend toward an increase in stature among both Japanese and Norwegians during the twentieth century is almost entirely a result of increases in lower limb length. Thus, the ratio of lower limb to trunk length has also increased significantly through time in these populations.[63] However, this cannot explain the more dramatic differences between the relative limb lengths of populations in modern high-latitude and tropical areas. If better nutrition and other living conditions that lead to "optimal" growth also lead to relatively long legs, then it would be logical to expect that most inhabitants of low-latitude developing countries would have relatively short legs. In fact, the opposite is actually observed.

It may make good evolutionary sense for certain physical characteristics to be relatively immune to nutritional influences, since such influences are likely to be short-term relative to climatic changes. Changes in stature do not affect the ratio of body surface area to body mass—a key factor in temperature regulation—as long as body breadth remains constant. Similarly, long limbs are always adaptive for dissipating heat. Thus, in a hot climate, the maintenance of a narrow body with long arms and legs, and in a cold climate, the maintenance of a wide body with short arms and legs may be strongly genetically determined or, at least, constrained within limits in both early and living hominids.

years ago[27,36] and KNM-WT 15000, an 11 to 12-year-old male *Homo erectus* from West Turkana, Kenya, is dated to about 1.5 million years ago.[26,37]

The skeletal outlines of these two individuals are shown in Figure 2. In the middle of the figure, A.L. 288-1 is depicted at actual size relative to KNM-WT 15000 and, on the right, expanded to the same height as KNM-WT 15000. What is most obvious on first comparison of these outlines is the tremendously greater stature of KNM-WT 15000. This difference is especially striking when one realizes that he was only 11 to 12 years old at the time of his death and would probably have grown another 15 to 20% by adulthood, perhaps reaching a height of about 185 cm (6 feet, 1 inch).[38] However, his body (bi-iliac) breadth, after reconstruction of his pelvis, is actually less than that of A.L. 288-1. Even at adulthood, his body breadth probably would have been only marginally greater than that of A.L. 288-1, even though he would have been about 78 cm (31 inches) taller.[22] Thus, KNMWT 15000 was not only much taller, but also much more linear than A.L. 288-1.

The estimated ratio of surface area to body mass for both fossils is similar to that prevailing among living tropical populations (compare Figs. 1 and 2). In contrast, if A.L. 288-1 is expanded to the same height as KNM-WT 15000, but her body proportions are maintained (Fig. 2, right), the estimated ratio of surface area to body mass falls well below the range for modern tropical populations. This is similar to what we saw when the hypothetical Pygmy was enlarged to the stature of a Nilotic (Fig. 1). As discussed earlier, this body morphology is maladaptive for tropical climates.

Less complete hominid fossils support the same general contrast in body shape between small early australopithecines and larger, later *Homo*. These include the *Australopithecus africanus* STS 14, which was about the same size and shape as A.L. 288-1, as well as several other early *Homo* individuals.[22,38] The average estimated stature of six African *Homo erectus* individuals dated to between 1.7 and 0.7 million years ago is 170 cm, tall even by modern standards.[38] Available pelvic remains of other early *Homo* are similar to the pelvis of KNM-WT 15000, suggesting that they also had relatively narrow body breadths.

All of this strongly suggests the presence of similar thermoregulatory constraints on the body shape of earlier hominids and modern humans. With an increase in body size from early *Australopithecus* to *Homo erectus,* the same body shape could not be retained along with a sufficiently high ratio of surface area to body mass. Thus, populations of large early *Homo* living in the tropics necessarily developed relatively linear bodies, despite the fact that a wider, australopithecine-like body would have had definite advantages, including easier delivery of a large-headed baby and more efficient balancing of the body over the hip joint during walking. In some ways the final body form of *Homo erectus* can be viewed as a compromise between these various factors.[22]

Ecological Implications

It is interesting and instructive that all present-day populations exhibiting the extreme linearity of body build illustrated by the Nilotic in Figure 1 inhabit not only hot environments, but also relatively open, dry environments, such as savannah grasslands.[39] As Wheeler has demonstrated theoretically,[25] a tall linear body is a distinct advantage when moving about in the open during the day. Relative to its mass, such a body leads to less heat gain from the sun, particularly near mid-day, and greater convective heat loss from the body, particularly in the morning and late afternoon. In contrast, in a closed, forested environment with little direct sunlight and little air movement, this kind of physique loses these advantages. In addition, the usefulness of a relatively large surface area for evaporative cooling by sweating is decreased in a humid environment. Thus, given the fact that heat production is related to body size, the best way to avoid over-heating under such conditions may be to limit body size itself. This is one interpretation of why present-day Pygmies, whether in Africa or elsewhere, are universally found in rainforest environments.[40,41]

These considerations make it likely that African *Homo erectus* was limited in distribution to relatively open, at least semi-arid environments, for these are where its physique would have been most adaptive. Smaller hominids, including *Australopithecus*, could have inhabited either closed and wet or open and dry environments. However, given the foregoing considerations as well as factors such as their relatively small stride length and difficulty in covering long distances on foot,[42] it seems most likely that they were limited to relatively closed, wet environments. This scenario of a shift from a more closed, wet to a more open, dry environment from *Australopithecus* to *Homo erectus* is consistent with evidence from other parts of the skeleton, such as the nasal region.[20] It may also have implications regarding these hominids' food procurement behaviors.[43–45]

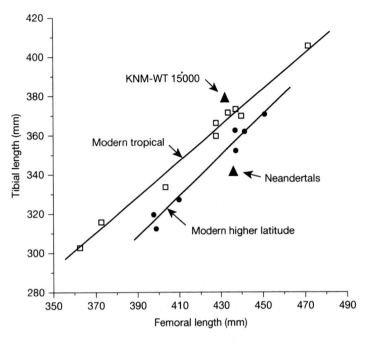

Figure 3. Tibial length versus femoral length in some modern populations and fossil specimens. Least squares regression lines are drawn through modern tropical and high-latitude samples (see text for details). Modern data points are population means; the Neandertal data point, based on the mean paired lengths of nine individuals, was obtained from Trinkaus[17]; all data combined sex. Lengths for KNM-WT 15000 are from Ruff and Walker.[38] Modern data are from Trinkaus[17] and Schultz,[69] Wolpoff personal communication, and my own measurements, converted, when necessary, to maximum lengths as described by Ruff and Walker.[38]

Later Hominids

We know that *Homo erectus* spread from Africa to other areas of the world more than one million years ago but, unfortunately, skeletal remains from the great majority of this period are so scanty that we have little idea of the body size and shape that characterized these populations. It is not until archaic *Homo sapiens* of the past 100,000 years that we begin to have enough evidence to reconstruct general body proportions.

The adult male Kebara 2 specimen from Israel, dated to about 60,000 years ago[46,47] is the only Neandertal pelvis that can be completely reconstructed, with mirror imaging of its right and left sides. The bi-iliac breadth of this specimen is very wide, more than 5 cm larger than either A.L. 288-1 or KNM-WT 15000 extrapolated to adult size.[22] In fact, this body breadth is at the extreme range of variation for modern humans. In both size and body proportions, the Kebara 2 individual was similar to a modern-day Eskimo, having an estimated ratio of surface area to body mass of 247 cm²/kg (compare with Fig. 1).

The Kebara remains are consistent with those of other Neandertals, including "Classic" Neandertals such as La Chapelle-aux-Saints 1, indicating a relatively wide body coupled with at least moderately large size.[48] As noted earlier, this body morphology, which among modern humans is always associated with cold environments, lends strong support to the view of Neandertals as "cold adapted."[9] It also indirectly supports the position that Neandertals originated and developed in higher latitudes, but made periodic incursions into more temperate regions such as the Middle East.[49] Interestingly, human populations directly following Neandertals in Europe and more "modern" populations interspersed in time with Neandertals in the Middle East are not characterized by these body proportions but, instead, they have moderate to linear forms.[48] This supports the concept of a more equatorial origin for these populations with subsequent north-ward migration into Europe, albeit with some possibly significant gene flow with at least some resident earlier "archaic" populations (i.e., Neandertals).[50]

LIMB PROPORTIONS

Another morphological characteristic of modern humans that has been shown to be strongly correlated with climate is relative limb length. In accordance with Allen's rule, populations inhabiting warmer climates have relatively long limbs, whereas those in colder climates have relatively short limbs. This has been demonstrated in living humans in a variety of ways, including limb length over body weight, arm span over stature, trunk length over stature, and lower limb length over trunk length.[33,51,52] The difference between the limb proportions of Africans and Europeans, at least, can-not be explained on the basis of nutrition[22] (see box).

Unfortunately, it is extremely difficult to quantify this proportional difference in skeletal remains, particularly given the incomplete remains characteristic of the vast majority of fossil hominids. Even A.L. 288-1 preserves only a few vertebrae and no complete tibiae, making both trunk length and lower limb length difficult to assess precisely. KNM-WT 15000 preserves more of these elements. However, because he is a juvenile, the epiphyses, or endplates of his vertebral bodies, had not yet fused, making it difficult to estimate his trunk length.

However, for several reasons which I have discussed elsewhere,[38] it is reasonable to use the ratio of the distal (lower) to proximal (upper) long bone segment of each limb to evaluate the length of the limb relative to the body or trunk. These crural (lower limb) or brachial (upper limb) ratios have long been noted to show the same geographic variability as limb length to body size indices, with high ratios occurring among tropical populations and low ratios among temperate to arctic populations.[17]

Another, more statistically valid way to compare the relative lengths of distal to proximal limb segments is to regress the length of one element against that of the other. This has been done in Figure 3 for the tibia against the femur of modern humans, KNM-WT 15000, and Neandertals. The modern humans have been divided into a tropical group (native Africans, Australian aborigines, and Melanesians) and a higher latitude group (Europeans, American Whites, and Eskimos). The tropical group clearly has a relatively longer tibia than the higher latitude group. Furthermore, KNM-WT 15000 falls above the modern tropical line, indicating a very high ratio of tibia length to femur length. I have shown elsewhere that the immaturity of KNM-WT 15000 should not affect this particular comparison.[38] Neandertals, in contrast, have relatively short tibiae, falling below the modern higher latitude populations. (A.L. 288-1 could not be included in this analysis because her one preserved tibia is missing a significant portion of its shaft.)

Thus, where it is possible to evaluate limb length proportions, earlier hominids that lived in hot climates (KNM-WT 15000) are found to have hyper-tropical proportions, whereas those that lived in colder climates (Neandertals) have hyper-arctic proportions. This is similar to what I found regarding the proportions of body breadth and height: KNM-WT 15000 is extremely linear relative to modern humans and Kebara 2 is extremely stocky.[22] These results are not too surprising, for it can be expected that cultural buffering against climatic stress would have been less effective in earlier hominids than in modern humans. In other words, biological adaptation to climate in earlier hominids was probably more important than it is today.

BROAD IMPLICATIONS

The finding that the body form of earlier hominids, like that of modern humans, appears to follow eco-geographical climatic rules, suggests various corollaries. First, it probably is not appropriate to characterize a species as having a single "typical or "average" body form, if that species spans a wide geographic range. This applies to both *Homo erectus* and *Homo sapiens,* whose remains have been found from tropical to at least cold temperate climatic conditions. In this regard, it is interesting that the *Homo erectus* fossils from Zhoukoudian, China, indicate a shorter stature than those of *Homo erectus* from Africa, including KNM-WT 15000 and others.[38]

Second, thermoregulatory factors should be considered when interpreting variation in body form among fossil hominids. For example, the body forms of A.L. 288-1 and KNM-WT 15000, although strikingly different in many ways (Fig. 2), are similar in terms of body heat regulation. Some observed differences between the pelves of taller and shorter australopithecines[34] may also be the result, at least in part, of thermoregulatory constraints on body breadth.

Third, when deriving estimates of stature or body weight from fragmentary fossil hominid remains, these systematic differences in body proportions should be taken into account. For example, stature estimates for KNM-WT 15000 based on his long bone lengths should obviously take into account his relatively long limbs. Thus, European-based formulae make him too tall, while the most reasonable estimates of his stature are derived from modern African populations.[38]

I emphasize the point that this general recommendation is not based on any special "racial" or "ethnic" affiliation between these modern groups and African *Homo erectus* (contra Feldesman, Kleckner, and Lundy[53]). Rather, it is based on a thermoregulatory similarity resulting from these groups' similar climatic environment, which is shared, for example, by such distantly related modern groups as Australian aborigines.[54] In fact, this is precisely the problem that earlier biological anthropologists encountered when they attempted to interpret morphological variation in broad racial terms. The patterning of geographic variation in morphological features among living and fossil hominids will depend on the particular environmental clines relevant to those features. In other words, the study of morphological variation and its significance, at least for those characteristics that are easily modified by the environment, should be couched in physiological rather than taxonomic terms.

Finally, thermoregulatory constraints on general body shape may have had even wider significance during human evolution. If body breadth was constrained during the increase in body size from *Australopithecus to Homo erectus,* this would also have constrained the size of the pelvic outlet for birth. Based on the obstetric dimensions of the KNM-WT 15000 pelvis extrapolated to the size of an adult female of his population and on his cranial capacity, it seems likely that this individual was much more similar to modern humans than to apes with regard to his degree of development at birth and his subsequent pattern of brain growth.[55] That is, he would have been born with a relatively small, undeveloped brain and in a helpless state, a condition referred to as secondarily altricial. In contrast, australopithecines probably did not follow this growth pattern, but were more similar to great apes.[56] This difference may have many broad implications regarding postnatal infant care, social organization, and cultural complexity in early *Homo.*

It is highly likely that the shape of the locomotor skeleton—i.e., the bones of the lower limb—was directly influenced by the relative narrowing of the body in *Homo erectus.* In particular, it has long been noted that the femur of many *Homo erectus* fossils has a highly distinctive shape, one that seems to indicate relatively large bending forces in one plane. These forces may be a natural consequence of the restructuring of the pelvis that occurred with the increase in the body size of early *Homo* and the attendant changes in muscle positioning and action about the hip joint.[22] Currently I am further examining this issue by measuring osteological samples of modern East Africans, who share the same general linearity of body shape. In collaboration with others, I am also contrasting these results with those obtained for modern humans of very different body shape (e.g., Eskimos and Aleuts). It is only by studying such natural variability among modern human populations within a physiological framework that we will better understand the significance of morphological variation in earlier hominids.

ACKNOWLEDGMENTS

I thank Alan Walker and Erik Trinkaus for their continuing collaboration on the projects described herein, the National Science Foundation for supporting this research and Elaine Kasmer for drawing Figure 2.

REFERENCES

1. Kennedy KAR (1976) *Human Variation in Space and Time.* Dubuque: Wm. C. Brown.
2. Ridgeway W (1908) The application of zoological laws to man. Brit Assoc Adv Sci, Trans Section H, Anthropology: 832–847.
3. Harris M (1968) *The Rise of Anthropological Theory.* New York: Thomas Y Crowell.
4. Coon CS, Garn SM, Birdsell JB (1950) *Races. A Study of the Problems of Race Formation in Man.* Springfield: Thomas.
5. Schneider E (1950) Geographical distribution of the body-weight/body-surface ratio. Nature *165:*286.
6. Schreider E (1951) Anatomical factors of body-heat regulation. Nature *167:*823–824.
7. Roberts DF (1953) Body weight, race and culture. Am J Phys Anthropol *11:*533–558.
8. Newman MT (1953) The applications of ecological rules to the racial anthropology of the aboriginal new world. Am Anthropol *55:*311–327.
9. Coon CS (1962) *The Origin of Races.* New York: Alfred A. Knopf.
10. Newburgh LH (eds) (1949) *Physiology of Heat Regulation and the Science of Clothing.* Philadelphia: W.B. Saunders.
11. Rensch B (1936) Studien uber klimatische parallelitat der merkmalauspragung bei vogeln und saugern. Arch Naturg *5:*317–363.
12. Mayr E (1942) *Systematics and the Origin of Species.* New York: Columbia University Press.
13. Hesse R, Allee WC, Schmidt KP (1951) *Ecological Animal Geography.* New York: John Wiley and Sons.
14. Dobzhansky T (1963) Possibility that *Homo sapiens* evolved independently 5 times is vanishingly small. Sci Am *208:*169–172.
15. Montagu A (1963) What is remarkable about varieties of man is likenesses, not differences. Cun Anthropol *4:*361–363.
16. Washburn SL (1963) The study of race. Am Anthropol *65:*521–531.
17. Trinkaus E (1981) Neanderthal limb proportions and cold adaptation. In Stringer CB (ed), *Aspects of Human Evolution,* pp 187–224. London: Taylor and Francis.
18. Beals KL, Smith CL, Dodd SM (1983) Climate and the evolution of brachycephalization. Am J Phys Anthropol *62:*425–437.
19. Beals KL, Smith CL, Dodd SM (1984) Brain size, cranial morphology, climate, and time machines. Curt Anthropol *25:*301–330.

20. Franciscus RG, Trinkaus E (1988) Nasal morphology and the emergence of *Homo erectus*. Am J Phys Anthropol *75*:517–527.

21. Falk D (1990) Brain evolution in *Homo:* The "radiator" theory. Behav Brain Sci *13*:333–381.

22. Ruff CB (1991) Climate, body size and body shape in hominid evolution. J Hum Evol *21*:81–105.

23. Wheeler PE (1991) The thermoregulatory advantages of hominid bipedalism in open equatorial environments: The contribution of increased convective heat loss and cutaneous evaporative cooling. J Hum Evol *21*:107–115.

24. Wheeler PE (1992) The thermoregulatory advantages of large body size for hominids foraging in savannah environments. J Hum Evol *23*:351–362.

25. Wheeler PE (1993) The influence of stature and body form on hominid energy and water budgets: A comparison of *Australopithecus and early Homo* physiques. J Hum Evol *24*:13–28.

26. Brown F, Harris J, Leakey R, Walker A (1985) Early *Homo erectus* skeleton from West Lake Turkana, Kenya. Nature *316*:788–792.

27. Johanson DC, Lovejoy CO, Kimbel WH, White TD, Ward SC, Bush ME, Latimer BM, Coppens Y (1982) Morphology of the Pliocene partial hominid skeleton (Al. 288-1) from the Hadar formation, Ethiopia. Am J Phys Anthropol *57*:403–451.

28. Bergmann C (1847) Uber die verhaltniesse der Warmeokonomie der thiere zu ihrer grosse. Gottingen Studien *1*:595–708.

29. Allen JA (1877) The influence of physical conditions on the genesis of species. Rad Rev *1*:108–140.

30. Hamilton TH (1961) The adaptive significances of intraspecific trends of variation in wing length and body size among bird species. Evolution *15*:180–195.

31. Mayr E (1963) *Animal Species and Evolution.* Cambridge: Harvard University Press.

32. Howells WW (1960) The distribution of man. Sci Am *203*:112–127.

33. Schreider E (1964) Ecological rules, body-heat regulation, and human evolution. Evolution *18*:1–9.

34. Robinson JT (1972) Early Hominid Posture and Locomotion. Chicago: University Chicago Press.

35. McHenry HM (1992) How big were early hominids? Evolutionary Anthropol *1*:15–20.

36. Sarna-Wojcicki AM, Meyer CE, Roth PH, Brown FH (1985) Ages of tuff beds at East African early hominid sites and sediments in the Gulf of Aden. Nature *313*:306–308.

37. Brown FH, McDougall I (1993) Geological setting and age. In Walker A, Leakey RE (eds), *The Nariokotome Homo erectus Skeleton,* pp 9–20. Cambridge: Harvard University Press.

38. Ruff CB, Walker A (1993) Body size and by shape. In Walker A, Leakey RE (eds), *The Nariokotome Homo erectus Skeleton,* pp 234–265. Cambridge: Harvard University Press.

39. Hiernaux J (1975) *The People of Africa.* New York: Scribner.

40. Coon CS (1955) Some problems of human variability and natural selection in climate and culture. Am Nat *89*:257–279.

41. Cavalli-Sforza LL (1986) *African Pygmies.* New York: Academic Press.

42. Jungers WL (1990) Scaling of hominoid femoral head size and the evolution of hominid bipedalism. Am J Phys Anthropol *81*:246.

43. Carrier DR (1984) The energetic paradox of human running and hominid evolution. Curt Anthropol *25*:483–495.

44. Sinclair ARE, Leakey MD, Norton-Griffiths M (1986) Migration and hominid bipedalism. Nature *324*:307–308.

45. Shipman P, Walker A (1989) The costs of being a predator. J Hum Evol *18*:373–392.

46. Rak Y, Arensburg B (1987) Kebara 2 neanderthal pelvis: First look at a complete inlet. Am J Phys Anthropol *73*:227–231.

47. Valladas H, Joron JL, Valladas G, Arens-burg B, Bar-Yosef O, Belfer-Cohen A, Goldberg P (1987) Thermoluminescence dates for the neanderthal burial site at Kebara in Israel. Nature *330*:159–160.

48. Ruff CB, Trinkaus E, Walker A, Larsen CS (1993) Postcranial robusticity in *Homo*, I: Temporal trends and mechanical interpretation. Am J Phys Anthropol *91*:21–53.

49. Valladas H, Reyss JL, Joron JL, Valladas G, Bar-Yosef O, Vandermeersch B (1988) Thermoluminescence dating of Mousterian "Proto-Cro-Magnon" remains from Israel and the origin of modern man. Nature *331*:614–616.

50. Smith FH, Trinkaus E (1991) Les origines de l'homme moderne en Europe centrale: Un cas de continuité. In Hublin JJ, Tillier AM (eds), *Aux Origines d'Homo sapiens*. Nouvelle Encyclopédie Diderot, pp 251–290. Paris: Presses Universitaires de France.

51. Roberts DF (1978) Climate and Human Variability, 2nd M. Menlo Park: Cummings.

52. Eveleth PB, Tanner JM (1976) *Worldwide Variation in Human Growth*. Cambridge: Cambridge University Press.

53. Feldesman MR, Kleckner JG, Lundy JK (1990) The femur/stature ratio and estimates of stature in mid- and late-Pleistocene fossil hominids. Am J Phys Anthropol *83*:359–372.

54. Abbie AA (1956–57) Metrical characters of a central Australian tribe. Oceania *27*:220–243.

55. Walker A, Ruff CB (1993) Reconstruction of the pelvis. In Walker A, Leakey RE (eds), *The Nariokotome Homo erectus Skeleton*, pp. 221–233. Cambridge: Harvard University Press.

56. Tague RG, Lovejoy CO (1986) The obstetric pelvis of A.L. 288-1 (Lucy). J Hum Evol *15*:237–255.

57. Newman MT (1960) Adaptations in the physique of American aborigines to nutritional factors. Hum Biol *32*:288–313.

58. Walter H (1976) Korperbauform and Klima. Z Morphol Anthropol *67*:241–263.

59. Froehlich JW (1970) Migration and the plasticity of physique in the Japanese-Americans of Hawaii. Am J Phys Anthropol *32*:429–442.

60. Bowles GT (1932) *New Types of Old Americans at Harvard*. Cambridge: Harvard University Press.

61. Takahashi E (1986) Secular trend of female body shape in Japan. Hum Biol *58*:293–301.

62. Benoist J (1971) Le gradient ecologique du rapport poids/surface chez des groupes d'Israeliens d'origines differentes. Biometrie Hum (Paris) *6*:36–45.

63. Tanner JM, Hayashi T, Preece MA, Cameron N (1982) Increase in length of leg relative to trunk in Japanese children and adults from 1957 to 1977: Comparison with British and with Japanese Americans. Ann Hum Biol *9*:411–423.

64. DuBois D, DuBois EF (1916) Clinical calorimetry: A formula to estimate the approximate surface area if height and weight be known. Arch Int Med *17*:863–871.

65. Jungers WL (1988) Lucy's length: Stature reconstruction in *Australopithecus afarensis* (A.L. 288-1) with implications for other small-bodied hominids. Am J Phys Anthropol *76*:227–231.

66. McHenry HM (1991) Sexual dimorphism in Australopithecus afarensis. J Hum Evol *20*:21–32.

67. Simons EL (1989) Human origins. Science *245*:1343–1350.

68. Schmid P (1983) Eine Rekonstruktion des Skelettes von A.L. 288-1 (Hadar) und deren Konsequenzen. Folia Primatol *40*:283–306.

69. Schultz AH (1937) Proportions, variability and asymmetries of the long bones of the limbs and the clavicles in man and apes. Hum Biol *9*:281–328.

Study Questions

1. How did Lucy move about, and how do we know?

2. What kind of habitat did Lucy live in, and how do we know?

3. What is it about the Nariokotome Boy's anatomy that lets us know about the habitat he lived in?

SECTION V

EVOLUTION OF AUSTRALOPITHECINES

.

The authors review the history of the discovery of fossils of *Australopithecus*, lay out the characteristics of the numerous species that belong to this genus, and explain how, with the discovery of new fossil material, the views of the evolutionary relationships among the different species of *Australopithecus* have changed over time.

13. The Australopithecines in Review

By L. C. Aiello and P. Andrews

The term australopithecine comes from the genus name *Australopithecus*. This genus was established in 1925 by Raymond Dart for an infant's skull (face, mandible and natural endocranial cast) that had been discovered the previous year at the Buxton lime quarry at Taungs in the northern Cape Province of South Africa. Although the name *Australopithecus* means southern ape (australo = southern; pithecus = ape), Dart emphasised the human-like reduced face and dentition of the Taung Child. He also noted that it most probably had a more erect posture than do the living apes. The foramen magnum was situated well forward, suggesting that the head would have been balanced on the vertebral column as it is in bipedal humans. Dart also felt that the endocranial cast suggested that the brain of the Taung Child had a more human-like organisation than that found in living apes, an assertion that is still actively contested (Falk, 1985, Holloway, 1985). The australopithecines, as represented by this child, were to Dart's mind intermediate between humans and apes. He called them man-apes and suggested that they be placed in their own taxonomic family, the *Homo-sunidae*.

Today, seventy-five years after the discovery of the Taung Child, we have many more australopithecine fossils from both southern and eastern Africa and, as a consequence, we have a much better idea of what these

L. C. Aiello and P. Andrews, "The Australopithecines in Review," *Human Evolution*, vol. 15, no. 1–2, pp. 17–38. Copyright © 2000 by Springer Science+Business Media. Reprinted with permission.

hominins[1] were like. There are now at least eight species of australopithecine that span the period between approximately 4.2–1.2 Ma (Fig. 1). The australopithecines have traditionally been divided into two groups, the 'gracile' australopithecines and the 'robust' australopithecines and this distinction is still heuristically useful. The 'gracile' australopithecines lived between about 4.2 and 2.0 Ma and include A. *anuniensis* and A. *afarensis* as well as the original species that Dart established for the Taung child, A. *africanus*. An additional species, A. *bahrelghazati*, from Chad is dated to between 3.0 and 3.5 million years ago (Brunet *et al.*, 1995). Too little is currently known about this species to say how it relates to the other 'gracile' australopithecines. Most recently, a new species of *Australopithecus*, A. *gahri*, has been established for material from the Middle Awash Valley, Ethiopia that dates to about 2.5 million years ago (Asfaw et al., 1999). It has been suggested to have been in the right place and at the right time to be the evolutionary link between the earlier A. *afarensis* and *Homo*. At the minimum, the growing number of 'gracile' australopithecine species suggests that the picture of hominin evolution at this time may be more complicated than the present fossil evidence indicates. The 'robust' australopithecines generally occur later in time than do the 'gracile' australopithecines, between about 2.7–1.2 Ma, They include A. *aethiopicus*, A. *rohustus* and A. *hoisei*.

Recently h has also been suggested that two species of early *Homo*, *Homo habilis* and *Homo rudolfensis*, be transferred to the genus *Australopithecus* (Wood and Collard, 1999). This is based on the fact that the morphology of the fossils referred to these species, as well as their inferred behavioural and lifehistory adaptations, are more similar to the australopithecines than to later and more convincing members of the genus *Homo*.

All of the australopithecines, including *Australopithecus habilis* and *Australopithecus rudolfensis*, share with modern humans the ability to walk on two legs. Over the years there have been a variety of explanations for the origin of bipedal locomotion (Rose, 1991). These include freeing the hands to carry and use tools (Bartholomew and Birdsell, 1953; Washburn, 1967; Marzke, 1986), enabling the hominins to see longer distances in an open environment (Ravey, 1978), increasing locomotor efficiency (Rodman and McHenry, 1980; but see Streudel, 1994), aiding the transport of food or offspring (Dnbrul, 1962; Sinclair et al., 1987), displaying or warning (Wescot, 1967; Jablonski and Chaplin, 1993). feeding (Jolly, 1970; Hunt, 1994) and thermo-regulation (Wheeler, 1984, 1985, 1991a, 199th, 1992a, 1992b, 1992c, 1993, 1994a, 19946; but see Chaplin *et al.*, 1994).

Because the reconstructed habitats of the 'gracile' australopithecines indicate that they lived in more wooded habitats than previously thought (Reed, 1997), many anthropologists now see australopithecine bipedalism as a forest adaptation For example, Hunt (1994) has proposed that bipedalism is a specific adaptation to feeding on small fruits in open-forest trees, where food was gathered either by standing on the ground or in the trees. This may he the case, but chimpanzees that feed in this fashion have not developed bipedal features of the pelvis and hindlimbs, Furthermore the Laetoii

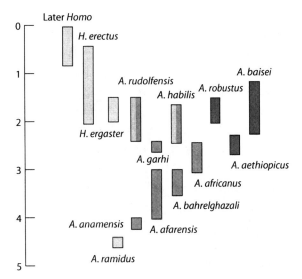

Figure 1. Plot of approximate time ranges of the hominin species. Black boxes = 'robust' australopithecines (paran-thropines), hatched hoses = 'gracile' austratopnheemes, stippled box = *Ardrpirhecus ranudus*, empty boxes = *Horno*, and half empty and half hatched = *Australopithecus habilis* and *Ausrralupithecos rudolfensis* that have recently been transferred from the genus *Homo* (Wood and Collard, 1999).

footprints suggest that early australopithecine bipedalism was for locomotion rather than merely postural. Because bipedalism is unique to hominins among primates and involves major skeletal modifications, it is logical to assume that its selective advantage relates to some unique aspect of the early australopithecine, or pre-australopithecine, niche. Wooded habitats are not necessarily homogenous and there is evidence that these early hominins occupied a variety of wooded habitats from closed forest to relatively open savannah-woodland. Few mammal species manage to live in both forest and open conditions, and the ability to exploit this range of habitats might have been the unique niche of the australopithecines. If this is the case hypotheses for the origin of bipedalism that incorporate energy efficiency (e.g. Isbell and Young, 1996) and/or thermoregulation (e.g. Wheeler, 1984) may have also been important in the early evolution of this unique locomotor adaptation.

Australopithecine bipedalism and body form were not like those found in modern humans or in early members of the genus *Homo*. Currently available evidence suggests that all of the australopithecines, with the possible exception of the newly described *A. garhi*, had shorter legs in relation to their forelimb lengths than does *Homo* (Jungers, 1982; Garuz *et al.,* 1988: Wood and Collard, 1999; but see McHenry and Berger, 1998a) and a pelvis that is considerably different in form from that of more modern hominins ("huge and Lovejoy, 1986: Berge et al., 1984: Berge and Kazmierczak, 1986). They were also heavily muscled for their stature, like modern apes (Aiello, 1992). Furthermore, many aspects of their skeletons, and particularly of their trunks, forelimbs, hands and shoulders, suggest that although bipedal when on the ground, they still were at home in the trees (Stern and Susman, 1983; Abitbol. 1995, Hunt. 1994). Recent estimates of australopithecine body mass show that there was little difference in size between the 'robust' and 'gracile' australopithecines (Mcllenry, 1992,1994), Average species body masses for all of the australopithecines range between about 40–49 kgs, with the females about 65–75% the mass of the males. There is also accumulating evidence that all of the australopithecines, including *Australopithecus hahtlis* and *Australopithecus rudolfensis,* had growth and development patterns that were more similar to the rapid growth in modern apes than to the slower growth in modern humans (Dean et. al., 1993; Smith, 1994; Wood and Collard, 1999; but see Lampl *et al.,* 1993).

Little is known about the postcrantal skeleton of the 'robust' australopithecines and currently the main difference between the two groups of australopithecines seems to be in the size of their teeth, jaws and faces. The 'robust' australopithecines tend to have more megadont cheek teeth, and smaller anterior teeth in relation to these cheek teeth, than do the 'gracile' australopithecines. Their jaws and faces are much more robust (Wood and Aiello, 1998), This implies that there was considerable variation in dietary adaptation between these two groups. This difference, its morphological correlates and the assumption that all of the 'robust' australopithecines are monophyletic, has lead some palaeoanthropologists to place the 'robust' australopithecines in their own genus, *Paranthropus.*

THE 'GRACILE' AUSTRALOPITHECINES

The two best-known species of 'gracile' australopithecine are *Australopithecus africanus* and *Australopithecus afarensis*. The remaining species. A. *bahre(ghazali, A.* anamensrs and *A. gahri* are less well represented by fossils and, because of their more recent establishment, are less well understood. An additional taxon, *Ardipitheeus rarnidus,* (White *et al.,* 1995) was originally referred to the genus *Australopithecus* (White et al., 1994). This taxon was established on the basis of 17 fossils from the Middle Awash, Ethiopia, that date between about 4.5 and 4.3 Ma (White *et al.,* 1994). Over 90 additional specimens making up about 45%

of a single skeleton were found in 1994 (Gee, 1995b) but these specimens have yet to be fully reported. The currently described specimens do not Include fossils of the pelvis or lower limbs which would confirm that A *rarnidus* was bipedal A. rarnidus has deciduous molars that are similar to ape deciduous molars and the permanent teeth that may be smaller in relation to inferred body size than is the case in the larger 'gracile' australopithecines. These two features would suggest that A. *ramidus* had not yet evolved the dietary adaptations and associated dental morphology that characterise the australopithecine species. At present all that can be said is that *Aridpithecus ramidus* represents a more primitive level of adaptation than the known australopithecines and is possibly ancestral to them.

I. Australopithecus Africanus

In the years since the discovery of the Taung Child, A. *africanus* fossils have been found at three other southern African sites: Sterkfontein and Gladysvale in the central Transvaal and Makapansgat in the northern Transvaal. Sterkfontein is by far the most prolific of the A. *africanus* sites, having yielded over 500 A. *africanus* fossils since it was first excavated in 1936 (Clarke, 1994). Makapansgat has produced 29 A. *africanus* specimens since 1947 (Rayner *et al.,* 1993) while Gladysvale, the most recently discovered site, yielded 2 tooth germs in 1992 (Berger *et al.,* 1993). No additional hominin specimens have been recovered from Taung (McKee and Tobias, 1994).

The main A *africanus* deposits at Sterkfontein (Member 4) are dated between approximately 2.8 and 2.2 Ma (Vrba, 1982). Based on faunal comparisons. Makapansgat may be earlier than this at about 3 Ma while Gladvsvale may be the most recent, dating between about 2,5 and 1.7 Ma (Berger *et al,,* 1993). There is no evidence that any of these sites were living sites nor is there evidence of stone or bone tools in the deposits containing *.4ustralopithecus africanus.* The australopithecine fossils seem to have been accumulated by carnivores, particularly leopards at Sterkfontein, hyenas at Makapansgat and eagles at Taung (Berger and Clark, 1995). Palaeoenvironmental reconstructions suggest that A. may have lived in a sub-tropical forest environment at Makapansgat (Rayner *et al.,* 1993) and in a more open environment at Sterkfontein. Stable carbon isotope analysis of A. *africanus* teeth from Makapansgat suggests that even these earlier hominins may have exploited relatively open environments such as woodlands or grasslands for food (Sponheimer and Lee-Thorpe, 1999). These analyses suggest that the australopithecines not only ate fruits and leaves like modern chimpanzees, but also large quantities of Carbon-13 enriched foods such as grasses and sedges or animals that ate these plants or both. The authors speculate that A. *africanus* may have consumed quantities of high-quality animal foods, a diet generally thought to be exclusive to the genus *Homo.*

There are two well-known A. *africanus* fossils from Sterkfontein, both found in 1947, which confirmed in adult specimens the bipedal hominin morphology that Dart had inferred for A. *africanus* on the basis of the Taung child. The first of these is a virtually complete skull (Sts 5), that is still affectionately known as 'Mrs. Ples' after one of the early taxonomic designations for the hominins from Sterkfontein, *Plesianthropus transvaalensis* (Broom, 1937). The second is a partially complete skeleton (Sts 14) comprising a distorted pelvis, a crushed femur, 15 vertebrae and some fragmentary ribs. Up until fairly recently, the general interpretation of *Australopithecus africanus* was that it represented a relatively homogenous taxon of bipedal hominin. Recent publication of a very large. presumed nmaleA *africanus* skull (Stw 505) (Conroy *et al.,* 1998) and analysis of the plethora of other hominin fossils from Member 4 at Sterkfontein has begun to change this interpretation. McHenry and Berger's (1998a, 1998b) initial analysis of Inferred body masses and relative limb lengths suggest that A. *africanus* was more ape-like it its body proportions that at least A. *afarensis,* while analyses of the tibia suggest that, although bipedal on the ground, A *africanus* would also have had the capability to move efficiently in the trees (Berger and Tobias 1996). Furthermore, there has been some suggestion that more than one species is represented among the A. *africanus* fossils. Quite extreme variation in size and morphology has been recognised among the mandibles from Makapansgat (Pilbeam 1972), while Clarke (1988, 1994) believes that the variation in crania from Sterkfontein justifies the conclusion that some fossils (e.g Sts 252 and Sts 36) might represent a species ancestral to the 'robust' australopithecines while others such as Sts 5 and Sts 52 would represent A. *africanus*. More recently, Lockwood (1999) has shown that the degree of variation in the A. *africanus* face, including the large Stw 505 cranium, is less than that found within *Australopithecus boisei* and compatible in pattern with the variation found within modern humans. The growing realization of the degree of size and morphological variation In the A. *africanus* collection, as well as in the other Plio-Pleistocene hominins, is one of the exciting current themes in australopithecine research.

Recently Sterkfontein also produced what is the earliest known hominin from southern Africa.. This hominin skeleton (Stw 573) comes from Member 2 at which is currently thought to he between 3,2 and 3.6 million years old. The foot bones suggest that it may have been more aboreally adapted than either *Australopithecus afarensis* or the later *Australopithecus hahdis (Homo* lrabitis) (Clarke and Tobias 1995). In this respect Stw 573 is consistent with the newer interpretations of the posteranial remains from the later Member 4 australopithecines. Whether Stw 573 proves to be A. *africanur* or another contemporary australopithecine, such as A. *afarensis,* must await further analysis of the remainder of this new discovery.

II. Australopithecus Afarensis

Up until. 1978, *Australopithecus africanus* was the only known 'gracile' australopithecine. But in that year Johanson and his co-workers established a new species, *A afarensis,* for fossils from the site of Hadar in Ethiopia and Letoli in Tanzania (Johanson *et al.,* 1978). In 1979 Johanson and White suggested that it represented the common ancestor for all later australopithecines on the one hand and Homo on the other, Since, 1979 fossils from Koobi Fora and Tabarin, Kenya and the Omo, Ethiopia have been referred to this taxon (Boas, 1988) as have further Ethiopian fossils from the Middle Awash (White *et* al., 1993) and Hadar itself (Kimbel *et al.,*1994).

A. *afarensis* is reasonably well dated by Potassium-Argon methods. The oldest currently known A. *afarensis is* a fragmentary frontal bone from the site of Belohdelie in the Middle Awash that is 3.9 Ma while the most recent is relatively complete skull (AL 444–2) from Kada Hadar Member at Hadar that is 3.0 Ma (Johanson et al., 1994). Palaeoenvironmental reconstruction of a number of A. *afarensis* sites suggested that it occupied a spectrum of environments from closed forest of the SH Member at Hadar to more open conditions at Laetoli, Tanzania (White *et* at., 1993; but see Andrews, 1989).

By far the most well known A afarensis fossil is Al. 228–1, a 40% complete skeleton that is affectionately known as Lucy. AL 288–1 was discovered in 1974 at Hadar, and because of its completeness it forms the basis for much that is known of A. *afarensis* skeletal anatomy. Careful reconstruction of the entire skeleton shows that Lucy would have stood 106 cm high (Schmid, 1983), about the height of a 4.5 year old European child. The pelvis is less distorted than, but similar to, the Sts 14 pelvis, and has sparked a heated controversy over the efficiency of A. *afarensis* bipedal locomotion (Lovejoy, 1988; Stern and Susman, 1983). There is little doubt, however, that A. afarensis was more capable of bipedal locomotion than are modern apes. Aspects of the knee, ankle joint and foot confirm this interpretation and show that during the stride her body weight would have been transferred in a straight line over the foot, passing directly over the toes at the end of the stride (Latimer *et al.,*1987). As modern humans, A. *afarensis* would have also had had moderate hip mobility and a more adducted femur (MacLatchy, 1996).

Many other aspects of A *afarensis* anatomy are primitive. For example, the size of the birth canal in relation to the inferred size of an *A. afarensis* infant suggests that Lucy would have had no trouble in bearing an infant at the relatively advanced stage of development common for today's apes (Leutenegger, 1987; but see Hauler and Schmid, 1995). The less developed condition of modern human neonates is a derived adaptation permitting birth before the infant's head becomes too large to pass through the constricted human birth canal. *A. afarensis* also has a ape-like funnel-shaped rib cage (Schmid, 1983, 1991) that is consistent with an adaptation to climbing in the trees (Hunt, 1994). The wide rib-cage and broad pelvis would also have provided room for a capacious gut, suggesting that *A. afarensis* did not have the high quality diet, and correspondingly relatively small gut, that is a necessary energetic concomitant of the enlarged brain in *Homo* (Aiello and Wheeler, 1995). Many additional parts of the skeleton, such as curved hand and foot phalanges, the shape of the scapula, the relatively mobile knee joint, and details of the humerus and elbow joint suggest *A. afarensis* was able to climb in the trees with much more agility than modern humans (Stern and Susman, 1983; Aiello and Dean, 1990).

There are no living primates that show in their skeletons the same mosaic of bipedal and arboreal features as does A. *afarensis,* and one of the main questions today is precisely how terrestrial A. *afarensis* was in its day-to-day locomotion. The remarkably preserved footprints at Laetoli, Tanzania, which date to between 3.6–3.75 Ma, clearly demonstrate that a hominin existed at this time that walked with an apparently efficient striding bipedal locomotion. The environment of Laetoli at the time of the footprint trail was open savannah-woodland. Raindrops preserved along with the footprints indicate that they were made at the beginning of the rainy season (Hay and Leakey, 1982) and the accompanying prints of many migratory animal species suggest that the hominins may have been participating in the annual game migrations. Some anthropologists suggest that the footprints are too modern to have been made by *A. afarensis* (Tuttle, 1981) and that another, more modern hominin species must have been in existence at the same time as A. *afarensis*. However, White and Sawa (1987) have argued convincingly that the footprints are compatible with what is known of A. *afarensis* foot morphology. The evidence of the Laetoli footprints, together with the many aboreally-adapted features of the A. afarensis skeleton, suggest that theses hominins had a mosaic locomotor pattern. This would have involved bipedalism while on the ground coupled with an arboreal adaptation that facilitated feeding and sleeping in the trees (Kimbel *et at.,* 1994; Aiello, 1994a; but see White *et al.,* 1993).

AL 288-1 is just one of a large number of fossils that have been referred to *A. afarensis* and a marked feature of the entire collection is an impressive difference in size. When the mandible, femur or humerus of AL 288-I, one of the smallest individuals, is compared to larger individuals, the degree of size difference is outside the range that would be expected in modern chimpanzees or humans, and just within the *95%* confidence limits for gorillas and orang-utans (Richmond and Jungers, 1995). This is an impressive degree of dimorphism for a species that has a relatively small average body size. ['his fact, together with possible morphological differences between the large and small individuals, has lead some researchers to suggest that more than one species is present in the A. *afarensis* collection (Olson, 1981, Sent and Tardieu, 1985). Other anthropologists argue that some of the morphological differences have been misinterpreted (Kimbel et al., 1984), or that they are merely a result of size (Asfaw, 1985) and/or have no functional significance (Latimer *et al.,* 1987).

At present the question of multiple species in the A. *afarensis* collection cannot be resolved. Discoveries in the Middle Awash and Hadar (Kimbel *et al.,* 1994; White *et al.,* 1993) suggest that the variation in size is continuous in time and space and cannot be sorted in two (or more) clear morphs that could be interpreted as different species. Furthermore, although the degree of dimorphism in A. *afarensis* is large, it is of the same order of magnitude as that found in other australopithecine species (McHenry, 1992, 1994; Aiello, 1994a).

It may be unusual for modern humans and chimpanzees, but not for the australopithecines. Evidence for very large and robust arm bones from both Hadar and the Middle Awash goes a long way to dispel earlier ideas (Stern and Susman, 1983; Lovejoy, 1981) that the larger morph of A. *afarensis* was any less adapted to arboreal locomotion than was the smaller morph. At present the fossil evidence is most consistent with the interpretation that A. *afarensis* was a highly dimorphic taxon with a mosaic locomotor pattern.

III. Australopithecus Anamensis

Australopithecus anarnensis was established in 1995 on the basis of nine hominin dental, cranial and post-cranial specimens from Kanapoi, Kenya and 12 specimens from Allia Bay, Kenya (Leakey. M.O. *et al.*, 1995). Subsequently further fossil material has been recovered from both sites and the antiquity has been established at between 4.17 ± 0.03 and 4.07 ± 0.02 million years ago (Leakey, M.G. et al., 1998) Not only is A. *anamensis* older than A. *afarensis* but it is also more primitive in certain aspects of its dental anatomy. and particularly in its large canine teeth. In these aspects it resembles more closely the earlier A. *afarensis* material from Laetoli, Tanzania, than the later material from Hadar, Ethiopia (Leakey, M.G. *et al.*, 1995). Its distal humerus is similar to that of A. *afarensis* (Lague and Jungers, 1996), the morphology of its 1st lower deciduous molar is intermediate between *Ardipithecus rarnidus* and A. *afareusis,* and its capilate is more ape-like than any *other known hominin. Based on current assessment of its morphology and on what is* presently known *of Ardipithecus rarnidus, Australopithecus anarnensis* could well be an intermediate species linking the earlier *Ardipithecas* with the later A. *afareusis.* Little is known from these early time periods, however, and the true evolutionary picture may prove to he considerably more 'bushy' than the present species suggest.

IV. Australopithecus garhi

The taxon *Australopithecus garhi* was established in 1999 for hominin fossils from the Hata Member of the Boar' Formation in the Middle Awash. Ethiopia. This material dates to 2.5 million years ago (Asfaw *et al.,* 1999). the taxon is roughly contemporaneous with A. *africanus* and post-dates the remainder of the 'gracile' australopithecines. The species name, *garhi,* means surprise in the Afar language, and the morphology of this australopithecine was a surprise. It is distinguished from A. *afarensis* by its absolutely very large postcanine dentition, from the australopithecines by the absence of their distinctive dental, facial and cranial features, and from A. *africanus, A. habihs* and A, *rudolfensis* by its primitive cranial and facial anatomy. Skeletal material from a nearby site, which most probably belongs to this taxon, also suggests that its femora where elongated in relation to its humeri as is the case in *Homo ergaster* and all more recent members of the genus *Homo.* It differs frum *Homo* in retaining relatively long forearms for its upper arms, however. Animal bones found at the sites also show clear evidence of cutmarks indicating butchery (Heinzelin et al., 1999). Although no stone tools have been found at the Hata sites, nearly contemporary deposits at Gona (96 km to the north) have abundant stone tools dated to 2.6 Ma. The inferred environment at Hata was a featureless, grassy lake margin. The absence of stone tools may reflect the absence of ready sources of raw materials and indicate that the hominins were 'curating' their tools and not leaving them behind. Although it is not possible to say with confidence that A *garhi* made stone tools and carried out the butchery, it is the only contemporary hominin in the deposits. If Asfaw and colleagues are correct in their attribution of these new fossils to *Australopithecus,* and if this taxon was responsible for the tool making and butchery, it would indicate that australopithecines in East African were both tool makers and meat eaters. As a result, the contemporary A, *africanus* in South Africa would not be the only australopithecine for which there is evidence of a high quality diet (Sponheimer and Lee-Thorpe, 1999).

THE 'ROBUST' AUSTRALOPITHECINES

Of the three species of 'robust' australopithecine, one *(Australopithecus robustus) occurs in South Africa and two (Australopithecus aethiopicus and Australopithecus boisei) occur in* East Africa with A. *boisei* known as far south as Malawi (Schrenk and Bromage, in press). The earliest 'robust' australopithecine, A. *aethiopicus, is* known from Kenya and Ethiopia and appears at about 2.7 Ma, while A. *boisei* appears about 2.3 Ma and A. *robustus* about 2.0 Ma.

The 'robust' australopithecines lived contemporaneously with either 'gracile' australopithecines or members of the *Homo* throughout their time range. The extreme masticatory system of the 'robust' australopithecines may indicate a divergence in dietary adaptation that would avoid competition with early *Homo*. Foley (1987) has suggest that if the environment was becoming increasing seasonal, the 'robust australopithecines might have opted for processing larger quantities of foods of relatively low nutritional value, while the more gracile hominins adopted a strategy whereby they broadened their dietary base to include a range of high quality food items such as animal-based products (see also Potts 1998).

Australopithecus Robustus

The first 'robust' australopithecine was found in 1938 by a schoolboy at the site of Kromdraai, which is not far from Sterkfontein in the Transvaal, South Africa (Broom and Schepers, 1946). This original discovery was a partial skeleton including a fragmentary skull, a mandible and parts of the posteranium. On the basis of the large teeth and robust jaws, this material was originally placed in a new taxon, *Paranthropus robustus*. Although some anthropologists continue to use the genus name, *Paranthropus* for all of the 'robust' australopithecines (eg. Dean, 1985; Caine, 1985; Wood and Collard. 1999), many prefer *to use Australopithecus and* thereby *to recognise the* grade similarities *in* adaptation shared with the 'gracile' australopithecines. The nearby site of Swartkrans has produced fossils representing 124 individuals of A. *robustus* since it was first excavated in 1948 (Brain, 1993a, 1994) and most recently 'robust' australopithecine teeth have been found at Sterkfontein (Member 5) (Kaman, 1994; Clarke, 1994) and at Gondolin in the Northwest Province of South Africa (Kuykendall, 1999). 'Robust' australopithecine fossils have also been found at the site of Drimolin hut these remain to be published.

Based on faunal comparisons, the australopithecine-bearing deposits at Swartkrans (Members 1-3) span the period between about 1.8–1.0 Ma (Brain, 1993a), while those at Sterkfontein (Member 5) are approximately 2.0–1.7 Ma (Kuman, 1994). The deposits at Kromdraai, may be more similar in age to the material from Sterkfontein than to that from Swartkrans. Deciduous molar teeth from Kromdraai are similar to the newly discovered teeth from Sterkfontein and different from Swartkrans deciduous molars. Grine (1982) feels that this difference is great enough to separate the fossils into two different species, *Paranthropus robustus* for the material from Kromdraai and *Paranthropus crassidens* for the material from Swartkrans. He also feels that the Swartkrans material is more specialised, and therefore more recent, than the Kromdraai fossils. Faunal comparisons also suggests an early date for Kromdraai (McKee *et al.*, 1995).

Swartkrans has yielded some fascinating insights into the behaviour of the 'robust' australopithecines (Brain, 1993a, 1994) Stable carbon isotope analysis of A. *robustus* tooth enamel suggests that these hominins were generalised feeders and could have included a significant component of animal-based foods in their diet (Lee-Thorpe and van der Merwe, 1093; Lee-Thorpe et al , 1994). This is consistent with interpretations drawn from their brain sizes which suggest that A. *robustus* could not have survived on a low-quality, vegetarian diet that has often been inferred for them on the basis of their robust masticatory anatomy (Aiello and Wheeler, 1995).

Bone tools found throughout the deposits show wear patterns that suggest repeated use as digging implements (Brain and Shipman, 1994). It is possible that they may have been used to reach ed1hle bulbs or tubers in the rocky terrain around the site. Other bone tools show wear that is consistent with working animal skins, and there are also stone tools throughout the deposits. It is currently impossible to determine whether *A. robustus* was the toolmaker. The reason is that early Homo is also found at Swartkrans in the same deposits as *A. robustus*. Susman (1988, 1994) argues that hand bones from the site indicate that *A. robustus* would have at least had the same manual ability to make and use tools as *Homo habilis,* but other anthropologists acknowledge the possibility that these hand bones may actually belong to *Homo* rather than to *A. robustus* (Trinkaus and Long, 1990; Aiello, 1994b).

The fossils at Swartkrans were largely accumulated as the result of carnivore predation. The smaller percentage of hominins in Member 3 (5.1%) in relation to the earlier Members 1 and 2 (9%, 16.7%) might even suggest that the Member 3 hominin were better at predator avoidance than the earlier hominins (Brain, 1993b, 1994). There is evidence for the controlled use of fire in Member 3 (Sillen and Hoering, 1993; Brain, 1993b, 1994) and the only hominins currently known from this member are the 'robust' australopithecines, Brain (1993b, 1994) suggests that Swartkrans in Member 3 times may have been a sleeping site for the 'robust' australopithecines, and that the decline in percentage representation of hominins in these deposits resulted from the protection provided by the presence of fires.

Australopithecus Boisei

Australopithecus robustus is only known from South Africa and *Australopithecus boisei* is only found at sites in Tanzania, Kenya, Ethiopia and Malawi. The first *A. boisei* fossil, a relatively complete and undistorted cranium, was found in 1959 by Mary Leakey at Olduvai Gorge, Tanzania. It is generally similar in form to the *A. robustus* crania from Kromdraai and Swartkrans, but has bigger molar teeth and more extreme facial features: the cheek bones are both higher and more flaring. The facial structure of *A. boisei* completes the trend seen in *A. a fricanus* and *A. robustus* towards the generation of increased chewing force (Rak, 1983). Discovery of the most complete *A. boisei* skull and mandible from Konso, Ethiopia, however, shows that there was considerable variation in the *A. boisei* skull (Sawa *et al.,* 1997).

This first *A. boisei* skull (Olduvai Hominid 5) was initially put in a separate taxon, *Zinjanthropus boisei* (L.S B. Leakey. 1959), but Robinson (1960) almost immediately suggested that it should be put in *Paranthropus boisei*. In 1967 Tobias reclassified it as *Australopithecus boisei,* pointing out the numerous similarities between it and the South African 'robust' australopithecines. Olduvai has only produced a few other *A. boisei* fossils (isolated teeth, parts of a fragmentary cranium, a fragmentary proximal femur and an almost complete ulna) that come from Beds I and II and date between about 1.85-1.20 Ma (Aiello *et al.,* 1999). During this time there was a saline lake in the area and the sites were located close to fresh water streams. Recent palaeoenvironmental analyses suggest a riparian to grassy woodland environment, at least Bed I times (Sikes, 1994; Plummer and Bishop, 1994).

In the years since the first discovery at Olduvai, further *A. boisei* material has come from Peninj in Tanzania, from Chesowanja, West Turkana and Koobi Fora in Kenya, the Omo in Ethiopia and in Malawi. The most important of these sites have been the Omo and Koobi Fora. Over 200 hominin specimens were recovered from the Omo between 1967–1976 and the Omo is also important because it has provided a well dated stratigraphic sequence for the Turkana Basin. Although the great majority of the Omo fossils are very fragmentary, we know that robust and non-robust hominins co-occur between about 2.7–1.4 Ma (Shungura Formation members C-K) (Suwa et al., 1996). The robust fossils from the earlier members (C-F) represent a different taxon, *Australopithecus aethiopicus* (see below and Wood, 1991 for a review).

Koobi Fora has been by far the most prolific of the East African hominin sites, and *Australopithecus boisei* is the most common hominin found. *A. boisei* fossils at Koobi Fora are found in the Upper Burgi, KBS and Okote Members and span the period from approximately 2.0–1.4 Ma. During this period there was a marked change in the environment in the Turkana basin. Between about 1.8–1.9 Ma there was a saline lake and sites are located along the lake margin as well as near river channels (Rogers *et al.*, 1994). After 1.7 Ma the lake disappeared to be replaced by a river. The climate also seems to have become drier (Rogers et al., 1994; Ceding, 1992). Whereas earlier australopithecines lived in fairly wooded, well watered environments, *A. boisei* (as well as the other 'robust' australopithecines) also lived in more open environments, but always near wetlands (Reed, 1997; see also Behrensmeyer, 1985; Shipman and Harris, 1988). *Homo* is the first hominin to be adapted to open and relatively and environments.

Two of the most important of the many *A. boisei* fossils from Koohi Fora are a virtually complete large cranium (KNM-ER 406) and a smaller half-cranium (KNM-ER 732). Both of these are from the KBS member and date to about 1.65–1.70 Ma. KNM-ER 406 is similar in its morphology to Olduvai Hominid 5 and both are presumed to be males. KNM-ER 732 is much smaller in size, but it preserves many features in common with the larger specimens. These include a large, inflated mastoid process, elongated glenoid fossil (articulation for the jaw) and a dish-shaped face. The size difference between KNM-ER 406 and KNM-ER 732 is commonly taken to represent the high level of sexual dimorphism present in *A. boisei*. A further important *A. boisei* fossil from Koobi Fora is the KNM-ER 1501) partial skeleton. This is from the Upper Burgi Member and is therefore older than the two crania, dating to about 1.88–1.90 Ma. Although this skeleton is very fragmentary and its allocation to *A. boisei* has been questioned (Aiello et al. 1999), it has body proportions similar to those of *A. afarensis* (Grausz *et al.*, 1988), with relatively small hindlimbs in relation to their forelimbs.

Considerable archaeological work has been carried out at Koobi Fora. Before about 1.6 Ma the stone tool assemblages were primarily restricted to relatively closed environments next to perennial water sources (Harris and Capaldo, 1993). After this time stone tools are found in a variety of habitat contexts and in varying densities. There is one site at Koobi Fora (FxJi 20 Main) which dates to 1.6 Ma and has evidence of controlled fire use in a context, like Swartkrans, that would suggest that the fire served as a source of light, heat and predator protection (Bellomo. 1994). Whether or not *A. boisei* was responsible for any of the archaeology at Koobi Fora is again impossible to determine with certainty. But Rogers *et al.* (1994) argue that the first appearance of early *Homo erectus* (*Homo ergasier*) and the apparent change in artifact distribution and occurrence around 1.6 Ma may be more that a coincidence. These authors strongly favour *Homo* as the tool user and fire maker at least in these later deposits.

V. Australopithecus Aethiopicus

In 1985 two 'robust' australopithecine specimens, a skull and a mandible, were found at two different localities on the Western shore of Lake Turkana (Walker *et al.*, 1986). The skull, found in the Lomekwi drainaget dates to about 2.50 Ma, while the mandible, from the nearby Kangatukuseo drainage, dates to about 2.45 Ma. This material is at least 500.000 years older than any of the previously known 'robust' australopithecines from sites other than the Omo, Ethiopia. The surprising thing about these fossils is not their age, but the fact that they represent a type of 'robust' australopithecine that was previously unknown. In particular, the skull (KNM-WT 17000) has a relatively small brain size and features of the occipital region that are characteristic of *A. afarensis*. But the teeth are among the largest 'robust' australopithecine teeth known and the face is massive and heavily buttressed. At an age that is roughly equivalent to *A.*

africanus in South Africa, this specimen did not fit into the expected trend in facial evolution that had been previously established by Rak (1983).

KNM-WT 17000 was originally assigned to *Australopithecus boisei on* the grounds of overall resemblance (Walker *et al.*, 1986) and the fact that it probably represents an early part of the evolving *A. boisei* lineage (see also Walker and Leakey, 1988). Other authors have pointed out that of the many features used in comparison, only a small number (eg. heart shaped foramen magnum. temporoparietal overlap at asterion) actually link this fossil exclusively with *A. boisei* (Delson, 1986; see also Kimble et al., 1988). The great majority of cranial features are either primitive, or link KNM-WT 17000 with all or some of the other 'robust' and 'gracile' australopithecines.

The taxon *Paraustralopithecus aethiopicas* was established by Arambourg and Coppens (1968) for an edentulous (without teeth) mandible (Omo 18-1967-18) from the Omo Shungura Member C (about 2.6 Ma). Because of the many features in which KNMWT 17000 differs from *A. boisei,* and because of some similarities between the Omo 18-1967-18 mandible, other early Omo mandibular fossils and the Kangatukuseo mandible, Kimbel *et al.* (1988) have referred both of the West Turkana specimens to the species *aethiopicus* and placed this species in the genus *Australopithecus*. *A. aethiopicus* is now considered to be a taxon that is more primitive than *A. boisei* (or *A. robustus*), but most probably in the *A.* boisei clade.

AUSTRALOPITHECINE PHYLOGENY

Ideas about australopithecine phylogeny have changed radically over the years with the discovery of each new taxon. In the 1950s the South African australopithecine sites had yet to be as precisely dated as they are today, but faunal comparisons suggested that the *A. africanus* sites of Sterkfontein and Makapansgat were older than the *A. robustus* sites of Kromdraai and Swartkrans. Robinson (1963) felt that the then known 'robust' australopithecines represented late survivors of an ancestral stock from which *A. africanus* and *Homo* evolved (Fig. 2a). He argued for a 'hominidizing' trend from *A. robustus* through *A. africanus* to *Homo*. This hypothesis lost support with the discovery of *A. boisei* at Olduvai in 1959 and the realisation that the large teeth and massive facial structure of the 'robust' australopithecines most probably represented specialised features that could easily have been derived from a more primitive *A. africanus*-like ancestor (Tobias, 1967). Because the Olduvai material was considered at that time to be roughly contemporaneous with the *A. africanus* deposits in South Africa Tobias (1967) suggested that a postulated Upper Pliocene australopithecine with teeth similar to *A. africanus* was ancestral to the contemporaneous Lower Pleistocene *A. africanus*, *A. hoisei* and *Homo habilis* (Fig. 2b). A rival hypothesis saw *A. boisei* and *Homo habilis* in East Africa as males and females of the same species, with a similar relationship between *A. africanus* and *A. robustus* in South Africa (Wolpoff, 1968). The 'single species hypothesis', as this idea came to be called, was not completely rejected until the mid-1970's. By this time the *A. africanus* levels of the South African cave sites were known not only to pre-date the *A. robustus* levels, but also to significantly pre-date the appearance of *Homo habilis* and *A. hoisei* in East Africa. Furthermore, a skull of early *Homo erectus* (*Homo ergaster*) (KNM-ER 3733) had been found in the same stratigraphic horizon as the *A. boisei* skull, KNM-ER 406 at Koobi Fora. Kenya (Leakey and Walker, 1976). The morphological variation of contemporaneous Plio-Pleistocene hominins was now too great, and the temporal duration too long, to be compatible with the 'single species hypothesis'.

For a few years in the late. 1970s it seemed clear that *A. africanus* was the probable common *ancestor of the* 'robust' australopithecines on the one hand and *Homo habilis* on the other (Eldredge *and* Tattersall, 1975; Delson *et al.*, 1977; Tattersall *and* Eldredge, 1977) (Fig 2c). However, the announcement of *A. afarensis*

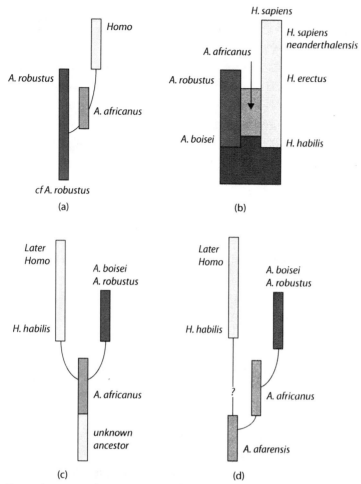

Figure 2. Historical interpretations of australopithecine phylogeny a) after Robinson (1963). b) after Tobias (1967). c) a phytogeny popular in the early 1970's, d) after Johanson and White (1979).

in 1978 resulted in yet another phylogenetic rethink. *A. afarensis* was not only older than *A. africanus,* but also more primitive In 1979 Johanson and White put forward the hypothesis that *A. afarensis* was the common ancestor of all of the other australopithecines on the one hand and of *Homo* on the other (Johanson and White, 1979) (Fig. 2d). In contrast, Tobias (1980) argued that *A. afarensis* was just an East African variant of the South African *A. africanus* and continued to support the idea that *A. africanus* was the common ancestor of *Homo* and the 'robust' australopithecine. Other anthropologists thought that the phylogeny was more complicated and recognised more than one species in the *A. afarensis* collection of fossils. In particular, Olson (1981) argued that both *Homo* and *A. africanus* were present, the smaller *A. afarensis* fossils representing an early species of *Homo* which lead through *A. africanus* (reclassified as *Homo africanus* by Olson) to modern humans. The larger *A. afarensis* fossils represented a early species of *Paranthropus* that was ancestral to the later robust forms (see also Falk, 1986, 1987).

During the 1980s there were numerous attempts to determine australopithecine phylogeny through the application of cladistic methodology (e.g. Skelton, McHenry and Drawhorn, 1986: Wood and Chamberlain, 1986). These analyses tended to produce conflicting results that depended primarily on which aspects of cranial morphology were used in the analyses. The phylogenetic confusion has been compounded more recently by the discovery of additional australopithecine taxa, and particularly by the discovery of the 'Black Skull' (KNM-WT 17000) in 1985 and the resulting acceptance of the taxon *Australopithecus aethiopicus,* by *Australopithecus anamensis* in 1995 and by *Australopithecus garhi in* 1999. Figure 3 illustrates two recent cladograms depicting the relationships between the various taxa. The cladistic hypothesis put forward by Wood and Collard (1999) (Fig. 3a) illustrates a monophylum *Homo ergaster* and all more recent members of the genus *Homo,* a monophylum for the 'robust' australopithecines (paranthropines), an equivocal position for *Australopithecus habilis* and *Australopithecus rudolfensis* and a more primitive basal position for *Australopithecus africanus* and *Australopithecus afarensis*. Note that these authors follow Strait *et al.,* (1997) in preferring the nomen *Praeauthropus africanus* for *Australopithecus afarensis* and also employ *Praeanthropus* as the genus for the 'robust' australopithecines. This nomenclature avoids the problem of paraphyly for the genus *Australopithecus and* accurately reflects the branching patterns in their cladistic hypothesis. They

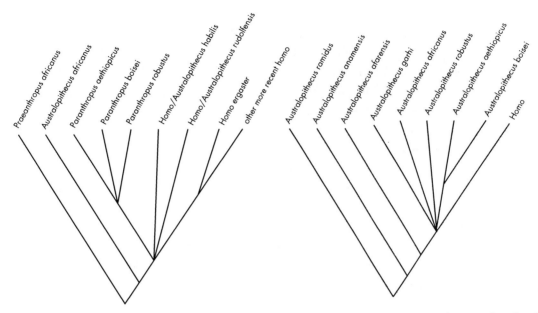

Figure 3. Two recently published cladograms depicting relationships between hominin taxa, a) after Wood and Collard (1999), b) after Suwa *et al.* (1999), See text for discussion.

recognise, however, that by transferring *Homo habilis* and *Homo rudolfensis* to the genus *Australopithecus* they are resurrecting the paraphyletic nature of the genus *Australopithecus* (Wood and Collard, 1999).

The second cladogram (Fig. 4b) includes both *Ardipithecus ramidus* and *Australopithecus garhi* (Asfaw et al, 1999), With the exception of the sister group relationship between *Australopithecus aedriopicus* and *Australopithecus boisei,* it postulates *an* unresolved polychotomy for *Australopithecus garhi* and all more recent australopithecines and *Homo.* Figure 4 provides some alternative phylogemes from Asfaw *et al.* (1999) some of which the authors note are not consistent with their cladogram. At present all that can be concluded is that it is not possible to resolve the phylogenetic relationships of the australopithecines with any degree of certainty One implication of these phylogenetic uncertainties is the realisation of the 'bushiness' of hominin evolution. It is also inevitable that additional species remain to be discovered.

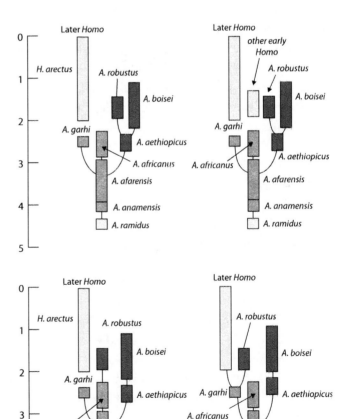

Figure 4. Some possible alternative phylogenics for homnin evolution (after Suwa *et al.,* 1999).

On the basis of present evidence it is probable that all of the australopithecines represent a single grade of evolution that was not only different from that of the genus *Homo* but also different from any extant primate. They mixed bipedal locomotion with an apparent arboreal capability, occupied a spectrum of habitats from closed forest to relatively open woodland, had a level of encephalization that was within the range of living primates (Aiello and Wheeler, 1995), and most probably had not yet developed the extended periods of infant dependency that are characteristic of modern humans. The major difference among the species is in the size of their masticatory apparatus which indicates an increasing reliance on foodstuffs requiring a greater degree of masticatory force in the later robust forms. This trend may have arisen in response both to environmental change and to competition not only with members of the genus *Homo*, but also with other terrestrial primates that were contemporaneous with them in both South and East Africa. The australopithecines represented a highly successful hominin adaptation that lasted for well over 3 million years. The only obvious explanation for their ultimate disappearance is that they finally lost the competitive struggle with the other primates, including members of the genus *Homo*, that were occupying similar niches in the African early Pleistocene.

ACKNOWLEDGEMENT

We would like to thank Professor Emduano Aguirre for inviting LA to speak at the International Symposium of the Ramon Areces Foundation in Madrid (11–13 March, 1998) and for the opportunity to prepare this paper for publication. We would also like to thank the Ramón Areces Foundation for making the symposium possible and for outstanding hospitality while in Madrid. We are also grateful to Bernard Wood and Mark Collard for numerous stimulating discussions on the problems and pitfalls of hominin cladistics and phylogenetic reconstruction.

REFERENCES

Abitbol, M.M. 1995. Lateral view of *Australopithecus afarensis:* primitive aspects of bipedal positional behavior in the earliest hominids. *Journal of Human Evolution* **28**: 211–229.

Aiello, L.C. 1992. Size and shape in human evolution *Journal of Human Evolution* **22**: 127.147.

Aiello, L.C. 1994a. Variable but singular *Nature* **368**: 399–400.

Aiello, L.C. 1994b. Thumbs up for our early ancestors. *Science* **265**: 1540–1541.

Aiello, L.C. and Dean, M.C. 1990. *An Introduction to Human Evolutionary Anatomy.* Academic Press: London.

Aiello, L.C. and Wheeler P. 1995. The expensive-tissue hypothesis: the brain and the digestive system in human and primate evolution. *Current Anthropology* 36.

Aiello, L.C., Wood, B.A., Key, C. and Lewis. M 1999 Morphological and taxonomic affinities of the Olduvai ulna (OH 36). *American Journal of Physical Anthropology* (in press).

Andrews, P. 1989. Pataeoeeology of Laetoli (Lead Review*). Journal of Human Evolution* **18**: 173–181.

Arambourg, C. and Coppens, Y. 1968. Découverte d'un Australopithécien nouveau dans 1es gisements de l'Omo (Ethiopie). *South African Journal of Science* **64**: 58–59.

Asfaw, B. 1985. Proximal femur articulation In Pliocene hominids. *American Journal of Physical Anthropology* **68**: 535–538.

Asfaw, B, White, T., Lovejoy. O, Latimer, B., Simpson, S. and Suwa. G. 1999. *Australopithecus garhi:* A new species of early hominid from Ethiopia. *Science* **284**: 629–635.

Bartholomew, G.A. and Birdsell, J.B. 1953. Ecology and the protohominids *American Anthropologist* **55**: 481–498.

Berge, C. and Kazmierczak, J.-B. 1986. Effects of size and locomotor adaptations on the hominid pelvis: evaluation of australopithecine bipedality with a new multivariate method, *Folia Prinratologia* **46**: 185–204.

Berger, C, Orban-Segebarth, R., and Schmid, P. 1984. Obstetrical interpretation of the australopithecine pelvic cavity *Journal of Human Evolution* **13**: 573–587.

Berger, L.R. and Clarke, R.J. 1995. Birds of prey and the taphonomy of the Taung child. *Journal of Human Evolution* **29**: 275–299.

Berger, L.R and Tobias, P.V. 1996. A chimpanzee-tike tibia from Sterkfontem. South Africa and Its Implications for the interpretation of bipedalism in *Australopithecus africanus. Journal of Human Evolution,* **30**: 343–348.

Berger L.R Mentei, CG and Thackeray, I.F. 1994. The renewal of excavation activities at Kromdraai, South Africa. *South African Journal of Science* **90**: 209–210.

Berger. L.R., Keyser A W., and Tobias, P.V. 1993. Brief Communication Gladysvale: first Early Hominid Site Discovered in South African Since, 1948. *American Journal of Physical Anthropology* **92**: 107–111.

Behrensmeyer, A.K., 1985. Taphonomy and the palenecologic reconstruction of hominid habitats in the Koobi Fora Formation. In *L'Environment des Homrnidés au Plio Pléistocene* (Y. Coppers, ed.) Paris: Masson, pp. 309–324.

Bellomo, RV. 1994. Methods of determining early hominid behavioral activities associated with the controlled use of fire at FxJi 20 Main. Koobi Fora. Kenya. *Journal of Human Evolution* **27**: 173–196.

Boas, N. 1988. *The status of Australopithecus afarensis. Yearbook of Physical Anthropology,* **31**: 85–113.

Brain. C.K. 1993a, *Swartkrans: A Cave's Chronicle of Early Man.* Transvaal Museum Monograph No. 8, Transvaal Museum, Pretoria.

Brain, C.K. 1993b. The occurrence of burnt bones at Swartkrans and their implications for the control of fire by early hominids. In: *Swartkrans, a cave's chronicle of carly man* (C.K. Brain, ed.) Transvaal Museum Monograph No. 8. pp. 229–242.

Brain, C.K. 1994. The Swartkrans Palaeontological research project in perspective: results and conclusions. *South African Journal of Science* **90**: 220–223.

Brain, C.K. and Shipman, P. 1993 The Swartkrans bone tools, In: *Swartkrans: a cave's chronicle of early man* (C.K. Brain, ed.) Transvaal Museum Monograph No. 8, pp. 195–216.

Broom, R. 1937. The Sterkfontein ape *Nature* **136**: 326.

Broom, R. and Schepers, G.W.H. 1946. *The South African fossil ape-man. The Australopirhecinae. Part 1. The occurrence and general structure of the South African ape-men.* Transvaal Museum Memorr 2.

Brunet, M., Beauvilain, A., Coppens, Y., Heintz, E., Moutaye, AHE. and Pilbeam, D 1995. The first australopithecine 2,500 kilometers west of the rift valley (Chad). *Nature* **378**: 273–275.

Cerling, T. 1992, development of grasslands and savannas in East Africa during the Neogene, *Palaeogeography, Palaeoclumatolgy and Palaeoecology* **97**: 241–247.

Chaplin. G., Jablonski, N.G. and Cable, N.T. 1994. Physiology, thermoregulation and bipedalism. *Journal of Human Evolution* **27**: 497–510.

Clarke, R.J 1988. A new *Australopithecus* cranium from Sterkfontein and its bearing on the ancestry of *Paranthropus.* In *Evolutionary History of the 'Robust' Australopithecures* (F. Grine. ed.) pp. 285–292. New York: Aldine de Gruyter.

Clarke. RJ. 1994. On some new interpretations of Sterkfontern stratigraphy *South African Journal of Science* **90**: 211–214.

Clarke, R.J, and Tobias, P.V. 1995. Sterkfontern Member 2 foot bones of the oldest South African hominid. *Science* **269**: 521–524.

Conroy, G.C., Weber, G.W., Seidler, H., Tobias. P.V., Kane, A., and Brunsden, B. 1998. Endocranial capacity in an early hominid cranium from Sterkfontein, South Africa *Science* **280**: 1730–1731.

Dart, R.A. 1925. *Australopithecus africanus*: the man-ape of South Africa. *Nature* **115**: 195–199.

Dean, M.C. 1985 The eruption pattern of the permanent incisors and first permanent molars in *Paranthropus robustus*. *American Journal of Physical Anthropology* **54**: 63–71.

Dean, M.C., Beynon, A.D. , Thackerav, J. F and Macho, G.A. 1993. Histological reconstruction of dental development and age at death of a juvenile *Paranthropus robustus* specimen, SK 63, from Swartkrans, South Africa. *American Journal of Physical Anthropology* **91**: 401–419.

Delson, E. 1986. Human phylogeny revised again. *Nature* **322**: 496–497.

Delson, E., Eldredge, N, and Tattersall, I 1977. Reconstruction of hominid phylogeny: a testable framework based on cladistic analysis. *Journal of Human Evolution* **6**: 263–278.

DuBrul. E.L. 1962. The general phenomenon of bipedalism. *American Zoologist* **2**: 205–398.

Eldredge, N. and Tattersall, I. 1975 Evolutionary models, phylogenetic reconstruction and another look at hominid phylogeny. *Contributions to Pharmatology* **5**: 218–242.

Falk, D. 1985. Apples. oranges and the lunate sulus. *American Journal of Physical Anthropology* 67: 313–315.

Falk, D. 1986. Evolution of cranial blood drainage in hominids enlarged occipital/marginal sinuses *and emissary foramina. Airwoman Journal of Physical Anthropology* **70**: 311–324.

Falk, D. 1987. Hominid palaeooneurology *Annual Review of Anthropology* **16**: 13–30.

Foley, R. 1987. *Another Unique Species* Harlow, Essex. Longman Group Limited.

Gee, H. 1995a. Uprooting the human family tree *Nature* **373**: 15.

Gee, H. 1995b. New hominid remains found in Ethiopia. *Nature* **373**: 272.

Grausz. H.M., Leakey, R.E., Walker. A.C. and Ward, C.V 1988. Associated Cranial and Postcranial *Bones of Australopithecus boisei.* In: *Evolutionary History of the 'robust' australopithecunes* (F.E. Grine, ed.) Aldine de Gruyter: New York. pp. 127–132.

Grine, F. 1982. A new juvenile hominid (Mammalia: Primates) from Member 3, Kromdraai Formation, Transvaal, South Africa. *Annals of the Transvaal Museum* **33**: 165–239.

Grine, F.E. 1985. Australopithecine evolution: the deciduous dental evidence. In: *Ancestors: the hard evidence* (E. Delson, ed.) pp. 153–167. Alan R. Liss, New York.

Harris, J.W.K. and Capaldo, S.D. 1993. The earliest stone tools: their implications for an understanding of the actisities and behaviour of late Pliocene hominids. In: *The use of tools by human and non-human primates* (A Bertheiet and J. Chavaillon, eds.) Oxford: Clarendon Press. pp., 196–220.

Hausler, M., and Schmid, P. 1995. Comparison of the pelves of Sts 14 and Al. 288–1: Implications for birth and sexual dimorphism in australopithecines. *Journal of Human Evolution.* **29**: 363–383.

Hay, R.L. and Leakey. M.D. 1988. The fossil footprints of Laetoli. *Scientific American* **246**: 38–45.

Hemzelin, J. de. Clark, J. D., White, T., Hart, W., Renne, P., WoldeGabriel. G., Beyene. Y., and Vrba, E. 1999. Environment and behavior of 2.5 million year old Bouri hominids. *Science* **284**: 615–629.

Holloway, R. 1973. Endocranial volumes of early African hominids and the role of the brain in human mosaic evolution. Journal *of Human Evolution* **2**: 449–458.

Holloway, R.L. 1985. *The past,* present and future significance of the Innate sulcus in early hominid evolution. In: *Hominid Evolution: Past, Present and Future* (P.V. Tobias, ed.) New York: Alan R. Liss, Inc. pp. 47–62.

Hunt. K. 1994. The evolution of human bipedality: ecology and functional morphology. *Journal of Human Evolution* **26**: 183–202.

Isbell. L.A., and Young, T.P. 1996. The evolution of bipedalism in hominids and reduced group size in chimpanzees - alternative responses to decreasing resource availability *Journal of Human Evolution* 30: 389–397.

Jablonski. N.G., and Chaplin, G. 1993. Origin of habitual terrestrial bipedalism in the ancestor of the Hominidae. *Journal of Human Evolution* **24**: 259–280.

Johanson. D.C., White, T. and Coppens, Y. 1978. A new species of the genus *Australopithecus* (Primates: Hominidae) from the Pliocene of eastern Africa. *Kirklandia,* No. 28, pp. 1–14.

Johanson. D.C. and White, T.D. 1979. A systematic assessment of early African hominids. *Science* **203**: 203, 321–330.

Jolly, C.J. 1970. The seed-eaters: a new model of hominid differentiation based on a baboon analogy. *Man* **5**: 1–26.

Jungers, W.L. 1982. Lucy's limbs: skeletal allometry and locomotion in *Australopithecus afarensis*. *Nature* **297**: 676–678.

Kimbel, W.H., White, T.C., and Johanson. D.C. 1998. Cranial morphology of *Australopithecus afarensis:* a comparative study based on a composite reconstruction of the adult skull. *American Journal of Physical Anthropology* **64**: 337–388.

Kimbel, W.H., White T.D., and Johanson, D.C. 1988. Implications of KNM-WT 17000 for the evolution of 'robust' australopithecines. In: *The Evolutionary History of the 'Robust' Australopithecines* (F. Grine, ed.) New York. Aldine de Gruyter pp. 259–268.

Kimbel, W.H., Johanson, D.C. and Rak, Y. 1994. The first skull and other new discoveries of *Australopithecus afarensis* at Hadar, Ethiopia. *Nature* **368**: 449–451.

Kuykendall, K.L. 1999. Description of the Gondolin Teeth: Hyper-robust hominids in South Africa? *American Journal of Physical Anthropology* **108(28)**: 176–177 (abstract).

Kuman, K 1994, The archaeology of Sterkfontein—past and present. *Journal of Human Evolution* **27**: 471–495.

Lague, M.R. and Jungers, W.L. 1996. Morphometric variation in Plio-Pleistocene hominid distal humeri. *American Journal of Physical Anthropology* **101**: 401–427.

Lampl, M., J.M. Monge, and A.E. Mann 1993. Further observations on a method for estimating hominoid dental developmental patterns. *American Journal of Physical Anthropology* **90**: 113–128.

Latimer, B., J.C. Ohman and C.O. Lovejoy 1987. Talocrural joint in African hominoids: implications for *Australopithecus afarensis*. American Journal of Physical Anthropology **74**: 155–175.

Leakey, L.S.B. 1959. A new fossil skull from Olduvai. *Nature* **184**: 491–493.

Leakey, M.G., Feibel, CS., McDougall I., and Walker A. 1995. New 4-million year old hominid species from Kanapoi and Allia Bay, Kenya. *Nature* **376**: 565–571.

Leakey, M.G., Feibel, C.S., McDougall, I., Ward, C. and Walker, A. 1998. New specimens and confirmation of an early age for *Australopithecus anamensis*. *Nature* **393**: 62–66.

Leakey, R.E.F. and Walker, A.C. 1976. *Australopithecus* and the single species hypothesis. *Nature* **261**: 572–574.

Lee-Thorpe, J. and van der Merwe, N.J. 1993. Stable carbon isotope studies of Swartkrans fossils. In: *Swartkrans: a cave's chronicle of early man* (C.K. Brain, ed.) Transvaal Museum Monograph No. 8, pp. 251–256.

Lee-Thorpe, J. van der Merwe, N.J. and Brain, C.K. 1994, Diet of *Australopithecus robustus* at Swartkrans from stable carbon isotopic analyse. *Journal of Human Evolution* **27**: 361–372.

Lockwood, C.A. 1999. Sexual dimorphism in the face of *Australopithecus africanus*. *American Journal of Physical Anthropology* **108**: 97–127.

Lovejoy, C.O. 1974. The gait of australpithecines. *Yearbook of Physical Anthropology* **17**: 147–161.

Lovejoy, C.O. 1981. The origin of man. *Science* **211**: 341–350.

Lovejoy, C.O. 1988. Evolution of human walking. *Scientific American* **259**: 82–89.

Leutenegger. W. 1987. Neonatal brain size and neurocranial dimensions in Pliocene hominids: implications for obstetrics. *Journal of Human Evolution* **16**: 291–296.

MacLatchy, L.M. 1996. Another look at the australopithecine hip. *Journal of Human Evolution* **31**: 455–476.

Marzke, M.W. 1986. Tool use and the evolution of hominid hands and bipedality. In: *Primate Evolution* (J. Else and P. Lee, eds.) Cambridge: Cambridge University Press, pp. 203–209.

McHenry, H. 1982. The pattern of human evolution: studies on bipedalism, mastication, and encephalizatian. *Annual Review of Anthropology* **11**: 151–173.

McHenry, H. 1992. Body size and proportions in early hominids. *American Journal of Physical Anthropology* **87**: 407–431.

McHenry, H. 1994. Behavioral ecological implications of early hominid body size. *Journal of Human Evolution* **27**: 77–87.

McHenry, H. and Berger L. R. 1998a. Limb lengths to Australopithecus and the origin of the genus *Homo*. *South African Journal of Science* **94**: 447–450.

McHenry, H. M., and Berger L.R. 1998b. Body proportions in *Australopithecus afarensis* and *A. africanus* and the origin of the genus *Homo*. *Journal of Human Evolution* **35**: 1–22.

McKee, J.K. and Tobias, P.V. 1994. Taung stratigraphy and taphonomy: preliminary results based on the 1988–1993 excavations. *South African Journal of Science* **90**: 233–235.

McKee, J. Thackeray, F. and Berger, L. (1995). Faunal assemblage sedation of southern African Pliocene and Pleistocene fossil deposits. *American Journal of Physical Anthropology* **96**: 235–250.

Olson. T.R. 1981. Basicranial morphology of the extant hominoids and Pliocene hominids: the new material from the Hadar formation. Ethiopia, and its significance in early human evolution and taxonomy. In: *Aspects of Human Evolution* (C.B. Stringer, ed.), pp. 99–128. Taylor and Francis, London.

Pilbeam, D. 1972. *The Ascent of Man, New York:* Macmillan Publishing Co. Inc.

Plummer. T.W. and Bishop, L.C. 1994. Hominid paleoecology at Olduvai Gorge, Tanzania as indicated by antelope remains. *Journal of Human Evolution,* **27**: 47–75.

Potts,. R 1998. Environmental hypotheses of hominin evolution. *Yearbook of Physical Anthropology,* **41**: 93–136.

Rak, Y. 1983. *The australopithecine face* Academic Press, London.

Ravey, M. 1978. Bipedelism: an early warning system for Miocene hominoids *Science,* **199**: 372.

Rayner. R.J., Moon, B.P. and Masters, J.C. 1993. The Makapansgat australopithecine environment. *Journal of Human Evolution* **24**: 219–231.

Reed, K.E. 1997 Early hominid evolution and ecological change through the African Plio-Pleistocene. *Journal of Human Evolution* **32**: 289–322.

Robinson. J.T., 1960 The affinities of the new Olduvai australopithecine. *Nature* **186**: 456–458.

Robinson. J.T., 1963. Adaptive radiation in the australopithecines and the origin of man. In: *African Ecology and Evolution* (G. Kurth ed.) Stuttgart. Gustav Fischer. pp. 120–140.

Robinson, J.T., 1972. *Early Hominid Posture and Locomotion.* Chicago: University of Chicago Press.

Rodman, P.S. and McHenry, H.M. 1980. Bioenergetics and the origin of hominid bipedalism. *American Journal of Physical Anthropology* **52**: 103–106.

Rogers, M.J., Feibel, C.S. and Harris, J.W.K. 1994, Changing patters of land use by Plio-Pleistocene hominids in the Lake Turkana Basis. *Journal of Human Evolution* **27**: 139–158.

Rose, M .D. 1991. The process of bipedalization in hominids. In: *Origine(s) de la Bipedie chez les Hominides (Cahiers de Paleonthropologie* (Y. Coppens and B. Senut, eds.), pp. 37–48. Paris: Editions du CNRS.

Schmid, P. 1991. The trunk of the australopithecines. In: *Origine(s) de la bipedie chez les hominides* (Y. Coppens and B. Senut, eds.) Paris: Primatologie Editions du CNRS. pp 225–234.

Schmid, P. 1983. Eine Rekonstrucklion des Skelettes von A.L. 288–1 (Hadar) und deren Konsequenzen. *Folia Primatologie* **40**: 283–306.

Schrenk, R., Bromage, T.G., Betzler, C.G., Ring. U, and Juwayeyi, Y. 1993. Oldest *Homo* and Pliocene biogeography of the Malawi Rift. *Nature* **365**: 833–836.

Senut, B. and Tardieu, C. 1985. Functional aspects of Plio-Pleistocene hominid limb bones: implications for taxonomy and phylogeny. In *Ancestors, the hard evidence* (E. Delson, ed.) New York: Alan R. Liss, Inc. pp., 193–201.

Shipman, P. and Harris, J.M. 1988. Habitat preference and paleoecology of *Australopithecus boisei* in Eastern Africa. In: *Evolutionary History of the 'Robust' Australopithecines* (F. Grine, ed.) New York: Aldine de Gruyter, pp. 343–382.

Sikes, N.E. 1994: Early hominid habitat preferences in East Africa: Paleosol carbon isotopic evidence. *Journal of Human Evolution* **27**: 25–45.

Sillen, A. and Hoering, T. 1993. Chemical characterization of burnt bones from Swartkrans. In: *Swartkrans: a cave's chronicle of early man* (C.K. Brain, ed.) Transvaal Museum Monograph No. 8, pp. 243–250.

Sinclair, A.R.E, Leakey, M.D. and Norton, Griffiths, M. 1986. Migration and hominid bipedalism. *Nature* **324**: 307–308.

Skelton, R.R. and McHenry, H.M. 1992. Evolutionary relationships among early hominids. *Journal of Human Evolution* **23**: 309–350.

Skelton, R.R., McHenry, H.M. and Drawhorn, G.M. 1986. Phylogenetic analysis of early hominids. *Current Anthropology* **27**: 21–43.

Smith, B.H. 1994. Patterns of dental development in *Homo, Australopethecus, Parn,* and *Gorilla. American Journal of Physical Anthropology* **94**: 307–326.

Sponheimer, M. and Lee-Thorpe, J. 1999. Isotopic evidence for the diet of an early hominid, *Australopithecus africanus. Science* **283**: 368–370.

Stern, J.T and Susman, R.L. 1983. The locomotor anatomy of *Australopithecus afarensis, American Journal of Physical Anthropology* **60**: 279–317.

Strait, D.S., Grine, F.E., and Moniz, M.A. 1997. A reappraisal of early hominid phylogeny. *Journal of Human Evolution* **32**: 17–82.

Steudel, K.L. 199. Locomotor energetics and hominid evolution. *Evolutionary Anthropology* **3**: 42–48.

Susman, R.L. 1988. Hand of *Paranthropus robustus* from Member 1, Swartkrans: fossil evidence for tool behavior. *Science* **240**: 781–784.

Susman, R.L. 1994. Fossil evidence for early hominid tool use *Science* **265**: 1570–1573.

Suwa, G., White, D.D., and Howell, F.C., 1996. Mandibular postcanine dentition from the Shungura Formation, Ethiopia: Crown morphology, taxonomic allocations, and Plio-Pleistocene hominid evolution. *American Journal of Physical Anthropology* **101**: 247–282.

Suwa, G., Asfaw, B., Beyene, Y., White, T.D., Katoh, S., Nagaoka, S., Nakaya, H., Uzawa, K., Renne, P., and WoldeGabriel, G. 1997. The first skull of *Australopithecus boisei. Nature* **389**: 489–492.

Tague, R.G. and Lovejoy, C.O. 1986. The obstetric pelvis of A.L. 288–1 (Lucy). *Journal of Human Evolution* **15**: 237–255.

Tartersali, I. and Eldredge, N. 1977. Fact, theory and fantasy in human paleontology. *American Scientist* **65**: 204–311.

Tobias. P.V. 1967. *Olduvai Gorge vol 2. The cranium and maxillary dentition of Australopithecus (Zinjanthropus) boisei.* Cambridge University Press: Cambridge.

Tobias. P.V. 1981. *"Australopithecus afarensis"* and *A. africanus:* critique and an alternative hypothesis. *Palaeontol Afr.* **23**: 117.

Trinkaus, E. and Long, J.C. 1990. Species attribution of the Swartkrans Member I first metacarpals: SK 84 and SKX 5020. *American Journal of Physical Anthropology* **83**: 419–424.

Tuttle, R H. Evolution of hominid bipedalism and prehensile capabilities. *Philosophical Transactions of the Royal Society B* **292**: 89–94.

Vrba, E., 1982. Biostratigraphy and chronology, based particularly on Bovidae, of southern hominid-associated assemblages: Makapansgat, Srerkfontein, Taung, Kromdraai, Swartkrans: also Elandsfuntern (Saldanah). Broken Hill (now Kabwe) and Cave of Hearths. *Congres International de Paléontologie Humane, ler Congres,* Tome I. pp. 707–752, Nice: CNRS.

Walker, A. and Leakey. R.E. 1988, The evolution of *Australopithecus boisei.* In: *The Evolutionary History of the 'Robust' Australopithecines* (F. Grine, ed.) New York: Aldine de Gruyter, pp. 247-258.

Walker, A., Leakey, R E., Harris, J.M. and Brown, F.H. 1986. 2.5 Myr *Australopithecus boisei* from west of Lake Turkana, Kenya. *Nature* **322**: 517–522.

Washburn, S.L. 1967. Behavior and the origin of man. *Proceedings of the Royal Anthropological Institute* **3**: 21–27.

Wescott, R.W, 1967. The exhibitionistic origin of human bipedalism. *Man* **2**: 630.

Wheeler, P.E. 1984. The evolution of bipedality and loss of functional body hair in hominids. *Journal of Haman Evolution* **13**: 91–98.

Wheeler, P.E. 1991a. The thermoregulatory advantages of hominid bipedalism in open equatorial environments: the contribution of increased convective heat loss and cutaneous evaporative cooling. *Journal of Human Evolution* **21**: 107–I15.

Wheeler, P.E. 1991b. The influence of bipedalism on the energy and water budgets of early hominids. *Journal of Human Evolution* **21**: 116–136.

Wheeler, P.E. 1992a. The influence of the loss of functional body hair on the energy and water budgets of early hominids. *Journal of Human Evolution* **23**: 379–388.

Wheeler, P.E. 1992b. The thermoregulatory advantages of large body size for hominids foraging in savannah environments. *Journal of Human Evolution* **23**: 351–362.

Wheeler, P.E. 1993. The influence of stature and body form on hominid energy and water budgets: a comparison of *Australopithecus* and early *Homo* physiques. *Journal of Human Evolution* **24**: 13–28.

Wheeler, P. E. 1994a. The thermoregulatory advantages of heat storage and shade-seeking behaviour to hominids foraging in equatorial savannah environments. *Journal of Human Evolution* **26**: 339–350.

Wheeler, P.E. 1994b. The foraging times of bipedal and quadrupedal hominids in open equatorial environments (a reply to Chaplin, Jablonski and Cable, 1994. *Journal of Human Evolution* **27**: 511–518.

White, T.D. and Suwa, G. 1987. Hominid footprints at Laetoli facts and interpretations. *American Journal of Physical Anthropology* **72**: 485–514.

White, T.D., Suwa, G., Hart, W.K., Walter, R.C., WoldeGabriel, G., Hemzelm, J. de, Clark, J.D., Asfaw, B. and Vrbha, E. 1993. New discoveries of *Australopithecus* at Maka in Ethiopia. *Nature* **366**: 261–265.

White, T.D., Suwa, G. and Asfaw, B. 1994. *Australopithecus ramidus.* a new species of early hominid from Aramis, Ethiopia. *Nature* **371**: 280–281.

White, T.D., Suwa, G. and Asfaw, B. 1995. *Australopithecus ramidus,* a new species of early hominid from Aramis. Ethiopia (correction). *Nature* **375**: 88.

Wolpoff, M.H. 1968. *Telanthropus* and the single species hypothesis. *American Anthropologist* **70**: 477–493.

Wood, B.A. 1991. *Koobi Fora Research Project, vol. 4: Homonid Cranial Remains,* Clarendon Press, Oxford.

Wood, B. A. 1993. Four legs good, two legs better. *Nature* **363**: 587–588.

Wood, B.A. 1994. The oldest hominid yet. *Nature* **371**: 280–281.

Wood, B.A. and Chamberlain, A.T. 1986. *Australopithecus:* Grade or Clade? In: *Major topics in primate and human evolution* (B.A. Wood, L. Martin and P. Andrews, eds.) Cambridge University Press. Cambridge, pp. 220–248.

Wood, B.A. and Aiello, L.C. 1998. Taxonomic and functional implications of mandibular scaling in early hominids. *American Journal of Physical Anthropology* **105**: 523–538.

Wood, BA. and Collard, M. 1999. The human genus. *Science,* **284**: 65–71.

Diet is a key element of an animal's adaptation. The authors describe the methods that are used to diagnose the diet of early hominins from examination of their teeth, and discuss the probable diets of many early hominin species.

14. Diet and the Evolution of the Earliest Human Ancestors

By Mark F. Teaford*† and Peter S. Ungar‡

S ince the discovery of *Australopithecus afarensis*, many researchers have emphasized the importance of bipedality in scenarios of human origins (1, 2). Surprisingly, less attention has been focused on the role played by diet in the ecology and evolution of the early hominids (as usually received). Recent work in a broad range of disciplines, such as paleoenvironmental studies (3, 4), behavioral ecology (5), primatology (6), and isotope analyses (7), has rekindled interests in early hominid diets. Moreover, important new fossils from the early Pliocene raise major questions about the role of dietary changes in the origins and early evolution of the Hominidae (8–10). In short, we need to focus not just on how the earliest hominids moved between food patches, but also on what they ate when they got there.

This paper presents a review of the fossil evidence for the diets of the Pliocene hominids *Ardipithecus ramidus*, *Australopithecus anamensis*, *Australopithecus afarensis*, and *Australopithecus africanus*. These hominids offer evidence for the first half of human evolution, from our split with prehistoric apes to the earliest members of our own genus, *Homo*. The taxa considered are viewed as a roughly linear sequence from *Ardipithecus* to *A. africanus*, spanning the time from 4.4 million to 2.5 million years ago. As such, they give us a unique opportunity to examine changes in dietary adaptations of our ancestors over nearly 2 million years. We also

Mark F. Teaford and Peter S. Ungar, "Diet and the Evolution of the Earliest Human Ancestors," *PNAS*, vol. 97, no. 25, pp. 13506–13511. Copyright © 2000 by National Academy of Sciences. Reprinted with permission.

trace what has been inferred concerning the diets of the Miocene hominoids to put changes in Pliocene hominid diets into a broader temporal perspective. From such a perspective, it becomes clear that the dietary capabilities of the early hominids changed dramatically in the time period between 4.4 million and 2.3 million years ago. Most of the evidence has come from five sources: analyses of tooth size, tooth shape, enamel structure, dental microwear, and jaw biomechanics. Taken together, they suggest a dietary shift in the early australopithecines, to increased dietary flexibility in the face of climatic variability. Moreover, changes in diet-related adaptations from *A. anamensis* to *A. afarensis* to *A. africanus* suggest that hard, abrasive foods became increasingly important through the Pliocene, perhaps as critical items in the diet.

TOOTH SIZE

In 1970, Jolly (11) noted that australopithecines had relatively small incisors compared with molars and speculated that this might be associated with terrestrial seed eating, as seen in *Theropithecus* today. Although this idea has been the subject of some controversy (12), Jolly's efforts have stimulated considerable research on the origins of hominid adaptations and on relative incisor size in a wide variety of living and fossil primates. Hylander (13), for example, examined the relationship of incisor row length (relative to body size) in a range of living anthropoids and found that those species with larger incisors tend to consume larger, tougher fruits, whereas those with smaller front teeth tend to feed on smaller foods, or those that require less extensive incisal preparation, such as leaves or berries. Since the work of Jolly and Hylander, numerous workers have looked to incisor size in early hominids and other fossil primates for clues concerning diet.

What can incisor size tell us of the diets of Miocene apes? Unfortunately, not as much as one would like. Ideally, to consider relative incisor sizes among taxa, we need estimates of species body weights based on attributes independent of the dentition. Such estimates are unavailable for most taxa. Furthermore, Miocene apes as a whole evidently had small incisors compared with extant hominoids, in much the same way that platyrrhines as a whole have relatively smaller incisors than do catarrhines, regardless of diet (14). Such phylogenetic effects make it difficult to find an extant comparative baseline series with which to compare these basal taxa of uncertain phyletic affinities.

On the other hand, incisor size might give us some clues to diet and tooth use for the early australopithecines, and we have good, consistent weight estimates from independent studies (15, 16) for many of these taxa. If we look at a regression of maxillary central incisor breadth on body size for species representing a variety of catarrhine genera, we see a separation of cercopithecines (with relatively larger incisors) above the line and colobines below (Fig. 1). Furthermore, more frugivorous chimpanzees and orangutans fall above the line, whereas gibbons and gorillas fall close to the line, with relatively smaller incisors. Indeed, values for the living frugivorous great apes fall above the 95% confidence limits of expected incisor size for modern catarrhines. The human values fall below the 95% confidence limits, indicating that we have very small incisors relative to body size.

Relative incisor sizes for the three "gracile" australopithecines are remarkably similar, and they fall very close to the regression line, much like the gorilla. These results are similar to those reported by Kay (21) and Ungar and Grine (17) and suggest that these hominids used their incisors in ingestion to a similar degree, although they all probably used these teeth less than either the chimpanzee or orangutan. These data can also give us some idea of whether a taxon often eats foods that require incisal preparation. For instance, lar gibbons have much smaller incisors than orangutans, and they depend on smaller fruits requiring little incisal preparation (17, 22, 23). From this perspective, the australopithecines probably put less emphasis on foods that require substantial incisor use, such as those with thick husks and those with flesh adherent to large, hard seeds. Body weight estimates and incisor size data for *Ardipithecus ramidus* and *Australopithecus garhi* should provide even more insights.

One of the hallmarks of the australopithecines has always been their large, relatively flat molars (24–29). There are certainly differences in the amount of occlusal relief between gracile and robust australopithecines (30) (see below). However, by comparison with other primates, the australopithecines' molars are still flat and huge. Even in the earliest hominids, this can be seen in a simple plot of mandibular postcanine tooth area (MD × BL, the product of maximal mesiodistal and buccolingual diameters), where most taxa have teeth larger than those of the modern orangutan (Fig. 2).

The only exception is *Ardipithecus*, which is more chimp-sized in the P_4–M_1 region, but intermediate between chimpanzees and orangutans in the M_2–M_3 region. Again, interpretations of such differences are hampered by the lack of body size estimates for *Ardipithecus*, but if a body size estimate of 51 kg is used for *A. anamensis* (the average of the two different estimates based on the tibia) (18), McHenry's "megadontia quotient" for this taxon is essentially identical to

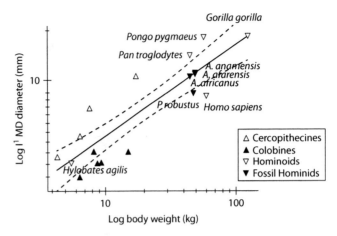

Fig. 1. Relative maxillary first incisor sizes in catarrhines. MD, mesiodistal. Dashed lines indicate 95% confidence limits of the least-squares regression plot (data from refs. 15 and 17–20).

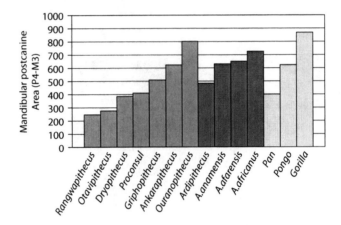

Fig. 2. Summed mandibular postcanine tooth areas (P4–M3) in Miocene apes, early hominids, and extant apes (data from refs. 8, 18–20, and 31–37).

that for *A. afarensis* (Fig. 3). In other words, its molars are large for a hominoid, but smaller than those of *A. africanus* or the "robust" australopithecines.

As one might expect, the Miocene hominoids show a tremendous range of mandibular molar sizes (Fig. 2). Many have postcanine tooth areas larger than that of *Ardipithecus*, and some (such as *Ouranopithecus*) even have larger postcanine tooth areas than that of *A. anamensis*, but as all body size estimates for them have been computed from dental remains, a megadontia quotient cannot be computed. The main message from a simple look at postcanine tooth size is that the earliest hominids make a nice progression leading into subsequent hominids, but they do not have larger postcanine teeth than all of the middle to late Miocene hominoids.

This might just mean that there are a variety of body sizes sampled in these taxa. However, as shown by the work of Lucas and colleagues (39), variations in tooth size are a means of adapting to changes in the external characteristics of foods, such as their size, shape, and abrasiveness. Clearly, some of these food characteristics were changing during the evolution of the earliest hominids, as postcanine teeth became relatively larger and larger. However, evidence from the middle to late Miocene shows that tooth size, by itself, cannot pinpoint the initial change to a hominid diet, at least not with the samples at hand.

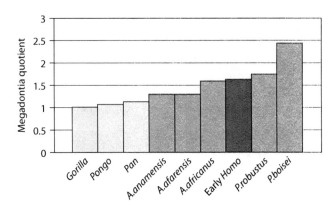

Fig. 3. Megadontia quotients for early hominids and extant primates (data from refs. 18, 20, 27, 31, and 38).

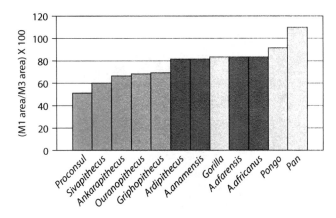

Fig. 4. Ratios of M1 to M3 areas, defined as the products of maximal mesiodistal and buccolingual diameters (data from refs. 8, 18–20, and 31–37).

One other way of looking at postcanine tooth size is to look at the ratio of the areas of M1 and M3 (Fig. 4). Lucas *et al.* (39) showed that this ratio was inversely related to the percentage of leaves, flowers, and shoots in the diet; that is, anthropoids with a high ratio of M1 to M3 area consumed more fruit than did those with a low M1 to M3 ratio. When this is computed for the earliest hominids, plus a sample of Miocene apes, a clear separation is evident, with the early hominids, including *Ardipithecus*, showing higher ratios than the Miocene apes. So, does this indicate more fruit in the diet of the earliest hominids? To begin to answer this question, we must look at analyses of tooth shape.

TOOTH SHAPE

Variations in tooth shape are a means of adapting to changes in the internal characteristics of foods, such as their strength, toughness, and deformability (39–43). Clearly, foods are complicated structures; thus it is impossible to describe all of the internal characteristics that might have confronted the earliest hominids' teeth. However, another approach is to describe the capabilities of those teeth.

For example, tough foods, those that are difficult to fracture, are generally sheared between the leading edges of sharp crests. In contrast, hard brittle foods, those that are easy to fracture but difficult to penetrate, are crushed between planar surfaces. As such, reciprocally concave, highly crested teeth have the capability of efficiently processing tough items such as insect exoskeletons and leaves, whereas rounder and flatter cusped teeth are best suited for a more frugivorous diet. Kay (21) has devised a "shearing quotient" as a measure of the relative shear potential of molar teeth. Basically, more folivorous species have the highest shearing quotients, followed by those that prefer brittle, soft fruits; finally, hard-object feeders have the lowest shearing quotients (21, 44).

Shearing crest studies have been conducted on early Miocene African apes and middle to late Miocene European apes. These studies suggest a considerable range of diets in these forms. For example, *Rangwapithecus* and *Oreopithecus* have relatively long shearing crests, suggesting folivory; *Ouranopithecus* has extremely short "crests," suggesting a hard-object specialization; whereas most other Miocene taxa studied, such as *Proconsul* and *Dryopithecus*, have the intermediate length crests of a frugivore (14, 45).

As for the early hominids, *A. africanus* had more occlusal relief than did *Paranthropus robustus*, suggesting a dietary difference between these species (30). Additional preliminary shearing quotient studies support this idea while reaffirming that the australopithecines, as a group, had relatively flat, blunt molar teeth and lacked the long shearing crests seen in some extant hominoids (28). By itself, this indicates that the earliest hominids would have had difficulty breaking down tough, pliant foods, such as soft seed coats and the veins and stems of leaves—although they probably were capable of processing buds, flowers, and shoots.

Interestingly, as suggested by Lucas and Peters (46), another tough pliant food they would have had difficulty processing is meat. In other words, the early hominids were not dentally preadapted to eat meat—they simply did not have the sharp, reciprocally concave shearing blades necessary to retain and cut such foods. In contrast, given their flat, blunt teeth, they were admirably equipped to process hard brittle objects. What about soft fruits? It really depends on the toughness of those fruits. If they were tough, then they would also need to be precisely retained and sliced between the teeth. Again, early hominids would be very inefficient at it. If they were not tough, then the hominids could certainly process soft fruits.

In sum, Miocene apes show a range of adaptations, including folivory, soft-fruit eating, and hard-object feeding. This range exceeds that of living hominoids and especially the early hominids. Although studies of shearing crest length have been conducted on only some of the early hominids, all evidence indicates that the australopithecines had relatively flat molar teeth compared with many living and fossil apes. These teeth were well suited for breaking down hard, brittle foods, including some fruits and nuts, and soft, weak foods, such as flowers and buds; but again, they were not well suited for breaking down tough pliant foods such as stems, soft seed pods, and meat.

ENAMEL STRUCTURE

Another area of interest regarding dental functional anatomy is the study of enamel thickness. There are certainly methodological differences between studies (47–52), but the consensus still seems to be that the australopithecines had relatively thick enamel compared with living primates, and that many of the Miocene apes also had thick enamel (24, 28, 48–49, 51, 53–54). Interestingly, this perspective may be changing as we get glimpses of more and more new taxa. For instance, Conroy *et al.* (55) have noted that *Otavipithecus* may have had thin enamel, and White *et al.* (8) have made the same observation for *Ardipithecus*. Granted, in neither case do we have a detailed series of measurements over the tooth crown, but still, the figures that have been quoted (less than 1 mm for *Otavipithecus* and 1.1–1.2 mm for *Ardipithecus*) are far less than those quoted for the australopithecines.

So what might be the functional significance of enamel thickness? The most frequently cited correlations are between the consumption of hard food items, or abrasive food items, and thick molar enamel (58–59). There are many potential complicating factors (51, 56, 59–60); thus it is perhaps not surprising that the correlation between enamel thickness and diet is not a perfect one (57). Moreover, thick enamel by itself does not necessarily provide protection against hard objects, which commonly cause fracture of enamel (61). The best protection against this is prism or crystallite decussation or interweaving. Maas (62, 63), Rensberger (64, 65), and others (42, 59) have shown that prism and crystallite orientations can give clues to intricate details of dental function, and that decussation can be an effective crack-stopping mechanism in many animals. Only anecdotal references to this phenomenon in Miocene apes and early hominids have been made thus far, largely because more detailed work generally requires the sectioning and etching of teeth. Still, after some discussion and debate (48–49, 53), a consensus now seems to be that they did have a significant degree of prism decussation. Thus, the thick enamel of the early hominids may have been a means of resisting breakage during the consumption of hard objects and an adaptation that prolonged the life of the tooth, given an abrasive diet.

DENTAL MICROWEAR

Numerous workers have recognized that microscopic wear on the incisors and molars of primates reflects tooth use and diet. For example, those primates that often use their front teeth in ingestion have high densities of microwear striations on their incisors. Furthermore, folivores have a high incidences of long narrow scratches on their molars, whereas frugivores have more pits on those surfaces. Among frugivores, hard-object feeders have even higher pit incidences than soft-fruit eaters. These and other relationships between microwear and feeding behaviors in living primates have been used to infer diet in fossil forms. Miocene apes have a remarkable range of microwear patterning, greatly exceeding that of living hominoids. For example, relatively high scratch densities suggest that *Micropithecus, Rangwapithecus,* and especially *Oreopithecus* (66) included more leaves in their diets. In contrast, high pit percentages suggest that *Griphopithecus* and *Ouranopithecus* (66) were hard-object specialists. Finally, intermediate microwear patterns suggest that most other species studied, such as *Gigantopithecus, Dendropithecus, Proconsul, Dryopithecus,* and, perhaps, *Sivapithecus* (66–68), had diets dominated by soft fruits. These data give us a glimpse of the extraordinary variation from which the last common ancestor of apes and hominids evidently arose.

Unfortunately, little is known about the microwear of early australopithecines. No microwear research has yet been published for either *Ardipithecus ramidus* or *A. anamensis,* although there has been some done on *A. afarensis* and *A. africanus.* The work done on *A. afarensis* has been largely qualitative and focused on the anterior teeth, and it suggests that these hominids were beginning to exploit savanna resources (69). Furthermore, Ryan and Johanson (70) argued that *A. afarensis* had a mosaic of gorilla-like fine wear striae and baboon-like pits and microflakes, indicating the use of incisors to strip gritty plant parts such as seeds, roots, and rhizomes. These authors also suggested that there was a functional shift in the P^3 complex from ape-like slicing and cutting to hominid puncture-crushing.

Work done on *A. africanus* has been more quantitative but has focused on comparing this taxon to *Paranthropus robustus* rather than to extant hominoids. Grine (71) found that *A. africanus* molars have lower incidences of pitting than seen for *Paranthropus. A. africanus* scratches are also longer and narrower and show more homogeneity in orientation. Grine argued that compared with the "robust" forms, *A. africanus* ate more soft fruits and leaves. Comparisons with work from Teaford (72) places *A. africanus* between *Cebus olivaceus* on one hand and *Pan troglodytes* on the other. Work on *A. africanus* incisors has shown that this taxon has higher microwear feature densities on all surfaces examined than does *Paranthropus* (17). This suggests that *A. africanus* processed a greater variety of foods with its front teeth, including larger, more abrasive ones, than were encountered by *Paranthropus.* Comparisons with an extant baseline series examined by Ungar (73) puts *Australopithecus* between *Pongo pygmaeus* and the seed predator/folivore *Presbytis thomasi* in degree of anterior tooth use in ingestion.

In sum, then, the microwear suggests that, by the end of the Miocene, hominoids had a wide range of diets. In contrast, *A. afarensis* probably focused on soft fruit but also began to incorporate into its diet abrasive, terrestrial resources that required incisal stripping. *A. africanus* may still have focused on soft fruit, particularly that which required a moderate amount of incisal preparation. Clearly, considerably more work is needed on these and other early hominids to put together a reasonable picture of diet based on microwear evidence.

MANDIBULAR BIOMECHANICS

Finally, there are other lines of evidence that we can examine to look for evidence of diet. Mandibular fragments are among the most common bony remains found at hominid fossil sites, and the architecture of this bone has been adapted to withstand stresses and strains associated with oral food processing. Thus its morphology probably reflects some aspects of diet. Analyses of australopithecine mandibular biomechanics have focused on corpus size and shape.

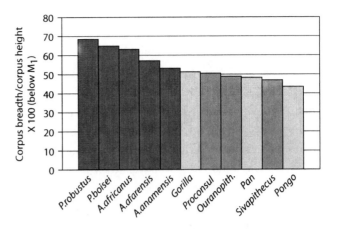

Fig. 5. Mandibular corpus shape (data from refs. 75, 76, and 85 and M. Leakey, personal communication).

Comparisons with extant hominoids have shown that *A. afarensis* and *A. africanus* have relatively thick mandibular corpora (74, 75). The same pattern was also found for *Paranthropus boisei* and *P. robustus*. Fig. 5 shows mandibular robusticity index values for extant great apes, some Miocene apes, and early australopithecines. The early hominids show relatively thicker mandibular corpora than extant great apes and Miocene catarrhines, suggesting a morphological shift in the former.

Both functional and nonfunctional interpretations have been offered to explain this phenomenon. For example, it may simply be that a thick mandibular corpus is an effect of large cheek teeth or a reduced canine. This is not a likely explanation, however, as australopithecines still have relatively broad mandibles when considered relative to molar size, and there appears to be no relationship between mandibular robusticity and relative canine size among the australopithecines (75).

Despite some inherent difficulties, it seems more likely that the unique shape of the australopithecine mandibular corpus relates to the functional demands of mastication. Thickened mandibles can act to resist extreme stresses associated with transverse bending (that is, "wishboning") and torsion. Because wishboning stresses decline toward the back of the corpus, torsion is likely a more important explanation. Corpus torsion can result from bite force and muscle activity during mastication. Therefore, it may be that australopithecine mandibular morphology reflects elevated stresses associated with unusual mechanical demands. Daegling and Grine (75) suggest that australopithecines may have eaten fibrous, coarse foods that required repetitive loading. While this fails to explain why colobines do not have thick corpora, it does suggest a fundamental difference between australopithecines and living great apes that may reflect a shift in diet in the early hominids.

Studies of corpus shape in *A. anamensis* and *Ardipithecus ramidus* will likely provide further clues regarding differences in mandibular architecture between great apes and later australo-pithecines. Corpus robusticity indices for *A. anamensis* below M_1 average 53.5 (M. Leakey, personal communication). These values fall at the upper range for extant hominoids (*Pan* = 39.2–57.8; *Gorilla* = 43.5–59.7; *Pongo* = 35.7–52.0) and at the lower end of the range for later fossil hominids (*A. afarensis* = 48.4–68.9, *A. africanus* = 54.8–79.0) (Fig. 5) (data from Daegling and Grine and Lockwood *et al.*) (75, 85).

In sum, the architecture of the mandibular corpus suggests that the "gracile" australopithecines differed from living apes in their abilities to dissipate masticatory stresses. Taken with other lines of evidence, this certainly suggests a difference in diet between living apes and *A. anamensis*, and between *A. anamensis* and later hominids, with *A. anamensis* intermediate between the African ape and later australopithecine conditions.

DISCUSSION

The australopithecines exhibited a complex of morphological fea-tures related to diet that are unique compared with living hominoids or Miocene apes. These early hominids all had small- to moderate-sized incisors; large, flat molars with little shear potential; a ratio of first to third molar area that was low compared with those of extant apes, but generally higher than those of Miocene apes; thick tooth enamel; and thick mandibular corpora. This suite of traits is distinctive of australopithecines and suggests a dietary shift at or near the stem of hominid evolution. Their thick-enameled, flattened molars would have had great difficulty propagating cracks through tough foods, suggesting that the australopithecines were not well suited for eating tough fruits, leaves, or meat. The dental microwear data agree with this conclusion, as the australopithecine patterns documented to date are most similar to those of modern-day seed predators and soft fruit eaters. Furthermore, given their comparatively small incisors, these hominids probably did not specialize in large, husked fruits or those requiring extensive incisal preparation. Instead, the australopithecines would have easily been able to break down hard, brittle foods. Their large flat molars would have served well for crushing, and their thick enamel would have withstood abrasion and fracture. Their mandibular corpora would probably have conferred an advantage for resisting failure, given high occlusal loads. In essence, for much of their history, the australopithecines had an adaptive package that allowed them ready access to hard objects, plus soft foods that were not particularly tough. The early hominids could also have eaten both abrasive and nonabrasive foods. This ability to eat both hard and soft foods, plus abrasive and nonabrasive foods, would have left the early hominids particularly well suited for life in a variety of habitats, ranging from gallery forest to open savanna.

Does this mean we can talk of a characteristic "australopithecine" dietary pattern? Perhaps to some extent, but although the australopithecines shared many features in common, they also differed from one another, suggesting a change in diet through time. Such morphological changes occurred as a mosaic, much as that seen for locomotor anatomy.

Much of the evidence for *Ardipithecus ramidus* is not yet available, but despite its thin molar enamel and absolutely smaller teeth than those of later hominids, it shows molar size proportions that may hint at dietary changes to come. *A. anamensis* shows the first indications of thicker molar enamel in a hominid, and its molar teeth were equivalent in size to those of *A. afarensis*. Still, its mandibular corpus is intermediate in robusticity between those of living great apes and later australopithecines. This combination of features suggests that *A. anamensis* might have been the first hominid to be able to effectively withstand the functional demands of hard and perhaps abrasive objects in its diet, whether or not such items were frequently eaten or were only an important occasional food source. *A. afarensis* was similar to *A. anamensis* in relative tooth sizes and probably enamel thickness, yet it did show a large increase in mandibular robusticity. This increase may be due to changes in peak force magnitude or degree of repetitive loading in mastication. Either way, hard and perhaps abrasive foods may have become even more important components of the diet of *A. afarensis*. *A. africanus* shows yet another increase in postcanine tooth size, which by itself would suggest an increase in the sizes and abrasiveness of foods. However, its molar microwear does not show the degree of pitting one might expect from a classic hard-object feeder. Thus, even *A. africanus* has evidently not begun to specialize in hard objects, but rather has emphasized dietary breadth. In contrast, subsequent "robust" australopithecines do show hard-object microwear and craniodental specializations, suggesting a substantial departure in feeding adaptive strategies early in the Pleistocene.

In sum, diet was probably an important factor in the origin and early evolution of our family. The earliest australopithecines show a unique suite of diet-related features unlike those of Miocene apes or living hominoids. Such features suggest that the earliest hominids may have begun to experiment with harder, more brittle foods at the expense of softer, tougher ones early on. This does not mean that all of the australopithecines were specialized hard-object feeders. It merely means that, through time, they acquired the ability to feed on hard objects. Many modern primates need to consume critical "fall-back foods" at certain times of the year (6), and it may well be that the earliest australopithecines resorted to the consumption of hard objects only in such situations, whereas the robust australopithecines relied on them far more regularly.

Another important aspect of early hominid trophic adaptations is evident from data presented here—the dietary shift from apes to early hominids did not involve an increase in the consumption of tough foods, and so the australopithecines were not preadapted for eating meat. This conclusion runs counter to (*i*) recent isotope work suggesting that the australopithecines did in fact consume significant amounts of meat (7) and (*ii*) nutritional work suggesting that meat may have provided critical nutrients for both young and old hominids (77–79). There would seem to be three different ways to reconcile these perspectives. First, the present study has reviewed only craniodental features related to diet. If the australopithecines used other means for ingesting and processing meat (e.g., tools), they might have been able to process meat more efficiently than the craniodental evidence suggests (80, 81). Second, the heavy C3 signature found in *A. africanus* (7) may reflect the consumption of underground storage organs of C3 plants rather than meat (82). Third, the functional analyses of the teeth assume that all meat has the same degree of toughness. This may not be the case. Studies of the physical properties of food have thus far focused on plant remains, with only brief mention of the toughness of materials like skin (40, 46). Variations in toughness between animal tissues might well be due to variations in the arrangement and density of collagen matrix. Furthermore, the physical effects of decomposition might render meat less tough and more readily processed by hominids. If this is so, it could be further evidence in support of scavenging as part of the early hominid way of life.

Investigators have tried to relate patterns of hominid evolution to patterns of climatic change for some time (3, 4). The focus of much of the recent work has been on the origin of the genus *Homo*. Can the dietary shifts in the earliest hominids also be tied to such changes? Whereas there is some evidence of large-scale climatic changes around the Mediterranean (83) and unusual faunal turn-over in parts of western Asia (84), there are no large-scale changes evident in sub-Saharan Africa until after the earliest hominids have arrived on the scene (i.e., not until 1.5–2.5 million years ago). There is the slow and inexorable cooling and drying of the Miocene, but perhaps the crucial result of this was an increase in microhabitat variability. Certainly, there are limits to our paleoecological evidence from this period, but as Potts (4) has noted, "in general, the oldest hominids were associated with a diverse range of habitats." These included lake and river margins, woodland, bushland, and savanna. Potts (4) has emphasized that locomotor versatility was a crucial adaptation of the earliest hominids in the face of such varied environmental conditions. We feel that this perspective needs to be extended to the dietary adaptations of the earliest hominids as well. In such a land of variable opportunities, the generalized craniodental toolkit of the earliest hominids may have had a distinct advantage, as it allowed our forbears the flexibility to cope with short-term and long-term climatic variations and the resultant changes in resource availability.

We are grateful to the Governments of Ethiopia, Kenya, and Tanzania and especially to the National Museums of Ethiopia, Kenya, and Tanzania for permission to study early hominid specimens in their care. This work was supported by National Science Foundation Grants SBR 9804882 and 9601766.

NOTES

1. Lovejoy, C. O. (1975) in *Primate Functional Morphology and Evolution,* ed. Tuttle, R. L. (Mouton, The Hague), pp. 291–326.

2. Susman, R. L., Stern, J. T. & Jungers, W. L. (1984) *Folia Primatol.* **43,** 113–156.

3. Vrba, E. S. (1995) in *Paleoclimate and Evolution, with Emphasis on Human Origins,* eds. Vrba, E. S., Denton, G. H., Partridge, T. C. & Burckle, L. H. (Yale Univ. Press, New Haven, CT), pp. 24–45.

4. Potts, R. (1998) *Yearbook Phys. Anthropol.* **41,** 93–136.

5. O'Connell, J. F., Hawkes, K. & Blurton Jones, N. G. (1999) *J. Hum. Evol.* **36,** 461–485.

6. Conklin-Brittain, N. L., Wrangham, R. W. & Hunt, K. D. (1998) *Int. J. Primatol.* **19,** 949–970.

7. Sponheimer, M. & Lee-Thorp, J. A. (1999) *Science* **283,** 368–370.

8. White, T. D., Suwa, G. & Asfaw, B. (1994) *Nature (London)* **371,** 306–312.

9. Asfaw, B., White, T., Lovejoy, O., Latimer, B., Simpson, S. & Suwa, G. (1999) *Science* **284,** 629–634.

10. Ward, C., Leakey, M. & Walker, A. (1999) *Evol. Anthropol.* **7,** 197–205.

11. Jolly, C. J. (1970) *Man* **5,** 1–26.

12. Dunbar, R. I. M. (1976) *J. Hum. Evol.* **5,** 161–167.

13. Hylander, W. L. (1975) *Science* **189,** 1095–1098.

14. Kay, R. F. & Ungar, P. S. (1997) in *Function, Phylogeny and Fossils: Miocene Hominoids and Great Ape and Human Origins,* eds. Begun, D. R., Ward, C. & Rose, M. (Plenum, New York), pp. 131–151.

15. Jungers, W. L. (1988) in *Evolutionary History of the "Robust" Australopithecines,* ed. Grine, F. E. (de Gruyter, New York), pp. 115–125.

16. McHenry, H. M. (1992) *Evol. Anthropol.* **1,** 15–20.

17. Ungar, P. S. & Grine, F. E. (1991) *J. Hum. Evol.* **20,** 313–340.

18. Leakey, M. G., Feibel, C. S., McDougall, I. & Walker, A. (1995) *Nature (London)* **376,** 565–571.

19. Wood, B. A. (1991) *Hominid Cranial Remains,* Koobi Fora Research Project (Clarendon, Oxford), Vol. 4.

20. Coffing, K., Feibel, C., Leakey, M. & Walker, A. (1994) *Am. J. Phys. Anthropol.* **93,** 55–65.

21. Kay, R. F. (1984) in *Adaptations for Foraging in Nonhuman Primates: Contributions to an Organismal Biology of Prosimians, Monkeys and Apes,* eds. Rodman, P. S. & Cant, J. G. H. (Columbia Univ. Press, New York), pp. 21–53.

22. Ungar, P. S. (1994) *Am. J. Phys. Anthropol.* **95,** 197–219.

23. Ungar, P. S. (1996) *Am. J. Primatol.* **38,** 145–156.

24. Robinson, J. T. (1956) *Mem. Transvaal Mus.* **9,** 1–179.

25. Wolpoff, M. H. (1973) *Am. J. Phys. Anthropol.* **39,** 375–394.

26. Wood, B. A. & Abbott, S. A. (1983) *J. Anat.* **136,** 197–219.

27. McHenry, H. M. (1984) *Am. J. Phys. Anthropol.* **64,** 297–306.

28. Kay, R. F. (1985) *Annu. Rev. Anthropol.* **14,** 315–341.

29. Suwa, G., Wood, B. A. & White, T. D. (1994) *Am. J. Phys. Anthropol.* **93,** 407–426.

30. Grine, F. E. (1981) *S. Afr. J. Sci.* **77,** 203–230.

31. Mahler, P. E. (1973) Ph.D. thesis (Univ. of Michigan, Ann Arbor).

32. Alpagut, B., Andrews, P. & Martin, L. (1990) *J. Hum. Evol.* **19,** 397–422.

33. Alpagut, B., Andrews, P., Fortelius, M., Kappelman, J., Temizsoy, I., Çelebi, H. & Lindsay, W. (1996) *Nature (London)* **382,** 349–351.

34. Andrews, P. (1978) *Bull. Br. Mus. (Nat. Hist.)* **30,** 85–224.

35. Begun, D. R. & Güleç, E. (1998) *Am. J. Phys. Anthropol.* **105,** 279–314.

36. de Bonis, L. & Melentis, J. (1984) *Cour. Forschungsinst. Senckenberg* **69,** 13–23.

37. Leakey, M. G., Feibel, C. S., McDougall, I., Ward, C. & Walker, A. (1998) *Nature (London)* **393,** 62–66.

38. McHenry, H. M. (1988) in *Evolutionary History of the "Robust" Australopithecines,* ed. Grine, F. E. (de Gruyter, New York), pp. 133–147.

39. Lucas, P. W., Corlett, R. T. & Luke, D. A. (1986) *Z. Morphol. Anthropol.* **76,** 253–276.

40. Lucas, P. W. & Teaford, M. F. (1994) in *Colobine Monkeys: Their Ecology, Behaviour and Evolution,* eds. Davies, A. G. & Oates, J. F. (Cambridge Univ. Press, Cambridge, U.K.), pp. 173–203.

41. Spears, I. R. & Crompton, R. H. (1996) *J. Hum. Evol.* **31,** 517–535.

42. Strait, S. G. (1997) *Evol. Anthropol.* **5,** 199–211.

43. Yamashita, N. (1998) *Am. J. Phys. Anthropol.* **106,** 169–188.

44. Meldrum, D. J. & Kay, R. F. (1997) *Am. J. Phys. Anthropol.* **102,** 407–428.

45. Ungar, P. S. & Kay, R. F. (1995) *Proc. Natl. Acad. Sci. USA* **92,** 5479–5481.

46. Lucas, P. W. & Peters, C. R. (2000) in *Development, Function and Evolution of Teeth,* eds. Teaford, M. F., Smith, M. M. & Ferguson, M. W. J. (Cambridge Univ. Press, Cambridge, U.K.), pp. 282–289.

47. Martin, L. B. (1985) *Nature (London)* **314,** 260–263.

48. Beynon, A. D. & Wood, B. A. (1986) *Am. J. Phys. Anthropol.* **70,** 177–193.

49. Grine, F. E. & Martin, L. B. (1988) in *Evolutionary History of the "Robust" Australopithecines,* ed. Grine, F. E. (de Gruyter, New York), pp. 3–42.

50. Beynon, A. D., Dean, M. C. & Reid, D. J. (1991) *Am. J. Phys. Anthropol.* **86,** 295–309.

51. Macho, G. A. & Thackeray, J. F. (1992) *Am. J. Phys. Anthropol.* **89,** 133–143.

52. Spoor, C. F., Zonneveld, F. W. & Macho, G. A. (1993) *Am. J. Phys. Anthropol.* **91,** 469–484.

53. Gantt, D. G. (1986) in *Comparative Primate Biology. Volume 1. Systematics, Evolution, and Anatomy.* Swindler, D. R. & Erwin, J. (Liss, New York), Vol. 1, pp. 453–475.

54. Andrews, P. & Martin, L. (1991) *Philos. Trans. R. Soc. London B* **334,** 199–209.

55. Conroy, G. C., Pickford, M., Senut, B., Van Couvering, J. & Mein, P. (1992) *Nature (London)* **356,** 144–148.

56. Martin, L. B. (1983) Ph.D. thesis (Univ. of London, London).

57. Maas, M. C. & Dumont, E. R. (1999) *Evol. Anthropol.* **8,** 133–152.

58. Kay, R. F. (1981) *Am. J. Phys. Anthropol.* **55,** 141–151.

59. Dumont, E. R. (1995) *J. Mammal.* **76,** 1127–1136.

60. Macho, G. A. & Berner, M. E. (1993) *Am. J. Phys. Anthropol.* **92,** 189–200.

61. Teaford, M. F., Maas, M. C. & Simons, E. L. (1996) *Am. J. Phys. Anthropol.* **101,** 527–544.

62. Maas, M. C. (1993) *Am. J. Phys. Anthropol.* **92,** 217–233.

63. Maas, M. C. (1994) *Am. J. Phys. Anthropol.* **95,** 221–242.

64. Rensberger, J. M. (1997) in *Tooth Enamel Microstructure,* eds. Koenigswald, W. v. & Sander, M. (Balkema, Rotterdam), pp. 237–257.

65. Rensberger, J. M. (2000) in *Development, Function and Evolution of Teeth,* eds. Teaford, M. F., Smith, M. M. & Ferguson, M. W. J. (Cambridge Univ. Press, Cambridge, U.K.), 252–268.

66. Ungar, P. S. (1996) *J. Hum. Evol.* **31,** 335–366.

67. Teaford, M. F. & Walker, A. C. (1984) *Am. J. Phys. Anthropol.* **64,** 191–200.

68. Daegling, D. J. & Grine, F. E. (1994) *S. Afr. J. Sci.* **90,** 527–532.

69. Puech, P.-F. & Albertini, H. (1984) *Am. J. Phys. Anthropol.* **65,** 87–91.

70. Ryan, A. S. & Johanson, D. C. (1989) *J. Hum. Evol.* **18,** 235–268.

71. Grine, F. E. (1986) *J. Hum. Evol.* **15,** 783–822.

72. Teaford, M. F. (1988) *Scanning Microsc.* **2,** 1149–1166.

73. Ungar, P. S. (1998) *Evol. Anthropol.* **6,** 205–217.

74. Hylander, W. L. (1988) in *Evolutionary History of the "Robust" Australopithecines,* ed. Grine, F. E. (de Gruyter, New York), pp. 55–58.

75. Daegling, D. J. & Grine, F. E. (1991) *Am. J. Phys. Anthropol.* **86,** 321–339.

76. Smith, R. J. (1980) Ph.D. dissertation (Yale Univ., New Haven, CT).

77. Milton, K. & Demment, M. (1988) *Am. J. Primatol.* **46,** 45–52.

78. Milton, K. (1999) *Evol. Anthropol.* **8,** 11–21.

79. Speth, J. D. (1989) *J. Hum. Evol.* **18,** 329–343.

80. Blumenschine, R. J. & Cavallo, J. A. (1992) *Sci. Am.* **267,** 90–96.

81. de Heinzelin, J., Clark, J. D., White, T., Hart, W., Renne, P., WoldeBabriel, G., Beyene, Y. & Vrba, E. (1999) *Science* **284,** 625–629.

82. Lee-Thorp, J. (2001) in *The Evolution of Human Diet,* eds. Ungar, P. S. & Teaford, M. F. (Greenwood, New Haven, CT), in press.

83. Bernor, R. L. (1983) in *New Interpretations of Ape and Human Ancestry,* eds. Ciochon, R. L. & Corruccini, R. S. (Plenum, New York), pp. 21–64.

84. Barry, J. C. (1995) in *Paleoclimate and Evolution, with Emphasis on Human Origins,* eds. Vrba, E. S., Denton, G. H., Partridge, T. C. & Burckle, L. H. (Yale Univ. Press, New Haven, CT), pp. 115–134.

85. Lockwood, C. A., Kimbel, W. H. & Johanson, D. C. (2000) *J. Hum. Evol.* **39,** 23–55.

The genus *Paranthropus* was at one time not distinguished from *Australpithecus*. The author explains why *Paranthropus* and *Australpithecus* should be considered distinct genera, the evolutionary relationships of the different species of *Paranthropus* to each other and to *Australopithecus*, and how the adaptation of *Paranthropus* can be inferred from its anatomy.

15. Paranthropus

By Frederick E. Grine

Genus name employed in reference to the clade that comprises the "robust" australopith fossils from the South African sites of Kromdraai, Swartkrans, and Drimolen (*Paranthropus robustus*), the geochronologically older sediments of the Shungura and Nachukui Formations of Ethiopia and Kenya (*P. aethiopicus*), and numerous later Plio-Pleistocene localities in Tanzania, Kenya, and Ethiopia (*P. boisei*).

The name *Paranthropus*, which means literally "beside man" or "next to man," was coined by R. Broom in 1938, when he described the first fossil hominid from the site of Kromdraai as belonging to the taxon *Paranthropus robustus*. Subsequently discovered australopith remains from the site of Swartkrans were also referred by Broom to *Paranthropus*, albeit to a separate species, *P. crassidens*. He regarded the Kromdraai and Swartkrans fossils as being so distinct from the *Australopithecus* specimens from Taung, Sterkfontein, and Makapansgat as to warrant their separation as a distinct subfamily, the Paranthropinae. Further work, principally by J.T. Robinson, served to substantiate the validity of recognizing the "robust" australopith fossils as representing a separate genus, *Paranthropus*, although he recognized the Kromdraai and Swartkrans fossils as composing a single species, *P. robustus*, and he did not consider that they were attributable to a separate subfamily. Robinson maintained that because *Paranthropus* and *Australopithecus* were on separate lines of evolution, and because they occupied different adaptive zones rather than different aspects of the same adaptive zone, their generic separation was fully justified. Robinson eventually came to view *Australopithecus* and *Homo* as constituting a single phyletic lineage and, therefore, proposed that the genus name *Australopithecus* be recognized as a junior synonym of *Homo*. In 1959, a massively built australopith cranium was discovered by M.D. Leakey in Bed I of Olduvai Gorge, Tanzania. It was attributed by L.S.B. Leakey to a novel taxon, *Zinjanthropus boisei*. Robinson, who was quick to recognize its close affinities to *P. robustus*, proposed that *Zinjanthropus* was a junior synonym of *Paranthropus*. Thus, according to him, the Olduvai cranium was attributable to *P. boisei*.

Subsequent studies by several workers, including P.V. Tobias and M.H. Wolpoff, in which all australopiths were viewed as composing a single evolutionary grade of organization, questioned the generic distinctiveness of *Paranthropus*. These grade-oriented, phenetic studies influenced opinion such that, in the mid-1990s, most students of (and almost all textbooks on) hominid evolution regarded *Paranthropus* as a junior synonym of *Australopithecus*. Indeed, some individuals have even argued that all australopith fossils simply represent size and/or temporal variants within the range of variation of a single anagenetic species lineage.

Additional discoveries of "robust" australopith fossils, most notably those recovered by R.E.F. Leakey and his colleagues on the eastern shores of Lake Turkana, Kenya, have led to numerous studies by workers such as B.A. Wood, M.C. Dean, R.J. Clarke, and F.E. Grine that have highlighted their distinctiveness. Thus, despite the overwhelming scholastic influence that the "grade" paradigm has had upon anthropologists, a strong body of evidence has accumulated in which *Paranthropus* specimens have been shown to possess a host of derived morphological specializations that probably reflect significant functional differences between them and other early hominid taxa. Although there have been arguments to the contrary, this morphological evidence points overwhelmingly to the fact that the "robust" australopiths represent a monophyletic clade. Their characteristic craniodental traits are almost certainly related to trophic (i.e., dietary) parameters. *Paranthropus* specimens display so many craniodental features distinguishing them from representatives of other hominid taxa that there is good reason to believe that they constitute a unique and specialized evolutionary lineage.

Along these lines, both Robinson and Clarke have argued that, since the morphological differences between *Paranthropus* and *Australopithecus* are notably greater than those separating *Australopithecus* and *Homo*, *Paranthropus* had probably been separate from *Australopithecus* for a longer time than had *Homo*. As Clarke stated (1985, p. 172): "… if it is valid to place *Homo habilis* in a genus distinct from *Australopithecus*, it is far more justifiable to separate *Paranthropus* from *Australopithecus*."

Robinson's view concerning early hominid phylogeny was adopted by T.R. Olson in his analysis of the Hadar and Laetoli fossils attributed by most workers to the species *A. afarensis*. Olson argued that the *Homo* and *Paranthropus* lineages were separate evolutionary entities and that they were already recognizable by the mid-Pliocene within the Hadar and Laetoli samples. Thus, according to him, the Hadar and Laetoli hypodigm of *Australopithecus afarensis* contains specimens belonging to different species, which made up the separate *Homo* and *Paranthropus* lineages. Accordingly, Olson has proposed that some of the Hadar fossils belong to the genus *Homo* (*H. aethiopicus*), while other of the Hadar and all of the Laetoli remains are attributable to the genus *Paranthropus* (*P. africanus*).

The question of the phylogenetic derivation of *Paranthropus* has been the focus of much of the work that has revolved around the interpretation of a nearly complete, albeit nearly edentulous cranium discovered in the 1980s by A.C. Walker in Pliocene sediments (ca. 2.5 Ma) of the Nachukui Formation on the western side of Lake Turkana. This specimen (with the catalog number KNM-WT 17000), which evinces a number of features that attest to its "robust" australopith affinities, has been interpreted by Walker and some of his colleagues as an early specimen of *Paranthropus* (= *Australopithecus*) *boisei*. They have argued that this fossil attests to the eastern African "robust" australopiths (= *A. boisei*) having evolved from *A. afarensis*, while the

South African "robust" form (= *A. robustus*) evolved independently from *A. africanus*. Should this unlikely phylogenetic scheme prove true, it would mean that the "robust" australopiths would have to be divided into two genera: *Paranthropus* for the South African form and *Zinjanthropus* for the "robust" australopith fossils from eastern Africa.

Other workers, including W.H. Kimbel, D.C. Johanson, T.D. White, E. Delson, and F.E. Grine, interpret the cranium from the Nachukui Formation as representing a species distinct from *P. boisei*. According to this interpretation, this cranium and a number of penecontemporaneous fossils from the Nachukui (Kenya) and Shungura (Ethiopia) Formations might be referred to the species *Paranthropus aethiopicus*. The most parsimonious interpretation of the phylogenetic relationships among these various species is that *P. boisei* and *P. robustus* are more closely related to each other and to *P. aethiopicus* than any of them are related to any other hominid species. Should this arrangement be accepted, there can be little doubt about the validity of *Paranthropus* as a monophyletic taxon. While this is superficially similar to the arrangement proposed by Olson, it differs in that it does not necessarily recognize *Paranthropus* elements in the Hadar and Laetoli hominid samples. Rather, those fossils, which appear to represent a single species that does not possess any recognizable "paranthropine" synapomorphies, will likely have to be assigned a new taxonomic designation (i.e., they will not belong to the genera *Homo*, *Paranthropus*, or *Australopithecus*), for which the nomen *Praeanthropus africanus* is available.

Thus, although there is considerable difference of opinion regarding not only the generic distinctiveness of *Paranthropus*, but also the number of "robust" australopith species that are represented in the fossil record, there is almost universal agreement that these specimens display an extensive suite of unique cranial and dental features probably related to trophic specializations involving the generation and distribution of powerful masticatory forces. The cranial remains are reasonably interpreted as evidence for the existence of at least three species, and their shared features almost certainly attest to their common ancestry.

CHARACTERISTICS OF PARANTHROPUS

The cranial and dental features that serve to distinguish the genus *Paranthropus* from other hominin genera include: a "dished" midface in which the pyriform aperture is set posterior to the level of the zygomatics; a depressed frontal trigone demarcated by strongly convergent superior temporal lines; a marked postorbital constriction; a nasion and a glabella that approximate each other in position; an internasal suture that tends to project above the frontomaxillary suture concomitant with superiorly expanded nasal bones; an infraorbital foramen that is situated in the lower half of the anterior surface of the zygomatic; a nasoalveolar clivus that passes smoothly into the nasal cavity; a hard palate that is very thick; a cranium that exhibits pneumatization and ectocranial superstructures (at least in presumptive males); a mastoid process that is laterally inflated relative to the supramastoid crest; a wide supraglenoid gutter; a thick zygomatic arch at the root of the frontal process; a petrous axis that is markedly angled to the sagittal plane, which results in a high petromedian angle; possibly a tendency for the occipital-marginal sinus to be enlarged relative to the transverse sinus; maxillary canine and incisor alveoli that tend to be aligned in the same coronal plane; incisors and canines that are relatively small compared to the sizes of molars and especially premolars; P_3 that tends to possess three roots; dP_3 "molarized" with anterior fovea centrally situated and walled by a complete mesial marginal ridge; very thick permanent molar enamel; a laterally inflated and relatively broad mandibular corpus with a large cross-sectional area at the level of M_1; a vertically oriented mandibular symphysis; and a wide extramolar sulcus of the mandible.

At least three species may be identified in the Plio-Pleistocene record of eastern (two species) and southern Africa (one species), although some workers, such as F.C. Howell and Grine, have maintained that the

Composite skull of Paranthropus from Swartkrans.

differences between the fossils from Swartkrans and Kromdraai attest to the presence of two *Paranthropus* species in South Africa. However, because the differences between the specimens from these two localities are subtle, and because the newly discovered fossils from Drimolen may warrant a reinterpretation of these differences, the "robust" australopith fossils from these three South African sites are considered to be attributable to a single taxon for present purposes. The three species recognized here are: *P. robustus*, *P. boisei*, and *P. aethiopicus*. Each is briefly discussed here and at greater length in separate entries.

P. AETHIOPICUS

This species is represented by the nearly edentulous adult cranium, KNM-WT 17000, from the Lokalalei Member of the Nachukui Formation, a partial juvenile cranium from Submember E3 of the Shungura Formation, a partial mandible with teeth from the Lokalalei Member, a partial, edentulous mandible (cataloged as Omo 18-1967-18) from Submember C8 of the Shungura Formation, which is the holotype of this taxon, and a number of isolated teeth that range from Shungura Members C through G. The Omo 18-1967-18 mandible was described in 1967 by C. Arambourg and Y. Coppens, who attributed it in 1968 to the novel taxon *Paraustralopithecus aethiopicus*.

The adult cranium (KNM-WT 17000) displays a number of features that serve to differentiate it from specimens of *P. robustus* and *P. boisei*, and some of the isolated teeth–most notably the premolars—from the Shungura Formation lack several of the highly derived features of *P. boisei* homologues, according to work of G. suwa, although penecontemporaneous deciduous premolars are virtually indistinguishable from those attributed to *P. boisei*. If the attribution of these various specimens to *P. aethiopicus* is correct, then this species may have a temporal range of between ca. 2.8 and 2.2 Ma. It shares with the other two species of *Paranthropus* almost all of the cranial derived features (synapomorphies) listed above as characterizing the genus, but few of the dental or mandibular features.

P. ROBUSTUS

This is the type species of the genus *Paranthropus*. The holotype specimen, cataloged as TM 1517 in the Transvaal Museum, Pretoria, derives from the South African site of Kromdraai. It was described in 1938 by R. Broom. To date, only a handful of hominid fossils have been recovered from Kromdraai, and it is likely that all derive from Member 3 of the Kromdraai B East formation. A decade after the recovery of the first Kromdraai specimen, Broom discovered fossils at the South African site of Swartkrans; these he assigned to another species, *P. crassidens*. Most workers consider the Kromdraai and Swartkrans fossils to represent a single species, *P. robustus*, with the vast bulk of the hypodigm of this taxon deriving from Swartkrans. Since 1992, specimens attributable to *P. robustus*, including a well-preserved cranium and mandible, have been recovered from the site of Drimolen, also in South Africa. *P. robustus* fossils are known primarily from Member 1 of the Swartkrans Formation, although recent excavations by C. K. Brain have yielded specimens from Members 2 and 3.

The geochronological age of *P. robustus* is presently determined by associated faunal remains from Members 1, 2, and 3 of the Swartkrans Formation. There is no significant difference among the assemblages from these three units, and the age of the largest Member 1 assemblage has been estimated to be between ca. 1.8 and 1.5 Ma. The geochronological age of the Kromdraai fossils is usually thought to be somewhat less than 1.5 Ma. The Drimolen *Paranthropus* fossils likely date from the same period of time.

Analyses of the faunal remains associated with *P. robustus* suggest that this species inhabited an environment that was somewhat more open than that associated with *Australopithecus africanus*. There are indications of riverine gallery forest habitats that appear to have been surrounded by large open grasslands.

P. BOISEI

The type of this species is a large, nearly complete cranium (cataloged as OH 5) that was discovered in 1959 in Bed I of Olduvai Gorge by M.D. Leakey. L.S.B. Leakey described it that same year as the new taxon *Zinjanthropus boisei*. The hypodigm of this species comprises fossils from Beds I and II of Olduvai Gorge and a mandible from the Humbu Formation at Peninj, near Lake Natton (Tanzania); a number of fine specimens from the Koobi Fora and Nachukui Formations (Kenya); a partial cranium from the Chemoigut Formation (Kenya); and a number of mandibles, isolated teeth, and a fragmentary cranium from the Shungura Formation (Ethiopia). A cranium attributable to *P. boisei* is known also from the site of Konso (Ethiopia).

The majority of the Koobi Fora fossils attributable to *P. boisei* derive from above the KBS Tuff, although several are known from below it (e.g., the mandibles KNM-ER 1469 and KNM-ER 1482 from the Upper Burgi Member). Undoubted *P. boisei* fossils are known from Members G, K, and L of the Shungura Formation, and from Bed II of Olduvai Gorge (i.e., specimen OH 3). Thus, undoubted *P. boisei* remains are known from ca. 2.3 to 1.4 Ma. Work by Wood and colleagues in 1994 suggests that *P. boisei* exhibited a degree of morphological stasis over this period.

The cheek teeth of *P. boisei* tend to be larger than those of *P. robustus;* dimensions for *P. boisei* premolars and molars are the largest recorded for any hominin taxon. Postcranial remains that are reasonably attributed to *P. boisei* suggest a species with some retained arboreal capabilities, especially in the configuration of its forearm skeleton. The proximal femur has a relatively small head and a relatively long anteroposteriorly flattened neck. Craniodental remains and postcranial bones that have been attributed to *P. boisei* indicate a species with a considerable degree of size (presumed sexual) dimorphism. Reasonable body size estimates based upon attributed postcranial remains range from ca. 35 to 85 kg for the smallest and largest bones, respectively.

See also Australopithecus Drimolen; Kromdraai; Olduvai Gorge; Paranthropus aethiopicus; Paranthropus boisei; Paranthropus robustus; Swartkrans; Synonym(y). [F.E.G.]

FURTHER READINGS

Clarke, R.J. (1985) *Australopithecus* and early *Homo* in southern Africa. In E. Delson (ed.): Ancestors: The Hard Evidence. New York: Liss, pp. 171–177.
Grine, F.E., ed. (1988) Evolutionary History of the "Robust" Australopithecines. New York: Aldine de Gruyter.

Olson, T.R. (1981) Basicranial morphology of the extant hominoids and Pliocene hominids: The new material from the Hadar Formation, Ethiopia, and its significance in early human evolution and taxonomy. In C.B. Stringer (ed.): Aspects of Human Evolution. London: Taylor and Francis, pp. 99–128.

Rak, Y. (1983) The Australopithecine Face. New York: Academic.

Robinson, J.T. (1954) The genera and species of the Australopithecinae. Am. J. Phys. Anthropol. 12:181–200.

Skelton, R.R., and McHenry, H.M. (1992) Evolutionary relationships among early hominids. J. Hum. Evol. 23:309–349.

Strait, D.S., Grine, F.E., and Moniz, M.A. (1997) A reappraisal of early hominid phylogeny. J. Hum. Evol. 32:17–82.

Suwa, G., White, T.D., and Howell, F.C. (1996) Mandibular postcanine dentition from the Shungura Formation, Ethiopia: Crown morphology, taxonomic allocation and Plio-Pleistocene hominid evolution. Am. J. Phys. Anthropol. 101:247–282.

Tobias, P.V. (1967) The cranium and maxillary dentition of Australopithecus (Zinjanthropus) boisei. Olduvai Gorge, Vol. 2. Cambridge: Cambridge University Press.

Walker, A.C., Leakey, R.E.F., Harris, J.M., and Brown, F.H. (1986) 2.5- My Australopithecus boisei from west of Lake Turkana, Kenya. Nature 322:517–522.

Wood, B.A., and Chamberlain, A.T. (1987) The nature and affinities of the "robust" australopithecines: A review. J. Hum. Evol. 16:625–641.

Wood, B.A., Wood, C., and Konigsberg, L. (1994) Paranthropus boisei: An example of evolutionary stasis? Am. J. Phys. Anthropol. 95:117–136.

PARANTHROPUS AETHIOPICUS

Taxonomic name used in reference to the earlier East African "robust" australopith fossils from the Shungura Formation (Ethiopia) and the Nachukui Formation (Kenya). These specimens span the time period ca. 2.8–2.2 Ma. The holotype specimen of this taxon is an edentulous mandible (cataloged as Omo 18-1967-18) from Submember C-8 of the Shungura Formation. It was described in 1967 by C. Arambourg and Y. Coppens, who attributed it in 1968 to the novel taxon *Paraustralopithecus aethiopicus.*

This species is represented by a nearly edentulous adult cranium (cataloged as KNM-WT 17000) from the Lokalalei Member of the Nachukui Formation, a partial juvenile cranium from Submember E-3 of the Shungura Formation, a partial mandible with teeth from the Lokalalei Member, and a number of isolated teeth that range from Shungura Members C through G. The adult cranium displays a number of derived features in common with *Paranthropus robustus* and *P. boisei,* which warrants its attribution to the same genus. On the other hand, KNM-WT 17000 differs from the crania of *P. robustus* and *P. boisei,* hence its attribution to a separate species. For the most part, the characters in which the *P. aethiopicus* cranium differs from those of *P. robustus* and *P. boisei* appear to evince more primitive states in the former. In additions, some of the isolated teeth–most notably the premolars—from the Shungura Formation lack several of the highly derived features of *P. boisei* homologues, although penecontemporaneous deciduous molars are virtually indistinguishable from those of *P. boisei.*

In their description and interpretation of KNM-WT 17000, A.C. Walker and colleagues suggested that, should this specimen be shown to be distinct from *P. boisei,* it might reasonably be accorded the taxonomic designation *P. aethiopicus,* the species name accorded the Omo 18-1967-18 mandible by Arambourg and Coppens. The Omo mandible and the 17000 cranium are of approximately the same geochronological age, but the KNM-WT 17000 cranium would have possessed very large mandible, and its attribution to *P. aethiopicus,* which is based upon a much smaller jaw, holds by a rather tenuous thread of logic. Whether or not the

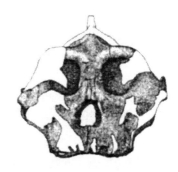

Lateral and facial views of the *Paranthropus aethiopicus* (KNM-WT 17000) cranium from West Turkana, Kenya Scales are 1 cm.

name *P. aethiopicus* proves to be validly applied to the KNM-WT 17000 cranium, the name is at least available for this purpose, and there are very good reasons to attribute this specimen to a separate species from *P. boisei* and *P. robustus*. Alternatively, the name *Paranthropus walkeri* has been proposed by W. Ferguson with WT 17000 as holotype. *P. aethiopicus* will no doubt enjoy increased use in taxonomic discussion of early Hominini.

P. aethiopicus shares with *P. robustus* and *P. boisei* the following derived features (synapomorphies) a "dished" midface with the facial surface of the zygoma anterior to the level of the pyriform aperture; coincident glabella and nasion; an internasal suture that rises above the level of the frontomaxillary suture and is superiorly expanded; a nasoalveolar clivus that passes smoothly into the floor of the nose; marked ectocranial superstructures (at least in presumptive males); pneumatization of the temporal squama with strongly flared parietral mastoid angle; a broad anterior palate with lateral incisor roots set medial to the lateral margins of the pyriform aperture; maxillary incisor and canine alveoli aligned nearly in the same coronal plane; a very thick palate; a tympanic plate that is deep; a petrous axis that is strongly inclined to the sagittal plane, resulting in a high petromedian angle; dP_3 molarized with a centrally placed anterior fovea that is fully enclosed by a high mesial marginal ridge; and very thick (hyperthick) permanent molar tooth enamel.

It is similar to *P. boisei* and differs from *P. robustus* in possessing a heart-shaped foramen magnum, lacking anterior pillars, having no (or only slight) Eustacian process of the tympanic bone; and in exhibiting parietal overlap of the occipital at asterion. On average, *P. aethiopicus* molar crowns approximate the sizes of *P. boisei* homologues, whereas *P. robustus* molars tend to be somewhat smaller. It is similar to *P. robustus,* and differs from *P. boisei* in possessing an interior margin of the orbit that is rounded laterally, a maxillary trigon (zygomaticomaxillary step), and a tympanic that is vertically inclined with·a distinct crest.

It differs from both *P. robustus* and *P. boisei,* and exhibits the presumably more primitive states (as evinced, for example, by *A. afarensis*) in the following features strong alveolar prognathism; an anteriorly very shallow palate; a smaller cranial capacity (410 cc estimate for KNM-WT 17000 vs. a value of 530 cc for *P. robustus* and estimates of 500–550 cc for *P. boisei*); a cerebellum that flares laterally and protrudes posteriorly; the presence of an asterionic notch; a relatively flattened cranial base; a shallow mandibular fossa that lacks a distinct articular eminence; an external auditory meatus that is medially positioned relative to the lateral edge of the suprameatal roof of the temporal bone; the absence or very slight development of the vaginal process of the tympanic bone; and a foramen magnum that is positioned at the level of the bi-tympanic line as opposed to being situated well anterior to the line. Indirect evidence suggests that *P. aethiopicus* displayed considerable size (presumably sexual) dimorphism, to judge from the difference in the size of the Omo 18-1967-18 mandible and the mandible that would have been associated with the KNM-WT 17000 cranium (the latter approximates KNM-ER 729, a large *P. boisei* mandible, in size).

Postcranial remains from the Shungura Formation that may be attributable to *P. aethiopicus* include a large ulna from Member E that is notable for its considerable length and substantial dorsoventral curvature.

See also Australopithecus; Australopithecus afarensis; Australopithecus africanus; Paranthropus; Paranthropus boisei; Paranthropus robustus. [F.E.G.]

FURTHER READINGS

Grine, F.E., ed. (1988) Evolutionary History of the "Robust" Australopithecines. New York: Aldine de Gruyter.
Walker, A.C., Leakey, R.E.F., Harris, J.M., and Brown, F.H. (1986) 2.5-My *Australopithecus boisei* from west of Lake Turkana, Kenya. Nature 322:517–522.

PARANTHROPUS BOISEI

Taxonomic name used in reference to the later East African "robust" australopith fossils from the Shungura Formation and Konso (Ethiopia); the Koobi Fora, Nachukui and Chemoigut Formations (Kenya); and Beds I and II of Olduvai Gorge and the Humbu Formation at Peninj (Tanzania). The type specimen (OH 5) was discovered by M.D. Leakey in Bed I of Olduvai Gorge in 1959. The earliest craniodental remains attributable to *P. boisei* are known from the Upper Burgi Member of the Koobi Fora Formation and from Member G of the Shungura Formation. The latest *P. boisei* specimen appears to derive from Konso. Thus, this species spans the temporal period from ca 2.3–1.4 Ma.

Many of the morphological features that characterize the skull and dentition of *P. boisei* are shared with *P. robustus* and *P. aethiopicus*. For example, all three *Paranthropus* species possess a "dished" midface (in which the pyriform aperture is set posterior to the facial plates of the zygomatics); a depressed frontal trigone demarcated by strongly convergent superior temporal lines; nasion and glabella in near approximation; a nasoalveolar clivus that extends smoothly into the nasal cavity, a very thick palate; a high petromedian angle; incisors and canines that are relatively small in comparison to the sizes of the molars and especially the premolars; and very thick permanent molar enamel.

P. boisei differs from *P. robustus* primarily in that the former has sharply defined inferolateral orbital margins, greater maxillary depth with a concomitantly shelved palate, a "heart-shaped" foramen magnum, a strong postero-inferior slope to the tympanic bone, and a tendency to develop an inferiorly extended zygomatic "visor." In addition, *P. boisei* lacks the maxillary trigone, the discernible anterior pillars, and the prominent Eustachian process of the tympanic possessed by *P. robustus*, *P. boisei* cheek teeth tend to be larger than those of *P. robustus*, *P. boisei* differs from *P. aethiopicus* principally in that the former has sharply defined inferolateral orbital margins; less alveolar prognathism; an anteriorly deeper (shelved) palate; a deeper glenoid fossa with a well-developed atricular eminence; a tympanic that extends to the lateral margin of the suprameatal roof; a more flexed cranial base; an anteriorly positioned foramen magnum; and a larger cranial capacity (500–550 cc vs. 410 cc).

Most of the morphological features that characterize the skull of *P. boisei* appear to be related to the generation and distribution of very powerful masticatory forces. In the absence of any contrary evidence, it seems reasonable to assume that these powerful forces were necessary to chew fibrous, rough, and/or hard objects. Such items would be consistent with a vegetarian diet that included fruits, seeds, and tubers.

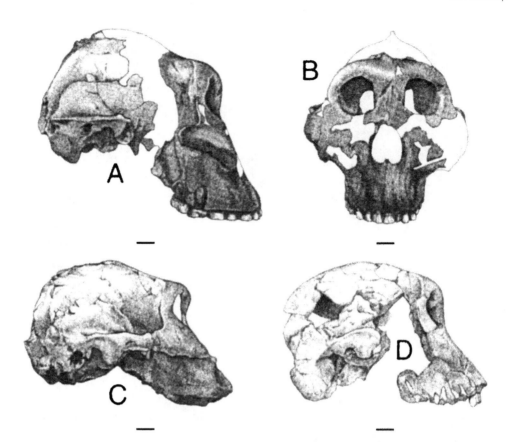

Crania of *Paranthropus boisei*: OH 5, Olduvai Gorge, Tanzania (A, B); KNM-ER 406, Koobi Fora, Kenya (C); KNM-ER 732 (D) OH 5 and ER 406 are thought to be male, ER 732 to be female. Scales are 1 cm.

Although crania, mandibles, and isolated teeth of *P. boisei* are by far the most abundant hominid fossils to be recovered from sediments that date to between about 2.3 and 1.4 Ma, there are comparatively few postcranial bones that can be attributed to *P. boisei* with reasonable certainty. These postcrania that can be referred to *P. boisei* suggest a species that retained some arboreal capabilities, especially in the configuration of its forearm skeleton. The proximal femur has a relatively small head and a relatively long, anteroposteriorly flattened neck. The calcaneus and talus are generally humanlike, indicating a bipedally adapted foot, although the pedal elements also display some apelike features, as well as some unique traits. Body-size estimates for *P. boisei* range from less than 30 kg to greater than 85 kg, and stature estimates have suggested values of ca. 148–168 cm. These estimates, although tenuous (because they are based on incomplete and referred long bones), indicate a species that exhibited considerable sexual dimorphism. This conclusion is supported by cranial and mandibular elements as well.

Recent studies have indicated that *P. boisei* probably exhibited a degree of morphological stasis in a variety of cranial and dental characters over the course of its ca. 1.0 Myr of existence. Reconstructions of the environment in which *P. boisei* fossils are found suggest that this species preferred fairly closed habitats that were in close proximity to water (e.g., gallery and marginal forests along rivers and lakes).

See also Africa, East; Australopithecus; Baringo Basin/Tugen Hills; Chesowanja; Konso: Natron-Eyasi Basin; Olduvai Gorge; Paranthropus; Paranthropus aethiopicus; Paranthropus robustus; Peninj; Turkana Basin. [F.E.G.]

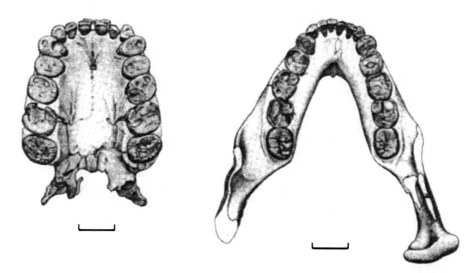

Left Palate of *P. boisei* OH 5, from Olduvai Gorge, Tanzania. Right: occlusal view of the *P. boisei* mandible from Peninj, Tanzania. Scale is 1cm.

FURTHER READINGS

Grine, F.E., ed. (1988) Evolutionary History of the "Robust" Australopithecines. New York: Aldine de Gruyter.

Howell, F.C. (1978) Hominidae. In V.J. Maglio and H.B.S Cooke (eds): Evolution of African Mammals. Cambridge, Mass.: Harvard University Press, pp. 154–248.

Rak, Y. (1983) The Australopithecine Face. New York: Academic.

Tobias, P.V. (1967) The cranium and maxillary dentition of *Australopithecus (Zinjanthropus) boisei:* Olduvai Gorge, Vol. 2. Cambridge: Cambridge University Press.

Wood, B.A. (1991) Koobi Fora Research Project, Vol. 4: Hominid Cranial Remains. Oxford: Oxford University Press.

Wood, B.A., and Chamberlain, A.T. (1987) The nature and affinities of the "robust" australopithecines: A review. J. Hum. Evol. 16:625–641.

Wood, B.A., Wood, C., and Konigsberg, L. (1994) *Paranthropus boisei:* An example of evolutonary stasis? Am. J. Phys. Anthropol. 95:117–136.

PARANTHROPUS ROBUSTUS

Taxonomic name used in reference to the "robust" australopith fossils from the South African sites of Kromdraai, Swartkrans, and Drimolen. The first of these specimens was discovered at Kromdraai in 1938. The fossil, which consists of the left half of a cranium, a right mandibular corpus, and several teeth, was obtained by R. Broom and described by him that same year. Broom noted that the face was flat, that the incisors and canines were small, and that the premolars and molars differed in their morphology and larger size from the Sterkfontein (South Africa) specimens of *Australopithecus*. He considered that the differences between the Kromdraai and the Sterkfontein fossils warranted their generic separation and made the Kromdraai specimen the type of a new taxon, *Paranthropus robustus*. A decade later, the first australopith fossil was recovered from the site of Swartkrans, several kilometers from Kromdraai along the Bloubank River. Broom observed that the mandibular corpus of the Swartkrans specimen was similar in its robusticity to that from Kromdraai and that the teeth were morphologically similar to, bur larger than, those from

Kromdraai. He considered that the Swartkrans and the Kromdraai fossils were attributable to the same genus, *Paranthropus* but that the subtle differences between them warranted their specific separation. Broom thus named the Swartkrans specimen *P. crassidens.*

Several years later, on the basis of his study of larger samples of australopith fossils from Swartkrans and Kromdraai, J.T. Robinson argued that they could be accommodated in a single species, *Paranthropus robustus.* Robinson noted, however, that the Kromdraai and the Swartkrans fossils differed from each other in subtle dental features, and he suggested that these forms could be regarded as two subspecies (*P. robustus robustus* and *P. robustus crassidens*). Some workers (e.g., F.C. Howell and F.E. Grine) have more recently argued that the differences between the Swartkrans and the Kromdraai fossils may, indeed, warrant their specific separation. Fossils discovered at the site of Drimolen since 1992 are morphologically similar to those from Kromdraai and Swartkrans and most likely represent the same species. *P. robustus* fossils are known from Members 1 (both Lower Bank and Hanging Remmant deposits), 2, and 3 of the Swartkrans Formation. The faunal assemblages from these different stratigraphic units do not vary significantly, nor do the *Paranthropus* fossils appear to vary appreciably from Member 1 through 3. They probably date to between ca. 1.8 and 1.5 Ma on the basis of associated faunal remains. A preliminary attempt at thermoluminescence (TL) dating of quartz sand grains from these units suggested that the Member 3 fossils may be as young as 850 Ka. This would make them the youngest *Paranthropus* remains known in either southern or eastern Africa. However, the absence of significant differences in the faunal assemblages among these stratigraphic units indicates that they are temporally closer to one another than implied by the TI date. The geochronological age of the Kromdraai hominid fossils is wholly unresolved; majority opinion would place them at somewhat less than 1.5 Ma. The Drimolen *Paranthropus* fossils also likely date from the same interval (i.e., ca 1.8–1.5 Ma).

A substantial suite of features characterizes *P. robustus.* Many of these are shared with *P. aethiopicus* and *P. boisei;* but, in several traits, *P. robustus*

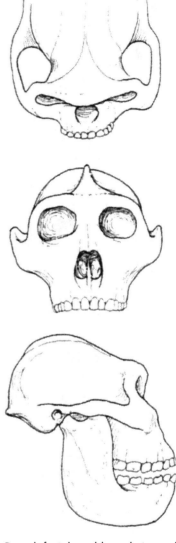

Dorsal, facial, and lateral views of *Paranthropus robustus* cranium. Courtesy of Frederisk E. Grine.

differs from the other two species. Among the features that characterize *P. robustus* are a robustly constructed cranium with ectocranial superstructures; substantial pneumatization of the cranium with marked lateral inflation of mastoid region; males with sagittal crest but lacking confluence of posteroinferior temporal and superior nuchal lines; temporal lines posteriorly divergent above lambda; a mastoid process not notably inflected and its tip medial to lateral margin of elongate and concave tympanic; marked angulation of the petrous axis to the sagittal plane resulting in a high petromedian angle; a tendency for the occipital-marginal sinus to be enlarged relative to the transverse sinus; a calvaria hafred to the facial skeleton at a low level, resulting in a low supraorbital height index; a low and slightly concave forehead with the frontal trigone delimited laterally by posteriorly convergent temporal crests; strong postorbital constriction; a strong and horizontally disposed supraorbital torus with a flattened "rib" of bone across the supraorbital margin and lacking twist between the medial and lateral components; a prominent glabella situated below the level of

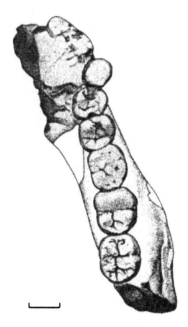

Occlusal view of the TM 1517 mandible of the *Paranthropus robustus* holotype from Kromdraai, South Africa. Scale is 1 cm.

the supraorbital margin; nearly coincident nasion and glabella as a result of a low glabella and a tendency for the internasal suture to project higher than the nasofrontale; an orthoganthous bony face of moderate height; the piriform aperture set in the central facial hollow; the nasoalveolar clivus passing smoothly into the floor of the nasal cavity without strong demarcation; incisive canals open into the horizontal surface of the nasal floor without the presence of capacious incisive fossa; a tendency of the alveolar margins of the maxillary canine and incisor sockets to lie in the same coronal plane; a palate that is deep posteriorly and shallow anteriorly; relatively small incisors and canines compared with the large sizes of premolars and molars; a tendency of P_3 to possess three roots; molarized dP_3 with the anterior fovea centrally situated and walled by a complete mesial marginal ridge; very thick permanent molar enamel; and a laterally inflated mandibular corpus.

Many of these traits appear to be related to the generation and distribution of powerful masticatory forces. Analyses of details of occluasal wear on the molar teeth indicate that the diets of *Australopithecus africanus* and *P. robustus* differed qualitatively and that the diet of *P. robustus* comprised hard objects. Studies of the carbon-isotope ratios of *P. robustus* tooth enamel indicate that this species had an overall reliance on C_3-based foods (trees, shrubs, forbs, and tubers) although C_4 grasses provided a substantial dietary contribution. Furthermore, strontium-calcium ratios determined from *P. robustus* cranial bones, if reliable, suggest that this species also may have consumed meat. Thus, the diet of *P. robustus* may have been fairly catholic, but its craniodental anatomy indicates a primary adaptation to the mastication of abrasive food items that required the application of powerful chewing forces.

Endocranial capacity estimates for *P. robustus* range between 450 and 550 ml, but only a single good specimen from Swartkrans is known (it has a volume of 530 ml). The paucity of good endocranial remains leaves this range of estimates open to question.

Because of the presence of *Homo* in the same sedimentary units at Swartkrans, it is difficult to correctly associate all of the hominid postcranial bones at that site. Nevertheless, there are several elements at Swartkrans that can be reasonably attributed to *P. robustus*, and there are a few from Kromdraai that also might belong to this species. In general, most of the postcranial remains of *P. robustus* appear to

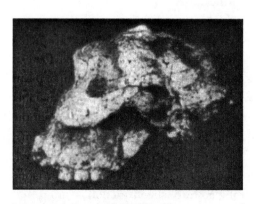

Lateral view of the SK 48 cranium of *Paranthropus robustus* from Swartkrans, South Africa. Courtesy of Frederick E. Grine.

be morphologically similar to those of other *Australopithecus* and *Paranthropus* species for which homologous elements are known. Thus, the femur of *P. robustus* has a relatively small head and relatively long, anteroposteriorly flattened neck. The radius exhibited enhanced stability against medial displacement during pronation and supination, and aspects of its morphology appear to be related to enhanced capabilities of forearm-flexor, hand-extensor, and hand-flexor muscles. This is suggestive of arboreal capabilities. Foot bones, on the other hand, are indicative of bipedal locomotion. Hand bones, especially pollical metacarpals, that may be attributable to *P. robustus* suggest an ability to have managed human-like precision grasping, which may relate to the capacity to manipulate tools; in this regard, *P. robustus* differs from species of *Australopithecus*, such as *A. afarensis* and *A. africanus*. However, the humanlike nature of the foot and hand bones may be related to their derivation from individuals of early *Homo* rather than from *Paranthropus*.

Reasonable estimates of body size for *P. robustus* that are based upon postcranial elements rather than on postcanine tooth size range from ca. 42 to more than 65 kg. Although we still have little idea of how robust these "robust" australopiths actually were, it appears that they may not have been substantially larger than some species of *Australopithecus* (e.g., *A. afarensis* and *A. africanus*). Size dimorphism (i.e., presumed sexual dimorphism) in cranial, mandibular, dental, and postcranial remains of *P. robustus* appears to be rather less than the differences in size between elements attributed to both *P. aethiopicus* and *P. boisei*, and to species of *Australopithecus*, such as *A. afarensis* and *A. africanus*. However, it is unclear whether this apparent pattern reflects a specific reduction of body-size (sexual?) dimorphism in *P. robustus*, or whether it is a taphonomic artifact that reflects the preferred prey size of the predator responsible for the accumulation of *P. robustus* remains.

See also Australopithecus; Broom, Robert; Drimolen; Kromdraai; Paranthropus; Paranthropus aethiopicus; Paranthropus boisei; Robinson, John Talbot; Swartkrans. [F.E.G.]

FURTHER READINGS

Brain, C.K. (1993) Swartkrans: A Cave' Chronicle of Early Man (Transvaal Museum Monographs No. 8). Pretoria. Transvaal Museum.

Grine, F.E. (1981) Trophic differences between "gracile" and "robust" australopithecines: A scanning electron microscope analysis of occlusal events. S. Afr. J. Sci. *77*:203–230.

Grine, F.E., and Susman, R.L. (1991) New *Paranthropus robustus* radius from Member 1, Swartkrans Formation: Comparative and functional morphology. Am. J. Phys. Anthropol. 84:229–248.

Howell, F.C. (1978) Hominidae. In V.J. Maglio and H.B.S. Cooke (eds.): Evolution of African Mammals. Cambridge, Mass.: Harvard University Press, pp. 154–248.

Lee-Thorpe, J.A., van der Merwe, N.J., and Brain, C.K. (1994) Diet of *Australopithecus robustus* at Swartkrans from stable carbon isotopic analysis. J. Hum. Evol. 27:361–372.

Rak, Y. (1983) The Australopithecine Face. New York: Academic.

Robinson, J.T. (1954) The genera and species of the Australopithecinae. Am. J. Phys. Anthropol. 12:181–200.

Sillen, A. (1992) Strontium-calcium ratios (Sr/Ca) of *Australopithecus robustus* and associated fauna from Swartkrans. J. Hum. Evol. 23:495–516.

Susman, R.L. (1988) Hand of *Paranthropus robustus* from Member 1, Swartkrans: Fossil evidence for tool behavior. Science 240:781–784.

Study Questions

1. What are the species included in the genus *Australopithecus*?

2. How do they differ from other apes?

3. How do they differ from one another?

4. What distinguishes the genus *Paranthropus* from other hominins?

5. What is likely to have been the diet of *Australopithecus* and *Paranthropus* and how do we know?

SECTION VI

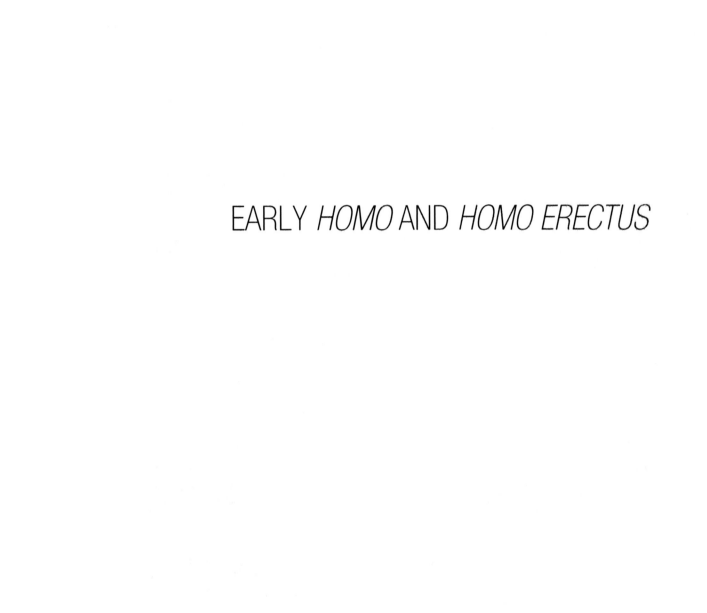

EARLY *HOMO* AND *HOMO ERECTUS*

The author discusses the lifeways of many species of early hominin and how they have changed over time.

16. Early African Hominids

Behavior and Environments

By Sally McBrearty

PLIOCENE AND EARLY PLEISTOCENE

Fossils discovered in the last 35 years have led to a new appreciation of the numbers of early species in the family Hominidae. There are now more than 1,300 known Pliocene and Early Pleistocene hominid fossil specimens. The Pliocene spans the period from 1.8 million to 5 million years ago. The Pleistocene, which dates from 10,000 to 1.8 million years ago, is subdivided into Early Pleistocene (750,000 to 1.8 million years ago), Middle Pleistocene (125,000 to 750,000 years ago), and Late Pleistocene (10,000 to 125,000 years ago) periods. The earliest-known hominid genus, *Ardipithecus*, is known from sediments dating to about 4.4 million years ago, and the oldest-known representative of *Australopithecus* dates to about 4.2 million years ago. The genus *Australopithecus* underwent an adaptive radiation in the Late Pliocene and Early Pleistocene. Some scholars place the more robust species of this radiation into a separate genus, *Paranthropus*. The earliest members of our genus, *Homo*, appeared as part of this radiation about 2.5 million years ago. The earliest stone artifacts and archaeological sites date to more than 2.6 million years ago, and the nearly simultaneous appearance of tools and *Homo* suggests to many researchers

Sally McBrearty, "Behavior and Environments of Early African Hominids," *Encyclopedia of Precolonial Africa*, ed. Joseph Vogel, pp. 269–275. Copyright © 1997 by Alta Mira Press. Reprinted with permission.

that members of the genus *Homo* are the makers of the tools. Others point out that the long-lived robust species *Australopithecus boisei* (or *Paranthropus boisei*) also appeared at this time and thus may qualify as the toolmaker.

The period from about 1.6 to 1.8 million years ago is particularly well represented in the fossil record. During this period, there were as many as six different contemporary hominid species in Africa. From our understanding of evolutionary processes, we expect these species to differ from one another not only in their appearance but also in their ways of life. While many details of these unique extinct adaptations are unknown, this article points out what they had in common and, where possible, how they may be expected to have differed.

Our knowledge of early hominids and their behavior depends in large part upon where they have become fossilized and, in the case of archaeological sites, where their living debris has been preserved. Finds of the earliest hominids are confined to the East African Rift Valley. Slightly younger fossils have been found in southern and northern Africa. None are currently known from western Africa, and scholars are uncertain whether early hominids did not inhabit this part of the continent, whether they did not encounter conditions suitable for fossilization, or whether fossils simply have not yet been discovered. The earliest archaeological sites, likewise, are found in the Rift Valley. While hominid fossils are found in caves in southern Africa, the fossils were incorporated in the cave fill through natural means. Hominids seem not to have used the caverns as lairs.

The earliest-known Pliocene hominids inhabited gallery forests surrounding the large Rift Valley riverine system and shared their habitat with the leaf-eating colobus monkey. Fossils of East African hominids of the Late Pliocene and Early Pleistocene have been found in lakeshore environments inhabited by lacustrine (lake) animals such as *Hippopotamus* and woodland animals such as *Giraffa*. The wooded habitat provided shade, food, and refuge from predators, as well as sleeping sites. All hominids are, by definition, bipedal, though each early species may have had its own style of bipedal walking, perhaps differing in gait, speed, and chosen substrate. The curved digits and long upper limbs of a number of early hominid species indicate a preference for life in the trees, and arboreal climbing for feeding, resting, escaping from predators, and sleeping at night may have been a common feature of hominid life until well into the Middle Pleistocene. The habitat away from the water was more open and capable of supporting herbivores (plant eaters) that fed on grass. The parklike appearance of today's East African savanna is maintained by frequent, deliberate burning, and this was not practiced until about 500,000 years ago. The attraction of more open environments for hominids may have been the protein source the animals provided as well as a different array of plant foods, including underground tubers.

Hominid species no doubt differed in their preferred foods, and we may also expect that there were dietary differences in the same species in separate parts of its geographic range, at successive seasons of the year, and over the tens or hundreds of thousands of years of its life span as a species. Like all primates, hominids are omnivores. They do not rely exclusively upon a single food but consume a mix of plant products, including fruit, leaves, bark, sap, seeds, stems, and roots.

One of the major debates in modern archaeology concerns the degree of reliance upon animal food by early hominids and how these animal products were obtained. Modern primate diet, as well as that of present-day tropical African foraging groups, is primarily vegetarian. Meat composes no more than 25 percent of the diet overall. Food derived from vertebrate animals no doubt included birds, fish, amphibians, and reptiles as well as mammals. Invertebrates, primarily insects, were also an important source of protein and fat.

A characteristic feature of *Australopithecus* and *Paranthropus* is their very large molar and premolar teeth with an extremely thick enamel covering—a feature that distinguishes them from *Homo*. These large rear teeth were probably used to process large quantities of tough, bulky, and perhaps low-quality vegetable food, and these hominids probably spent the major portion of their waking hours feeding. *Homo* is also distinguished from *Australopithecus* and *Paranthropus* on the basis of its relatively larger brain size, a characteristic that provides another argument for the theory that *Homo* was the maker of the earliest stone tools. However, from their anatomy, *Australopithecus* and *Paranthropus* appear potentially as dexterous as early *Homo*, and chimpanzees with brain sizes equivalent to *Australopithecus* or *Paranthropus* are known to use simple tools in the wild.

Animal bones at some of the earliest archaeological sites include those of very large, aggressive animals, including elephants, hippopotamuses, and rhinoceroses, which have exceptionally thick hides. Many archaeologists believe that comparatively small-bodied hominids, with very simple implements, were not capable of killing and butchering these animals. It was argued in the early years of the discipline that the presence of large carcasses at sites implied cooperative hunting, but it has since been observed that modern primates, even those who hunt in groups, do not take animals larger than themselves. For example, at the Tai National Forest, Ivory Coast, the favored prey of the common chimpanzee, with a mean body size for males of 50 kilograms, is the red colobus monkey, which weighs only about 5 to 10 kilograms. From the study of breakage and other damage to bone at early archaeological sites, it has been suggested that scavenging from the kills of contemporary large predators, especially hyenas and large cats, was the major source of animal food in early hominid diet.

The earliest stone tools included flakes, which may have been used to slice meat and tendons from bones, and hammers, which may have been used to smash bones to extract the marrow inside. Early stone hammers were no doubt also used to crack open nuts and hard fruits and to pound tubers and stems to make them palatable and to extract liquid. Some of the most important early inventions were probably made of perishable materials that have not survived. A critical early implement was the digging stick, which enabled hominids to tap important underground resources. Ethnographers have observed that modern human foragers in East Africa are able to obtain as many as 5 kilograms of edible tubers, with a food value of more than 3,000 calories, in a single hour's work with a digging stick. Other important inventions were wooden clubs or spears and trays or containers of bark or wood. Stone tools provided the means to skin animals and prepare hides. While not needed for warmth in much of low-altitude, tropical Africa, hides would have provided welcome protection from sun, rain, rocks, and thorns. There is no direct evidence before the Late Pleistocene for the joining of hides into clothing or footwear, but informal pointed stone tools could have been used to punch holes in hides, which could then be joined with sinew. Carrying slings of hide or skin would also have been particularly important in freeing the hands during the transport of foodstuffs, implements, or offspring, and while there is no evidence for the manufacture of twine or cord, strips made of grass, sinew, or hide could serve to join objects into bundles.

Two familiar features of modern life, shelter and fire, apparently were not present in the Pliocene or Early Pleistocene. While claims have been made for evidence of the controlled used of fire as early as 1.4 million years ago, such use was probably not routine, and food was consumed uncooked. There is little good evidence for the construction of shelters or the occupation of caves until the Middle Pleistocene, when the use of fire probably allowed hominids to drive predators from their lairs and keep them at bay with burning embers. Concentrations of lava boulders, artifacts, and broken bone at sites in Bed I at Olduvai Gorge were originally interpreted by archaeologists as the remains of huts or windbreaks, but these interpretations are now actively disputed. As foragers, hominid groups were mobile in their search for food, and, to avoid attracting predators, they did not sleep repeatedly in the same place. It does appear that hominids, perhaps attracted to a particular shady spot, fruiting tree, or source of stone for making artifacts, visited some early sites repeatedly over periods of years. However, there is no evidence that they occupied sites for long periods of time or that they altered sites deliberately to suit their needs, though they may well have constructed sleeping nests or other ephemeral structures that have not survived.

While it is conceivable that the largest vegetarian hominids might be nearly solitary, much as the modern orangutan, most early hominids no doubt lived in groups. Group size depends upon a number of factors, including dietary requirements, habitat, and pressure from predators. Considering their body size, it is unlikely that any early hominids lived in groups exceeding 40 or 50 individuals, and daily foraging groups were probably much smaller, perhaps as few as four or five. The amount of landscape with which any individual hominid was acquainted was not large. Small-bodied, more exclusively vegetarian species would have required a smaller territory to support the group, whereas those that depended in part upon hunting or scavenging would have needed a somewhat larger home range, perhaps 250 square kilometers. Sources of stone for tool manufacture at some early sites are known, and before the Middle Pleistocene, there is no evidence that hominids transported tools or the stone used to make them for distances greater than about 10 kilometers.

Hominids needed to drink every day, and without watertight containers, they could not stray more than a day's walk from a potable water source. Since trees provided their main refuge from predators, they would probably hesitate to stray far beyond a patch of woods. Low population densities prohibited the harboring of endemic infectious diseases, and the most common cause of death for early hominids was probably predation. A fairly large number of individuals in arboreal populations would have suffered injuries through falls. Survival would not normally exceed an individual's reproductive years, with a probable maximum life span for most species of about 35 years. Fairly small group sizes and home ranges meant that an individual would probably meet fewer than 200 members of his or her own species in a lifetime, and most of these individuals would be kin.

Physical differences between the sexes (sexual dimorphism) were fairly pronounced among early hominid species, with the most dimorphic in body size probably being the larger forms. Female body weights may have been as little as 60 to 70 percent of male body weight among *Australopithecus boisei* (*Paranthropus boisei*), for example. Size differences decreased with the appearance of *Homo erectus*, but pronounced size dimorphism probably remained an important feature of hominid life until the end of the Middle Pleistocene. Dimorphic primate species show sexual differences in foraging behavior that reflect both the animals' size and their individual energy requirements. The largest male apes, for example, may not be able to travel to the ends of smaller branches, where most fruit is found, because the boughs will not bear their weight. A pregnant or lactating female requires greater amounts of high-quality forage, and among some primate species, females range less widely than males, remaining closer to predictable food sources. While male primates are more likely to engage in hunting, it is not an exclusively male activity, and chimpanzee females have been observed to pursue and capture heavy prey in the forest canopy, even while carrying infants.

The nature of social relations between the sexes among early hominids has been a major source of debate in paleoanthropology. All modern primates species show a lasting social bond between a mother and her offspring, but there is great variety in mating patterns, group size, territoriality, and kin relations among group members. These behaviors no doubt varied among early hominid species. Polygyny is the norm among modern primate species with marked sexual dimorphism in body size and was likely a common form of social organization among early hominid species.

Two nearly universal features of modern human societies are the formalization of sexual relations and the economic cooperation of males and females in the rearing of young. Many paleoanthropologists believe these features to be of prime importance in the evolution of human societies and have attempted to pinpoint when they appeared in evolutionary history. In modern societies, food sharing plays a crucial role in creating lasting economic ties between males and females. Among modern primates, while individuals may occasionally share food or tolerate begging from offspring or potential mates, sharing food is not daily routine, and there is no agreement among paleoanthropologists about when it originated among Hominidae. Some contend that it appeared with the first tools and archaeological sites, while others link it to the appearance of bipedalism, well over 2 million years earlier, and still others postulate that long-term habitual economic cooperation between the sexes did not appear until the Late Pleistocene, more than 2 million years later.

One important clue to early hominid social organization lies in infant brain size. While adult brain size in early *Homo* is greater than those of *Australopithecus* or *Paranthropus*, the early *Homo* pelvis was still quite narrow. A small birth canal means a small brain size for the newborn and suggests a period of accelerated growth in early infancy to achieve large adult brain size. The modern human infant undergoes such a period of rapid postnatal brain growth, during which it is helpless and utterly dependent upon its mother. This prolonged infant dependency has profound implications for maternal behavior and provides much of the glue that binds modern human society together.

If culture, taken to mean a society's shared set of symbols, beliefs, and ideas about appropriate behavior, existed in the Early or Middle Pleistocene, it has left no tangible sign, and whether early hominids could convey their thoughts to one another through spoken language is hotly debated by paleoanthropologists. Speech required enlargement and reorganization of the primate brain and alteration of the larynx, tongue, jaw, and resonating cavities in the palate and cranium. These developments, together with the invention of a series of complex linguistic devices including syntax, may have occurred in a series of steps over a long period of time. Modern nonhuman primates communicate not only vocally but also through gesture, posture, and facial expression. It is quite possible that a rudimentary form of speech, perhaps incorporating many of these elements, was practiced by early *Homo*. Divergent trajectories among groups in the evolution of speech would have provided a strong mechanism isolating different early hominid species.

MIDDLE PLEISTOCENE

The Middle Pleistocene (125,000 to 750,000 years ago) is important in the development of human behavior because it saw the beginnings of behavioral modernity. With the extinction of *Australopithecus* and *Paranthropus* by about 1.4 million years ago, species diversity within the Hominidae was substantially reduced. Early members of the genus *Homo*, such as *Homo ergaster*, may have survived into the Middle Pleistocene, and *Homo erectus* became firmly established. Climatic change, technological innovation, or population pressure probably provided the impetus for a number of expansions of hominid populations out of Africa.

There is a possibility that *Homo erectus* found its way to Asia as early as 1.8 million years ago, but it was clearly present there by 1 million years ago. By about 500,000 years ago, archaic members of our own species, *Homo sapiens*, had appeared in Africa, Europe, and Asia. African archaic *Homo sapiens* populations probably gave rise to the first modern humans, *Homo sapiens sapiens*. Fossilized remains of these earliest modern humans have been found in South Africa and Ethiopia, and date to as much as 130,000 years ago. A rapid expansion of this modern human population out of Africa in the Late Pleistocene seems to have resulted in the displacement or extinction of archaic hominid populations in Eurasia, though some paleoanthropologists argue for an independent or parallel origin of modern humans elsewhere.

Homo erectus and archaic *Homo sapiens* had body proportions similar to modern humans, and their arboreal adaptation had probably become a thing of the past. Male adult height in some cases reached as much as 180 centimeters, which is in the range of the tallest populations of modern humans. Postcranial skeletons were very robust, indicating that these hominids had a high level of endurance for a strenuous and demanding way of life. There are no examples of very aged individuals from this period, and the maximum life span was probably about 40 years. The increased numbers of fossils and archaeological sites indicate that hominids existed in greater numbers, but population densities were still low enough to discourage endemic disease, and the common cause of death was probably traumatic injury or predation. However, one female *Homo erectus* (KNM-ER 1808) is known to have perished through a severe infection or dietary disorder, and a male archaic *Homo sapiens* (from a site at Kabwe) shows signs of serious periodontal disease.

Homo erectus seems to have occupied the entire African continent, with the possible exception of the portions of western and central Africa that are now forested (however, artifacts and fossilized remains of *Homo erectus* may yet be found there). The African geographic range of archaic *Homo sapiens* appears to have been broader still. A tolerance for a wider range of habitats may be due to the advanced nature of Middle Pleistocene technology over that of the preceding period. Perhaps manufacture of watertight containers freed hominids at this time to forage farther from a water source.

About 1.5 million years ago, the ad hoc stone-fracturing techniques of the Olduwan industry gave way to the Acheulian, whose hand axes and cleavers are characterized by standardized tool forms and often careful, bifacial workmanship. Flakes were produced by more formalized methods, including the Levallois technique. By about 200,000 years ago, Middle Stone Age technology had replaced the Acheulian in Africa. Hand axes and cleavers ceased to be made, and smaller tools made on flakes produced by the Levallois and other formal techniques became the norm. Stone tools do not seem to have been designed for particular uses, but individual tools were used for multiple tasks. The use of stone tools to make other artifacts in perishable materials, such as wood, skin, or grass, was probably common. In the later Middle Stone Age, scrapers and points made on flakes show clear signs of hafting onto handles or spears.

Some Middle Pleistocene populations appear to have practiced a new type of foraging, with repeated, perhaps seasonal, reoccupation of favored sites. With the possible exception of circular hut foundations at Middle Stone Age sites in the Orange River Valley in South Africa, signs of occupation structures are still rare and their interpretation problematic. While most sites are found in the open, the occupation of caves became more frequent. The disturbance and damage to bone debris in Acheulian cave occupations indicates that competition with predators was still a serious problem, but living in caves seems to have become more routine for some Middle Stone Age populations. Instrumental in this development was the controlled use of fire, and deliberately fashioned hearths are known from both Acheulian and Middle Stone Age contexts.

The importance of the use of fire cannot be overemphasized. While there is no indication of the use of cooking vessels, tuberous vegetables and meat were probably roasted, rendering a wider array of foods edible and nutritious. Chewing cooked food places substantially less stress on the teeth and jaws, and natural selection for a reduced dentition and masticatory musculature strongly affected the shape of the hominid face.

Charring and scraping is an important technique in woodworking, and a club, spear, and tray apparently made by this method have been recovered at the Acheulian site of Kalambo Falls, Zambia. The use of fire also had an important impact on the African landscape. Repeated, perhaps seasonal, burnings cleared dense brush and encouraged the growth of fire-resistant tree species and grass. It is not known whether the fires escaped from hominid control, or whether the burning was deliberate, in the manner of some modern foragers and pastoralists, but the process made possible the open landscape that supports the large ungulate herds of today's African savanna.

Homo erectus is thought by many to have consumed more meat than its predecessors and to have practiced cooperative hunting. It is also frequently argued that cooperative hunting or learning to manufacture the standardized and more technically demanding tool forms of the Acheulian and Middle Stone Age required speech. It should be remembered, however, that lions, hyenas, and wolves hunt cooperatively and that birds and insects construct intricate and standardized nests, all without benefit of the spoken word. Nonetheless, with its larger body size, with a brain from one-half to two-thirds the size of a modern human brain, and armed with fire and an improved tool kit, *Homo erectus* seems well matched to its quarry. Examination of faunal remains shows that competition with predators was still a serious issue and that scavenging may have been common at both Acheulian and Middle Stone Age sites. Longer-term occupation of sites and the use of fire indicate that Acheulian hunters had established more secure territorial claims and had moved up in the carnivore hierarchy, but it may not have been until the early part of the Late Pleistocene that Middle Stone Age peoples routinely hunted dangerous game animals.

While sexual dimorphism was reduced in *Homo erectus* and archaic *Homo sapiens*, it seems to have been greater than among modern human populations. Brow ridge development, in particular, was far greater among males than females, and this characteristic feature of the hominid face reached its apogee in the Middle Pleistocene, perhaps maintained by sexual selection. Hominid social organization remains nearly as enigmatic as for earlier periods. There is no unambiguous evidence for symbolic behavior or ritual in African *Homo erectus*. Cut marks made by stone tools on a cranium of archaic *Homo sapiens* from Bodo, Ethiopia, however, can be interpreted as evidence for either cannibalism or ritual defleshing. Clear signs of cannibalism can be seen on the charred and broken early-modern human bones from the Middle Stone Age context at the Klasies River Mouth, South Africa, connoting either symbolic behavior or an all too familiar pattern of interpersonal or inter-group violence. A number of deliberate early-modern human burials are known from the Middle Stone Age levels at Border Cave, South Africa, though it is possible that these are intrusive from a later level.

From the archaeological record of the African Middle Stone Age, there are additional hints of modern behavior dating to many tens of thousands of years before such behavior appears outside Africa. Definite regional styles of artifact manufacture in the Middle Stone Age suggest the beginnings of ethnic identity. Blades occur in the Kapthurin Formation, Kenya, dating to about 240,000 years ago, and sophisticated bone harpoons, dating to 90,000 years ago, have been found at Katanda, Zaire. Faunal remains and projectile points from the Middle Stone Age site at /=Gi, Botswana, dating to about 77,000 years ago, indicate hunting of dangerous game animals and a deliberate, scheduled use of resources at different seasons of the year. The Middle Stone Age also sees the first extensive use of marine resources by coastal populations. Obsidian that was traded or transported from a source 190 kilometers away has been found in a Middle Stone Age level at the site of Muguruk, Kenya, implying either widespread trade among neighboring groups or acquaintance with distant landscapes or populations, both quite unknown in previous periods. Traces of similar modern behaviors appear quite suddenly in Eurasia about 40,000 years ago, when modern humans apparently arrived from Africa.

BIBLIOGRAPHY

Brooks, A. S., D. M. Helgren, J. S. Cramer, A. Franklin, W. Hornyak, J. M. Heating, R. G. Klein, W. J. Rink, H. Schwarcz, J. N. Leith Smith, K. Stewart, N. E. Todd, J. Verniers, and J. E. Yellen. 1995. Dating and context of three Middle Stone Age sites with bone points in the Upper Semliki Valley, Zaire. *Science* 268: 548–553.

Campbell, B. 1966. *Human evolution*. New York: Aldine Publishing Company.

Clark, J. D. 1970. *The prehistory of Africa*. New York: Praeger.

_____. 1988. The Middle Stone Age of East Africa and the beginnings of regional identity. *Journal of World Prehistory* 2: 235–303

_____. 1992. African and Asian perspectives on the origins of modern humans. *Philosophical Transactions of the Royal Society of London Series B* 337: 201–215.

Fleagle, J. G. 1988. *Primate adaptation and evolution*. San Diego: Academic Press.

Foley, R. 1984. *Another unique species*. London: Longman.

Isaac, G. Ll. 1982. The earliest archaeological traces. In *The Cambridge history of Africa, vol. 1: From the earliest times to 500 B.C.*, ed. J. D. Clark, 157–247. Cambridge: Cambridge University Press.

Klein, R. G. 1989. *The human career*. Chicago: Chicago University Press.

McBrearty, S. 1989. Cutlery and carnivory. *Journal of Human Evolution* 18: 277–282.

Toth, N., and K. Schick. 1986. The first million years: The archaeology of protohuman culture. *Advances in Archaeological Method and Theory* 9: 1–96.

Volman, T. P. 1984. Early prehistory of southern Africa. In *Southern African prehistory and paleoenvironments*, ed. R. G. Klein, 169–395. Rotterdam: A. A. Balkema.

Yellen, J. E., A. S. Brooks, E. Cornelissen, M. H. Mehlman, and K. Stewart. 1995. A Middle Stone Age worked bone assemblage from Katanda, Upper Semliki Valley, Zaire. *Science* 268: 553–556.

The author describes the specific anatomical features in early hominins, their probable function, how species of early hominins might be related to each other, and how speciation in early hominins may have occurred.

17. Tempo and Mode in Human Evolution

By Henry M. McHenry

In the 50 yr since the publication of Simpson's *Tempo and Mode in Evolution* (1) the paleontological record of Hominidae has improved more than a 100-fold. The improvements include precise geological dating and rich collections of well-preserved fossil hominids. Particularly valuable are newly discovered postcranial remains of early species that permit body-size estimation (2–4). These new data show that the pattern of morphological change in the hominid lineage was mosaic. Different parts of the body evolved at different times and at various rates. This report focuses on hominid phylogeny and the tempo and mode of evolution of bipedalism, the hominid dental configuration, and encephalization.

SPECIES, CLADES, AND PHYLOGENY

Views differ on the definitions of fossil hominid species and their phylogenetic relationships for many reasons but especially because of (*i*) the difficulty in identifying paleospecies (5–8) and (*ii*) the pervasiveness of homoplasy (9). One view (9) consists of five species of *Australopithecus* (*A. afarensis*, *A. aethiopicus*,

Henry M. McHenry, "Tempo and Mode in Human Evolution," *PNAS*, vol. 91, no. 15, pp. 6780–6786. Copyright © 1994 by National Academy of Sciences. Reprinted with permission.

A. africanus, A. boisei, and *A. robustus*) and three of *Homo* (*H. habilis, H. erectus,* and *H. sapiens*). Table 1 presents the geological dates and the estimated body, brain, and tooth sizes of these species.

Analysis of the states of 77 craniodental characters in these species of *Australopithecus* and *H. habilis* (9) reveals that the cladogram in Fig. 1*A* is the most parsimonious (tree length = 12,796, consistency index = 0.72). The two late "robust" australopithecines, A. robustus and A. boisei are the most highly derived and form a sister group with early *Homo.* This branch links with *A. africanus* to form a clade containing *A. africanus, A. robustus, A. boisei,* and early *Homo. A. aethiopicus* branches from this clade next with *A. afarensis* as a sister species to all later hominids.

Fig. 1*B* displays the phylogenetic tree implied by the most parsimonious cladogram. This phylogeny implies that *A. afarensis* is the most primitive hominid and that all later hominids shared a common ancestor that was more derived than *A. afarensis.* This post-*afarensis* hypothetical ancestor may someday be discovered. Its morphology can be reconstructed by observing the many ways *A. aethiopicus* resembles later hominids (especially *A. africanus*) and not *A. afarensis.* For example, the canine eminences of the face are prominent in the outgroup and in *A. afarensis* but are reduced or absent in all other species of hominid, which implies that the common ancestor of all post-*afarensis* species had canine eminences that were also reduced. This hypothetical ancestor would have a strongly developed metaconid on the lower first premolar. It would not, however, resemble *A. aethiopicus* in traits related to masticatory hypertrophy (heavy chewing), nor would it resemble any other post-*afarensis* species because they are all too derived in flexion of the base of the skull, orthognathism (flat faced), and encephalization to have been the ancestor of *A. aethiopicus.* After the divergence of *A. aethiopicus,* this phylogeny depicts a common ancestor of *A. africanus, A. robustus, A. boisei,* and *Homo* that resembled *A. africanus* in its development of anterior dentition, basicranial flexion, orthognathism, and encephalization. A second hypothetical common ancestor appears in Fig. 1*B* to account for the numerous derived traits shared by *A. robustus, A. boisei,* and early *Homo* that are not seen in *A. africanus.* This ancestor would have the degree of basicranial flexion and orthognathism seen in early *Homo* and the amount of encephalization seen in *A. robustus* and *boisei.* This phylogeny proposes a third hypothetical ancestor that would be at the root of the lineage leading to *A. robustus* and *A. boisei.* This ancestor probably resembled *A. robustus* in traits related to heavy chewing.

Although the most parsimonious cladogram implies this phylogeny, other cladograms are possible but less probable. A cladogram linking *A. aethiopicus* to *A. boisei* and *robustus* as one branch and *A. africanus*/ early *Homo* as another requires more evolutionary steps (tree length = 13332; consistency index = 0.69) because the later "robusts" resemble early *Homo* in so many features. These features include many aspects of basicranial flexion, loss of prognathism (muzzle), changes in the anterior dentition, and encephalization. The postcrania, although not included in this analysis, support the view that at least *A. robustus* and early *Homo* are monophyletic relative to other species of early hominid.

Whatever the true phylogeny is, and there can be only one, the fact remains that homoplasy is commonplace. Some resemblances appeared independently and not because of evolution from a common ancestor that possessed the same feature. Either adaptations for heavy chewing evolved twice or basicranial flexion, orthognathism, reduced anterior dentition, and encephalization each evolved more than once.

BIPEDALISM AND THE POSTCRANIUM

However the specific phylogeny of Hominidae is reconstructed, the important point is that these species are closely related to *H. sapiens,* and, in general, the more recent in time the species is, the more derived

Table 1. Species of *Australopithecus, Homo,* and modern African apes with geological ages, estimated body weights, brain volumes, relative brain sizes (EQ), cheek-tooth area, and relative cheek-tooth area (MQ)

SPECIES	DATES, MYR	BODY WEIGHT, KG*		BRAIN VOLUME,[†] CM³	EQ[‡]	TOOTH AREA,[§] MM²	MQ[¶]
		MALE	FEMALE				
A. afarensis	4–2.8	45	29	384	2.2	460	1.7
A. africanus	3–2.3	41	30	420	2.5	516	2.0
A. aethiopicus	2.7–2.3			399		688	
A. boisei	2.1–1.3	49	34	488	2.6	756	2.5
A. robustus	1.8–1.0	40	32	502	2.9	588	2.2
H. habilis	2.4–1.6	52	32	597	3.1	502	1.7
Early *H. erectus*	1.8–1.5	58	52	804	3.3	377	1.0
Late *H. erectus*	0.5–0.3	60	55	980	4.0	390	1.0
H. sapiens	0.4–0	58	49	1350	5.8	334	0.9
Pan paniscus	0	38	32	343	2.0	227	0.9
Pan troglodytes	0	49	41	395	2.0	294	0.9
Gorilla gorilla	0	140	70	505	1.7	654	1.0

*See refs. 2 and 10.

[†]Endocranial volume is transformed into brain volume by formula 4 in ref. 11.

[‡]Expected brain volume is 0.0589 (species body weight in g)0.76; see ref. 12.

[§]Tooth area is the sum of the md × bl diameters of P_4, M_1, and M_2; see ref. 13.

[¶]MQ, ratio of observed tooth area and expected area; expected area is 12.15 (species body weight in kg)$^{0.86}$; see ref. 13.

[‖]Two species may be represented in this sample. Using Wood's 1988 classification, I calculate the values for *H. habilis sensu stricto* and *Homo rudolfensis* as follows: male body weight, 37 and 60 kg; female body weight, 32 and 51 kg; brain volume, 579 and 709 cm³; EQ, 3.5 and 3.0; tooth area, 478 and 570 mm²; MQ, 1.9 and 1.5 kg; see ref. 10.

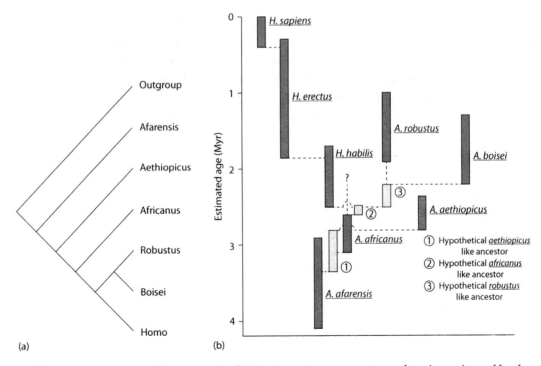

FIG. 1. (A) The most parsimonious cladogram using all 77 traits or using summary scores from the analyses of five functional complexes or seven anatomical regions. Tree length is 12,796 and consistency index is 0.722. (B) The phylogeny implied by the most parsimonious cladogram. Three hypothetical ancestors are predicted.

features it shares with our species. The earliest species, *A. afarensis,* is the most primitive in the sense that it shares the fewest of these derived traits and retains a remarkable resemblance to the common ancestor of African apes and people in many craniodental features. Its postcranium, however, is highly derived (14). It is fundamentally reorganized from that typical of apes to that specific to Hominidae (14–24).

Fig. 2 presents features in which the postcranium of *A. afarensis* differs from African apes and approaches the condition characteristic of humans. The most significant features for bipedalism include shortened iliac blades, lumbar curve, knees approaching midline, distal articular surface of tibia nearly perpendicular to the shaft, robust metatarsal I with expanded head, convergent hallux (big toe), and proximal foot phalanges with dorsally oriented proximal articular surfaces. A commitment to bipedalism in *A. afarensis* is also shown by the 3.5 million year (Myr) Laetoli footprints, which show very human-like proportions, arches, heel strike, and convergent big toes (24–27).

The nature of *A. afarensis* implies that bipedalism evolved well before the appearance of most other hominid characteristics. The appearance of bipedalism is sudden in the sense that it involved a complex alteration of structure in a relatively short period of time. Unfortunately, the fossil record does not yet include hominid postcrania predating 4.0 Myr that would document the transition from ape-like to hominid locomotion. The fundamental changes had already taken place in *A. afarensis.*

These bipedal alterations seen in *A. afarensis* are incomplete relative to modern *H. sapiens,* however (23, 28–40). Fig. 3 presents traits in which this species differs in its postcranium from later species of Hominidae. These plesiomorphies probably imply that the bipedalism of *A. afarensis* was kinematically and energetically different from modern humans and may imply that they were more efficient tree climbers than modern humans. This arborealism would have been different from ape-like tree climbing, however, because the hindlimb was specialized for bipedality and had lost essential climbing adaptations such as hallucial divergence.

The pattern of change in these traits in later species of Hominidae is complex. Most of the postcranial elements that can be directly compared reveal a period of stasis with no change between *A. afarensis* and *A. africanus* (23, 32). This is particularly striking in the capitate bone in the wrist and pelvis. Both have the identical combination of modern pongid, modern human, and unique characteristics. In the metacarpals and hand phalanges, however, *A. africanus* has some *Homo*-like features absent in *A. afarensis* (41, 42). The distal thumb phalanx of *A. africanus,* for example, is very human-like with its broad apical tuft that contrasts sharply with the relatively narrow, chimp-like tufts of the distal phalanges of *A. afarensis.* Limb proportions remain similar to *A. afarensis* in all species until the appearance of *H. erectus* at 1.7 Myr (2). Even *H. erectus* retains some primitive characteristics relative to *H. sapiens* (7). The most conspicuous of these is the relatively small cross-sectional area of the lumbar and sacral bodies (43). Narrow pelvic inlets and long femoral necks are characteristic of *A. afarensis, A. africanus,* and *H. erectus* and are probably related to parturition of smaller-head neonates (21, 44–49).

Body size remains relatively small in all species of *Australopithecus,* including the surprisingly petite bodies of the "robust" australopithecines (refs. 2–4, 49; Table 1, column 3). Sexual dimorphism in body size decreases from *A. afarensis* to *A. africanus* to *A. robustus.* Specimens attributed to *H. habilis* vary enormously in size and may imply (with other evidence) the existence of two species (3, 10, 14, 50). A sudden change occurs at 1.8 Myr with the appearance of *H. erectus* with body weights as high as 68 kg and a substantial reduction in sexual dimorphism. There is no evidence of a gradual trend of increased body weight through time, as might be expected from Cope's law.

Lumbar lordosis and sacral retroflexion

Sacral ala expanded laterally

Sacroiliac and hip joints closely approximated

Pelvis with:

- Mediolaterally expanded, superinferiorly shortened, and anteriorly rotated iliac blades
- Robust anterior iliac spines
- Distinct sciatic notch
- Distinct iliopsoas groove
- Rugose and large area for sacrotuberous ligament
- Retroflexed auricular surface with extensive retroauricular area
- Robust posterior superior iliac spine
- Sigmoid curvature of iliac crest
- Dorsoventrally thickened pubic symphysis
- Retroflexion of hamstring tuberosity
- Shortened ischial shank

Femoroal neck long with human-like distribution of cortical and spongy bone

Distal femur with:

- High bicondylar angle
- Elliptical lateral condyle
- Deep patellar groove with high lateral lip

Calcaneus with:

- Massive body
- Deep dorsoplantar dimension
- Ovoid transverse section
- Horizontally oriented sustentacular shelf

Midtarsal region is:

- Stout
- Anteroposteriorly expanded
- Strong transverse and longitudinal arch

Relative small forelimbs

Proximal humerus with open and shallow bicipital groove

Distal humerus with:

- Rounded lateral well of olecranon fossa
- Gracile lateral epicondyle
- Moderate-sized and cranially facing medial epicondyle
- Moderate development of supracondylar ridge

Radiocarpal joint perpendicular to shaft axis

Capitate with:

- Proximodistally shortened axis
- Single and elongated facet for MCII
- Shallow excavations for MCIII articulations

Metacarpals II-V relatively short with no dorsal transverse ridge on heads

Phalanges relatively short

Tibia with straight shaft

Distal tibia with articular surface nearly perpendicular to shaft axis

Metatarsal I with:

- Robust and triangular diaphysis
- Expanded head

Metatarsals II-V with:

- Heads expanded superiorly
- MTV powerfully built with large tuberosity

Hallux is convergent

Toes relatively short

Proximal phalanges with dorsally oriented proximal articular surfaces

FIG. 2. Derived postcranial traits shared by *A. afarensis* and *H. sapiens*. MC, metacarpal. MT, metatarsal

MASTICATION

The distinction between the hominid and pongid dental pattern was sharply delineated before the discovery of *A. afarensis* (51), but that species bridged the gap (52, 53). Overall, the dentition of the earliest species of hominid is more similar to the inferred last common ancestor than it is to *H. sapiens*. Most notable primitive traits include large central and small lateral upper incisors, projecting upper canine with marginal attrition facets, small metaconid of the lower first premolar and parallel or convergent tooth rows. The positions of the masticatory muscles are also primitive, particularly the posterior placement of the main fibers of the temporalis. But there are numerous derived features shared with later hominids as well. The most conspicuous of these is the reduced canines with apical wear.

Distal phalanges with:
- Weakly developed apical tufts
- Strong capsular cuffs
- Well-developed tubercles for collateral ligaments

Middle Phalanges with:
- Pronounced ridges lateral to the insertion of flexor digitorum superficialis
- Strong impressions for the insertion of this muscle tendon

Proximal phalanx of thumb attenuated

Proximal phalanges II-V
- Slender
- Curved
- With strong flexor sheath

Metacarpal I with:
- Highly concavoconvex proximal surface
- Attenuated shaft

Metacarpals II-V with:
- Large heads and bases
- Curved shafts

Pisiform:
- Elongate
- Rod-shaped

Trapezium with concavoconvex articular surface for MCI

Capitate with:
- Reduced area for styloid process
- Dorsally placed trapezoid facet
- Mediolaterally constricted MCIII facet
- Prominent palmar beak
- Waisted neck

Middle phalanges relatively long

Proximal phalanges:
- Long
- Curved
- Broad-based
- Narrow bodied in dorsal view
- Mediolateral flare of body for flexor sheath
- More highly circumferential trochlea

Metatarsal I with rounded head

Navicular with:
- Low maximum dorsoplantar height
- Large cuboid facet which faces at right angles to the lateral cuneiform

Lateral cuneiform with pongid-like plantar tuberosity

Long and narrow tuberosites ulnae and incisura trochlearis

Long and narrow collum radii and tuberosites radii

Radial head with broad articular area for zona conoidea of humerus

Distal humerus with:
- Strongly developd lateral crest on the anterior surface of the trochlea
- Distally extended capitular surface
- Proximal setting of the lateral epicondyle
- Lateral shaft margin parallel with shaft

Scapula with cranially oriented glenoid

Sacrum with:
- Only slightly developed ventral concavity
- Weakly developed transverse process of S1
- No upper lateral angles on superior surface of the transverse processes of S1

Thorax funnel-shaped

Proximal femur with:
- Poorly developed prolongation of articular surface along anteriosuperior margin of neck
- Short neck relative to femoral length

Short femur

Distal tibia with posterior tilt

Distal fibula with:
- Proximal border of distal articular surface running obliquely
- Articular surface facing inferomedially
- Less acute angle between distal articular and subcutaneous surfaces
- Broad and deep peroneal groove

Knee with:
- Rectangular shape
- Wide intercondylar notch
- Marked asymmetry of femoral condyles
- Single attachment for lateral meniscus

* **Midthoracic vertebrae with ventrally-expanded centra**

Lumbar and sacral centra relatively small in cross-section

Iliac blades face posteriorly

Ischium relatively long with hamstring surface area facing mostly inferiorly

Acetabulum with diminutive anterior horn

FIG. 3. Primitive postcranial traits of *A. afarensis* shared with the reconstructed common ancestor of African apes and humans. MC, metacarpal.

Hominid species postdating *A. afarensis* lose this species' primitive dental characteristics. *A. africanus* is variable in size and shape of its anterior teeth, but some specimens are more *Homo*-like (5, 50). Its lower first premolar is decidedly bicuspid. The mass of the temporalis muscle has moved forward into a more *Homo*-like position. Prognathism is reduced. The primitive dental features of *A. afarensis* are lost in hominid species postdating the appearance of *A. africanus*.

One unexpected characteristic of all early hominid species is postcanine megadontia and associated features related to heavy chewing (9, 13, 54–63). Relative to body size, the cheek-teeth of *A. afarensis* are 1.7 times larger than expected from that seen in modern species of Hominoidea (Table 1, column 8). Relative cheek-tooth size is higher in *A. africanus* (2.0) and higher still in *A. robustus* (2.2) and *A. boisei* (2.5). The appearance of *Homo* is marked by a reduction to 1.7. From the earliest *Homo* species to *H. erectus* to *H. sapiens* there has been dental reduction. Presumably the masticatory hypertrophy within species *of Australopithecus* is related to diet and to the amount of grit entering the mouth. Reduction of tooth size in *Homo* may reflect dietary change, but also it is probably related to the use of tools in preparing food.

The phylogeny presented in Fig. 1*B* implies traits related to heavy chewing evolved by parallel evolution in two lineages. One of these is the lineage from *A. afarensis* to *A. aethiopicus*. The second is the lineage from *A. afarensis* to *A. africanus* to the late "robust" australopithecines, *A. robustus* and *A. boisei*. This is a surprising result because *A. aethiopicus* and *A. boisei* share a suite of unique character states such as extreme anterior projection of the zygomatic bone, huge cheek teeth, enormous mandibular robusticity, a heart-shaped foramen magnum, and temporoparietal overlap of the occipital at asterion (at least in males).

All of these traits, except for the heart-shaped foramen magnum, are related to the functional complex of heavy chewing. The huge cheek-teeth and robust mandibles of both species are obviously part of masticatory hypertrophy. The anterior projection of the zygomatic bones brings the masseter muscles into a position of maximum power. The encroachment by the root of the zygomaticoalveolar crest obscures the expression of the anterior pillars and upper canine jugae. Even the morphology of the temporoparietal overlap with occipital is related to the function of the forces generated by the chewing muscles (9).

Theoretically, it is understandable how such detailed similarity could be due to parallel evolution. These species are closely related and share "… so much in common in their constitution" (64) that similar selective forces produce similar morphologies. The selective forces in this case are related to a feeding adaptation that is associated with a specialized ecological niche. As Mayr (ref. 65, p. 125) points out "… most adaptations for special niches are far less revealing taxonomically than they are conspicuous. Occupation of a special food niche and the correlated adaptations have a particularly low taxonomic value." In fact, many of the same traits characteristic of *A. aethiopicus* and the other "robust" australopithecines reappear in distantly related species adapted to heavy chewing. Expansion of the cheek-teeth, shortening of the muzzle, and anterior migration of the attachment areas of the chewing muscles are seen in other primates whose diet requires heavy chewing (e.g., *Hadropithecus*, *Theropithecus*, probably *Gigantopithecus*, and *Ekmowehashala*).

ENCEPHALIZATION

Table 1, column 5 presents brain sizes in species of Hominidae. Absolute brain volume has more than tripled from *A. afarensis* to *H. sapiens,* and relative size has more than doubled (6, 8, 11, 12, 22, 66–84). Given the very human-like postcranium of *A. afarensis*, it is interesting that this species has a relative brain size very close to that of modern chimpanzees. Lamarck, Huxley, Haeckel, and Darwin speculated that bipedalism preceded encephalization, but they had no fossil proof (78). The early species of *Australopithecus* confirm their prediction.

Both absolute and relative brain size increase through time in the series from *A. afarensis* [384 cc, 2.2 ratio of brain volume and expected volume (EQ)] to *A. africanus* (420 cc, 2.5 EQ) to *A. boisei* (488 cc, 2.6 EQ) to *A. robustus* (502 cc, 2.9 EQ). Superficially, this increase through time appears to be by gradual increments, but samples are small and body weight determinations are inexact (2). The sample of endocasts of *A. afarensis* consists of three specimens and of these, all are fragmentary, and one is the estimated

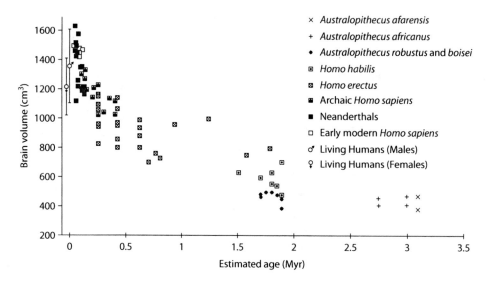

FIG. 4. Brain size (in cm³) plotted against time (Myr) for specimens attributed to Hominidae.

adult size from a 2.5-yr-old child (68). Although there are six endocasts of *A. africanus,* three of these needed substantial reconstruction (74). There is only one endocast of *A. robustus,* four of *A. boisei,* seven of *H. habilis,* five for early *H. erectus,* and five for late *H. erectus.* Body weight estimates may be off the mark, but the sample of postcranial specimens is sufficient to show that body weight remained at about the same relatively small size in all species of *Australopithecus.* This result implies that the apparent increase in brain size through time in species of *Australopithecus* is not due merely to an increase in body size. Body size and brain size are variable in specimens attributed to *H. habilis* with individuals as small as 32 kg and 484 cc and others as large as 57 kg and 709 cc. Although there are reasons to keep *H. habilis* as a single species (6), dividing the sample into two species is justifiable (8, 50). With either taxonomy, the absolute brain sizes of these early *Homo* specimens lie between *Australopithecus* and *H. erectus,* although relative brain sizes of early members of *H. erectus* overlap the range of the smaller-bodied specimens of *H. habilis.* The relative brain size of early *H. erectus* is surprisingly small because body size is so large. By 1.7 Myr, individuals attributed to *H. erectus* grew to > 180 cm, and by 1.5 Myr one individual (KNM-WT 15000) may have stood 185 cm and weighed 68 kg as an adult (4). Despite the fact that the average early *H. erectus* brain was > 200 cc larger than the average brain of *H. habilis,* the relative brain sizes are only slightly different (EQ = 3.1 and 3.3).

The pattern of encephalization since early *H. erectus* is difficult to interpret because geological dates are less accurate, variability is high, and body weights are difficult to establish. Fig. 4 plots brain size against time. For its first million years, *H. erectus* has absolute brain volumes that do not increase through time and therefore represent a period of stasis (85). It is difficult to establish whether relative brain sizes increased because there are very few postcranial fossils of *H. erectus* after 1.5 Myr from which to estimate body size. The few femora that are known are similar in size to those from early *H. erectus.* When taken over its entire range, the current sample of *H. erectus* does show a weak, but significant, positive increase in brain size through time (76). The sample of archaic *H. sapiens* (0.4–0.125 Myr) shows a strong positive trend (76). Variability is high. Many specimens as old as 0.4 Myr are within the modern human range of variation, and after 0.25 Myr all specimens are within this range. The average for the Neanderthals is 1369 cc compared with 1462 cc for early modern *H. sapiens.*

STASIS, PUNCTUATION, AND TRENDS

It is useful to regard evolutionary change in the hominid lineage from the point of view of Mayr's peripatric theory of speciation (86). Presumably, most of our samples derive from central populations of species and not from the small, isolated, and peripheral groups that are the most likely source of new species. When one of these peripheral isolates becomes reproductively isolated from the central species and its geographical range expands, it may overlap with the parent species, resulting in the coexistence of ancestral and descendant species. As depicted in Fig. 1*B*, ancestral species overlap in time with descendants in most cases in hominid evolution, which is not what would be expected from gradual transformations by anagenesis (87). Trends through time observed in the fossil record are not necessarily the result of gradual change but rather "… an accumulation of discrete speciation events" (ref. 86; p. 223).

These events can be obscured by defining paleospecies too broadly, however. For example, it is conventional to define *H. erectus* as including specimens from deposits as old as 1.8 Myr and as young as 0.2 Myr (85). There is a slight trend in brain-size increase in this series (76), but the earliest and smallest brained specimens are regarded by some as a separate species, *Homo ergaster* (50, 88, 89). Another example is the inclusion of specimens into *H. sapiens* that date back to perhaps 0.5 Myr, despite their decidedly archaic features. By this attribution, there is a strong positive trend in brain size through time (76). An argument can be made, however, that this sample consists of several species (90).

This view does not exclude the presence of change through time within species, however. As the original proponents of the theory of punctuated equilibrium point out (86), this view concerns the relative frequency of stasis, punctuation, and phyletic gradualism. Even within the multiple-species hypothesis of Middle to Late Pleistocene *Homo* (90), all change through time does not occur at speciation events. For example, brain size and cranial morphology change from early to late specimens referred to *Homo neanderthalensis*. It is interesting, however, how little change occurs within most hominid species through time.

I thank the organizers of this symposium and particularly Francisco Ayala and Walter Fitch for the invitation to contribute this paper. I am indebted to my colleague, R. R. Skelton, with whom I did the phylogenetic analysis reported here. I thank all those whose work led to the discovery of the fossils and especially M. D. Leakey, R. E. Leakey, F. C. Howell, D. C. Johanson, Tadessa Terfa, Mammo Tessema, C. K. Brain, P. V. Tobias, the late A. R. Hughes, and T. White for many kindnesses and permission to study the original fossil material. I thank the curators of the comparative samples used in this study. Partial funding was provided by the Committee on Research of the University of California, Davis.

REFERENCES

1. Simpson, G. G. (1944) *Tempo and Mode in Evolution* (Columbia Univ. Press, New York).
2. McHenry, H. M. (1992) *Am. J. Phys. Anthropol.* **87,** 407–431.
3. McHenry, H. M. (1994) *J. Hum. Evol.* **27,** in press.
4. Ruff, C. B. & Walker, A. (1993) in *The Nariokotome Homo erectus Skeleton,* eds. Walker, A. & Leakey, R. (Harvard Univ. Press, Cambridge, MA), pp. 234–265.
5. Kimbel, W. H. & Martin, L. B. (1993) in *Species, Species Concepts, and Primate Evolution,* eds. Kimbel, W. H. & Martin, L. B. (Plenum, New York), pp. 539–553.
6. Tobias, P. V. (1991) *Olduvai Gorge Volume 4: The Skulls, Endocasts and Teeth of Homo habilis* (Cambridge Univ. Press, Cambridge, U.K.).

7. Walker, A. & Leakey, R. (1993) in *The Nariokotome Homo erectus Skeleton*, eds. Walker, A. & Leakey, R. (Harvard Univ. Press, Cambridge, MA).

8. Wood, B. A. (1991) *Koobi Fora Research Project IV: Hominid Cranial Remains from Koobi Fora* (Clarendon, Oxford).

9. Skelton, R. R. & McHenry, H. M. (1992) *J. Hum. Evol.* **23**, 309–349.

10. McHenry, H. M. (1994) in *Power, Sex, and Tradition: The Archaeology of Human Ancestry*, eds. Shennan, S. & Steele, J. (Routledge & Kegan Paul, London), in press.

11. Aiello, L. C. & Dunbar, R. I. M. (1993) *Curr. Anthropol.* **34**, 184–193.

12. Martin, R. D. (1981) *Nature (London)* **293**, 57–60.

13. McHenry, H. M. (1984) *Am. J. Phys. Anthropol.* **64**, 297–306.

14. McHenry, H. M. (1994) in *Integrative Pathways to the Past: Paleoanthropological Papers in Honor of F. Clark Howell*, eds. Corruccini, R. S. & Ciochon, R. L. (Prentice-Hall, Engelwood Cliffs, NJ), pp. 251–268.

15. Berge, C. (1993) *L'Évolution de la Hanche et du Pelvis des Hominidés: Bipedie, Parturition, Croissance, Allometrie* (Presses du CNRS, Paris).

16. Johanson, D. C., Taieb, M. Coppens, Y. (1982) *Am. J. Phys. Anthropol.* **57**, 373–402.

17. Latimer, B. (1991) in *Origine(s) de la Bipédie chez les Hominidés*, eds. Coppens, Y. & Senut, B. (Presses du CNRS, Paris), pp. 169–176.

18. Latimer, B. M. & Lovejoy, C. O. (1989) *Am. J. Phys. Anthropol.* **78**, 369–386.

19. Latimer, B. & Lovejoy, C. O. (1990) *Am. J. Phys. Anthropol.* **82**, 125–134.

20. Latimer, B. & Lovejoy, C. O. (1990) *Am. J. Phys. Anthropol.* **83**, 13–23.

21. Lovejoy, C. O. (1988) *Sci. Am.* **259**, 118–126.

22. McHenry, H. M. (1982) *Annu. Rev. Anthropol.* **11**, 151–173.

23. McHenry, H. M. (1986) *J. Hum. Evol.* **15**, 177–191.

24. McHenry, H. (1991) in *Origine(s) de la Bipédie chez les Hominidés*, eds. Coppens, Y. & Senut, B. (Presses du CNRS, Paris), pp. 133–142.

25. Leakey, M. D. & Hay, R. L. (1979) *Science* **278**, 317–323.

26. Tuttle, R. H. (1987) in *Laetoli: A Pliocene Site in Northern Tanzania*, eds. Leakey, M. D. & Harris, J. M. (Clarendon, Oxford), pp. 503–523.

27. White, T. D. (1980) *Science* **208**, 175–176.

28. Deloison, Y. (1991) in *Origine(s) de la Bipédie chez les Hominidés*, eds. Coppens, Y. & Senut, B. (Presses du CNRS, Paris), pp. 177–186.

29. Jungers, W. L. (1982) *Nature (London)* **297**, 676–678.

30. Jungers, W. L. (1988) *J. Hum. Evol.* **17**, 247–266.

31. Senut, B. (1981) *L'Humérus et Ses Articulations chez les Hominidés Plio-Pléistocene* (Presses du CNRS, Paris).

32. McHenry, H. M. (1983) *Am. J. Phys. Anthropol.* **62**, 187–198.

33. Schmid, P. (1983) *Folia Primatol.* **40**, 283–306.

34. Schmid, P. (1991) in *Origine(s) de la Bipédie chez les Hominidés*, eds. Coppens, Y. & Senut, B. (Presses du CNRS, Paris), pp. 225–234.

35. Senut, B. & Tardieu, C. (1985) in *Ancestors: The Hard Evidence*, ed. Delson, E. (Liss, New York), pp. 193–201.

36. Senut, B. (1991) in *Origine(s) de la Bipédie chez les Hominidés*, eds. Coppens, Y. & Senut, B. (Presses du CNRS, Paris), pp. 245–258.

37. Stern, J. T. & Susman, R. L. (1983) *Am. J. Phys. Anthropol.* **60**, 279–318.

38. Susman, R. L., Stern, J. T. & Jungers, W. L. (1984) *Folia Primatol.* **43**, 113–156.

39. Tardieu, C. (1983) *L'articulation du Genou* (Presses du CNRS, Paris).

40. Tuttle, R. H. (1981) *Philos. Trans. R. Soc. London B* **292**, 89–94.

41. Ricklan, D. E. (1987) *J. Hum. Evol.* **16,** 643–664.

42. Ricklan, D. E. (1990) in *From Apes to Angels: Essays in Honor of Phillip V. Tobias,* ed. Sperber, G. H. (Wiley-Liss, New York), pp. 171–183.

43. Latimer, B. & Ward, C. V. (1993) in *The Nariokotome Homo erectus Skeleton,* eds. Walker, A. & Leakey, R. (Harvard Univ. Press, Cambridge, MA), pp. 266–293.

44. Berge, C., Orban-Segebarth, R., & Schmid, P. (1984) *J. Hum. Evol.* **13,** 573–587.

45. Lovejoy, C. O. (1978) in *Early Hominids of Africa,* ed. Jolly, C. J. (St. Martins, New York), pp. 403–429.

46. McHenry, H. M. (1975) *J. Hum. Evol.* **4,** 343–356.

47. Tague, R. G. & Lovejoy, C. O. (1986) *J. Hum. Evol.* **15,** 237–255.

48. Walker, A. (1993) in *The Nariokotome Homo erectus Skeleton,* eds. Walker, A. & Leakey, R. (Harvard Univ. Press, Cambridge, MA), pp. 411–430.

49. Walker, A. & Ruff, C. B. (1993) in *The Nariokotome Homo erectus Skeleton,* eds. Walker, A. & Leakey, R. (Harvard Univ. Press, Cambridge, MA), pp. 221–233.

50. Wood, B. A. (1992) *Nature (London)* **355,** 783–790.

51. Clark, W. E. L. (1967) *Man-Apes or Ape-Men* (Holt, Rinehart & Winston, New York).

52. Johanson, D. C. & White, T. D. (1979) *Science* **203,** 321–330.

53. White, T. D., Johanson, D. C. & Kimbel, W. H. (1981) *S. Afr. J. Sci.* **77,** 445–470.

54. Aiello, L. & Dean, C. (1990) *An Introduction to Human Evolutionary Anatomy* (Academic, London).

55. Grine, F. E., ed. (1988) in *Evolutionary History of the Robust Australopithecines* (de Gruyter, New York), 509–510.

56. Rak, Y. (1983) *The Australopithecine Face* (Academic, New York).

57. Tobias, P. V. (1967) *Olduvai Gorge: The Cranium and Maxillary Dentition of Australopithecus (Zinjanthropus) boisei* (Cambridge Univ. Press, Cambridge, U.K.).

58. Tobias, P. V. (1991) in *Evolution of Life Fossils, Molecules, and Culture,* eds. Osawa, S. & Honjo, T. (Springer, Tokyo), pp. 363–377.

59. Turner, A. & Wood, B. (1993) *J. Hum. Evol.* **24,** 301–318.

60. Turner, A. & Wood, B. (1993) *J. Hum. Evol.* **24,** 147–168.

61. Walker, A., Leakey, R. E. F., Harris, J. M. & Brown, F. H. (1986) *Nature (London)* **322,** 517–522.

62. Wood, B. A. (1988) in *Evolutionary History of the "Robust" Australopithecines,* ed. Grine, E. F. (de Gruyter, New York), pp. 269–284.

63. Wood, B. A. & Chamberlain, A. T. (1987) *J. Hum. Evol.* **16,** 625–642.

64. Darwin, C. (1872) *The Origin of Species* (Random House, New York), 6th Ed.

65. Mayr, E. (1969) *Principles of Systematic Zoology* (McGraw-Hill, New York).

66. Begun, D. & Walker, A. (1993) in *The Nariokotome Homo erectus Skeleton,* eds. Walker, A. & Leakey, R. (Harvard Univ. Press, Cambridge, MA), pp. 326–358.

67. Blumenberg, B. (1983) *Curr. Anthropol.* **24,** 589–623.

68. Falk, D. (1987) *Annu. Rev. Anthropol.* **16,** pp. 13–30.

69. Foley, R. A. (1992) in *Evolutionary Ecology and Human Behaviour,* eds. Smith, E. A. & Winterhalder, B. (de Gruyter, New York), pp. 131–164.

70. Godfrey, L. & Jacobs, K. H. (1981) *J. Hum. Evol.* **10,** 255–272.

71. Gould, S. J. (1975) *Contrib. Primatol.* **5,** 244–292.

72. Hofman, M. A. (1983) *Brain Behav. Evol.* **22,** 102–177.

73. Holloway, R. L. & Post, D. G. (1982) in *Primate Brain Evolution: Methods and Concepts,* eds. Armstrong, E. & Falk, E. (Plenum, New York), pp. 57–76.

74. Holloway, R. L. (1983) *Hum. Neurobiol.* **2,** 105–114.

75. Jerison, H. (1973) *Evolution of the Brain and Intelligence* (Academic, New York).

76. Leigh, S. R. (1992) *Am. J. Phys. Anthropol.* **87,** 1–13.

77. Martin, R. D. (1983) *Human Brain Evolution in an Ecological Context* (Am. Mus. Nat. Hist., New York).

78. McHenry, H. M. (1975) *Science* **190,** 425–431.

79. McHenry, H. M. (1974) *Am. J. Phys. Anthropol.* **40,** 329–340.

80. Parker, S. T. (1990) in *"Language" and Intelligence in Monkeys and Apes,* eds. Parker, S. T. & Gibson, K. R. (Cambridge Univ. Press, Cambridge, U.K.), pp. 129–154.

81. Passingham, R. E. (1985) *Brain Behav. Evol.* **26,** 167–175.

82. Pilbeam, D. R. & Gould, S. J. (1974) *Science* **186,** 892–901.

83. Shea, B. T. (1987) *Int. J. Primatol.* **8,** 139–156.

84. Tobias, P. V. (1971) *The Brain in Hominid Evolution* (Columbia Univ. Press, New York).

85. Rightmire, G. P. (1990) *The Evolution of Homo erectus* (Cambridge Univ. Press, Cambridge, U.K.).

86. Gould, S. J. & Eldredge, N. (1993) *Nature (London)* **366,** 223–227.

87. MacFadden, B. J. (1992) *Fossil Horses: Systematics, Paleobiology, and Evolution of the Family Equidae* (Cambridge Univ. Press, Cambridge, U.K.).

88. Groves, C. P. (1989) *A Theory of Human and Primate Evolution* (Clarendon, Oxford).

89. Wood, B. (1993) in *Species, Species Concepts, and Primate Evolution,* eds. Kimbel, W. H. & Martin, L. B. (Plenum, New York), pp. 485–522.

90. Stringer, C. B. (1994) in *Issues in Hominid Evolution,* ed. Howell, F. C. (California Acad. Sci., San Francisco), in press.

Recognizing the earliest members of our genus requires a sound definition of the genus. The authors suggest a novel combination of clade and grade characteristics to define genus *Homo*. They recognize several species of early *Homo* in the African fossil record, but not all of them conform to their genus definition. They suggest that *Homo erectus* may be the first "real" member of the human genus.

18. The Changing Face of Genus *Homo*

By Bernard Wood and Mark Collard

The genus *Homo* was established by Carolus Linnaeus[1] as part of the *binomial* system he introduced in the tenth edition of his *Systema Naturae*. As conceived by Linnaeus, the genus *Homo* subsumed two species; the name *Homo sapiens* was attached to the more diurnal of the two. Within *H. sapiens*, Linnaeus recognized six groups. Four of these are geographical variants drawn from the four continents, Africa, America, Asia and Europe, that were known to Linnaeus. The other two groups, namely the wild and the monstrous men, are of sociohistorical rather than biological interest. The same is true of the second species, also called *Homo sylvestris*, *Homo troglodytes* which is part myth and part orangutan.

CHANGING INTERPRETATIONS

The process of relaxing the criteria for allocating species to *Homo* has proceeded in a series of steps. Some of these coincided with the recognition of new fossil species. Others resulted from the discovery of previously unknown features of a species or from reinterpretations of existing evidence.

Bernard Wood and Mark Collard, "The Changing Face of Genus Homo," *Evolutionary Anthropology,* vol. 8, no. 6, pp. 195–207. Copyright © 1999 by John Wiley & Sons, Inc. Reprinted with permission.

Homo neanderthalensis

The first step in the process of broadening the scope of *Homo* was William King's[2] decision to recognize a new *Homo* species for the Neanderthal specimen. He considered naming a new genus for the Feldhofer skeleton, but eventually decided that it was sufficiently similar to *H. sapiens* to warrant its inclusion in *Homo* as *H. neanderthalensis* King, 1864. In the same year, George Busk[3] reported to the British Association for the Advancement of Science on what we now know to be a Neanderthal cranium from Gibraltar. Although Busk acknowledged the strength of the resemblance between the Gibraltar cranium and the one from the Neanderthal cave, he judged the former to belong to *H. sapiens*, albeit a member of the species that was more similar to living Tasmanians and Australians than to contemporary Europeans. Interestingly, these additions to the genus *Homo* were made four years before the first fossils were allocated to *H. sapiens*.[4]

The inclusion of the Neanderthal skeleton within *Homo* expanded the ranges of both the cranial and postcranial morphology of the genus. The morphology of the type specimen, together with evidence gleaned from discoveries made prior to 1859 and thereafter in Western Eurasia, show that Neanderthal crania differ from those of living and fossil *H. sapiens* in several respects.[5,6] Typically, they have discrete and rounded supraorbital ridges, faces that project anteriorly in the midline, laterally projecting and rounded parietal bones, a rounded, posteriorly projecting occipital bone, a derived nasal morphology, large incisor teeth, and postcanine teeth with large root canals. Their brains were as large as, if not larger, than those of modern humans. Postcranial peculiarities include limb bones with stout shafts and relatively large joint surfaces, especially well-marked areas for the attachment of a muscle that helps to control movement at the shoulder, and an elongated pubic ramus of the pelvis. Despite the latter trait, there is no indication that the Neanderthals were anything other than upright, obligate, bipeds.

Deliberate burials or rock falls have resulted in an unusually good sample of immature Neanderthals. These show that the peculiar cranial and postcranial morphology of the Neanderthals occurs in the skeletal remains of very young children as well as adults.[7,8] This is evidence that these features are under genetic control. Thus they cannot be dismissed as being behaviorally induced and, in consequence, taxonomically and phylogenetically irrelevant.

Homo Heidelbergensis

The second step in the process of relaxing the criteria for including fossil evidence within *Homo* was the addition of *Homo heidelbergensis* Schoetensack, 1908. The type specimen of *H. heidelbergensis* is a mandible found in 1907 during excavations to extract sand from a quarry at Mauer, near Heidelberg, Germany.[9] The next evidence within Europe came in 1933 from a gravel pit at Steinheim, Germany, but in the meantime evidence had been found in Africa (Kabwe, 1921 and 1925). These remains and others like them were initially labeled as "archaic" *H. sapiens*, but now they are being increasingly often referred to as *H. heidelbergensis*.[10–13]

The brain cases of *H. heidelbergensis* are often, but not always, smaller than those of modern humans (for example, Steinheim), but they are always more robustly built, with large ridges above the orbits and a thickened occipital region. The Mauer mandible has no chin, and the corpus is substantially larger than those of modern Europeans. Postcranially, the shapes of the limb bones are much like those of *H. sapiens* except that the shafts of the long bones are generally thicker, with higher robusticity indices. They have some, but not all, of the features of *H. erectus* crania, but lack the derived features of Neanderthal crania.

If there is to be a single species name to cover the archaic material from Europe, Africa and Asia,[12,13] then the name with priority is *H. heidelbergensis* Schoetensack, 1908. However, if there was evidence that the two other regions sampled equally good species, then the name that would have priority for the African

Box 1. Principles and Practice of Nomenclature

"... biological nomenclature has to be an exact tool that will convey a precise meaning for persons in all generations."

J. Chester Bradley in the Preface to the 1st edition of the International Code of Zoological Nomenclature[129]

The need to have conventions for the application and use of names for species groups has been recognized since Linnaeus[1] introduced the binomial system in 1758. The first formal code to regulate zoological nomenclature was devised by Hugh Strickland, and both Charles Darwin and Richard Owen were on the Committee that presented it to the British Association for the Advancement of Science in 1842. Entitled a "Series of Propositions for Rendering the Nomenclature of Zoology Uniform and Permanent," it was widely adopted in France, Italy, and the United States. The code was further refined by discussions, at and between, successive International Congresses of Zoology in 1889, 1895, and 1898. The direct descendant of Strickland's "Propositions" was the "Règles internationales de la Nomenclature zoologique," published in 1905. This code remained in force until 1961, when an international commission published the first edition of the *International Code of Zoological Nomenclature*, hereafter referred to as the Code. In 1973, responsibility for the Commission and the Code was transferred from the organizers of the International Zoological Congresses to the International Union of Biological Sciences in 1973, which sponsored the third and most recent edition of the Code in 1985.[130]

The purpose of the Code[130] is to "promote stability and universality in the scientific names of animals and to ensure that the name of each taxon is unique and distinct" (p. 3). Its basic principle is priority, in which normally "the valid name of a taxon is the oldest available name applied to it" (pp. 262–263). The Code is effective but cumbersome to use. It is made up of 88 Articles that are given Arabic numbers (1–88) and five Appendices (A–F). Each article has subsections that are identified by lower-case letters, and these sometimes are broken down into sub-subsections using either Arabic or lower-case

italic numbers. For example, Article 31, subsection (a) (ii) (i.e. 31, (a) (ii)) sets out the procedure to be followed for choosing the ending of a new species name depending on whether the person to whom the name refers is male or female or, when there is more than one person a mixture of males and females. This may seem arcane, but the provisions of the Code do bring uniformity to a system that could easily descend into chaos. It must be emphasized that the Code has both "rules" and "recommendations." If the rules are not followed, then a nomenclatural act may be overturned, but the failure to follow recommendations cannot invalidate a proposal.

When a new species is established, the correct sequence must be followed; in the examples given below, the relevant articles and subsections are given in parentheses. The proposed name must be available and it must be published. The name must be a word of more than one letter or a compound word (11, (h), (i)), that is capable of being rendered into Latin (11, (b), (iii)). It must not have been used for another taxon, and Article 13, (a), (I) stipulates that its publication must include "a description or definition that states in words characters that are purported to differentiate the taxon." The Code does not specify how comprehensive these descriptions should be, and this imprecision leads to potential difficulties: one researcher may deem a description to be satisfactory, while another may judge it to be inadequate. Disagreement about whether or not Alexeev[131] did this adequately for *Homo rudolfensis* lies at the heart of a recent exchange about hominin nomenclature.[132,133] A "publication" is defined very precisely in the Code. It must be public, intended for the scientific record, and freely available, either gratis or for purchase, but not by private subscription or in a limited addition. All copies of the publication

(continue)

(continued)

must be identical. Two appendices to the Code, D and E, provide useful recommendations about matters such as the choice of title and whether illustrations are necessary, but these are recommendations and need not be followed. Thus, for example, researchers are not required to give the etymology of a species name nor to specify a type specimen. However, the original description is the only opportunity to specify a type specimen. Subsequently, the only way to identify a replacement for the type is to select one of the original specimens as the "lectotype."[129,133]

The Code recommends, but does not stipulate, that the binomial should be followed by the name of the describer who has priority and the date of publication: for example, *Sinanthropus pekinensis* Black, 1927.[134] If subsequent research suggests that the species should be subsumed into a genus with priority, then the original author's name is put in parenthesis, and the name of the reviser is added. Thus, *Sinanthropus pekinensis* Black, 1927 effectively became *Pithecanthropus pekinensis* (Black, 1927) von Koenigswald and Weidenreich, 1939[16] when the latter authors reduced the differences between the two genera to no more than the differences between "two different races of present mankind" (p. 928). First Mayr,[19,20] and then later Le Gros Clark,[15] ceased to distinguish between *Pithecanthropus erectus* from Indonesia and *Pithecanthropus pekinensis* from Zhoukoudian, and subsumed *Pithecanthropus* into *Homo*. Thus, because of the priority it enjoys, the species *Anthropopithecus erectus* Dubois, 1892, which two years later became *Pithecanthropus erectus* (Dubois, 1892) Dubois, 1894[135] provides the species name *Homo erectus* (Dubois, 1892) Mayr, 1944 for the new, amalgamated taxon. Although this is the full, formal, name of the species, authors normally use the shortened version, *Homo erectus* (Dubois, 1892).

species would be *H. rhodesiensis* Woodward, 1921. Further, if the Ngandong material is not to be included in *H. erectus* (see below), the appropriate name for a distinctive Asian "archaic" *Homo* species would be *H. soloensis* Oppe-noorth, 1932.

Homo Erectus

The third step in the process of expanding the range of morphology within *Homo* began in 1944, when Mayr[19] recommended that *Pithecanthropus erectus* Dubois, 1892 should be transferred to the genus *Homo*, and was completed by Le Gros Clark[15] exactly a hundred years after *H. neanderthalensis* was incorporated into *Homo*. Until the taxonomy was rationalized, the main subsets of the hypodigm of what is now referred to as *H. erectus* were attributed to five genera. Two of these, *Pithecanthropus* and *Meganthropus* von Koenigswald, 1950, were known from Java, and one, *Sinanthropus* Black, 1927, from China. Two African genera, *Telanthropus* Broom and Robinson, 1949 from southern Africa and *Atlanthropus* Arambourg, 1954 from North Africa made up the balance.

This has meant that the hypodigm of *H. erectus* has had a complicated nomenclatural history. The type specimen was originally referred to as *Anthropopithecus erectus* Dubois, 1892,[14] but was transferred two years later to *Pithecanthropus erectus* (Dubois, 1892) Dubois, 1894. The next taxonomic revision was signaled when von Koenigswald and Weidenreich[16] concluded that *Sinanthropus* and *Pithecanthropus* differed no more than "two different races of present mankind" (p. 928). This conclusion was formalized four years later when Weidenreich[17] sank *Sinanthropus* into *Pithecanthropus*. Just over a decade later in the first edition of *The Fossil Evidence for Human Evolution*, Le Gros Clark[18] placed both *Sinanthropus* Black, 1927 and *Meganthropus* von Koenigswald, 1950 into *Pithecanthropus* (Dubois, 1892). In the meantime, however, Mayr had proposed that *Pithecanthropus*,[19] *Meganthropus*,[20] and *Telanthropus*[20] be transferred to

Homo. Lastly, in the second edition of his text, Le Gros Clark[15] proposed that *Atlanthropus* as well as *Pithecanthropus* be transferred to *Homo*.

Compared with *H. sapiens*, *H. neanderthalensis*, and *H. heidelbergensis*, fossils attributed to *H. erectus* have a smaller neurocranium, a lower vault, a broader base relative to the vault, and more complex pre-molar roots. They also have a substantial, essentially continuous torus above the orbits, behind which is a sulcus. There is usually a sagittal torus and an angular torus that runs toward the mastoid process. The occipital region is sharply angulated, with a well-marked supra-toral sulcus, and the inner and outer tables of the vault are thickened. Despite the relatively large number of crania that had been recovered from Java, China, and elsewhere, relatively little was known about the postcranial morphology of what was to become *H. erectus*. Discoveries from East African sites provided crucial evidence in the form of a pelvis and femur from Olduvai Gorge (OH 28), two fragmentary partial skeletons from East Turkana (KNM-ER 803 and 1808), and the unusually well-preserved skeleton from West Turkana (KNM-WT 15000). The cortical bone of the postcranial skeleton is generally thick. The long bones are robust; the shaft of the femur is relatively flattened from front to back while that of the tibia is relatively flattened from side to side in comparison with those of other *Homo* species. These are referred to as platymeria and platyenemia, respectively. However, all the postcranial elements are consistent with a habitually upright posture and bipedalism.

Some workers have suggested that the "early African" component of *H. erectus* is significantly more primitive than is *H. erectus sensu stricto* and have proposed that this subset of the hypodigm be assigned to a separate species, *H. ergaster* Groves and Mazák, 1975,[10,11,21–24] However, not all researchers accept the need to subdivide the *H. erectus* hypodigm in this way.[25–30]

Homo habilis

The fourth step in the process of relaxing the criteria for allocating species to *Homo* came in 1964, when Leakey, Tobias, and Napier, set out the case for recognizing a new species for the "gracile" hominid remains recovered at Olduvai Gorge from 1960 onward. Even more contentiously, they proposed that the new species should be accommodated within the genus *Homo* as *H. habilis* Leakey, Tobias, and Napier, 1964.[31] The addition of *H. habilis* to the genus *Homo* meant that Le Gros Clark's[18] diagnosis of *Homo* needed amendment. This involved Leakey and coworkers[31] relaxing some criteria such as brain size, so that the relatively small-brained (600 to 700 cm^3) crania from Olduvai could be included. It was claimed that other criteria, such as dexterity, an erect posture, and a bipedal gait, did not need to be changed because Leakey, Tobias, and Napier's[31] interpretation of the functional capabilities of the *H. habilis* remains from Olduvai was such that the type specimen and the para-types complied with these functional criteria.[31] Ultimately, new discoveries and the reinterpretation of existing evidence has led others to offer rather different functional assessments of the same material.

Early Homo

The fifth step in the process of changing and relaxing the criteria for allocating species to the genus *Homo* began in 1972 with the discovery of KNM-ER 1470. Although this specimen was not formally assigned to *H. habilis* (initially it was attributed to *Homo* sp. indet.[32]), it was the first in a sequence of fossil discoveries at Koobi Fora, among them KNM-ER 1590, 1802, 1805, 1813, and 3732, that were informally referred to as "early *Homo*." The morphology of KNM-ER 1470 showed the unique combination of an "advanced" neurocranium with a "primitive" australopith-like face. The presence of these two morphologies in the same cranium posed a difficulty for researchers. Which was the homoplasy, the large brain or the large, broad face? Alone among the early commentators, Walker[33] cautioned that KNM-ER 1470 may represent a large-brained *Australopithecus*. Most researchers chose the face as the site of homoplasy[34,35] and argued that the large neurocranium allied the new cranium with *Homo*. As a consequence, from 1973 onward, the genus *Homo* subsumed a substantially wider range of facial and basicranial morphology[36] than it did prior to the discovery of KNM-ER 1470.

In due course, important additional specimens from Koobi Fora (for example, KNM-ER 1590, 1802, 1813, and 3732)[36] and Olduvai Gorge (OH 62)[37] were added to the early *Homo* hypodigm, as was fossil evidence from Members G and H of the Shungura Formation,[38-40] Member 5 at Sterkfontein,[41,42] and Member 1 at Swart-krans.[43-46] This additional material subsumes a wide range of cranial morphology, with endocranial volumes ranging from just less than 500 cm³ to about 800 cm³. The mandibles also vary in size, with those from the larger individuals having robust bodies and premolar teeth with complex crowns and roots.

The discovery of OH 62 was particularly significant in connection with the postcranial skeleton of *H. habilis*. Although the preservation of this specimen is poor, enough of the skull is preserved to allow virtual certainty that the partial skeleton does not belong to *Paranthropus boisei*. Thus, unless it is the first evidence from Bed I of a novel taxon, OH 62 must belong to *H. habilis*, the only other hominin species known from that time range at Olduvai Gorge. Although several isolated postcranial specimens from Bed I had been attributed to *H. habilis*,[31] it was subsequently pointed out that it is at least equally likely that this postcranial evidence belongs to *P. boisei*.[47] If the logic we have set out is followed, the discovery of OH 62 provided the first unequivocal postcranial evidence of *H. habilis*. It was all the more significant, therefore, that OH 62 apparently had limb proportions that were at least as ape-like as those of individuals attributed to *Australopithecus afarensis*.[37,48] If the associated skeleton KNM-ER 3735 from Koobi Fora also proves to belong to *H. habilis*,[36,49,50] this will provide further evidence of that taxon's postcranial morphology.

Changing Functional Interpretations of *H. habilis*

The final contribution to the increasing inclusiveness of *Homo* came as the result of reassessing the functional implications of the original postcranial remains attributed to *H. habilis* from Olduvai Gorge. The type and paratypes of *H. habilis* included fossil evidence from both the forelimb (OH 7) and the hindlimb (OH 8, 10, and 35).[31] Some investigators have argued that OH 8 and 35 are from the same individual,[51] but an analysis of the shapes of the reciprocal joint surfaces suggests otherwise.[52] The initial assessment of the functional implications of the evidence from the leg and foot stressed the ways in which the Olduvai material resembled *H. sapiens*,[53] but authors who have considered these specimens in more detail were more cautious. For example, they stressed that the knee was imperfectly adapted to bipedalism[54] and that the foot may not have been from an individual capable of modern human-like striding bipedalism.[55] However, in their revised diagnosis of the genus *Homo*, Leakey and coworkers[31] were clear that inclusion in *Homo* implied "habitual erect posture and bipedal gait" and, with respect to the upper limb, evidence of a "power grip" and a "simple and usually well developed precision grip" (p. 7).

With regard to the OH 8 foot, reassessments of its functional morphology have stressed its potential for climbing and pointed out that it retains several of the morphological features seen in living nonhuman primates.[51,56-58] Researchers have suggested that although OH 8 has the articular mechanisms that convert the foot into a rigid lever during the support phase of walking,[57] it apparently lacks some functional elements such as the lateral deviation of the heel and the propulsive great toe that are present in *H. sapiens*.[59] Similarly, considerations of the Olduvai OH 7 hand have suggested that earlier functional interpretations may need to

---

Box 2. Species Groups Within Homo

The following taxa have been proposed as component species of the genus *Homo;* temporal and geographic distribution and the type specimen are given for each taxon.

Genus *Homo* Linnaeus, 1758[1] [includes, for example, *Pithecanthropus* Dubois, 1894; *Protanthropus* Haeckel, 1895; *Sinanthropus* Black, 1927; *Cyphanthropus* Pycraft, 1928; *Meganthropus* Weidenreich, 1945; *Atlanthropus* Arambourg, 1954; *Telanthropus* Broom and Robinson, 1949]. Pliocene-present, world-wide.

Species *Homo sapiens* Linnaeus, 1758.[1] Pleistocene–present, worldwide. There is no designated type specimen for *H. sapiens*.

Species *Homo neanderthalensis* King, 1864.[2] Pleistocene, western Eurasia. Type: Neanderthal 1, adult calotte and partial skeleton. Found at Neanderthal, Elberfield, Germany, 1856.

Species *Homo erectus* (Dubois, 1892)[14] Mayr, 1944.[19] Pleistocene, Africa and Eurasia. Type: Trinil 2, adult calotte. Found at Trinil, Ngawi, 1891.

Species *Homo heidelbergensis* Schoetensack, 1908.[9] Pleistocene, Africa and Eurasia. Type: Mauer 1, adult mandible. Found at Mauer, Heidelberg, Germany, 1907.

Species *Homo habilis* Leakey, Tobias and Napier, 1964.[31] Pliocene, Africa. Type: OH 7, partial calotte and hand bones. Found at site FLKNN 1 in Bed I at Olduvai Gorge, Serengeti, Tanzania, 1960.

Species *Homo ergaster* Groves and Mazák, 1975.[136] Plio-Pleistocene, Africa and possibly Eurasia. Type: KNM-ER 992, adult mandible. Found in Okote Member, Koobi Fora Formation, Area 3 at Koobi Fora, East Turkana, NFD, Northern Kenya, 1971.

Species *Homo rudolfensis* (Alexeev, 1986)[131] sensu Wood, 1992.[23] Pliocene, East Africa. Type: KNM-ER 1470, adult cranium. Found in the Upper Burgi Member, Koobi Fora Formation, Area 131 at Koobi Fora, East Turkana, NFD, Northern Kenya, 1972.

Species *Homo antecessor* Bermudez de Castro et al., 1997.[137] Pleistocene, Europe. Type: ATD6-5–mandible and associated teeth. Found at Gran Dolina, Atapuerca, Spain, 1994.

---

be revised in the light of evidence that it displays a mosaic of features ranging from an ape-like carpus and phalanges, to a thumb that some have interpreted as being compatible with pulp-to-pulp opposition.[60-63]

HAVE THE LIMITS OF *HOMO* BEEN STRETCHED TOO FAR?

Depending on the type of taxonomic interpretation adopted,[64] the genus *Homo* contains as many as seven fossil species: *H. neanderthalensis, H. heidelbergensis, H. erectus, H. habilis, H. ergaster, H. rudolfensis,* and *H. antecessor*. These species run the gamut of morphology from the australopith-like postcranial skeletal morphology and proportions of *H. habilis* to the very different morphology and limb proportions of modern humans. Notwithstanding the existence of comprehensive morphological diagnoses of *Homo*,[15,31,65] in practice species have been and are being assigned to that genus on the basis of four criteria. The first criterion concerns absolute brain size. The notion of a "cerebral rubicon" for membership in *Homo* is closely linked with Keith,[66] who located it at 750 cm³, midway between the highest gorilla and the lowest "aborigine" endocranial volumes (pp. 205–206). In Leakey, Tobias, and Napier's[31] diagnosis of *Homo*, the rubicon was lowered to its present level of 600 cm³ in order to accommodate *H. habilis*. The second criterion is the possession of language. Tobias,[67] in particular, has championed the link between *Homo* and the ability to communicate through spoken language. He based this primarily on evidence from endocranial casts and wrote that "in the endocranial casts of *H. habilis*, for the first time in the early hominid fossil record, there are prominences corresponding to both a well-developed speech area of Broca and a secondary speech area

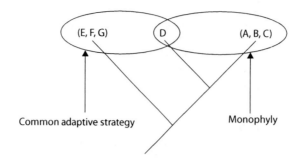

Figure 1. An illustration of the conflict between defining a genus using cladistic and evolutionary systematic criteria. With which group of species should species D be classified? If it is grouped with species A, B, and C, the resulting genus would be monophyletic but not adoptively coherent, whereas if It is grouped with species E, F, and G, the resulting genus would be adoptively coherent but not monophyletic.

of Wernicke. These are two of the most important neural bases for language ability in the human brain" (p. 836). *H. habilis* was, he claimed, "the first language-dependent primate" (p. 840). The third criterion is the ability to manufacture stone tools.[31,67] The connection between stone-tool manufacture and *Homo* is a longstanding one[68] that Kenneth Oakley made explicit in the content and the title of his book *Man the Tool-Maker.*[69] Although for five years *Zinjanthropus*[70] was credited with being "the oldest yet discovered maker of stone tools" (p. 493), the mantle was swiftly passed on to *H. habilis.*[31] Thereafter, the putative link between stone tools and *Homo* has been maintained by workers such as Hill and coworkers[71] and Kimbel and coworkers.[72] The fourth criterion for including species in *Homo* is the possession of a modern human-like precision grip based on a well-developed, opposable pollex.[31]

It is now evident that none of these criteria is satisfactory. The "cerebral rubicon" is problematic because cranial capacity is of questionable biological significance unless it is related to estimates of body mass.[73] Likewise, there is compelling evidence that language function cannot be reliably inferred from the gross appearance of endocasts.[74–77] Moreover, the language-related parts of the brain are not as well-localized as earlier studies had implied. While it is attractive to link language with the appearance of the genus *Homo*, there is little sound evidence to support such a scenario. The connection between *Homo* and stone-tool manufacture is also difficult to substantiate, for there is now overwhelming evidence that for much of the Plio-Pleistocene in East Africa hominin species were both synchronic and sympatric. The earliest stone tools, which come from about 2.6–2.3 Myr deposits in East Africa, were almost certainly contemporaneous with both early *Homo* and *Paranthropus.*[78–81] Furthermore, functional morphological analyses of the hands of the early hominins have either suggested that a modern human-like grip is not restricted to *Homo*[63,82–88] or indicated that we cannot yet be certain about the potential range of precision grips of any of the early hominins.[62] Thus there is a need to rethink the criteria we use to assign species to *Homo*.

A REVISED DEFINITION OF THE GENUS *HOMO*

Systematists are currently debating the definition of the genus category as part of a wider discussion about the implications of the cladistic method of phylogenetic reconstruction for the Linnaean system of classification.[89–94] At present, there are two main, competing definitions of the genus category. The first, which is associated with the evolutionary systematic method of classification, states that a genus is a species or group of species of common ancestry that occupies a different ecological situation or "adaptive zone" than that occupied by the species of another genus.[95] A group of species of common ancestry under this definition can be either monophyletic, comprising a common ancestor and all its descendants, or paraphyletic, comprising a subset of a monophyletic group. In the second definition, which is associated with the cladistic method of classification, a genus is a group of species that are more closely related to one another than they are to any species assigned to another genus.[90] In other words, under this definition a genus can only be monophyletic; it cannot be paraphyletic.

These definitions differ critically over the classification of ancestral species that have different adaptive strategies than their descendants, as well as over terminal taxa that form a monophyletic group with one taxon but share an adaptive strategy with another taxon. For example, in Fig. 1 species A, B, and C are monophyletic and adaptively similar, but their sister taxon, species D, shares an adaptive strategy with a monophyletic group comprising species E, F, and G. With which taxon should species D be classified? Should it be grouped with species A, B, and C, in which case the resulting genus would be monophyletic but not adaptively coherent? Or should it be grouped with species E, F, and G, in which case the resulting genus would be adaptively coherent but not monophyletic? The latter option would be selected under the evolutionary systematic definition, whereas the former option would be favored under the cladistic definition.

The evolutionary systematic definition of the genus category is rejected by cladists because they do not consider paraphyletic taxa to be real evolutionary units.[90] However, defining genera solely on the basis of monophyly is equally problematic, for this definition does not specify how many species should be included in a genus. Because all species are related to one another, a genus defined on the basis of monophyly could comprise, depending on personal preference, between three species and all species that have ever existed. Of course it would be possible for systematists to agree, for example, that a genus should comprise no more than two species and their common ancestor, a tribe no more than two genera, a family no more than two tribes, and so on. Provided sister taxa were granted equivalent rank, such a system would yield objectively defined taxa. However, it would also demand an impracticably large number of categories. Moreover, because such a phylogenetic classification, by definition, imparts information only about descent, it ignores the equally important modification component of evolution.[94]

We have suggested elsewhere[64] that the evolutionary systematic definition of the genus category should be modified so that paraphyletic taxa are inadmissible. Because the cladistic methodology cannot distinguish between ancestor-descendant and sister-group relationships, there is no way of recognizing ancestors empirically. In practice, therefore, the problem of how to classify an ancestral species having an adaptive strategy that differs from that of its descendants simply does not arise. On the other hand, the problem of how to classify a terminal species that forms a monophyletic group with one taxon but which shares an adaptive strategy with another can be overcome by recognizing it as a monotypic genus. We suggested, therefore, that a genus should be defined as a species, or monophylum, whose members occupy a single adaptive zone.[64]

Cladistics is the most effective method of identifying monophyletic groups of species, but how can we best determine hominin adaptive strategies? For a species to persist long enough to be sampled in the hominin fossil record, individuals must be able to maintain themselves in homeostasis despite fluctuations in ambient temperature, humidity, and the availability of water. They also have to procure and process sufficient food to meet their minimum requirements for energy and essential nutrients. Last, they must be able to mate in order to produce offspring. The ways in which the members of a hominin species meet these fundamental requirements comprise that species' adaptive strategy. Thus, if *H. rudolfensis*, *H. habilis*, *H. ergaster*, *H. erectus*, *H. heidelbergensis* and *H. neanderthalensis* have been allocated to the correct genus, two conditions must be met. First, cladistic analyses should indicate that the species are more closely related to *H. sapiens* than they are to the australopiths (the shorthand we will use for the species within *Australopithecus*, *Paranthropus*, and *Ardipithecus*). Second, functional analyses should indicate that the strategies used by the fossil *Homo* species to maintain homeostasis, acquire food, and produce offspring are more similar to the strategies used by the *H. sapiens* than they are to the strategies employed by the australopiths.

PHYLOGENETIC RELATIONSHIPS OF FOSSIL *HOMO* SPECIES

Hominin phylogenetic relationships have been reconstructed using cladistic analysis for more than two decades, but no published analysis has included all the fossil hominins or examined all the possible hypotheses of relationships among the species. Nevertheless, there is a clear consensus that *H. ergaster*, *H. heidelbergensis*, and *H. neanderthalensis* are more closely related to *H. sapiens* than they are to australopith genera. The relationships of *H. ergaster* have been examined in three studies,[23,36,96] all of which suggested that *H. ergaster* shares a common ancestor with *H. sapiens* to the exclusion of *Australopithecus* or *Paranthropus*. Notably, in a bootstrap reanalysis using PAUP (1,000 replication, heuristic, TBR)[97] of Strait, Grine, and Moniz's[96] character-state data matrix a (*H. ergaster*, *H. sapiens*) clade was recovered in 98% of the replicates.[64]

The only exhaustive examination of the relationships of *H. heidelbergensis* among the Hominini has suggested that *H. heidelbergensis* is the sister taxon of modern *H. sapiens* to the exclusion of all the other taxa in the sample.[98] A bootstrap reanalysis of the character-state data matrix using PAUP (options as above) found a sister group relationship between *H. heidelbergensis* and *H. sapiens* in 100% of the replicates.[64] In line with this, when MacClade[99] was used to alter the topology of the most parsimonious tree so that *H. heidelbergensis* was the sister taxon of the (*A. africanus*, *H. rudolfensis*, *Paranthropus*) clade, the tree length increased markedly from 297 to 335, and the consistency index (CI) declined from 0.66 to 0.58.[64]

No cladistic analysis has included *H. neanderthalensis* and examined all the possible hypotheses regarding relationships among the in-group taxa. Nevertheless, the number of almost certainly derived cranial and postcranial similarities between *H. neanderthalensis* and *H. sapiens* is such that it is highly unlikely that *H. neanderthalensis* is more closely related to the species assigned to australopith genera than it is to *H. sapiens*. The close relationship between the Neanderthals and modern humans is reflected in the recent debate as to whether the Neanderthals should be considered a separate species or included within *H. sapiens* as a subspecies.[10,11,100]

It is also clear from the analyses that *H. erectus* shares a common ancestor with *H. sapiens* to the exclusion of the australopith genera, although the relationship is possibly less reliable than those linking *H. ergaster*, *H. heidelbergensis*, and *H. neanderthalensis* to *H. sapiens*. The relationships of *H. erectus* within Hominini have been analyzed in two studies,[23,98] both of which suggest that *H. erectus* is more closely related to *H. sapiens* than it is to *Australopithecus* or *Paranthropus*. However, a bootstrap reanalysis (1,000 replication, heuristic, TBR) of the second study's data matrix using PAUP indicated that the clade linking *H. erectus* and *H. sapiens* to the exclusion of *Australopithecus* and *Paranthropus* was not supported at the 50% level.[64] When MacClade was used to constrain the cladogram so that *H. erectus* was the sister taxon of a (*Paranthropus*, *A. africanus*, *H. rudolfensis*) clade, tree length increased by just six steps to 303 and the CI declined by just 0.02 to 0.64.[64]

In contrast, neither *H. habilis* nor *H. rudolfensis* can be assumed with any degree of reliability to be more closely related to *H. sapiens* than they are to species allocated to other genera. Six studies have investigated the relationships of *H. habilis* and *H. rudolfensis* within Hominini.[23,36,96,98,101,102] In three of the favored cladograms (Fig. 1A in Strait, Grine, and Moniz,[96] Fig. 7.2 in Wood,[36] and Fig. 3 in Chamberlain and Wood[101]) *H. habilis* and *H. rudolfensis* are more closely related to the other *Homo* species than either is to *Australopithecus* or *Paranthropus*. In the fourth cladogram (Fig. 4 in Chamberlain and Wood[101]), *H.*

habilis is the sister taxon of a *(A. africanus, Paranthropus, H. rudolfensis, H. erectus, H. sapiens)* clade, and *H. rudolfensis* is more closely related to *Paranthropus* than it is to *H. sapiens*. In the remaining cladogram (Fig. 1a in Lieberman, Wood, and Pilbeam[102]), *H. habilis* is the sister taxon of *H. ergaster*, but that clade is more closely related to *A. africanus* than it is to *H. rudolfensis*. The most parsimonious cladograms do not, therefore, consistently indicate that *H. habilis* and *H. rudolfensis* share a common ancestor with *H. sapiens* to the exclusion of *Australopithecus* or *Paranthropus*. Moreover, even in the cladograms in which *H. habilis* and *H. rudolfensis* are grouped with the other *Homo* species, the links are weak. For example, Wood[36] found that a cladogram in which *H. rudolfensis* is the sister taxon of *Paranthropus* was only one step longer than the cladogram in which *Homo* is monophyletic. Likewise, a reanalysis of Strait, Grine, and Moniz's[96] data using MacClade indicated that their favored

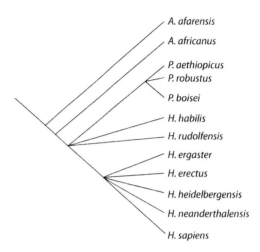

Figure 2. Consensus cladogram showing the relationship between hominin species. Because *A. afarensis* is consistently placed as the basal taxon, there are grounds for removing it from *Australopithecus*.[96]

cladogram is only two steps shorter than one in which *H. rudolfensis* is the sister taxon of *Paranthropus* and only three steps shorter than a cladogram in which *H. habilis* is the sister taxon of *Paranthropus*.[64]

Figure 2 depicts what we consider, on current evidence, to be the best estimate of the phylogenetic relationships between the species assigned to *Homo* or to the other hominin genera. It should be noted, however, that there are other, more pessimistic assessments of what can be determined about hominin relationships using cladistic methods.[103] Indeed the results of a recent study suggest that the type of morphology preserved in the hominin fossil record may not be a reliable source of information about phylogeny.[104,105] It is clear from Figure 2 that the current interpretation of the genus. *Homo* does not satisfy the first condition for a genus, for the fossil species assigned to it do not unequivocally form a monophyletic group with *H. sapiens*. It is probable that *H. erectus, H. ergaster, H. heidelbergensis*, and *H. neanderthalensis are* more closely related to *H. sapiens* than any of them to the species assigned to *Australopithecus* or *Paranthropus* (too little is currently known about *Ardipithecus* to include it in these analyses). However, *H. habilis* and especially *H. rudolfensis* are as likely to form clades with *Australopithecus* or *Paranthropus* as they are with *H. sapiens*.[64]

ADAPTIVE STRATEGIES OF FOSSIL *HOMO* SPECIES

Many aspects of a primates phenotype help it maintain homeostasis, acquire food, and produce offspring. However, not all of these aspects can be reliably reconstructed from the fossil record. Arguably, the most important of those that can be determined using palaeontological evidence are body size and shape, locomotor behavior, relative brain size, pattern of development, and the relative size of the masticatory apparatus. Using these as criteria, what evidence is there that *H. erectus, H. ergaster, H. habilis, H. heidelbergensis, H. neanderthalensis*, and *H. rudolfensis* share a functionally coherent adaptive strategy with *H. sapiens* rather than with the australopiths? We have reviewed this evidence elsewhere[64] and concluded that on the basis of the information that is available about early hominin body size and shape, locomotion, development, and the relative size of their masticatory apparatus, the hominins fall into two broad groups (Box 3).

The first group has a relatively low body mass; a body shape that, in terms of thermoregulation, is interpreted as being better suited to a relatively closed environment; and a postcranial skeleton that

Box 3. Summary of Results of Functional Analyses Carried Out by Wood and Collard[64]
(H) indicates a modern human-like pattern, (A) an australopith-like pattern,
and (I) an Intermediate pattern.

	Body Size	Body Shape	Locomotion	Jaws and Teeth	Development	Brain Size
H. rudolfensis	?	?	?	A	A	A
H. habilis	A	A	A	A	A	A
H. ergaster	H	H	H	H	H	A
H. erectus	H	?	H	H	?	I
H. heidelbergensis	H	?	H	H	?	A
H. neanderthalensis	H	H	H	H	H	H

suggests a combination of terrestrial bipedalism with proficient climbing. The first group also has teeth and jaws that were apparently adapted to a considerably more mechanically demanding diet than that of *H. sapiens*, and a developmental schedule more closely resembling that of apes than modern humans. This broad grouping may subsume more than one adaptive strategy, but the details are beyond the scope of this review.

The second group has a larger body mass, a more modern-human-like, open-habitat-adapted physique, and a postcranial skeleton consistent with a form of locomotion similar to that of modern humans (terrestrial bipedalism with, in adults, a limited ability for climbing). The teeth and jaws of the second group were apparently adapted to a diet which, when ingested, had similar mechanical properties to that of *H. sapiens*, and its developmental pattern was more modern human-like. This group may also subsume more than one adaptive zone.

It is noteworthy that relative brain size does not group the fossil hominins in the same way. This suggests that the link between relative brain size and adaptive zone is more complex than is conventionally assumed.[106]

With varying degrees of certainty, species within *Australopithecus*, including the recently announced *Australopithecus garhi*,[107] and *Paranthropus*, together with *H. habilis* and *H. rudolfensis*, can all be assigned to the first group, whereas *H. erectus*, *H. ergaster*, *H. heidelbergensis*, and *H. neanderthalensis* can be assigned to the second. We presently know too little about *Ardipithecus ramidus* and *Australopithecus anamensis* to be confident about even an approximate assessment of their adaptive strategies. When these observations are combined with the uncertainly about the phylogenetic relationships of *H. habilis* and *H. rudolfensis*, it is clear that the species currently assigned to *Homo* do not form a monophylum whose members occupy a single adaptive zone. In other words, with the hypodigms of *H. habilis* and *H. rudolfensis* assigned to it, the genus *Homo* fails to measure up to the criteria for a genus.

TAXONOMIC IMPLICATIONS

When the twin criteria of monophyly and adaptive coherence are applied to the fossil species presently included within *Homo*, it is apparent that on both counts *H. neanderthalensis*, *H. erectus*, *H. heidelbergensis*, and *H. ergaster* in large measure satisfy both criteria, whereas *H. habilis* and *H. rudolfensis* signally fail to meet them.[64] This suggests that *H. habilis* and *H. rudolfensis* should be removed from *Homo*.

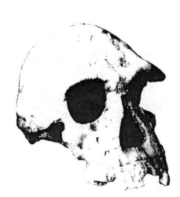

Figure 3. Oblique views of KNM-ER 1470, the lectotype[132] of *Homo rudolfensis*, and KNM-ER 1813, the best-preserved cranium of *Homo habilis* sensu stricto.[31] It has been proposed that both these taxa should be transferred from *Homo* to *Australopithecus*. These species would thus become, respectively, *Australopithecus rudolfensis* (Alexeev, 1986)130 Wood and Collard, 1999[64] and *Australopithecus habilis* (Leakey, Tobias, and Napier, 1964)[31] Wood and Collard, 1999.[64]

If *H. habilis* and *H. rudolfensis* are removed from *Homo*, does a new genus or new genera have to be established, or is it possible to transfer the two species to an existing genus or genera? Although *H. habilis* is adaptively like the australopiths, several aspects of its cranial morphology distinguish it from *Australopithecus*.[23,36,50,67,107,108] Likewise, although some aspects of cranial morphology align *H. rudolfensis* with *Paranthropus*,[102] other evidence, such as enamel structure,[36,109,110] suggests that, particularly until associated postcranial remains of *H. rudolfensis* are forthcoming, it may be premature to incorporate that species into *Paranthropus*. Moreover, the mosaic nature of the *A. garhi* cranial remains reemphasize how important it is to be circumspect about linking hominin species in an ancestor-descendant sequence on the basis of assumed synapomorphies.[108]

As if these were not sufficient grounds for taxonomic caution, there also is the fact that cranial and dental remains, those parts of the hominin fossil record normally employed in phylogenetic analyses, may be reliable for reconstructing the phylogenetic relationships of species and genera.[91,103–105,107,111] Thus, we cannot be as confident about the composition of hominin clades as we would like to be. Further, because the identification of clades is one of the two components of the genus definition we have put forward, decisions about higher-order taxa should be conservative until we can demonstrate that we have the means to generate more robust and reliable cladistic hypotheses. It is for these reasons that we have suggested elsewhere that, pro tern, it is most appropriate to refer to the two species displaced from *Homo* as, *Australopithecus habilis* and *Australopithecus rudolfensis*.[64] In the case of *A. habilis*, this means reverting to a taxonomy that at one time or another was supported or proposed by Tobias (see Washburn[112]), Howell,[113] Robinson,[114] Pilbeam,[115] and Walker,[33] among others. We anticipate that the results of future research may well justify erecting one or more new genera for these taxa in order to better reflect hypotheses about their phylogenetic relationships and adaptive regimes. It may also be necessary to reassess the taxonomic homogeneity of *A. habilis*.[45,46]

EVOLUTIONARY IMPLICATIONS

One of the main objectives of paleontology is the identification of adaptive radiations. These are episodes of species generation and diversification, and are usually associated with a shift in "grade."[116] Some refer to the process as the emergence of a new adaptive zone,[95,117] the species diversification being based on the

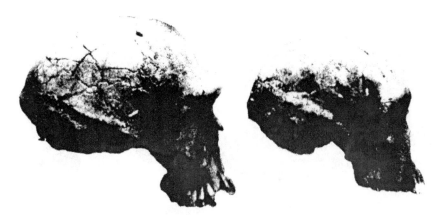

Figure 4. Lateral views of KNM-ER 3733, a representative of *Homo ergaster*, and KNM-ER 1813, a representative of *Australopithecus habilis*.

appearance of one or more "key innovations."[118–120] Researchers have argued that there is a concept in neontology, the "fitness-generating" or "G-function,"[121] which provides a model for how grades may have emerged in the fossil record.[122]

The fitness-generating function is an equation used to calculate the fitness of a phenotype.[123] The equation takes into account "all the fitness tradeoffs in terms of the costs and the benefits an organism receives for doing its business a certain way in a particular time and place...."[122] (p. 204). Thus, a new "adaptive type" is a species grouping with a function that has a less severe fitness trade-off than that of the group it supersedes. Rosenzweig, Brown, and Vincent[123] provide a compelling example from among the reptiles. In the Americas, and increasingly in the Old World, true vipers are being replaced by members of the pit viper group, comprising rattlesnakes, copperheads, and coppermouths. It is hypothesized that the reason for the success of the latter group relates to a key innovation in its visual system. True vipers have to trade off visual acuity against spectral band width; they cannot focus sharply on both infrared and visible light. Members of the pit viper group have overcome this problem by developing loreal pits for the reception of light in the infrared part of the spectrum, reserving their "real" eyes for the reception of visible light. By avoiding the compromise between wavelength and sharpness of image, pit vipers have effected a fitness trade-off that is superior to that of the true vipers. In other words, Rosenzweig, Brown, and Vincent[123] claim that we are observing the emergence of a new grade of vipers.

We suggest that if the genus *Homo* is to have any meaning, its lower boundary should mark a distinct shift in hominin adaptive strategy involving morphological and behavioral innovations. In other words, it should be a new adaptive type. The additional interpretative challenge is that this adaptive shift must be capable of identification in the hominin fossil record and therefore must involve those parts of the skeleton and other hard tissues that are relatively abundant in the hominin fossil record. It is highly unlikely that interpretations based on the fossil record are going to falsely identify adaptive shifts (a false-positive result or Type II error). Indeed, it is much more likely that many adaptive shifts will escape detection by those who have to rely on the fossil record for evidence of their existence. For example, there may be bony evidence of the viper's loreal pit, but it would be difficult to unravel the details of Rozensweig, Brown, and Vincent's example from the fossil record.

If we accept that the lower boundary of *Homo* should be redrawn to include *H. ergaster* but exclude *H. habilis* and *H. rudolfensis*, what is the basis of the hypothesis that this would result in a genus that more closely corresponds to one adaptive zone? The most likely candidate for a key innovation is diet, for this would be consistent with the reduction in tooth and mandible size. However, it does not seem to correspond in all particulars to the type of dietary shift that is envisaged in the "expensive-tissue hypothesis."[124]

Although there is skeletal evidence that the relative gut size of *H. ergaster* was reduced as compared to those of the australopiths, *H. ergaster* does not show evidence of any substantial shift in absolute or relative brain size.[64] These changes do not appear until much later in hominin evolution. We have suggested elsewhere,[125] as have others,[126,127] that extra-oral preparation of food by cooking may be the key innovation. Others have pointed to the likelihood that a switch to the consumption of underground storage organs such as tubers may have occurred around this time.[126,127]

It is also possible, indeed probable, that *Homo*, even when redefined in the way we suggest, may still be too inclusive. Although it may be difficult to detect in the hominin fossil record, the emergence of a complex spoken language and the shift to the manufacture of precision tool-kits[128] may have coevolved as joint key innovations that ushered in, at least in behavioral terms, a new and distinct adaptive zone. Did an increasingly sophisticated hominin culture blunt the process of species generation and diversification and thus block what in other circumstances would have been a classic adaptive radiation?

ACKNOWLEDGMENTS

Bernard Wood is supported by The Henry Luce Foundation, and Mark Collard by The Wellcome Trust. We are grateful to Arthur Cain for translating the 10th edition of Linnaeus' *Systema Naturae* and to A. Chamberlain for making his data available. We also thank Fred Grine and Alan Bilsborough for helpful comments on an earlier version of this paper. We are also grateful to the NERC and The Lever-hulme Trust for past support for research that has been incorporated into this study.

REFERENCES

1. Linnaeus C. 1758. Systema naturae. Stockholm: Laurentii Salvii.
2. King W. 1864. The reputed fossil man of the Neanderthal. Q J Sci 1:88–97.
3. Busk G. 1865. On a very ancient cranium from Gibraltar. Rep Br Assoc Adv Sci Bath, 1864:91–92.
4. Lartet L., 1868. Une sépultive des Troglodvtes du Périgord (cranes des Eyzies). Bull Soc Anthropol Paris 3:335–349.
5. Trinkaus F., 1983. The Shanidar neanderthals. New York: Academic Press.
6. Stringer C. Gamble C. 1993. In search of the neanderthals. London: Thames and Hudson.
7. Tillier AM. 1989. The evolution of modern humans: evidence from young Mousterian individuals. In: Mellars P, Stringer C, editors. The human revolution. Edinburgh: Edinburgh University Press, p 286–297.
8. Rak Y, Kimbel WH, Hovers E. 1996. On Neanderthal autapomorphies discernible in Neandertal infants: a response to Creed Miles et al. J Hum Evol 30:155–158.
9. Schoetensack O. 1908. Der Unterkiefer des *Homo heidelbergensis* aus den Sanden von Mauer bei Heidelberg. Leipzig 1–67.
10. Tattersall I. 1986. Species recognition in human paleontology. J Hum Evol 15:165–175.
11. Tattersall I. 1992. Species concepts and species identification in human evolution. J Hum Evol 22:341–349.
12. Rightmire GP. 1996. The human cranium from Bodo, Ethiopia: Evidence for speciation in the Middle Pleistocene. J Hum Evol 31:21–39.
13. Rightmire GP. 1998. Human evolution in the Middle Pleistocene: the role of *Homo heidelbergensis*. Evol Anthropol 6:218–227.
14. Dubois E. 1892. Palaeontologische onderzoekingen op Java. Versl Mijnw, Batavia 3:10–14.

15. Le Gros Clark WE. 1964. The fossil evidence for human evolution: an introduction to the study of paleoanthropology, 2nd ed. Chicago: University of Chicago Press.

16. von Koenigswald GHR, Weidenreich F. 1939. The relationship between *Pithecanthropus* and *Sinanthropus*. Nature 144:926–929.

17. Weidenreich F. 1943. The skull of *Sinanthropus pekinensis:* A comparative study of a hominid skull. Palaeontol Sinica series D 10:1–484.

18. Le Gros Clark WE. 1955. The fossil evidence for human evolution, 1st ed. Chicago: University of Chicago Press.

19. Mayr E. 1944. On the concepts and terminology of vertical subspecies and species. National Research Council Committee on Common Problems of Genetics, Paleontology and Systematics Bulletin No. 2, p 11–16.

20. Mayr E. 1950. Taxonomic categories in fossil hominids. Cold Spring Harbor Symp Quant Biol 15:109–118.

21. Andrews P. 1984. An alternative interpretation of the characters used to define *Homo erectus*. Cour Forsch Inst Senckenberg. 69:167–175.

22. Wood BA. 1984. The origin of *Homo erectus*. Cour Forsch Inst Senckenberg 69:99–111.

23. Wood BA. 1992. Early hominid species. J Hum Evol 22:351–365.

24. Wood BA. 1994. Taxonomy and evolutionary relationships of *Homo erectus*. Cour Forsch Inst Senckenberg 171:159–165.

25. Turner A, Chamberlain AT. 1989. Speciation, morphological change and the status of African *Homo erectus*. J Hum Evol 18:115–130.

26. Rightmire GP. 1990. The evolution of *Homo erectus*. Cambridge: Cambridge University Press.

27. Rightmire GP. 1993. Variation among early *Homo* crania from Olduvai Gorge and the Koobi Fora region. Am J Phys Anthropol 90:1–33.

28. Brauer G. 1994. How different are Asian and African *Homo erectus*? In: Franzen JL, editor. 100 years of Pithecanthropus: the *Homo erectus* problem. Cour Forschungs-Institut Senckenberg. 171: 301–318.

29. Brauer G, Mbua E. 1992. *Homo erectus* features used in cladistics and their variability in Asian and African hominids. J Hum Evol 22:79–108.

30. Kramer A. 1993. Human taxonomic diversity in the Pleistocene: Does *Homo erectus* represent multiple hominid species? Am J Phys Anthropol 91:161–171.

31. Leakey LSB, Tobias PV, Napier JR. 1964. A new species of the genus *Homo* from Olduvai Gorge. Nature 202:7–9.

32. Leakey REF. 1973. Evidence for an advanced Plio-Pleistocene hominid from East Rudolf, Kenya. Nature 242:447–450.

33. Walker A. 1976. Remains attributable to *Australopithecus* in the East Rudolf succession. In: Coppens Y, Howell FC, Isaac GL, Leakey REF, editors. Earliest man and environments in the Lake Rudolf Basin. Chicago: University of Chicago Press. p 484–489.

34. Leakey REF. 1973. Evidence for an advanced Plio-Pleistocene hominid from East Rudolf, Kenya. Nature 242:447–450.

35. Bilsborough A, Wood BA. 1988. Cranial morphometry of early hominids I. facial region. Am J Phys Anthropol 76:61–86.

36. Wood BA. 1991. Koobi Fora research project, vol. 4: hominid cranial remains. Oxford: Clarendon Press.

37. Johanson DC, Masao FT, Eck GG, White TD, Walter RC, Kimbel WH, Asfaw B, Manega P, Ndessokia P, Suwa G. 1987. New partial skeleton of *Homo habilis* from Olduvai Gorge, Tanzania. Nature 327:205–209.

38. Howell FC, Coppens Y. 1976. An overview of the Hominidae from the Omo succession, Ethiopia. In: Coppens Y, Howell FC, Isaac G, Leakey REF, editors. Earliest man and environments in the Lake Rudolf Basin. Chicago: University of Chicago Press, p 522–532.

39. Boaz NT, Howell FC. 1977. A gracile hominid cranium from Upper Member G of the Shungura Formation, Ethiopia. Am J Phys Anthropol 46:93–108.

40. Coppens Y. 1980. The differences between *Australopithecus* and *Homo;* preliminary conclusions from the Omo Research Expeditions studies. In: Königsson LK, editor. Current argument on early man. Oxford: Pergamon Press. p 207–225.

41. Hughes AR, Tobias PV. 1977. A fossil skull probably of the genus *Homo* from Sterkfontein, Transvaal. Nature 265:310–312.

42. Clarke RJ. 1985. *Australopithecus* and early *Homo* in Southern Africa. In: Delson E, editor. Ancestors: the hard evidence. New York: Alan R. Liss. p 171–177.

43. Clarke RJ, Howell FC. 1972. Affinities of the Swartkrans 847 Hominid cranium. Am J Phys Anthropol 37:319–336.

44. Grine FE, Strait DS. 1994. New hominid fossils from Member 1 "Hanging Remnant," Swartkrans, Formation, South Africa. J Hum Evol 26:57–75.

45. Grine FE, Demes B, Jungers WL, Cole TM. 1993. Taxonomic affinity of the early *Homo* cranium from Swartkrans, South Africa. Am J Phys Anthropol 92:411–426.

46. Grine FE, Jungers WL, Schultz J. 1996. Phenetic affinities among early *Homo* crania from East and South Africa. J Hum Evol 30:189–225.

47. Wood BA. 1974. Olduvai Bed I post-cranial fossils: a reassessment. J Hum Evol 3:373–378.

48. Hartwig-Scherer S, Martin RD. 1991. Was "Lucy" more human than her "child"? Observations on early hominid post-cranial skeletons. J Hum Evol 21:439–449.

49. Leakey REF, Walker A, Ward CV, Grausz HM. 1989. A partial skeleton of a gracile hominid from the Upper Burgi Member of the Koobi Fora Formation, East Lake Turkana, Kenya. In: Giacobini G, editor. Proceedings of the 2nd International Congress on Human Paleontology, pp 167–173. Milan: Jaca Books.

50. Wood BA. 1992. Origin and evolution of the genus *Homo*. Nature 355:783–790.

51. Susman RL, Stern JT. 1982. Functional morphology of *Homo habilis*. Science 217:931–934.

52. Wood BA, Aiello L, Wood C, Key C. 1998. A technique for establishing the identity of "isolated" fossil hominin limb bones. J Anat 193:61–72.

53. Napier JR. 1964. The evolution of bipedal walking in the hominids. Arch Biol (Liège) 75(suppl):673–708.

54. Davis PR. 1964. Hominid fossils from Bed I, Olduvai Gorge, Tanganyika: a tibia and fibula. Nature 201:967.

55. Day MN, Napier JR. 1964. Hominid fossils from Bed I, Olduvai Gorge,' Tanganyika: fossil foot bones. Nature 201:968–970.

56. Lewis OJ. 1983. The joints of the evolving foot. part III: the fossil evidence. J Anat 131:275–298.

57. Lewis OJ. 1989. Functional morphology of the evolving hand and foot. Oxford: Clarendon Press.

58. Kidd RS, Higgins PO, Oxnard CE. 1996. The OH8 foot: a reappraisal of the functional morphology of the hind foot utilizing a multivariate analysis. J Hum Evol 31:269–291.

59. Lewis OJ. 1972. The evolution of the hallucial tarsometatarsal joint in the Anthropoidea. Am J Phys Anthropol 37:13–34.

60. Susman RL, Creel N. 1979. Functional and morphological affinities of the subadult hand (OH 7) from Olduvai Gorge. Am J Phys Anthropol 51:311–332.

61. Susman RL, Stern JT, Jungers WL. 1984. Arboreality and bipedality in the Hadar hominids. Folia Primatol 43:113–156.

62. Marzke MW. 1997. Precision grips, hand morphology, and tools. Am J Phys Anthropol 102:91–110.

63. Susman RL. 1998. Hand function and tool behavior in early hominids. J Hum Evol 35:23–46.

64. Wood B, Collard M. 1999. The human genus. Science. 284:65–71.

65. Robinson JT. 1968. The origin and adaptive radiation of the australopithecines. In: Kurth G, editor. Evolution and hominisation, 2nd ed. Stuttgart: Fischer Verlag. p 150–175.

66. Keith A. 1948. A new theory of human evolution. London: C.A. Watts.

67. Tobias PV. 1991. Olduvai Gorge: Vol. 4. The skulls, endocasts and teeth of *Homo habilis*. Cambridge: Cambridge University Press.

68. Wood B, Collard M. 1999. Is *Homo* defined by culture? Proc Br Acad 99:11–23.

69. Oakley KP. 1949. Man the toolmaker. London: British Museum (Natural History).

70. Leakey LSB. 1959. A new fossil skull from Olduvai. Nature 184:491–493.

71. Hill A, Ward S, Deino A, Curtis G, Drake R. 1992. Earliest *Homo*. Nature 355:719–722.

72. Kimbel WH, Walter RC, Johanson DC, Reed KE, Aronson JL, Assefa Z, Marean CW, Eck GG, Bobe R, Hovers E, Rak Y, Vondra C, Chen Y, Evensen NM, Smith PE. 1996. Late Pliocene *Homo* and Oldowan tools from the Hadar Formation (Kada Hadar Member), Ethiopia. J Hum Evol 31:549–561.

73. Martin RD. 1983. Human brain evolution in an ecological context. New York: American Museum of Natural History.

74. Galaburda AM, Pandya DN. 1982. Role of architectonics and connections in the study of primate brain evolution. In: Armstrong E, Falk D, editors. Primate brain evolution. New York: Plenum Press, p 203–216.

75. Gannon PJ, Holloway RL, Broadfield DC, Braun AR. 1998. Asymmetry of chimpanzee planum temporale: humanlike pattern of Wernicke's brain language area homolog. Science 279:220–222.

76. Gilissen E, Amunts K, Schlaug G, Zilles K. 1998. Left-right asymmetries in the temporoparietal intrasylvian cortex of common chimpanzees. Am J Phys Anthropol 26(suppl):86.

77. Gannon PJ, Kheck NM. 1999. Primate brain 'language' area evolution: anatomy of Heschl's gyrus and planum temporale in hominids, hylobatids and macaques and of planum parietale in *Pan troglodytes*. Am J Phys Anthropol 28(suppl): 132–133.

78. Kibunjia M, Roche H, Brown FH, Leakey REF. 1992. Pliocene and Pleistocene archaeological sites west of Lake Turkana, Kenya. J Hum Evol 23:431–438.

79. Kibunjia M. 1994. Pliocene archaeological occurrences in the Lake Turkana Basin. J Hum Evol 27:159–171.

80. Wood BA, Wood CW, Konigsberg LW. 1994. *Paranthropus boisei*–an example of evolutionary stasis? Am J Phys Anthropol 95:117–136

81. Semaw S, Renne P, Harris JWK, Feibel CS, Bernor RL, Fesseha N, Mowbray K. 1997. 2.5 million-year-old stone tools from Gona, Ethiopia. Nature 385:333–336.

82. Napier JR. 1962. The evolution of the hand. Sci Am 204:2–9.

83. Napier JR. 1962. Fossil hand bones from Olduvai Gorge. Nature 196:409–411.

84. Susman RL. 1988. Hand of *Paranthropus robustus* from Member I of Swartkrans: fossil evidence for tool behaviour. Science 240:781–784.

85. Susman RL. 1991. Who made the Oldowan stone tools? Fossil evidence for tool behaviour in Plio-Pleistocene hominids. J Anthropol Res 47: 129–151.

86. Susman RL. 1994. Fossil evidence for early hominid tool use. Science 265:1570–1573.

87. Ricklan DE. 1990. The precision grip of *Australopithecus africanus*: anatomical and behavioral correlates. In: Sperber GH, editor. From apes to angels: essays in anthropology in honor of Phillip V. Tobias. New York: Wiley Liss. p 171–183.

88. Hamrick MW, Churchill SE, Schmitt D, Hylander WL. 1998. EMG of the human flexor pollicis longus muscle: implications for the evolution of hominid tool use. J Hum Evol 34:123–136.

89. Clayton WD. 1983. The genus concept in practice. Kew Bull 38:149–153.

90. Stevens PF. 1984. The genus concept in practice–but for what practice? Kew Bull 40:457–465.

91. Harrison T. 1993. Cladistic concepts and the species problem in hominoid evolution. In: Kimbel WH, Martin LB, editors. Species, species concepts and primate evolution. New York: Plenum Press, p 345–371.

92. de Queiroz K, Gauthier J. 1994. Toward a phylogenetic system of biological nomenclature. Trends Ecol Evol 9:27–31.

93. Valentine JW, May CL. 1996. Hierarchies in biology and paleontology. Paleobiology 22:23–33.

94. Knox EB. 1998. The use of hierarchies as organizational models in systematics. Biol J Linnaeus Soc 63:1–49.

95. Mayr E. 1963. Animal species and their evolution. Cambridge, MA: Belknap.

96. Strait DS, Grine FE, Moniz MA. 1997. A reappraisal of early hominid phylogeny. J Hum Evol 32:17–82.

97. Swofford DL. 1991. Phylogenetic analysis using parsimony, version 3.0s. Champaign: Illinois Natural History Survey.

98. Chamberlain AT. 1987. A taxonomic review and phylogenetic analysis of *Homo habilis*. Ph.D. thesis, the University of Liverpool, England.

99. Maddison WP, Maddison DR. 1992. MacClade: analysis of phylogeny and character evolution, version 3. Sunderland, MA: Sinauer Assoc.

100. Krings M, Stone A, Schmitz RW, Krainitzk H, Stoneking M, Pääbo S. 1997. Neandertal DNA sequences and the origin of modern humans. Cell 90:19–30.

101. Chamberlain AT, Wood BA. 1987. Early hominid phylogeny. J Hum Evol 16:119–133.

102. Lieberman DE, Wood BA, Pilbeam DE. 1996. Homoplasy and early *Homo:* an analysis of the evolutionary relationships of *H. habilis* and *H. rudolfensis*. J Hum Evol 30:97–120.

103. Corruccini RS. 1994. In: Corruccini RS, Ciochon RL, editors. Integrative paths to the past: paleoanthropological advances in honor of F. Clark Howell. Englewood Cliffs: Prentice Hall, p 167–183.

104. Collard M, Wood BA. 1998. Cladistics and the estimation of hominid phylogeny. Am J Phys Anthropol 26(suppl):122.

105. Collard M, Wood BA. submitted. Reliability of human phylogenetic hypotheses. Proc Natl Acad Sci.

106. Deacon TW. 1990. Problems of ontogeny and phylogeny in brain size evolution. Int J Primatol 11:237–282.

107. Asfaw B, White T, Lovejoy O, Latimer B, Simpson S, Suwa G. 1999. *Australopithecus garhi:* a new species of early hominid from Ethiopia. Science 284:629–635.

108. Wood BA. 1996. Origin and evolution of the genus *Homo*. In: Meikle WE, Howell FC, Jablonski NG, editors. Contemporary issues in human evolution, memoir 21. San Francisco: California Academy of Sciences, p 105–114.

109. Beynon AD, Wood BA. 1986. Variations in enamel thickness and structure in East African hominids. Am J Phys Anthropol 70:177–193.

110. Beynon AD, Wood BA. 1987. Patterns and rates of enamel growth in the molar teeth of early hominids. Nature 326:493–496.

111. Hartman SE. 1988. A cladistic analysis of hominoid molars. J Hum Evol 17:489–502.

112. Washburn SL. 1963. Behavior and human evolution. In: Washburn S, editor. Classification and human evolution, Chicago: Aldine de Gruyter.

113. Howell FC. 1965. Comment on "New discoveries in Tanganyika: Their bearing on hominid evolution," by PV Tobias. Curr Anthropol 6:399–401.

114. Robinson JT. 1965. *Homo "habilis"* and the australopithecines. Nature 205:121–124.

115. Pilbeam D. 1972. The ascent of man. New York: Macmillan.

116. Huxley JS. 1958. Evolutionary processes and taxonomy with special reference to grades. Uppsala Universitets årsskrift. 6:21–38.

117. Simpson GG. 1961. Principles of animal taxonomy. New York: Columbia University Press.

118. Miller AH. 1949. Some ecologic and morphologic considerations in the evolution of higher taxonomic categories. In: Mayr E, Schüz E, editors. Ornithologie als Biologische Wissenschaft. Berlin: Carl Winter, p 84–88.

119. Jensen JS. 1990. Plausibility and testability: assessing the consequences of evolutionary innovation. In: Nitecki MH, editor. Evolutionary innovations. Chicago: Chicago University Press, p 171–190.

120. Hunter JP. 1998. Key innovations and the ecology of macroevolution. Trends Ecol Evol 13:31–36.

121. Brown JS, Vincent TL. 1987. A theory for the evolutionary game. Theoretical Popul Biol 31:140–166.

122. Rosenzweig ML, McCord RD. 1991. Incumbent replacement: evidence for long-term evolutionary progress. Paleobiology 17:23–27.

123. Rosenzweig ML, Brown JS, Vincent TL. 1987. Red Queen and ESS: The coevolution of evolutionary rates. Evol Ecol 1:59–94.

124. Aiello LC, Wheeler PE. 1995. The expensive-tissue hypothesis: the brain and the digestive system in human and primate evolution. Curr Anthropol 36:199–221.

125. Collard M, Wood B. 1999. Grades among the African early hominids. In: Bromage T, Schrenk F, editors. African biogeography, climate change and early hominid evolution. New York: Oxford University Press, p 316–327.

126. O'Connell JF, Hawkes K, Blurton Jones NG. 1999. Grandmothering and the evolution of *Homo erectus*. J Hum Evol 36:461–485.

127. Wrangham RW, Jones JH, Laden G, Pilbeam D, Conklin-Brittain N. in press. The raw and the stolen: cooking and the ecology of human origins. Curr Anthropol.

128. Brooks AS. 1996. Behavior and human evolution. In: Meikle WE, Howell FC, Jablonski NG, editors. Contemporary issues in human evolution, Memoir 21. San Francisco: California Academy of Sciences. p 135–166.

129. Bradley J. 1961. International Code of Zoological Nomenclature adopted by XV International Congress of Zoology, London, July 1958. London: International Trust for Zoological Nomenclature.

130. Ride WDI., 1985. International code of zoological nomenclature, 3rd ed. Berkeley: University of California Press.

131. Alexeev VP. 1986. The origin of the human race. Moscow: Progress Publishers.

132. Kennedy GE. 1999. Is *"Homo rudolfensis"* a valid species? J Hum Evol 36:119–121.

133. Wood BA. 1999. *"Homo rudolfensis"* Alexeev, 1986–fact or phantom? J Hum Evol 36:115–118.

134. Black D. 1927. On a lower molar hominid tooth from the Chou Kou Tien deposit. Palaeontologia Sinica (N.S.D.)7:l–28.

135. Dubois E. 1894. *Pithecanthropus erectus*, eine menschenähuliche Uebergangsform aus Java, Batavia Landes-Druckere.

136. Groves CP, Mazák V. 1975. An approach to the taxonomy of the Hominidae: gracile Villafranchian hominids of Africa. Cas Miner Geol 20:225–247.

137. Bermudez de Castro JM, Arsuaga JL, Carbonell E, Rosas A. Martinez I, Mosqueria M. 1997. A hominid from the Lower Pleistocene of Atapuerca, Spain: possible ancestor to Neandertals and modern humans. Science 276:1392–1395.

The author discusses what can be learned about how members of early *Homo* lived from evidence preserved at the oldest archaeological sites. The action of natural processes upon early archaeological remains provides a challenge to accurate interpretation of the behavior of early *Homo*.

19. Cutlery & Carnivory

By Sally McBrearty

The late Glynn Isaac was fond of pointing out that the earliest evidence for human behavior is nothing more than piles of stones and bones. These ancient trash heaps were his life's work, but they mean little if divorced from their contexts. How did these objects get there, and how can we trace their history to its source in hominid behavior? Actualistic studies are one path to the answer. Actualism or uniformitarianism is the examination of present-day natural processes to provide analogs for past events. Schick and Blumenschine, both former students of Glynn Isaac, have undertaken two very different actualistic projects, but the aim of each is to provide the means to distinguish the effects of ancient hominid behavior from those of other agents. Schick deals with stones, Blumenschine bones.

Archaeologists of the Plio-Pleistocene have traditionally treated archaeological sites as the pure fossilized remains of ancient hominid behavior, largely ignoring the profound transformations brought about by depositional and diagenetic processes. Realization that this attitude is unrealistic has been accelerated by accumulating data regarding site formation and disturbance (e.g., Behrensmeyer, 1975; Wood & Johnson, 1978; Gifford-Gonzalez, 1981; Villa, 1982; Schiffer, 1983). The vast majority of African Pleistocene artifacts have become buried by the action of water, and telltale signs of fluvial disturbance, such as artifact

Sally McBrearty, "Cutlery & Carnivory," *Journal of Human Evolution*, vol. 18, no. 3, pp. 277–282. Copyright © 1989 by Academic Press Ltd. Reprinted with permission by Elsevier Science and Technology.

abrasion, are taught to every student. Archaeologists concentrate on "primary context" undisturbed sites, but because such ideal sites are so rare, an archaeologist may be tempted to ignore the fluvial signatures that jeopardize valuable conclusions. Schick's study replaces the "primary context" vs. "disturbed" dichotomy with a more useful system of scoring according to degrees of disturbance. Thus sites can be ranked, and archaeologists are free to ask questions appropriate to the information preserved.

Schick's methods included a series of flume experiments, followed by site replication studies in which the effects of fluvial processes on simple Plio-Pleistocene cultural products were monitored. Her resulting criteria for site ranking include aspects of geologic context, especially sediment grain size, as well as artifact size distribution, damage, orientation, and conjoinability. These criteria are then used to evaluate the sites at Koobi Fora in Kenya.

Schick's experimental findings confirm that interpreting early hominid behavior is impossible without a firm grasp of geologic principles. Plio-Pleistocene site formation processes act to destroy meaningful spatial patterns and artifact associations; they also create spurious patterns and associations. Specifically, they may elongate the spatial distribution of artifacts in a downstream direction, sort artifacts by size, remove small pieces, reduce the density of objects, and create new concentrations of pieces downstream from the original scatter.

Acknowledging these effects, it is still interesting to inquire into the behavior of the earliest tool makers. By identifying the sources of raw materials used in stone tool manufacture, Leakey (1971) and Hay (1976) demonstrated that Pleistocene hominids at Olduvai Gorge transported stone over distances in excess of 10 km. At Koobi Fora, raw material sources are more dispersed, but from Schick's refitting of artifacts and the reduction sequences worked out by Toth (1982), it is now appreciated that Plio-Pleistocene hominids carried both artifactual and nonartifactual stone from place to place about the Koobi Fora landscape.

The question then arises as to how and why stone and bone end up concentrated at the particular localities that archaeologists call sites. Schick approaches this question as a paleolithic economist. She examines the flow of artifacts into and out of sites, and points out that sites form when the import rate exceeds the export rate. What is more difficult to determine is the motive for this accumulation: deliberate discard, accidental loss, forced abandonment, waste accumulation, or as Potts (1983, 1987, 1988a) has suggested, the storage of materials for future use. Schick makes the novel suggestion that these piles of debris are the result of "passive storage", or an "anxiety/security" cycle of resource availability. Objects may be carried around "just in case", and when the perceived future need for the object disappears, such as when a new raw material source is approached, the object is dropped and becomes part of the archaeological record. Reduced pressure to remove stone from such a locality would lead to a net accumulation of stone detritus. These conditions would be met if, for example, foraging was planned for the immediate area, if activities not requiring stone tools were anticipated, or if raw material was known to be plentiful in the next area to be exploited. Stone tools are our first evidence for deliberate human modification of natural objects, and if Schick is correct, it may be that this important message was dispatched to us in quite an offhand fashion.

Blumenschine's volume reports an actualistic study that grows out of the subdiscipline of taphonomy. His work addresses a fundamental issue in paleoanthropology, the role of hunting in the evolution of human society. Hunting has been thought central to the development of human cooperative behavior, language, and sex roles (e.g. Washburn & Lancaster, 1968, Lovejoy, 1981). Isaac (1978, 1982) incorporated these ideas into his interpretation of Koobi Fora Plio-Pleistocene sites as foci of intense social activity where sharing the products of the hunt took place.

Taphonomic studies, such as those of Behrensmeyer (1975) and Hill (1975), by examining what happens to mammalian carcasses on the modern East African landscape, implicated nonhuman bone accumulating and modifying agencies. Scanning electron microscopy, however, when applied to stone artifacts from Koobi Fora (Keeley & Toth, 1981), demonstrated clearly that the tools had been used by hominids to deflesh bones. When similar techniques were applied to bones from sites at Olduvai Gorge and Koobi Fora, however, it became clear that cut marks made by stone tools and tooth marks made by carnivores were both represented (Bunn, 1981, Potts & Shipman, 1981), and appreciation of the role of carnivores in Plio-Pleistocenc site formation grew. Studies by Hill (1983, 1984), Kruuk (1972), Mills (1984), Binford (1981), and others on the behavior of social carnivores have allowed new, better informed reconstructions of classic sites, such as Brains's (1981) re-examination of the South African australopithecine caves, and Potts' (1988a) reanalysis of Beds I and II at Olduvai Gorge.

In this climate of healthy respect for carnivores, early hominids are seen as one potential meat eater among many, most of whom are better equipped for the job. It has frequently been suggested that meat was obtained not by hunting but by the less glamorous means of scavenging (Potts, 1983, 1984; Binford, 1981, 1985; Binford, *et al.*, 1988; Shipman, 1983, 1986a, 1986b); Binford (1984) and Klein (1988) contend that scavenging persisted as the chief means of procuring meat until the end of the Middle Pleistocene. Archaeologists of the Plio-Pleistocene have accepted that some scavenging took place on an *ad hoc* basis, particularly of the largest animals (Leakey, 1971: Isaac, 1982), and it has been hypothesized that the requirements of a scavenging adaptation provided the stimulus for bipedalism (Shipman, 1986a, Sinclair *et al.,* 1986).

The question for a paleoecologically minded investigator, then, is whether scavenging was a practical full-time adaptation for a Plio-Pleistocene hominid, and this is the question Blumenschine addresses. He documented the quantity and quality of carcasses made available by predators on a day-to-day basis, by monitoring several hundred square kilometers of the Serengeti National Park and adjacent Ngorongoro crater for a period of eleven months. His findings have been summarized more briefly elsewhere (Blumenschine, 1987).

The Serengeti and Ngorongoro regions span a variety of habitat types, including wooded savanna, riverine woodland, and dry open country and lacustrine woodlands surrounding two perennial rift lakes; these comprise a fairly good array of analogs for the habitats occupied by Plio-Pleistocene hominids. By registering the numbers of carcasses encountered, their taxonomic identity, their completeness, and the amount of edible tissues available. Blumenschine quantifies how much food would be available to a potential hominid scavenger, the quality of that food, and what effort would be required to harvest it. Through observation of the presence or absence of predators at or near the kill site, the risk of competition with other carnivores and scavengers is assessed.

Blumenschine finds that kills of small ungulates disappear rapidly, as they are often nearly completely consumed by their initial predators, whereas larger carcasses may persist as food resources for a number of days. Recently abandoned felid kills provide a good source of food, consisting primarily of marrow bones and head contents which felid jaws cannot penetrate. He concludes that the major constraint on a Plio-Pleistocene hominid scavenger is competition with another group of very efficient scavengers, the hyenas.

Stone tools enabled hominids to pierce hide and crush bone, activities for which they were poorly equipped by nature. Blumenschine assumes that early hominids would be armed with stone tools, would limit their activities to the daylight hours, and would not attempt directly to usurp the kills of very large carnivores. Habitat type, season, and predator density emerge as crucial factors to scavenging in his analysis. The open savanna at the end of the dry season provides a resource glut for Serengeti scavengers through natural mortality of the migrating herds, but because the natural deaths at the end of the dry season are stress related, the animal food available is of low nutritional value. High quality felid kills persist in riparian woodland during the dry season due to the absence of hyenas. Thus Blumenschine favors a dry season riparian woodland habitat as the Plio-Pleistocene hominid scavenging niche. By applying cost to benefit modelling to this proposed scavenging behavior, Blumenschine arrives at the conclusion that routed foraging in the sense of Binford (1984) rather than the central place model favored by Isaac (1981, 1982, 1983) was the norm.

For archaeologists, a valuable byproduct of Blumenschine's observations reported here is a set of criteria whereby scavenged bone assemblages may be distinguished from deliberately hunted ones (see also Blumenschine, 1986). Scavengers have relatively late access to a carcass, at a point when nearly all of a small animal, and significant parts of a large one, have been consumed by the initial predator. Thus, contrary to Binford (1984), but in keeping with Klein (1982) and Vrba (1980), Blumenschine predicts that a collection of bones resulting from scavenging will contain primarily adults of large and medium sized ungulate species. He further predicts that head and lower limb bones will predominate, and that defleshing cut marks will be found preferentially on these parts. This is an important contribution as it is in direct conflict with usual interpretations of archaeological bone assemblages. It would appear from the work of Bunn (1983, 1986) and Potts (1983, 1988a) that some of the traits predicted by Blumenschine do characterize early bone assemblages from Koobi Fora and Olduvai Gorge. But collections in which head and lower limb bones predominate are usually construed as butchery stations from which the more nutritious parts have been removed for consumption elsewhere. For example, in a recent reanalysis of the Olduvai Bed I FLK Zinj floor (FLK 22) Bunn and Kroll (1986) conclude from the high proportion of limb bones represented, and from the midshaft location of many of the cutmarks, that the Olduvai hominids had access to meaty carcasses and that these were most likely obtained by deliberate hunting.

If Blumenschine's reasoning is correct, he has provided evidence that during the dry season our Plio-Pleistocene ancestors supplemented their otherwise vegetarian diet with head contents and bone marrow scavenged from the kills of large carnivores, and that the very human activities that accompany deliberate hunting must be sought later in the archaeological record. This scenario for early hominid behavior is a much needed alternative to the "just so" stories drawn from the modern ethnographic record that were the stuff of archaeological interpretation ten years ago. It is part of a healthy trend in paleoanthropology that seeks to find interesting differences between ourselves and Plio-Pleistocene hominids, and to avoid projecting suites of modern human behaviors onto our early ancestors.

However, Blumenschine's is only one of many possible reconstructions. As Potts (1988b) has pointed out, hunting and scavenging need not be mutually exclusive behaviors. The diversity in both species and body parts represented in the Olduvai bone assemblages suggests to him neither a specialized hunting nor scavenging adaptation. Many modern social carnivores practice both hunting and scavenging as part of flexible foraging strategies designed to obtain animal protein. At sites where many feeding episodes are represented, it may be unrealistic to expect to distinguish between hunting and scavenging behaviors, strictly defined.

Both Schick's and Blumenschine's volumes confirm the premise that detailed observations of the modern natural world are crucial ingredients in constructing an interpretive framework to understand events in the remote past. They are to be recommended to the actualistically minded paleoanthropologist, and to anyone who would like a glimpse into specific details of the habits and habitats of our early hominid ancestors. According to Blumenschine, a smörgasbord of animal protein was available for the scavenging, though not without the risk of running afoul of large dangerous felids and canids. It was stone tools that provided the means to tap this resource, and from the work of Schick and others, we know that these implements were carried by hominids from place to place. From this we may derive a maxim for success in Plio-Pleistocene life: watch out for carnivores and bring your own cutlery.

ACKNOWLEDGEMENTS

I would like to thank Alison Brooks, Andrew Hill, Richard Klein, and Rick Potts for their thoughtful comments on the manuscript.

REFERENCES

Behrensmeyer, A. K. (1975). The taphonomy and paleoecology of Plio-Pleistocene vertebrate assemblages east of Lake Rudolf, Kenya. *Mus. Comp. Zool. Bul.* **146,** 473–578.

Binford, L. R. (1981). *Bones: Ancient Men and Modern Myths.* New York: Academic Press.

Binford, L. R. (1984). *Faunal Remains from Klasies River Mouth.* New York: Academic Press.

Binford, L. R. (1985). Human ancestors: changing views of their behavior. *J. Anthropol. Archaeol.* **4,** 292–327.

Binford, L. R., M. G. L. Mills & N. M. Stone. (1988). Hyena scavenging behavior and its implications for the interpretation of faunal assemblages from FLK 22 (the Zinj floor) at Olduvai Gorge. *J. Anthropol. Archaeol.* **7,** 99–135.

Blumenschine, R. J. (1986). Carcass consumption sequences and the archaeological distinction of scavenging and hunting. *J. hum. Evol.* **15,** 639–660.

Blumenschine, R. J. (1987). Characteristics of an early hominid scavenging niche. *Curr. Anthropol.* **28,** 383–408.

Brain, C. K. (1981). *Hunters or the Hunted?* University of Chicago Press.

Bunn, H. T. (1981). Archaeological evidence for meat eating by Plio-Pleistocene hominids from Koobi Fora and Olduvai Gorge. *Nature* **291,** 574–577.

Bunn, H. T. (1983). Evidence of the diet and subsistence patterns of Plio-Pleistocene hominids at Koobi Fora, Kenya and at Olduvai Gorge, Tanzania. In (J. Clutton-Brock & C. Grigson, Eds) *Animals and Archaeology: Hunters and Their Prey.* Oxford: B.A.R. International Series **163,** 21–30.

Bunn, H. T. (1986). Patterns of skeletal representation and hominid subsistence activities at Olduvai Gorge, Tanzania, and Koobi Fora, Kenya. *J. hum. Evol.* **15,** 673–690.

Bunn, H. T. & Kroll, E. M. (1986). Systematic butchery by Plio/Pleistocene hominids at Olduvai Gorge, Tanzania. *Curr. Anthropol.* **27,** 431–452.

Gifford-Gonzalez, D. P. (1981). Taphonomy and paleoecology: a critical review of archaeology's sister disciplines. *Advances in Archaeological Method and Theory* **4,** 365–438.

Hay, R. D. (1976). *Geology of Olduvai Gorge, a Study of Sedimentation in a Semi-arid Basin.* Berkeley: University of California Press.

Hill, A. P. (1975). *Taphonomy of Contemporary and Late Cenozoic East African Vertebrates.* Ph.D. Dissertation, University of London.

Hill, A. P. (1983). Hyaenas and early hominids. In (J. Clutton-Brock & C. Grigson, Eds) *Animals and Archaeology: Hunters and Their Prey.* Oxford: B.A.R. International Series **163,** 87–92.

Hill, A. P. (1984). Hyaenas and hominids: taphonomy and hypothesis testing. In (R. Foley, Ed.) *Hominid Evolution and Community Ecology.* London: Academic Press, pp. 111–128.

Isaac, G. L1. (1978). The food sharing behavior of protohuman hominids. *J. Anthropol. Res.* **34,** 311–325.

Isaac, G. L1. (1981). Emergence of human behavior patterns: archaeological tests of alternative models of early hominid behaviour: excavation and experiments. *Philos. Trans. Roy. Soc. Lond.* **B292,** 177–188.

Isaac, G. L1. (1982). The earliest archaeological traces. In (J. D. Clark, Ed.) *Cambridge History of Africa,* vol. 1. Cambridge University Press, pp. 157–247.

Isaac, G. L1. (1983). Bones in contention: competing explanations from the juxtaposition of Early Pleistocene arti-facts and faunal remains. In (J. Clutton-Brock & C. Grigson, Eds) *Animals and Archaeology: Hunters and Their Prey.* Oxford: B.A.R. Monograph Series **163**, 3–19.

Keeley, L. H. & N. Toth (1981). Microwear polishes on early stone tools from Koobi Fora, Kenya. *Nature* **293**, 464–465.

Klein, R. G. (1982). Age (mortality) profiles as a means of distinguishing hunted species from scavenged ones in Stone Age archaeological sites. *Paleobiol.* **8**, 151–158.

Klein, R. G. (1988). The archaeological significance of animal bones from Acheulean sites in southern Africa *African Archaeological Review* **6**, 3–26.

Kruuk, H. (1976). *The Spotted Hyena: a Study of Predation and Social Behavior.* University of Chicago Press.

Leakey, M. D. (1971). *Olduvai Gorge,* vol. 3. Cambridge University Press.

Lovejoy, O. (1981). The origin of man. *Science* **211**, 341–350.

Mills, M. G. L. (1984). Prey selection and the feeding habits of the large carnivores in the southern Kalahari. *Koedoe Suppl.* 281–294.

Potts, R. (1983). Foraging for faunal resources by early hominids at Olduvai Gorge, Tanzania. In (J. Clutton-Brock & C. Grigson, Eds) *Animals and Archaeology: Hunters and Their Prey.* Oxford: B.A.R. Monograph Series **163**, 51–62.

Potts, R. (1984). Hominid hunters? Problems in identifying the earliest hunter/gatherers. In (R. Foley, Ed.) *Hominid Evolution and Community Ecology,* pp. 129–166. London: Academic Press.

Potts, R. (1987). Transportation of resources: reconstructions of early hominid socioecology: a critique of primate models. In (W. G. Kinzey, Ed.) *The Evolution of Human Behavior: Primate Models,* pp. 28–50. Albany: State University of New York Press.

Potts, R. (1988a). *Early Hominid Activities at Olduvai.* New York: Aldine de Gruyter.

Potts, R. (1988b). On an early hominid scavenging niche. *Curr. Anthropol.* **29**, 153–155.

Potts, R. & P. Shipman. (1981). Cutmarks made by stone tools from Olduvai Gorge, Tanzania. *Nature* **291**, 577–580.

Schiffer, M. B. (1983). Toward the identification of site formation processes. *Amer. Antiq.* **48**, 675–706.

Shipman, P. (1983). Early hominid lifestyle: hunting and gathering or foraging and scavenging? In (J. Clutton-Brock & C. Grigson, Eds) *Animals and Archaeology: Hunters and Their Prey.* Oxford: B.A.R. International Series **163**, 31–49.

Shipman, P. (1986a). Scavenging or hunting in early hominids: theoretical framework and tests. *Amer. Anthropol.* **88**, 27–43.

Shipman, P. (1986b). Studies of hominid–faunal interactions at Olduvai Gorge. J. *hum. Evol.* **15**, 691–706.

Sinclair, A. R. E., M. D. Leakey, & M. Norton-Griffiths (1986). Migration and hominid bipedalism. *Nature* **324**, 307–308.

Toth, N. (1982). *The Technologies of Early Hominids at Koobi Fora, Kenya: an Experimental Approach.* Ph.D. Dissertation, Department of Anthropology, University of California, Berkeley.

Villa, P. (1982). Conjoinable pieces and site formation processes. *American Antiquity* **47**, 276–289.

Vrba, E. S. (1980). The significance of bovid remains as indicators of environment and predation patterns. In (A. K. Behrensmeyer & A. P. Hill, Eds) *Fossils in the Making,* pp. 247–271. University of Chicago Press.

Washburn, S. L. & Lancaster, C. S. (1968). The evolution of hunting. In (R. B. Lee & I. de Vore, Eds) *Man the Hunter,* pp. 293–303. Chicago: Aldine.

Wood, W. R. & D. L. Johnson. (1978). A survey of disturbance processes in archaeological site formation. *Advances in Archaeological Method and Theory* **1**, 315–381.

For many years archaeologists believed that the practice of hunting by early hominins was the feature that distinguished the human line from that of the apes. As we have seen in an earlier chapter, some apes hunt fairly frequently. The authors show, by observation of the behavior of modern carnivores, that on the African landscape there are other ways to obtain meat.

20. Scavenging and Human Evolution

By Robert J. Blumenschine and John A. Cavallo

Although meat eating helped to shape the evolution of human brains, behavior and toolmaking, our early ancestors seem to have been better scavengers than hunters.

Man the Hunter is a phrase that rings. Who would not rather be numbered with the lion than with the vulture? Hunting seems nobler than scavenging and, at first glance, more profitable, too. What better way to reaffirm our evolutionary success than to portray our earliest hominid ancestors as mighty hunters? Many anthropologists agree that eating the meat of large animals helped to form the physical and social environment that selected for the traits that most distinguish humans from apes. But was that meat acquired by predation or by scavenging? This question matters perhaps as much as any in evolutionary studies because it touches on the definition of human nature. Unfortunately, the answer given by the theory of Man the Hunter is based more on sexual and other prejudices than on the fossil record and the ecology of finding food.

Scavenging has received little notice, we believe, because many anthropologists have been too quick to project current ways of life into the past. They use hunter-gatherers, apes or carnivores as surrogates for

Robert J. Blumenschine and John A. Cavallo, "Scavenging and Human Evolution," *Scientific American*, vol. 267, no. 4, pp. 90–96.

aspects of early hominid life that have been obscured by the passage of time—a practice that strips the hominids of the very adaptations that made them unique. Advocates of the hunting theory also elevate hominids above other organisms, as if our ancestors were immune to most of the pressures that shape relations between predators and prey. In all these matters, they assume that early hominids found hunting to be bountiful, predictable and safe and scavenging to be marginal, opportunistic and risky.

Our research reaches quite different conclusions. Scavenging may have been more common than hunting two million years ago, at the boundary between the Pliocene and Pleistocene epochs. Flaked-stone toolmaking, the practice of butchering large animals and the evolution of big-brained *Homo* all make their first known appearance in the physical record at this time. Because much of the evidence lies at such east African sites as Olduvai Gorge in Tanzania, we attempted to learn how to decipher the residues of ancient subsistence patterns at nearby game reserves: Tanzania's Serengeti National Park and Ngorongoro Conservation Area. We also tried to test objectively the prevailing notion that scavenging would have been inferior to hunting.

In independent stints over a period of 20 months, we noted how predators and scavengers got their meat and what they did to the bones they left behind. Our fieldwork thus united ethology with taphonomy—the study of how postmortem events alter carcasses in the fossil record. Further, we integrated these results with paleontological and archaeological evidence for the behavior of protohominids. This approach reads into the past only those aspects of present behavior and ecology that leave preservable residues. It thus avoids a wholesale imposition of the way of life of a modern species that happens to suit one's ideals.

Scavenging Opportunities differed by size, terrain, season and cause of death. Riparian woodlands probably offered the best returns because the trees provided hominids with refuge and hid carcasses from vultures. Arboreal leopard kills (1) were probably available year-round; lion kills (2) came mainly in the dry season. Saber-toothed cats seem to

That no substitute exists in anthropology for such actualistic studies may be demonstrated by what zoologists have shown about the behavior of the hyena—the popular symbol of scavenging—and the lion—the prototypical predator. Until 30 years ago, no one conceived that each carnivore both hunts and scavenges. If biases can so cloud the truth about living carnivores, how much more careful must scientists be in reconstructing the subsistence of extinct hominids?

The theory of Man the Hunter has never been constrained by fossil evidence. Charles Darwin was the first to present hunting as the behavioral catalyst that selected for an enlarged brain, tool use, reduced canine teeth and bipedalism, thus splitting the lineages of humans and apes. He laid out his hypothesis in *The Descent of Man* (1871), before any fossils earlier than the Neanderthals had been found. When more ancient specimens turned up in the early decades of this century, workers linked them directly to Darwin's scheme. Raymond A. Dart, discoverer of the *Australopithecus* genus, spent some 30 years trying to show that this hominid could have hunted the animals whose bones were so often found mingled with its own. To circumvent the problem of the absence of stone tools at these sites, Dart invoked an "osteodontokeratic" tool and weapon kit made from animal bones, teeth and horn.

This interpretation gained popular support in the many accounts of humanity's "killer ape" forebears. It fell apart, however, under the critical tests of the pioneering taphonomist C. K. Brain of South Africa's Transvaal Museum. He showed that the australopithecines had played no role in gathering the bones of the animals found in association with their own skeletons. Instead, these studies suggested, both hominids and ungulates had ended together when the leopards that hunted them discarded their carcasses at the base of

have left large carcasses (3) in these habitats in all seasons. Open-country kills of lions, cheetahs (4) and hyenas (5) were less attractive to hominids, who lagged behind the vultures and hyenas and had no place to escape from larger carnivores. Drownings (6) and starvation (7) afforded windfall opportunities, not all of which were safe to exploit.

Scavenging on the open plain requires speed and strength beyond what early hominids possessed. These spotted hyenas reached this lion kill before vultures stripped it and could outrun any lion that might return.

their favored feeding trees. Yet the hunting hypothesis remained intact; now, however, it was made to apply to the later stage in evolutionary history that began with the appearance of large-brained *Homo habilis*.

The arguments for this theory reached full flower in the papers collected in Richard B. Lee and Irven DeVore's *Man the Hunter* (1968). The contributors sketched the following scenario. Protohominids encroach on the savanna by eking out their accustomed vegetarian diet with increasing amounts of hunted flesh. Hunting puts a premium on foresight and dexterity, selecting for larger brains and nimbler hands. These traits increase the capacity for technology, raising the payoff of intelligence and augmenting the original selective pressure. Hunting becomes the engine of a self-sustaining cycle of social and intellectual evolution.

This theory prevailed until the late 1970s, when an influential article by the late Glynn Isaac shifted the emphasis from the gathering of meat to the sharing of it [see "The Food-Sharing Behavior of Protohuman Hominids," by Glynn Isaac; SCIENTIFIC AMERICAN, April 1978]. Isaac, an archaeologist at the University of California at Berkeley, showed that early hominids had home bases—a behavioral innovation—which, he argued, implied a sexual division of labor—another innovation. To enhance the omnivorous strategy, males ranged far in search of scavengeable meat or hunted quarry, females gathered fruits and tubers nearer home and families shared the take. Eventually this altruistic behavior and social cooperation began to select for intelligence, language and culture.

Lewis R. Binford, now at Southern Methodist University, carried such analysis further in 1981. In a taphonomic reanalysis of Mary Leakey's data from the early Olduvai bone assemblages, Binford argued that neither hunting nor food sharing had evolved by *H. habilis* times. Hominids had merely processed the meager leftovers of more capable carnivores by breaking open bones to get at the marrow. He said scavenging could not have provided the surpluses of meat needed to sustain food sharing. Instead the social and nutritional aspects of protohominid feeding resembled the mainly vegetarian diets of modern apes.

Binford later argued, on similar grounds, that even the early modern *Homo sapiens* of southern Africa and the contemporaneous Neanderthals of Europe relied on scavenging to get large animals and hunted only small ones. Thus, Binford, too, retained the hunting hypothesis by moving it closer to the present—within the past 100,000 years. His reconstruction accepts that scavenging was a penurious enterprise and that hunting and its attendant pattern of food sharing was a driving evolutionary force, albeit one that took effect very late in our evolution.

We began our critique of this entire approach by appraising the hunting prowess of early hominids. The physiques of *Australopithecus* and early *Homo* were unprepossessing. Females stood about four feet tall, males under five; females weighed about 70 pounds and males around 100. Their long arms suggest they still took refuge in trees. No doubt they had frequent occasion to do so, confronted as they were by such proficient predators as lions, saber-toothed cats and hyenas. As for their tools, even *Homo* wielded a very primitive kit of rough-hewn scrapers and unworked hammerstones. No true weapons are apparent.

Yet the archaeological evidence shows that these puny primates encroached on the large carnivores' niche. At Olduvai and elsewhere, archaeologists have found simple stone artifacts in association with fossilized bone fragments from animals as small as a gazelle and as big as an elephant. Surfaces of some of these bones bear the tooth marks of carnivores. Some of these and other bones also carry cut marks made when the associated tools were used to remove meat and disarticulate bones. Many bones are fractured and marked by a hammerstone, used to get at the marrow. Could protohumans have killed animals as fleet and formidable as these? We think scavenging deserves a closer look.

Proponents of hunting have argued that a diurnal hominid would have had difficulty in locating the kills of wider-ranging predators and that any they might have chanced on would have been thoroughly eaten by hyenas, the only animal that can crush bones for marrow with its teeth. But these arguments miss two scavenging opportunities that we identified in Tanzania—big-cat kills in riparian woodlands and the carcasses of very large animals that die of disease or by drowning. Hominids foraging in this habitat may have pieced together a niche no other scavenger could exploit so well [see illustration on pages 90 and 91].

Riparian woodlands would have suited partially arboreal bipeds by providing sanctuary and by hiding carcasses from vultures, the lead spotters of the scavenger tribe. Large ungulate carcasses crop up in these regions mainly in the dry season, when lions abandon their defleshed, zebra-size kills. Leopard kills, on the other hand, consist of smaller ungulates and are available year-round. These kills are shielded best of all because they are typically stored in trees. Two million years ago saber-toothed cats may have provided hominids with a third opportunity, also in riparian woodlands. Kills of these extinct predators would have provided very large carcasses and abundant meat.

We hypothesize that scavenging may have been most important in the dry season, when plant foods are scarcest and scavenging opportunities are most diverse. Aside from leopard kills, wet-season predation does not have the predictable riparian focus but instead is scattered in broader and more open habitats. Hyenas are quick to find and consume these exposed carcasses. Because scavenging may have made carnivory and herbivory seasonally complementary feeding strategies, we do not assume—as proponents of Man the Hunter do—that getting meat was the core of hominid adaptation. As dental evidence suggests, hominids have always been omnivores. The mere existence of stone tools and animal bones does not demonstrate that meat eating was common.

Yet scavenging may have made the dry season a time of plenty. It is then that starvation and predation produce many carcasses. Even the most marginal abandoned lion kill, retaining only marrow and brain, could provide much more than an adult's daily caloric requirements at the cost of half an hour's effort with a hammerstone. This rate of food return is higher than can be obtained by harvesting plants. If efficiency guided foraging decisions, hominids would have always preferred scavenging to harvesting, whenever scavenging was possible.

This preference would have been most marked at the height of the dry season, when plant productivity reaches its nadir and big-cat kills become predictable, shortening searches for these resources. A similar

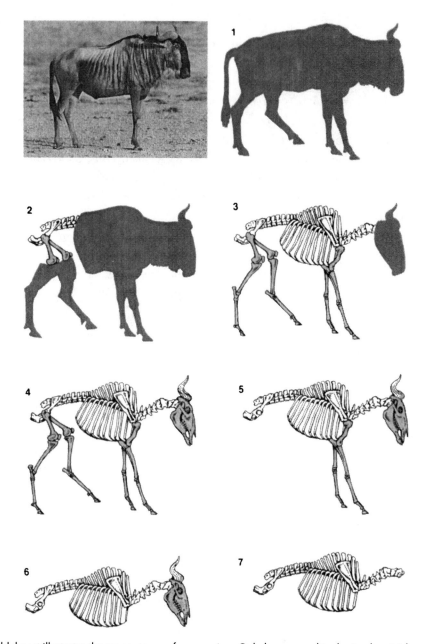

Vanishing Wildebeest illustrates the seven stages of scavenging. Only hyenas and tool-using hominids can exploit carcasses of this size beyond stage four by breaking limb bones for the marrow and opening skulls for the brains. In his study of *FLK Zinjanthropus*, an east African archaeological site dated to about two million years ago, Henry T. Bunn of the University of Wisconsin at Madison found a preponderance of head and limb bones. The finding matches stage 4, suggesting that the hominids scavenged defleshed carcasses.

economy applies in the comparison with hunting: less energy is spent in picking one's food out of a tree or up off the ground if one does not first have to chase it.

Scavenging also incurs less risk than hunting. Any meat that attracts hominids can also attract lions, which, when they arrive, may ignore the dead in order to pursue the living. Our research showed, however, that large carnivores often leave certain classes of carcasses unattended for long periods. In the interim, the sites would have been safe.

Defleshed lion kills in riparian woodlands are particularly safe. We found that bone-crushing hyenas usually do not discover these carcasses until a day after they are abandoned by lions—a good window of

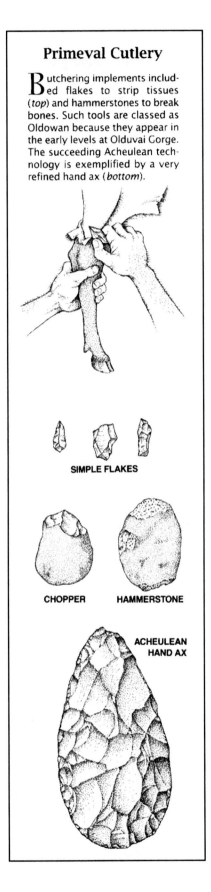

Primeval Cutlery

Butchering implements included flakes to strip tissues (*top*) and hammerstones to break bones. Such tools are classed as Oldowan because they appear in the early levels at Olduvai Gorge. The succeeding Acheulean technology is exemplified by a very refined hand ax (*bottom*).

SIMPLE FLAKES

CHOPPER   HAMMERSTONE

ACHEULEAN HAND AX

opportunity for any hominid capable of wielding a hammer-stone. Tree-stored leopard kills provide more food (flesh as well as marrow) at less risk, especially when the cache contains several kills. Leopards tend to be solitary, and even a baboon or chimpanzee can sometimes scare one away. Moreover, leopards often abandon their kills voluntarily for as long as eight to 12 hours during the day, leaving some of them in a complete condition. Hominids in these woodlands would appear to have faced no more danger in scavenging than in foraging for plant foods in the same regions.

But risks may have outweighed benefits in the open plains, despite the plentiful opportunities for displacing the timid cheetah and jackal from their kills, exploiting abandoned lion kills in wet periods and benefiting from natural deaths during drought. The reason for this judgment is the scarcity of trees, which deprived the arboreally adapted hominids of sanctuary. Yet this drawback applies with at least equal force to hunting. Big herbivores have ways of defending themselves, and even if one can be killed, the conspicuousness of the killing quickly attracts scavengers. Many of these would have been more than a match for rock-wielding bipeds.

Hunting enthusiasts might respond that game is more wholesome than carrion. In the Serengeti, however, we found that few carcasses left on the ground retain scavengeable food as long as 48 hours, the time it takes for putrefaction to set in. But even then, most edible tissues remain encased in skin or bone that excludes insects and other postmortem disease vectors. Even carcasses produced by "natural" death generally carry no dangerous parasites, because most such deaths result from malnutrition, not disease.

Scavenging has also been faulted as nutritionally unsound. John D. Speth of the University of Michigan has suggested that animals that died of hunger would provide protein without enough fat for balance, a diet that can lead to a form of starvation. (Backwoodsmen called it "rabbit fever" because it came from living exclusively on rabbits and other lean game.) Yet hominids have always gotten most of their calories from the carbohydrates and oils of plants, and the most regular dry-season scavenging possibilities are predator kills of animals with fat in their marrow.

Which came first, scavenging or hunting? Answers have been proffered on ethological grounds, only to be controverted by new evidence. Hunting was uniquely human until Jane Goodall documented it in chimpanzees. Scavenging was beneath the dignity of a primate until workers discovered chimpanzees and baboons usurping the kills of cheetahs and leopards. It was foreign to human nature until 1988, when an ethnographic study of 20 years' duration documented avid scavenging by the Hadza and San foragers of sub-Saharan Africa. The delayed observation testifies to the prejudice against scavenging.

The earliest hominids probably scavenged and took small prey with their hands, as chimpanzees and baboons do. Only their next step was unique: they began to use tools to butcher large carcasses that non-human primates cannot exploit. The difficulty of this leap belies the charge that scavenging offers no challenge that might select for human qualities.

Our fieldwork suggests that scavenging is not at all easy for a slow, small, dull-toothed primate. To locate scavengeable carcasses before others did, we had to learn how to interpret the diverse cues to the presence of a carcass in riparian woodlands. They include the labored, low-level, early-morning, bee-line flight of a single vulture toward a kill; vultures perched in mid-canopy rather than at the crown of a tree, where they nest; appendages of a concealed leopard or of its kill dangling from a branch; and tufts of ungulate hair or fresh claw marks at the base of a leopard's feeding tree. At night, the loud "laughing" of hyenas at a fresh kill, the panicked braying of a zebra being attacked, the grunting of a frightened wildebeest—all serve notice of where to find an abandoned carcass when morning comes.

Higher primates make "mental maps" of their ranges and use them to predict where the next batch of fruit will ripen. Hominids might have applied this ready-made skill to predict the future availability and location of carcasses. We learned how to do it, with great effort. Every day we monitored the movements, hunting and feeding schedules, and belly sizes of predators, as well as the general activity of their prey. Apart from its possible nutritional payoffs, hominids might have used such information routinely to avoid predators.

Social skills would not have advanced, however, unless scavenging also selected for social cooperation. Scavenged carcasses that fed only one individual, leaving no surplus to share, would probably have promoted competition. But if our research results are correct and big-cat kills gave early hominids a food surplus, then Isaac's model of cooperative foraging, processing and food sharing would work. Similarly, if such carcass foods did not usually coincide with plant foods, the emergent social skills might have expanded to include a division of labor, with corporate foraging about a common home base. To add to our ancestors' challenges, one need only hypothesize that they generally found carcasses in one place and stone for butchery tools in another. Uniting the tools with their objects would have thus required deep planning depth, detailed mental mapping and social cooperation.

West African chimpanzees are the only nonhuman primates that have enough planning depth to bring stone tools to food sources, as they do when they transport stone hammers and anvils to break the hard nuts of kola and Panda trees. Still, they do not carry the stone very far—*H. habilis* transported stone as far as 10 kilometers (six miles)—and the nuts are not nearly as ephemeral as the scavengeable carcasses the early hominids butchered.

Technological skills necessary for exploiting most scavenging options are embodied in the earliest, Oldowan, tool kit [*see box on opposite page*]—sharp-edged stone flakes to deflesh and disarticulate and natural cobbles to break marrow bones and skulls. No tools clearly designed as weapons are apparent in either this complex or those of the more sophisticated tools of the Acheulean age, which ranged from 1.5 million to 200,000 years ago.

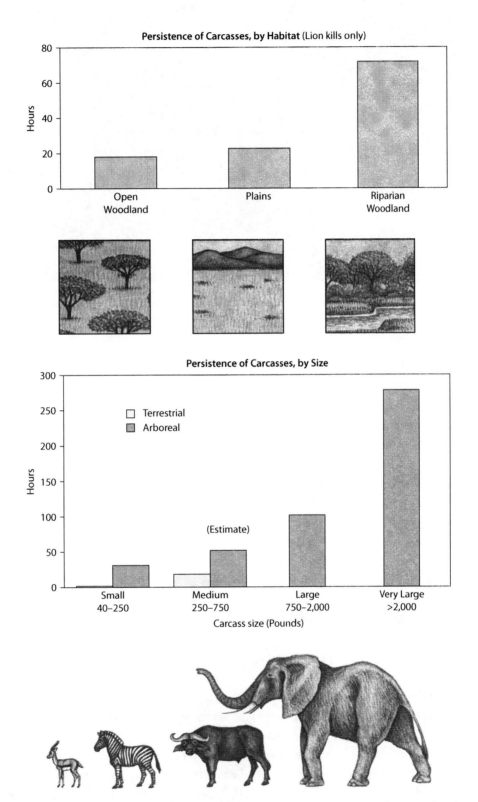

Persistence of Carcasses, by Habitat (Lion kills only)

Persistence of Carcasses, by Size

CARCASS PERSISTENCE in the Serengeti varies by habitat and size. Large carcasses on the ground outlast small ones, tree-stored kills outlast terrestrial ones and carcasses in dense riparian woodlands outlast those in open woodlands and savannas.

Leopard's larder keeps carcasses out of reach and out of sight to all except hominids. Because such tree-stored kills may retain flesh as well as marrow, they would have been particularly valuable to hominids with butchering tools.

Such considerations lead us to conclude that Oldowan hominids may have created a scavenging niche that can account both for the earliest assemblages of tools and large mammal bones and for many uniquely human traits assumed to have arisen from hunting. A scavenging option may have started as a supplement to plant foraging, appearing in the following stages.

Hominids may have begun eating large animals long before *Homo* appeared. *Australopithecus* could have pioneered the strategy when it occupied the savannas and woodlands that became widespread by six million years ago, in the wake of global climatic change. These open environments would have offered far better scavenging opportunities than the closed woodlands and forests of hominid predecessors—habitats in which the apes have remained to this day.

The earliest hominids may have come across defleshed kills while foraging for plants in thin ribbons of riparian woodlands. These resources would require only unmodified cobbles to extract the remaining marrow and brain from their bony cases. The butchery of these rich sources of energy and protein might have left a record that has so far eluded archaeologists because it occurred before the invention of flake tools, whose manufacture leaves a conspicuous litter of stone chips.

If so, diurnal hominids may have started to supplant hyenas by getting to the kill first. This hypothesis finds some confirmation in the extinction of several hyena species about two million years ago. The advent of a flaked stone technology by about 2.5 million years ago may then have enabled hominids to encroach on a new component of the large mammal scavenging niche. Now they could get flesh as well as marrow. With flaked stone, hominids held in their hands fabricated versions of the flesh-shearing carnassial teeth of carnivores. With them, the hominids could butcher a leopard's tree-stored kills. The flesh from the much larger prey of the saber-toothed cats would also have been accessible, an observation that leads us to suggest that hominids may have had something to do with this species' extinction some 1.5 million years ago. It may be significant that these big cats persisted longer in Europe and the Americas than in Africa, going extinct only after hominids first colonized these continents.

Hunting of very small prey by hominids may have been an ancient strategy, and the late development of projectile weapons made early *H. sapiens* a predator more capable than any other primate. But scavenging has probably had a much more pervasive effect on human evolution than has hitherto been appreciated.

FURTHER READING

The Serengeti Lion: A Study Of Predator-Prey Relations. George B. Schaller. University of Chicago Press, 1976.

Serengeti: Dynamics of an Ecosystem. A. R. Sinclair and M. Norton-Griffiths. University of Chicago Press, 1984.

Last Days in Eden. Elspeth Huxley and Hugo Van Lawick. Amaryllis Press, 1984.

Another Unique Species: Patterns in Human Evolutionary Ecology. Robert Foley. John Wiley and Sons, Inc., 1987.

The First Technology. Nicholas Toth in *Scientific American*, Vol. 256, No. 4, pages 112–121; April 1987.

As the first hominin to disperse throughout the entire Old World, *Homo erectus* was adapted to many different habitats. But by studying fossils of *Homo erectus* and the stone tools associated with them, and by diagnosing the nature of the ancient environments where those fossils were found, it is possible to reconstruct the overall behavior of this species, what it required to survive, and how it dispersed from Africa.

21. The Paleobiology of *Homo Erectus*

Implications for Understanding the Adaptive Zone of this Species

By Susan Cachel and John W. K. Harris

ANATOMICAL IMPLICATIONS OF NICHE STRUCTURE IN *HOMO ERECTUS*

Several lines of evidence (anatomy, palaeoecology, lithic technology, and archaeological survey) converge to suggest that the niche of the taxon Homo erectus differed significantly from the niches of earlier hominid taxa. We delineate this evidence in the following sections, as we attempt to reconstruct the adaptive zone of this species.

In recent years, archaeological and human paleontological records in the Old World have been interpreted to show evidence of distinct species within the hypodigm of *Homo erectus* and the dispersal of hominids out of sub-Saharan Africa. Regardless of the minutiae of various debates, hominid dispersal from sub-Saharan Africa is a major evolutionary event, and East Africa, the Horn of Africa, and the Middle East are targeted as the principal corridor for dispersal into Eurasia. Given the recent radiometric dating of Javan *Homo erectus* to 1.8 mya (Swisher *et at.* 1994), a date equivalent to the oldest *Homo erectus* site in Africa

(Koobi Fora), it is possible that hominids began to spread from sub-Saharan Africa even before 2 mya. In spite of the equivalence of the earliest dates in Java and Koobi Fora, we consider that *Homo erectus* emerged in Africa. Australopithecines have been found only in sub-Saharan Africa, and do not occur in other tropical areas of the Old World. Furthermore, a remarkably complete sub-adult specimen of *Homo erectus* from the western Kenyan site of Nariokotome (KNM-WT 15000) shows a funnel-shaped thorax, long femoral neck, small femoral neck-shaft angle, and iliac flare that indicate this species emerged from the australopithecine subfamily.

The KNM-WT 15000 specimen is dated at 1.53 mya, and, in spite of anatomical traits indicating descent from an australopithecine, it shows significantly different postcranial anatomy from the australopithecine (Walker and Leakey 1993). The horizontal orientation of the clavicle and glenoid cavity argue for increased terrestriality. A major feature of the specimen is its modern limb propor tions: the lower limb has increased in length, so that the relative proportion of upper to lower limbs is like that found in modern hominids. The relatively long legs of modern hominids are usually explained by presumed efficiency in bipedal locomotion. Yet recent experimental studies of locomotor efficiency in modern humans demonstrate that relatively longer legs have no important effect on locomotor efficiency (Steudel and Beattie 1994; Steudel 1995; Webb 1994). If leg length does not affect locomotor efficiency, then the evolution of relatively long lower limbs in *Homo erectus*, as exemplified by KNM-WT 15000, was driven by selection pressures either for speed or for heat adaptation. Speed is unlikely to have been a factor in increasing relative length of the legs: Heat adaptation, however, was probably a major selection factor in the increasing relative length of the Nariokotome lower limb, particularly given the long distal limb segments and exaggerated ectomorphy of the whole specimen (Ruff and Walker 1993). Ruff (1991) argues that narrow pelvic bi-iliac breadth in all Plio/Pleistocene specimens complete enough to examine indicates a fundamental hominid adaptation to heat, but the greater stature and long limbs of the Nariokotome specimen indicate further adaptation to open, arid, hot environments.

Why did heat adaptation become a factor in East Africa? Increasing aridity and the spread of grasslands may have been important. Yet paleosol carbonates and organic matter from sites in the Kenya Rift Valley show that an environmental mosaic appears to have persisted for the last 15.5 my. There is no evidence here of a shift to a dominant open grassland regime at any time (Kingston *et at.* 1994). Carbon isotope signals taken from herbivore teeth from the same succession of sites in Kenya show that C4 grasses are present in herbivore diets at 15.3 mya, although these grasses are not the primary food resource until 7 mya (Morgan *et al.* 1994). One researcher believes that modern Serengeti-type grasslands had a brief peak in East Africa at 1.7 mya, and a slightly less pronounced peak between 1.6-1.4 mya (Cerling 1992). It is important to note that hominid anatomy by itself indicates climatic adaptation, irrespective of the palaeoenvironmental evidence. Narrow pelvic width demonstrates adaptation to heat (Ruff 1991), and the long legs and pro-nounced ectomorphy of the Nariokotome specimen imply arid, open-country adaptation.

The predicted full stature of the sub-adult Nariokotome specimen indicates large size, even by modern standards, although any prediction is affected by assumptions about the existence and de gree of an adolescent growth spurt. In non-human primates, the growth spurt may not exist, or it may be sexually dimorphic; in modern humans, the adolescent growth spurt can be quite variable across populations. Certainly adult body size was larger in the Nariokotome species than in specimens of early genus *Homo* from Olduvai Gorge. This indicates a difference in nutrition, and a probable dietary shift in the Nariokotome species.

If, as seems likely, large adult stature occurred in the Nariokotome specimen, then relative brain size is affected. Relative brain size may not have been markedly larger in *Homo erectus* than in earlier hominids. Walker (1993a) uses a figure of 909 cc. for the adult cranial capacity of the KNM-WT 15000 specimen, and estimates the relative brain size as being equivalent to that of earlier members of genus *Homo*. Because the difference in relative brain size between early genus *Homo* and the australopithecines is not marked, this indicates that the great increase in relative brain size often thought to be characteristic of genus *Homo* is, in fact, only found in this genus after the Middle Pleistocene.

A critical and frequently overlooked factor in hominid evolutionary ecology is that the Nariokotome individual and his conspecifics coexisted with *Australopithecus boisei* and perhaps other species of the genus *Homo*. A theoretical model for the coexistence of competing species predicts that seasonal variation in resource abundance generates species diversity by creating tradeoffs between maintenance and foraging efficiency (Brown 1989). Heat adaptation affects the ability to range and forage in equatorial environments, and particularly affects mid-day activity levels (Wheeler 1993). Given access to abundant, potable water, the ancestors of *Homo erectus* in East Africa may have reacted to seasonality and competition from sympatric hominid species by evolving additional morphological adaptations to dissipate heat by increasing stature, relative leg length, and ectomorphy. Foraging efficiency would increase. Earlier postcranial evidence is sparse; we have no knowledge of body form and limb proportions in *Homo erectus* prior to 1.53 mya. We assume that the spread of *Homo erectus* in the Old World was associated with the postcranial anatomy of the Nariokotome specimen, but no comparable North African, European, or Javanese specimen has been discovered.

The Nariokotome species must have had a higher quality diet and a better nutritional base to support large adult body size, in contrast to members of early genus *Homo* discovered at Olduvai Gorge. Walker has argued that hominid stature and body weight increased when relatively habitual hunting was first established at 1.5 mya (Walker 1993b); the dispersal of *Homo erectus* from Africa was caused by new, or more efficient, hunting abilities (Walker 1984). As evidence of such hunting abilities, a partial adult skeleton of *Homo erectus* dated to 1.7 mya (KNM-ER 1808) has extensive pathological remodeling of the bone surface. This periosteal inflammation has been attributed to hypervitaminosis A, which Walker *et al.* (1981) suggest was caused by ingestion of an adult carnivore liver. It may be unnecessary to invoke hunting to explain hominid dispersal. Home range size in animals increases isometrically or allometrically with body size; yet carnivorous mammals do show a greater home range size increase with body size increase than herbivorous or omnivorous mammals (Calder 1984).

ARCHAEOLOGICAL IMPLICATIONS OF NICHE STRUCTURE IN *HOMO ERECTUS*

Just after the earliest occurrence of *Homo erectus* at Koobi Fora (1.8 mya), the archaeological rycord in East Africa becomes increasingly complex. 1.7 mya marks the advent of the Karari Indus try. The coincidence of these dates suggests that *Homo erectus* (unlike earlier or sympatric hominids) was experiencing selection pressure to exploit resources that were widely distributed across early Pleistocene landscapes. By 1.7-1.5 mya, archaeological traces are found in a variety of habitats within the Lake Turkana Basin (Rogers *et al.* 1994). This contrasts with survey results from two earlier intervals within this lake basin, and confirms the increase in home-range size and wider habitat exploitation suggested by the anatomy of *Homo erectus* and the efficient exploitation of resources implied by Karari artifacts.

By 1.6 mya in Africa, lithic assemblages become highly variable both in terms of individual artifact size and shape, as well as in densities across ancient landscapes. Moreover, during the interval between 2.0-1.5 mya, the nature and distribution of archaeological traces across the ancient landscape yield evidence for hominid activities and ranging patterns from such well documented localities as Olduvai Gorge Bed II and the Okote

Member at Koobi Fora. Comparing the evidence, one sees the influence of local conditions in eliciting very different hominid behavioral responses between the two areas (Potts 1988; Cachel and Harris n.d.).

CHARACTER RELEASE AFFECTING MORPHOLOGY AND BEHAVIOR

Natural selection affects the phenotype, which comprises both morphology and behavior. Variability within the hypodigm of *Homo erectus* has recently been interpreted as evidence of multiple species (Groves 1989; Tattersall 1992; Wood 1992). These analyses emphasize a marked distinction between Asian and African specimens and raise doubt about the presence of *Homo erectus* in Europe. A more parsimonious explanation for phenotypic variability in *Homo erectus* is that such variability reflects character or ecological release occurring during colonization of novel environments that offer no competition (Cachel and Harris n.d.). During ecological release (Van Valen 1965), species encountering no competitors in new environments may alter their behavior and morphology, causing increasing variability of the phenotype or phenotypic character release. Character release also ensures the likelihood that a widely dispersed species like *Homo erectus* would demonstrate great morphological and behavioral variability (Cachel and Harris in press). This would explain morphological differences within the *Homo erectus* hypodigm which some researchers recognize with taxonomic distinctions between African, European, and Asian specimens. Explaining variation in Acheulean assemblages has long been a staple of research in lithic technology (e.g., Gowlett and Crompton 1994). Character release would also explain differences in the behavioral phenotype, as seen by the evidence of stone artifact traits and the distribution of artifacts in diverse contexts. Some examples that may illustrate this phenomenon in younger time periods during the Lower Pleistocene are regional variants of the Acheulean industry that occur on the northwest Mediterranean coast of Africa at Sidi Abderrahman and Ternifine. Other stone tool industries exist where hand-axes are rare or absent. Examples in Europe are the Buda, Tayacian and Clactonian industries. Olduwan artifacts are found in association with the 1.8-1.6 mya Dmanisi mandible (Gabunia and Vekua 1995). The Nihewan Basin in northern China has yielded several sites dated between 1-0.7 mya with Olduwan artifacts (Schick and Toth 1995). If behavioral character release were occurring in migrating hominids, it may be no accident that Acheulean variants or alternate industries are found far from tropical African habitats.

FACTORS AFFECTING DISPERSION

Five factors probably affected hominid dispersion out of the Rift regions of East Africa. 1. Tectonic changes in East Africa, associated with the development of East African and Red Sea rifting beginning at 25 mya (Harland *et at.* 1989: Fig. 7.3), contribute to the origin of regional faunas through habitat fragmentation. Regional faunas affect mammalian diversity (Flessa 1975). Events associated with tectonism or Pleistocene climatic fluctuations would therefore create regional faunas, and contribute to species diversity through habitat fragmentation. 2. It is unlikely, however, that a large-bodied mammal species like *Homo erectus* was limited even by extensive habitat fragmentation, because dispersal ability is directly proportional to body size in land mammals. 3. According to Rapoport's Rule (Stevens 1989), high-latitude species have greater latitudinal range than low-latitude species, and are less affected by the occurrence or degree of seasonality. Consequently, once hominids disperse from low latitudes, the less constrained they are likely to be in terms of range or seasonal perturbations.

4. Because the niche of a species may vary with geographic range, it is possible that the niche of *Homo erectus* in sub-Saharan Africa was different from that of *Homo erectus* in North Africa or in the Far East, simply because of the wide distribution of this taxon. A wide distribution coupled with low population sizes would ensure the operation of genetic drift; phenotypic morphological or behavioral traits may have therefore sometimes been caused by random processes, rather than natural selection. 5. The phenomenon of ecological or character release may also have been important (Cachel and Harris in press).

EMERGENCE AND DISPERSAL OF *HOMO ERECTUS*

Palaeontology and archaeology demonstrate that *Homo erectus* emerged in areas of tropical sub-Saharan Africa where habitat disruption, caused by Pleistocene climatic fluctuations, tectonic movements, and volcanism was prevalent. The successful migration of *Homo erectus* out of the African tropics is not necessarily dependent upon material culture, because the Old World monkey genus Macaca occurs in many temperate areas during the Pleistocene (England, Germany, the Netherlands, northern China) without benefit of tool behavior or the ability to create artificial shelters or control fire. We suggest that *Homo erectus* (perhaps like some modern macaque [Richard *et at.* 1989] and baboon species) thrived on environmental disruption, and emerged as a "weed" taxon in areas of tropical Africa disrupted by Pleistocene climatic and tectonic perturbations (Cachel and Harris in press).

Archaeological survey yields evidence that a variety of habitats were being occupied (Rogers *et al.* 1994). For the first time, there are indications that hominids occupied much higher elevations. In the Ethiopian highlands, sites occur just below the forest zone at 2000 meters (Clark and Harris 1985). Ethiopian sites such as Gadeb and Melka Konture experience extreme fluctuations in daily temperature, with freezing or near freezing conditions at night. It therefore appears significant that some of the earliest evidence of hominid control of fire occurs at the Gadeb site, which dates to 1.4 mya. Here hominid control of fire may have been initiated to combat nocturnal freezing, but it also facilitated the movements of hominids into new habitats, some of which were at higher elevations. The dispersal of *Homo erectus* into new and possibly marginal regions of Eurasia is a result of a weed-like ability to thrive in disrupted environments. Many researchers attribute the first control of fire to this taxon (Balter 1995), and the use of fire by this hominid species may have contributed to local environmental disruption. If *Homo erectus* is present in Java at 1.8 mya (Swisher *et al.* 1994), hominid dispersal from sub-Saharan Africa probably occurred prior to 2 mya. A date of 1.8-1.6 mya for the *Homo erectus* mandible from Dmanisi in Georgia also suggests an earlier dispersal (Mchedlidze 1993; Dean and Delson 1995; Gabunia and Vekua 1995). A 2 mya migration pre-dates the earliest Acheulean artifacts, which are found in the Ethiopian site of Konso-Gardula, dated to 1.4 mya, where abundant Acheulean artifacts occur with a mandibular specimen of *Homo erectus* (Asfaw *et al.* 1992). If hominids migrated from sub-Saharan Africa at 2 mya, this might explain the absence of the Acheulean industry in China and Java, although we consider character release to be the more probable explanation, because it accounts for both morphological and behavioral variation. Clark *et at.* (1994) argue that advanced morphological features appear first in Africa, but character release may explain morphological variation between African and Eurasian specimens of *Homo erectus* .

Various routes have been proposed for the dispersal of Lower Pleistocene hominids from Africa. The most likely route is by way of the Afar Depression, through the shallow termination of the Red Sea and across the southwestern point of the Arabian Peninsula. During the early and middle Pleistocene, land today covered by the Red Sea may have been intermittently subaerially exposed to allow hominid movements between northeast Africa and the Arabian Peninsula and north into the Levant and thence to Eurasia (the Levantine

Corridor [Bar-Yosef and Goren-lnbar 1993]). Available geophysical evidence supports this possible route. The Asal Rift segment of the Afar Depression is now subaerially exposed because crustal thinning and subsidence is balanced by the injection of magma (de Chabalier and Avouac 1994). This is a modern example of an emergent area in the Afar Depression caused by processes presumably operating through the Pleistocene. Hominid dispersal into Eurasia may well have occurred in this region along a broad front. The site of Ubeidiya is crucial in understanding the timing of migration, as well as behavioral and ecological factors involved in the dispersal of hominids. The earliest artifact levels date to 1.5 mya (Tchernov 1987). The broad similarities in the lithic assemblages of Ubeidiya and Olduvai Bed II suggest a stone tool tradition that may have African origins. The dating of Ubeidiya indicates that hominids had already dispersed out of Africa and established a foothold in Eurasia by 1.5 mya. Dmaniti, in Georgia (1.8-1.6 mya), also lies on the vector of dispersal through the Levant into Asia.

A major turnover in the large mammal fauna of Europe appears to have occurred at 800,000 ya (Turner 1992), which would certainly affect hominid paleoecology. Whatever the first migration date from Africa may be, it is clear that hominid presence in Europe is ephemeral until about 500,000 ya (Turner 1992). Evidence of a more permanent hominid occupation after 500,000 ya is provided by the Mauer and Boxgrove sites in central and northern Europe. The latter contains a hominid fossil, Acheulean implements with debitage, and butchered animal remains (Roberts *et al.* 1994).

We believe that the combined archaeological and paleontological records in East Africa and the Middle East may be dense enough, and dated well enough, to begin to test ideas about the adaptive zone of *Homo erectus*. Because of its novel adaptive zone, this taxon was the first widely dispersed hominid species, and its dispersal occurred at an early date.

REFERENCES

Asfaw, B. *et at.* 1992. The earliest Acheulean from Konso-Gardula. *Nature* 360:732–735.

Balter, M. 1995. Did *Homo erectus* tame fire first? Science 268:1570.

Bar-Yosef, O. and Goren-Inbar, N. 1993. *The Lithic Ass emblages of Ubeidiya*. Monographs of the Institute of Archaeology, Hebrew University of Jerusalem.

Brown, J.S. 1989. Coexistence on a seasonal resource. *American Naturalist* 133:168–182.

Cachel, S. and Harris, J.W.K. in press. Ranging patterns, land-use, and subsistence in *Homo erectus* from the perspective of evolutionary ecology. In *Proceedings of the Pithecanthropus Centennial, 1893–1993; Vol. I, Palaeoanthropology: Evolution and Ecology of Homo erectus* (eds. J.R.F. Bower and S. Sartono). Leiden: Leiden University Press.

Cachel, S. and Harris, J.W.K. n.d. *The lifeway of Homo erectus from the perspective of evolutionary ecology.*

Calder, III, W.A. 1984. *Size, Function, and Life History.* Cambridge (Mass.): Harvard University Press.

Cerling, T.E. 1992. Development of grasslands and savannas in East Africa during the Neogene. *Palaeogeography, Palaeoclimatology, Palaeoecology* 97:241–247.

de Chabalier, J-B. and Avouac, J-P. 1994. Kinematics of the Asal Rift (Djibouti) as determined from the deformation of Fieale Volcano. Science 265:1677–1681.

Clark, J.D. and Harris, J.W.K. 1985. Fire and its roles in early hominid lifeways. *The African Archaeological Review* 3:3–27.

Clark, J.D. *et al.* 1994. African *Homo erectus* : Old radiometric ages and young Olduwan assemblages in the Middle Awash Valley, Ethiopia. *Science* 264:1907–1910.

Dean, D. and Delson, E. 1995. *Homo* at the gates of Europe. *Nature* 373:472–473.

Flessa, K.W. 1975. Area, continental drift and mammalian diversity. *Paleobiology* 1:189–194.

Gabunia, L. and Vekua, A. 1995. A Plio-Pleistocene hominid from Dmanisi, East Georgia, Caucasus. *Nature* 373:509–512.

Gowlett, J.A.J. and Crompton, R.H. 1994. Kariandusi: Acheulean morphology and the question of allometry. *The African Archaeological Review* 12:3–42.

Groves, C.P. 1989. *A Theory of Human and Primate Evolution*. Oxford: Clarendon Press.

Harland, W.B. *et al.* 1989. *A Geologic Time Scale 1989*. Cambridge: Cambridge University Press.

Kingston, J.D. *et al.* 1994. Isotopic evidence for Neogene hominid paleoenvironments in the Kenya Rift Valley. *Science* 264:955–959.

Mchedlidze, G. 1993. News from the Georgian Republic. *Society of Vertebrate Paleontology News Bulletin* 158: 19–21.

Morgan, M.E. *et at.* 1994. Carbon isotopic evidence for the emergence of C4 plants in the Neogene from Pakistan and Kenya. *Nature* 367:162–165.

Potts, R. 1988. *Early Hominid Activities at Olduvai*. New York: Aldine de Gruyter.

Richard, A.F. *et al.* 1989. Weed macaques: The evolutionary implications of macaque feeding ecology. *International Journal of Primatology* 10:569–594.

Roberts, M.B. *et al.* 1994. A hominid tibia from Middle Pleistocene sediments at Boxgrove, UK. *Nature* 369:311–313.

Rogers, M.J., Harris, J.W.K. and Feibel, C.S. 1994. Changing patterns of land use by Plio/ Pleistocene hominids in the Lake Turkana Basin. *Journal of Human Evolution* 27:139–158.

Ruff, C.B. 1991. Climate and body shape in hominid evolution. *Journal of Human Evolution* 21:81–105.

Ruff, C.B. and Walker, A. 1993. Body size and body shape. In *The Nanokotome Homo erectus skeleton* (eds. A. Walker and R. Leakey): pp. 234–265. Cambridge (Mass.): Harvard University Press.

Schick' K.D. and Toth, N. 1995. Continuing archaeological research in the Nihewan Basin, China. *Abstracts, Fourth Annual Meeting of the Paleoanthropology Society,* Oakland, CA.

Steudel, K.L. 1995. Locomotor energetics and hominid evolution. *Evolutionary Anthropology* 5(1):42–48.

Steudel, K. and Beattie, J. 1994. Was locomotor efficiency an important adaptive constraint in the evolution of the hominid lower limb? *American Journal of Physical Anthropology* 93 (supplement 18):187 (abstract).

Stevens, G.C. 1989. The latitudinal gradient in geographical range: how so many species coexist in the tropics. *American Naturalist* 133:240–256.

Swisher, III, C.C. *et al.* 1994. Age of the earliest known hominids in Java, Indonesia. *Science* 263:1118–1121.

Tattersall, I. 1992. Species concepts and species recognition in human evolution. *Journal of Human Evolution* 22:341–349.

Tchernov, E. 1987. The age of the Ubeidiya Formation, an early hominid site in the Jordan Valley. *Israel Journal of Earth Sciences* 36:3–36.

Turner, A. 1992. Large carnivores and earliest European hominids: Changing determinants of resource availability during the Lower and Middle Pleistocene. *Journal of Human Evolution* 22:109–126.

Van Valen, L. 1965. Morphological variation and width of the ecological niche. *American Naturalist* 94:377–390.

Walker, A. 1984. Extinction in hominid evolution. In *Extinctions* (ed. M.H. Nitecki): pp. 119- 152. Chicago: University of Chicago Press.

Walker, A. 1993a. The origin of the genus *Homo*. In *The Origin and Evolution of Humans and Humanness* (ed. D.T. Rasmussen): pp. 29–47. Boston: Jones and Bartlett Publisher.

Walker, A. 1993b. Perspectives on the Nariokotome discovery. In *The Nariokotome Homo erectus* Skeleton (eds. A. Walker and R. Leakey): pp. 411–430. Cambridge (Mass.): Harvard University Press.

Walker, A. and Leakey, R. 1993. The postcranial bones. In *The Nariokotome Homo erectus Skeleton* (eds. A. Walker and R. Leakey): pp. 95–160. Cambridge (Mass.): Harvard University Press.

Walker, A. *et al.* 1981. A possible case of hypervitaminosis A in *Homo erectus* . *Nature* 296:248–250.

Webb, D. 1994. Why people run and the evolutionary implications of lower limb length. *American Journal of Physical Anthropology* 93 (supplement 18): 204–205 (abstract).

Wheeler, P.E. 1993. The influence of stature and body form on hominid energy and water budgets: A comparison of *Australopithecus* and early *Homo* physiques. *Journal of Human Evolution* 24:13–28.

Wood, B. 1992. Origin and evolution of the genus *Homo. Nature* 355:783–790.

Study Questions

1. How did the behavior and social life of early hominins differ from that of modern people?

2. Is *Australpithecus afarensis* ancestral to all subsequent hominin species? Why or why not?

3. What are the problems in identifying the earliest members of genus *Homo*?

4. How can fossils of early *Homo* be distinguished from those of *Australopithecus*?

5. What anatomical features define the genus *Paranthropus*, and what do they tell us about the way of life of these early hominins?

6. What are the earliest archaeological sites composed of, and what do these remains tell us about the adaptation of early *Homo*?

7. What distinguishes *Homo erectus* from other species of early *Homo*?

8. What was the likely route of dispersal of *Homo erectus* out of Africa?

SECTION VII

NEANDERTHALS

Neanderthals lived a tough and challenging life. Not only were they adapted for survival in extreme environments, but their bones show that they suffered repeated injury as part of an extremely active life.

22. Hard Times Among the Neanderthals

By Erik Trinkaus

Although life was difficult, these prehistoric people may not have been as exclusively brutish as usually supposed.

Throughout the century that followed the discovery in 1856 of the first recognized human fossil remains in the Neander Valley (*Neanderthal* in German) near Düsseldorf, Germany, the field of human paleontology has been beset with controversies. This has been especially true of interpretations of the Neanderthals, those frequently maligned people who occupied Europe and the Near East from about 100,000 years ago until the appearance of anatomically modern humans about 35,000 years ago.

During the last two decades, however, a number of fossil discoveries, new analyses of previously known remains, and more sophisticated models for interpreting subtle anatomical differences have led to a reevaluation of the Neanderthals and their place in human evolution.

This recent work has shown that the often quoted reconstruction of the Neanderthals as semierect, lumbering caricatures of humanity is inaccurate. It was based on faulty anatomical interpretations that were reinforced by the intellectual biases of the turn of the century. Detailed comparisons of Neanderthal skeletal remains with those of modern humans have shown that there is nothing in Neanderthal anatomy that conclusively indicates locomotor, manipulative, intellectual, or linguistic abilities inferior to those of modern humans. Neanderthals have therefore been added to the same species as ourselves—*Homo sapiens*—although they are usually placed in their own subspecies, *Homo sapiens neanderthalensis*.

Despite these revisions, it is apparent that there are significant anatomical differences between the Neanderthals and present-day humans. If we are to understand the Neanderthals, we must formulate hypotheses as to why they evolved from earlier humans about 100,000 years ago in Europe and the Near East, and why they were suddenly replaced about 35,000 years ago by peoples largely indistinguishable from ourselves. We must determine, therefore, the behavioral significance of the anatomical differences between the Neanderthals and other human groups, since it is patterns of successful behavior that dictate the direction of natural selection for a species.

In the past, behavioral reconstructions of the Neanderthals and other prehistoric humans have been based largely on archeological data. Research has now reached the stage at which behavioral interpretations from the archeological record can be significantly supplemented by analyses of the fossils themselves. These analyses promise to tell us a considerable amount about the ways of the Neanderthals and may eventually help us to determine their evolutionary fate.

One of the most characteristic features of the Neanderthals is the exaggerated massiveness of their trunk and limb bones. All of the preserved bones suggest a strength seldom attained by modern humans. Furthermore, not only is this robustness present among the adult males, as one might expect, but it is also evident in the adult females, adolescents, and even children. The bones themselves reflect this hardiness in several ways.

First, the muscle and ligament attachment areas are consistently enlarged and strongly marked. This implies large, highly developed muscles and ligaments capable of generating and sustaining great mechanical stress. Secondly, since the skeleton must be capable of supporting these levels of stress, which are frequently several times as great as body weight, the enlarged attachments for muscles and ligaments are associated with arm and leg bone shafts that have been reinforced. The shafts of all of the arm and leg bones are modified tubular structures that have to absorb stress from bending and twisting without fracturing. When the habitual load on a bone increases, the bone responds by laying down more bone in those areas under the greatest stress.

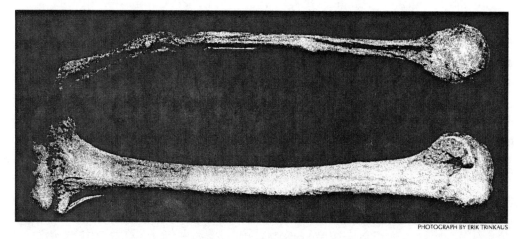

PHOTOGRAPH BY ERIK TRINKAUS

Diagonal lines on these two arm bones from Shanidar 1 are healed fractures. The bottom bone is normal. That on the top is atrophied and has a pathological tip, caused by either amputation or an improperly healed elbow fracture.

In addition, musculature and body momentum generate large forces across the joints. The cartilage, which covers joint surfaces, can be relatively easily overworked to the point where it degenerates, as is indicated by the prevalence of arthritis in joints subjected to significant wear and tear over the years. When the surface area of a joint is increased, the force per unit area of cartilage is reduced, decreasing the pressure on the cartilage.

Most of the robustness of Neanderthal arm bones is seen in muscle and ligament attachments. All of the muscles that go from the trunk or the shoulder blade to the upper end of the arm show massive development. This applies in particular to the muscles responsible for powerful downward movements of the arm and, to a lesser extent, to muscles that stabilize the shoulder during vigorous movements.

Virtually every major muscle or ligament attachment on the hand bones is clearly marked by a large roughened area or a crest, especially the muscles used in grasping objects. In fact, Neanderthal hand bones frequently have clear bony crests, where on modern human ones it is barely possible to discern the attachment of the muscle on the dried bone.

In addition, the flattened areas on the ends of the fingers, which provide support for the nail and the pulp of the finger tip, are enormous among the Neanderthals. These areas on the thumb and the index and middle fingers are usually two to three times as large as those of similarly sized modern human hands. The overall impression is one of arms to rival those of the mightiest blacksmith.

Neanderthal legs are equally massive; their strength is best illustrated in the development of the shafts of the leg bones. Modern human thigh and shin bones possess characteristic shaft shapes adapted to the habitual levels and directions of the stresses acting upon them. The shaft shapes of the Neanderthals are similar to those in modern humans, but the cross-sectional areas of the shafts are much greater. This implies significantly higher levels of stress.

Further evidence of the massiveness of Neanderthal lower limbs is provided by the dimensions of their knee and ankle joints. All of these are larger than in modern humans, especially with respect to the overall lengths of the bones.

The development of their limb bones suggests that the Neanderthals frequently generated high levels of mechanical stress in their limbs. Since most mechanical stress in the body is produced by body momentum and muscular contraction, it appears that the Neanderthals led extremely active lives. It is hard to conceive of what could have required such exertion, especially since the maintenance of vigorous muscular activity would have required considerable expenditure of energy. That level of energy expenditure would undoubtedly have been maladaptive had it not been necessary for survival.

The available evidence from the archeological material associated with the Neanderthals is equivocal on this matter. Most of the archeological evidence at Middle Paleolithic sites concerns stone tool technology and hunting activities. After relatively little change in technology during the Middle Paleolithic (from about 100,000 years to 35,000 years before the present), the advent of the Upper Paleolithic appears to have brought significant technological advances. This transition about 35,000 years ago is approximately coincident with the replacement of the Neanderthals by the earliest anatomically modern humans. However, the evidence for a significant change in hunting patterns is not evident in the animal remains left behind. Yet even if a correlation between the robustness of body build and the level of hunting efficiency could be demonstrated, it would only explain the ruggedness of the Neanderthal males. Since hunting is exclusively or at least predominantly a male activity among humans, and since Neanderthal females were in all respects as strongly built as the males, an alternative explanation is required for the females.

Some insight into why the Neanderthals consistently possessed such massiveness is provided by a series of partial skeletons of Neanderthals from the Shanidar Cave in northern Iraq. These fossils were excavated between 1953 and 1960 by anthropologist Ralph Solecki of Columbia University and have been studied

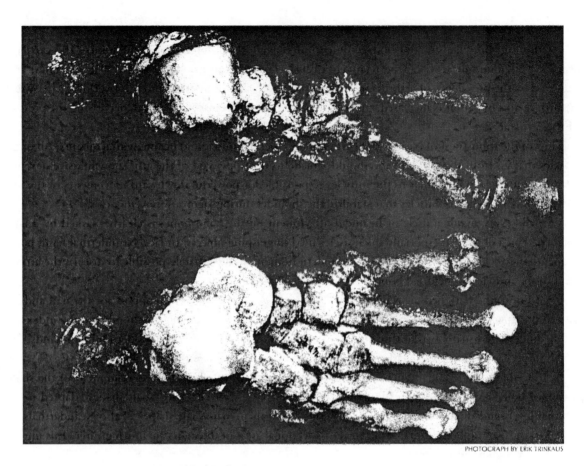

The ankle and big toe of Shanidar 1's bottom foot show evidence of arthritis, which suggests an injury to those parts. The top foot is normal though incomplete.

principally by T. Dale Stewart, an anthropologist at the Smithsonian Institution, and myself. The most remarkable aspect of these skeletons is the number of healed injuries they contain. Four of the six reasonably complete adult skeletons show evidence of trauma during life.

The identification of traumatic injury in human fossil remains has plagued paleontologists for years. There has been a tendency to consider any form of damage to a fossil as conclusive evidence of prehistoric violence between humans if it resembles the breakage patterns caused by a direct blow with a heavy object. Hence a jaw with the teeth pushed in or a skull with a depressed fracture of the vault would be construed to indicate blows to the head.

The central problem with these interpretations is that they ignore the possibility of damage after death. Bone is relatively fragile, especially as compared with the rock and other sediment in which it is buried during fossilization. Therefore when several feet of sediment caused compression around fossil remains, the fossils will almost always break. In fact, among the innumerable cases of suggested violence between humans cited over the years, there are only a few exceptional examples that cannot be readily explained as the result of natural geologic forces acting after the death and burial of the individual.

One of these examples is the trauma of the left ninth rib of the skeleton of Shanidar 3, a partially healed wound inflicted by a sharp object. The implement cut obliquely across the top of the ninth rib and probably pierced the underlying lung. Shanidar 3 almost certainly suffered a collapsed left lung and died several days or weeks later, probably as a result of secondary complications. This is deduced from the presence of bony spurs and increased density of the bone around the cut.

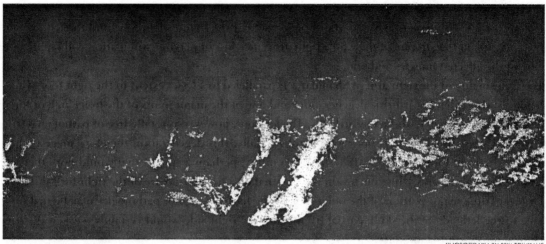

PHOTOGRAPH BY ERIK TRINKAUS

The scar on the left ninth rib of Shanidar 3 is a partially healed wound inflicted by a sharp object. This wound is one of the few examples of trauma caused by violence.

The position of the wound on the rib, the angle of the incision, and the cleanness of the cut make it highly unlikely that the injury was accidentally inflicted. In fact, the incision is almost exactly what would have resulted if Shanidar 3 had been stabbed in the side by a right-handed adversary in face-to-face conflict. This would therefore provide conclusive evidence of violence between humans, the *only* evidence so far found of such violence among the Neanderthals.

In most cases, however, it is impossible to determine from fossilized remains the cause of an individual's death. The instances that can be positively identified as prehistoric traumatic injury are those in which the injury was inflicted prior to death and some healing took place. Shortly after an injury to bone, whether a cut or a fracture, the damaged bone tissue is resorbed by the body and new bone tissue is laid down around the injured area. As long as irritation persists, new bone is deposited, creating a bulge or spurs of irregular bone extending into the soft tissue. If the irritation ceases, the bone will slowly re-form so as to approximate its previous, normal condition. However, except for superficial injuries or those sustained during early childhood, some trace of damage persists for the life of the individual.

In terms of trauma, the most impressive of the Shanidar Neanderthals is the first adult discovered, known as Shanidar 1. This individual suffered a number of injuries, some of which may be related. On the right forehead there are scars from minor surface injuries, probably superficial scalp cuts. The outside of the left eye socket sustained a major blow that partially collapsed that part of the bony cavity, giving it a flat rather than a rounded contour. This injury possibly caused loss of sight in the left eye and pathological alterations of the right side of the body.

Shanidar 1's left arm is largely preserved and fully normal. The right arm, however, consists of a highly atrophied but otherwise normal collarbone and shoulder blade and a highly abnormal upper arm bone shaft. That shaft is atrophied to a fraction of the diameter of the left one but retains most of its original length. Furthermore, the lower end of the right arm bone has a healed fracture of the atrophied shaft and an irregular, pathological tip. The arm was apparently either intentionally amputated just above the elbow or fractured at the elbow and never healed.

This abnormal condition of the right arm does not appear to be a congenital malformation, since the length of the bone is close to the estimated length of the normal left upper arm bone. If, however, the injury to the left eye socket also affected the left side of the brain, directly or indirectly, by disrupting the blood supply to part of the brain, the result could have been partial paralysis of the right side. Motor and sensory control areas for the right side are located on the left side of the brain, slightly behind the left eye socket. This would explain the atrophy of the whole right arm since loss of nervous stimulation will rapidly lead to atrophy of the affected muscles and bone.

The abnormality of the right arm of Shanidar 1 is paralleled to a lesser extent in the right foot. The right ankle joint shows extensive arthritic degeneration, and one of the major joints of the inner arch of the right foot has been completely reworked by arthritis. The left foot, however, is totally free of pathology. Arthritis from normal stress usually affects both lower limbs equally; this degeneration therefore suggests that the arthritis in the right foot is a secondary result of an injury, perhaps a sprain, that would not otherwise be evident on skeletal remains. This conclusion is supported by a healed fracture of the right fifth instep bone, which makes up a major portion of the outer arch of the foot. These foot pathologies may be tied into the damage to the left side of the skull; partial paralysis of the right side would certainly weaken the leg and make it more susceptible to injury.

The trauma evident on the other Shanidar Neanderthals is relatively minor by comparison. Shanidar 3, the individual who died of the rib wound, suffered debilitating arthritis of the right ankle and neighboring foot joints, but lacks any evidence of pathology on the left foot; this suggests a superficial injury similar to the one sustained by Shanidar 1. Shanidar 4 had a healed broken rib. Shanidar 5 received a transverse blow across the left forehead that left a large scar on the bone but does not appear to have affected the brain.

None of these injuries necessarily provides evidence of deliberate violence among the Neanderthals; all of them could have been accidentally self-inflicted or accidentally caused by another individual. In either case, the impression gained of the Shanidar Neanderthals is of a group of invalids. The crucial variable,

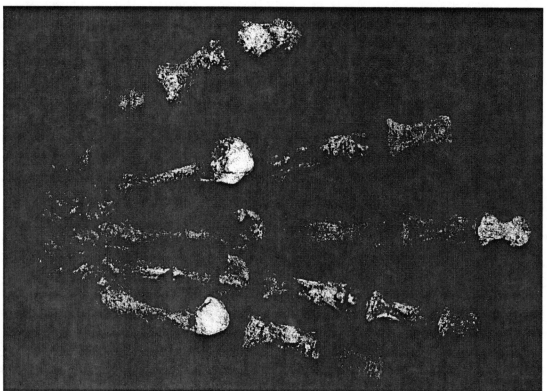

PHOTOGRAPH BY ERIK TRINKAUS

The right hand of Shanidar 4 demonstrates the enlarged finger tips and strong muscle markings characteristic of Neanderthal hands.

however, appears to be age. All four of these individuals died at relatively advanced ages, probably between 40 and 60 years (estimating the age at death for Neanderthals beyond the age of 25 is extremely difficult); they therefore had considerable time to accumulate the scars of past injuries. Shanidar 2 and 6, the other reasonably complete Shanidar adults, lack evidence of trauma, but they both died young, probably before reaching 30.

Other Neanderthal remains, all from Europe, exhibit the same pattern. Every fairly complete skeleton of an elderly adult shows evidence of traumatic injuries. The original male skeleton from the Neander Valley had a fracture just below the elbow of the left arm, which probably limited movement of that arm for life. The "old man" from La Chapelle-aux-Saints, France, on whom most traditional reconstructions of the Neanderthals have been based, suffered a broken rib. La Ferrassi 1, the old adult male from La Ferrassie, France, sustained a severe injury to the right hip, which may have impaired his mobility.

In addition, several younger specimens and ones of uncertain age show traces of trauma. La Quina 5, the young adult female from La Quina, France, was wounded on her right upper arm. A young adult from Sala, Czechoslovakia, was superficially wounded on the right forehead just above the brow. And an individual of unknown age and sex from the site of Krapina, Yugoslavia, suffered a broken forearm, in which the bones never reunited after the fracture.

The evidence suggests several things. First, life for the Neanderthals was rigorous. If they lived through childhood and early adulthood, they did so bearing the scars of a harsh and dangerous life. Furthermore, this incident of trauma correlates with the massiveness of the Neanderthals; a life style that so consistently involved injury would have required considerable strength and fortitude for survival.

There is, however, another, more optimistic side to this. The presence of so many injuries in a prehistoric human group, many of which were debilitating and sustained years before death, shows that individuals were taken care of long after their economic usefulness to the social group had ceased. It is perhaps no accident that among the Neanderthals, for the first time in human history, people lived to a comparatively old age. We also find among the Neanderthals the first intentional burials of the dead, some of which involved offerings. Despite the hardships of their life style, the Neanderthals apparently had a deep-seated respect and concern for each other.

Taken together, these different pieces of information paint a picture of life among the Neanderthals that, while harsh and dangerous, was not without personal security. Certainly the hardships the Neanderthals endured were beyond those commonly experienced in the prehistoric record of human caring and respect as well as of violence between individuals. Perhaps for these reasons, despite their physical appearance, the Neanderthals should be considered the first modern humans.

The recovery of fragmentary DNA from Neanderthal fossils has made it possible to compare ancient Neanderthal DNA with the DNA of living people. This analysis has established Neanderthals as a distinct species, and suggests the divergence time of the two species, but recent work suggests that members of the two lineages may have interbred at some point since their divergence.

23. No Evidence of Neandertal mtDNA Contribution to Early Modern Humans

David Serre[1], André Langaney[2,3], Mario Chech[2], Maria Teschler-Nicola[4], Maja Paunovic[5‡] Philippe Mennecier[2], Michael Hofreiter[1],Göran Possnert[6], Svante Pääbo[1*]

Ancient mitochondrial DNA (mtDNA), extracted from the fossils of four Neanderthals, preserved under exceptional circumstances, is described here. This study compares these Neanderthal mtDNA sequences to those of five Homo sapiens individuals from the same time period and geographic region. Earlier research has discovered mtDNA mutations that are peculiar to the Neanderthals. Because the Homo sapiens individuals examined did not carry any of these Neanderthal mutations, the authors conclude that there was little or no interbreeding between the two groups.*

INTRODUCTION

Despite intense research efforts, no consensus has been reached about the genetic relationship between early modern humans and archaic human forms such as the Neandertals. While supporters of ''multiregional

* Abstract from Neves, G. M. & Serves, M. 2013. Extremely Rare Interbreeding Events Can Explain Neanderthal DNA in Living Humans. *PLoS ONE 7*

evolution" argue for genetic exchange or even continuity between archaic and modern humans (Weidenreich 1943; Wolpoff et al. 1984, 2000; Duarte et al. 1999; Hawks and Wolpoff 2001), proponents of a "single African origin" of contemporary humans claim that negligible genetic interaction took place (Cann et al. 1987; Stringer and Andrews 1988; Ingman et al. 2000; Underhill et al. 2000; Stringer 2002). Mitochondrial DNA (mtDNA) sequences from early modern humans would in principle be able to resolve the question of a contribution of Neandertal mtDNA to modern humans. However, human DNA is pervasive in palae-ontological and archaeological remains as well as in most laboratory environments (e.g., Krings et al. 2000; Hofreiter et al. 2001b; Wandeler et al. 2003). It is therefore currently impossible to differentiate contaminat-ing modern DNA sequences from endogenous human DNA in human remains. Thus, although mtDNA sequences have been reported from remains of early modern humans (Adcock et al. 2001; Caramelli et al. 2003), it is not possible to determine whether such DNA sequences indeed represent endogenous DNA sequences (Abbott 2003). A related problem is that if a Neandertal fossil yields modern human-like DNA sequences, those might be discarded as putative contaminations (Nordborg 1998; Trinkaus 2001), even if they may be endogenous and represent evidence for a close genetic relationship or interbreeding between the two groups.

To explore the genetic relationship between early modern humans and Neandertals in spite of these difficulties, we made use of the fact that the four Neandertal mtDNA sequences determined to date can easily be distinguished from those of modern humans (Krings et al. 1997, 2000; Ovchinnikov et al. 2000; Schmitz et al. 2002; Knight 2003). This allowed us to ask whether all well-preserved Neandertal remains contain Neandertal-like mtDNA and whether all well-preserved early modern human remains fail to contain such DNA sequences. Thus, we did not attempt to determine DNA sequences that are similar to present-day human mtDNA. Instead, we determined whether Neandertal-like mtDNA sequences were present or absent in well-preserved remains of Neandertals and of early modern humans.

RESULTS AND DISCUSSION

The preservation of endogenous DNA in fossils is correlated with the amount, composition, and chemical preservation of amino acids (Poinar et al. 1996). We find that endogenous DNA can be amplified from Pleistocene remains when the amino acid content is more than 30,000 parts per million (ppm), the ratio of glycine to aspartic acid between two and ten, and the aspartic acid racemization (i.e., the stereoisomeric D/L ratio) less than 0.10 (Poinar et al. 1996; Krings et al. 1997, 2000; Schmitz et al. 2002; data not shown). We analyzed the amino acid preservation of 24 Neandertal and 40 early modern human fossils (Table S1). Several important Neandertal fossils, such as La Ferrassie and Krapina, as well as important modern human fossils, such as Veternica, proved to be too poorly preserved to be likely to allow DNA retrieval. Thus, further destructive sampling of these specimens was not considered justified. However, four Neandertal and five early modern human fossils fulfilled the above criteria for amino acid preservation and were thus expected to contain endogenous DNA (Figure 1; Table 1). These samples were geographically well distrib-uted across Europe (Figure 2) and included remains whose morphology is typical of Neandertals (e.g., La Chapelle-aux-Saints) and of modern humans (La Madeleine, Cro-Magnon). They also included samples that have sometimes been considered "transitional" between Neandertals and modern humans, based on their morphological features: Vindija (Smith 1984) and Mladeč (Frayer 1986, 1992; Wolpoff 1999).

If low amounts of DNA are preserved in a specimen, some extracts will fail to contain DNA molecules by chance (Hofreiter et al. 2001a). Therefore, except in the case of Mladeč: 2, in which the amount of material available permitted only two extractions, we extracted each of the four Neandertal and the five early modern human samples three times. For each extraction, amplifications were performed using two primer pairs: (i) "hominoid primers" that amplify homologous mtDNA sequences from the previously determined Neandertals and contemporary modern humans, as well as African great apes; (ii) "Neandertal primers" that, under the conditions used, amplify only Neandertal mtDNAs even in the presence of a large excess of modern human DNA (Krings et al. 2000; Schmitz et al. 2002). Since authentic ancient DNA is typically highly degraded, both primer pairs

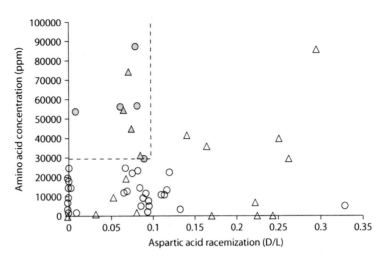

Figure 1. Amino Acid Analyses of 64 Hominid Remains

For each bone, the extent of aspartic acid racemization (D/L) and the amino acid concentration (ppm) is given. The dash lines delimit the area of amino acid preservation compatible with DNA retrieval. Circles and triangles represent early modern humans and Nean-dertals, respectively. The samples from which DNA extractions were performed are green (see also Table S1). DOI: 10.1371/journal.pbio.0020057.g001

were designed to amplify short mtDNA fragments (72 and 31 bp, respectively, excluding primers). In each of these fragments, two substitutions allow the discrimination of previously determined Neandertal mtDNA sequences from contemporary modern human sequences. The sensitivity of both primer pairs is similar, as shown by the fact that they are both able to amplify single template molecules as judged from

Table 1. DNA Retrieved from Late Pleistocene Fossils in This Study

SPECIMEN	Primers Used and Products Obtained[a]	
	"HOMINOID"	"NEANDERTAL"
Neandertal remains		
Vindija 77 (Vi-77) (Croatia)	3/3	2/3
Vindija 80 (Vi-80) (Croatia)	3/3	1/1[b]
Engis 2 (Belgium)	2/3	2/3
La Chapelle-aux-Saints (France)	**3/3**	2/3
Early modern human remains		
Mladč 25c (Czech Republic)	3/3	0/3
Mladč 2 (Czech Republic)	2/2	0/2
Cro-Magnon (France)	3/3	0/3
Abri Pataud (France)	3/3	0/3
La Madeleine (France)	2/3	0/3
Six cave bears	13/18	0/18

[a]For each specimen and primer pair, the number of amplifications yielding a specific product is given followed by the total number of amplification attempted.
[b]A single amplification using the indicated "Neandertal" primers was attempted. The sequence was confirmed by amplification of larger overlapping fragments (cf. Figure S1).
DOI: 10.1371/journal.pbio.0020057.t001

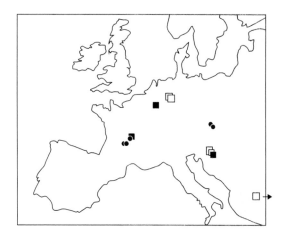

Figure 2. Geographical Origin of Neandertal and Early Modern Human Samples from Which mtDNA Sequences Have Been Analyzed

Filled squares and filled circles represent Neandertal and early modern human remains, respectively, analyzed in this study. The four Neandertal remains formerly analyzed are represented by empty squares.
DOI: 10.1371/journal.pbio.0020057.g002

nucleotide misincorporation patterns (Hofreiter et al. 2001a). In order to determine the nature of the DNA sequences amplified, each amplification product was cloned and approximately 30 clones were sequenced for each "hominoid product" and ten clones for each "Neandertal product."

When amplified with the hominoid primers, all Neandertal and all early modern human remains yielded modern human DNA sequences (see Table 1). In addition, five cave bear teeth from Vindija, Croatia, and one from Gamssulzen, Austria, extracted in parallel with the hominid samples, all yielded human sequences. This confirms previous results in showing that most, if not all, ancient remains yield human DNA sequences when amplification conditions that allow single DNA molecules to be detected are used (Hofreiter et al. 2001b). For three Neandertal and all five modern human remains, several different mtDNA sequences were retrieved from individual extractions, and in the case of one Neandertal and one modern human, at least two of the sequences were also found in an independent extraction from the same specimen. Additionally, one of the cave bear teeth yielded a human sequence found in two independent extracts. Thus, the fact that a DNA sequence is found in two independent extracts is a necessary, but not sufficient, criterion of authenticity when human remains are analyzed. This implies that in the absence of further technical improvements, it is impossible to produce undisputable human mtDNA sequences from ancient human remains. In addition to DNA sequences identical to those previously amplified from present-day humans, the Neandertal bones Vi-77 and Vi-80 from Vindija yielded four out of 89 and 73 out of 85 mtDNA sequences, respectively, that were identical to previously determined Neandertal sequences. Thus, these two specimens contain a proportion of Neandertal-like mtDNA sequences (i.e., sequences that carry two substitutions that differentiate Neandertal mtDNA sequences from modern human mtDNA sequences as described above) that is high enough to detect using primers that amplify also modern human DNA.

When amplified with Neandertal-specific primers, Neandertal-like mtDNA sequences were amplified from two independent extractions from all Neandertal fossils (see Table 1; Figure 3). For one of these, Vi-80 from Vindija, DNA preservation was sufficient to allow the retrieval of longer fragments and thus the reconstruction of 357 bp of the hypervariable region I (see Supporting Information section; Figure S1). This mtDNA sequence was identical to that retrieved from another bone from the same locality (Vi-75; Krings et al. 2000). In contrast to the Neandertal remains, none of the early modern human extracts yielded any amplification products with the Neandertal primers, although these remains are similar in chemical preservation to the Neandertal remains (see Figure 1).

Thus, all Neandertal remains analyzed yielded mtDNA sequences that are not found in the human mtDNA gene pool today but are similar to those found in four previously published Neandertals (Krings et al. 1997, 2000; Ovchinnikov et al. 2000; Schmitz et al. 2002) (see Figure 3). This is compatible with results suggesting that the extent of Neandertal mtDNA diversity was similar to that of current humans and lower than that of the great apes (Krings et al. 2000; Schmitz et al. 2002). It is noteworthy that this result is not an artifact created by discarding "modern-like" mtDNA sequences amplified from Neandertals (Trinkaus 2001), since all Neandertal remains with good biomolecular preservation yield "Neandertal-like" mtDNA sequence. Furthermore, none of the five early modern humans yields "Neandertal-like" mtDNA sequences in spite of the fact that these remains are as well preserved in terms of amino acids as the Neandertal remains. Thus, we fail to detect any evidence of mtDNA gene flow from Neandertals to early modern humans or from early modern humans to Neandertals.

However, a relevant question is what extent of gene flow between Neandertals and early modern humans the current data allow us to exclude. In this regard, it is of relevance that the five early modern humans analyzed lived much closer in time to the Neandertals than do contemporary individuals. The probability that mtDNA sequences potentially contributed to modern humans by Neandertals were lost by drift (Nordborg 1998) or swamped by continuous influx of modern human mtDNAs (Enflo et al. 2001) in the Neandertal gene pool is therefore much smaller than when contemporary humans are analyzed (e.g., Relethford 1999). In fact, the five early modern humans analyzed almost double the amount of information about the Upper Pleistocene mtDNA gene pool since, under a model of constant effective population size, all contemporary humans trace their mtDNA ancestors back to only four to seven mtDNA lineages 20,000 to 30,000 years ago (Figure 4A; Figure S2), while all other mtDNA sequences present in the gene pool at that time have been lost by random genetic drift. Since the probability is very low ($p < 0.007$) that one or more of the five early modern humans analyzed here are among these few ancestors of current humans, the five Upper Pleistocene individuals can be added to the ancestors of the current mtDNA gene pool to allow us to ask what extent of Neandertal mtDNA contribution to early modern humans can be statistically excluded using the coalescent. Under the model of a constant human effective population size (Tavare 1984; Nordborg 1998) of 10,000 over time (Figure 4A), any contribution of Neandertal mtDNA to modern humans 30,000 years ago larger than 25% can be excluded at the 5% level (Figure S3). A more realistic scenario may be that the spread of modern humans was accompanied by an increase in population size before and during their migration out of Africa and subsequent colonization of western Eurasia (see Figure 4B). In that case, the Neandertal contribution that can be excluded is smaller (i.e., less gene flow could have taken place), but that depends critically on when and how the expansion occurred. Finally, under the unlikely scenario that population size was constant during the migration out of Africa and colonization of Europe and expanded only after a putative merging with Neandertals, the Neandertal contribution could have been larger, but this also depends on the nature of the growth (see Figure 4C).

```
Cambridge Reference Sequence   TCACACATCAACTGCAACTCCAAAGCCACCC
Vi80                           ...T.........A............A.G...
Vi77                           ...T.........A............A.G...
Engis 2                        ...T.........A............A.....
La Chapelle-aux-Saints         ...T.........A............A.....

Feldhofer                      ...T.........A............A.G...
Mezmaiskaya                    ...T.........A............A.....
Vi75                           ...T.........A............A.G...
Feldhofer II                   ...T.........A............A.....
```

Figure 3. Sequences Obtained from the Neandertal Remains Using the "Neandertal Primers"

Dots indicate identity to the human reference sequence (Anderson et al. 1981) given above. The four upper DNA sequences were determined in this study. Previously determined DNA sequences are shown below.
DOI: 10.1371 journal.pbio.0020057.g003

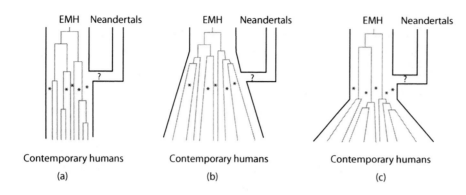

Figure 4. Schematic Model of Putative Contribution of Neandertal mtDNA to the Gene Pool of Modern Humans

(A) Under the assumption of a constant effective population size of 10,000 for modern humans, contemporary mtD-NAs trace back to approximately five mtDNA lineages 25,000 years ago. The modern human fossils represent five additional samples from around the time of putative admixture (stars). The contemporary and early modern human (EMH) samples reject a Neandertal contribution of 25% or more to modern humans about 30,000 years ago (p < 0.05).
(B) Under the more realistic scenario of an expansion of the human population during and after the colonization of Europe, a smaller Neandertal contribution can be excluded because the number of ancestors of the current human gene pool was larger 30,000 years ago. However, the contribution that can be excluded would depend on when and how the expansion occurred.
(C) Under the scenario that population size was constant before a putative merging with the Neandertal population and expanded only thereafter, the Neandertal contribution could have been larger, but similarly depends on how the expansion occurred.
DOI: 10.1371/journal.pbio.0020057.g004

CONCLUDING REMARKS

It is noteworthy that under the model of constant population size, about 50 early modern human remains would need to be studied to exclude a Neandertal mtDNA contribution of 10%. To exclude a 5% contribution, one would need to study more early modern human remains than have been discovered to date. Thus, definitive knowledge of the extent of a putative contribution of Neandertals to the modern human gene pool will not be possible, although extensive studies of variation in the current human gene pool may clarify this question (Wall 2000). It is, however, worthwhile to note that samples considered as anatomically ''transitional'' between modern humans and Neandertals, such as Vindija (Smith 1984; Wolpoff 1999) and Mladec (Frayer 1986, 1992; Wolpoff 1999), analyzed here, fail to show any evidence of mtDNA admixture between the two groups. Thus, while it cannot be excluded that Neandertals contributed variants at some genetic loci to contemporary humans, no positive evidence of any such contribution has yet been detected.

MATERIALS AND METHODS

Amino acid preservation. About 10 mg of bone were removed from each specimen and analyzed as in Schmitz et al. (2002) with minor modifications. In brief, proteins are hydrolyzed and amino acids labeled with *o*-phtaldialdehyde/*N*-acetyl-L-cysteine and analyzed by high performance liquid chromatography (Shimadzu, Kyoto, Japan) under conditions that separate the different amino acids as well as their stereoisomers. Eight amino acids are analyzed and their respective concentration measured: D- and I-alanine, glycine, D-and I-aspartic acid, serine, glutamic acid, valine, D- and I-leucine, and isoleucine.

DNA extraction and amplification. DNA extractions were performed in a laboratory dedicated to ancient DNA work. In this laboratory, positive air pressure is maintained with filtered air at all times, and all areas and equipment are treated with UV light when the laboratory is not used. A maximum of six bone or teeth samples were processed together with two blank extractions. Neandertal samples were always processed together with early modern human samples or cave bear samples. For each extraction, the samples were ground and between 30 mg and 120 mg of bone powder was extracted as in Krings et al. (1997). mtDNA sequences were amplified by polymerase chain reaction (PCR) using 5 µl of extract and 60 cycles. In addition, a minimum of four blank PCRs were performed together with each amplification from extracts. The "Neandertal-specific" amplification was carried out using the primers NL16230/NH16262 (Krings et al. 1997) and an annealing temperature of 60°C. We consider it highly unlikely that the Neandertal-specific mtDNA fragments represent contaminations from other Neandertals, given that none of the extracts of modern humans or cave bears processed in parallel with the Neandertal remains yielded such products. The "hominoid" amplification was performed with the primers L16022/ H16095 (Krings et al. 1997) and an annealing temperature of 54°C. PCR products were cloned into *Escherichia coli* using the TOPO TA cloning kit (Invitrogen, Leek, The Netherlands), and ten or 30 clones of each amplification were sequenced on a ABI 3700 (Applied Biosystems, Foster City, California, United States).

Estimation of admixture. Given that previous analyses of mtDNA sequences have rejected a model of complete panmixia between Neandertals and early modern humans (Nordborg 1998), we focused on the estimation of the level of admixture between Neandertals and early modern humans that can be excluded. For this purpose, we considered a population of early modern humans that merged at Tm with a (genetically different) population of Neandertal individuals (see Figure 4) from which point the fused population was panmictic. The probability of picking K individuals by chance in the merged population that all carry a modern human mtDNA sequence is $(1 - c)^K$, where c represents the Neandertal genetic contribution to the merged population. If none of n mtDNA sequences sampled in the merged population is Neandertal-like, we can exclude (at the 5% level) contributions that give a probability smaller than 0.05 of observing only modern human sequences, i.e., $(1 - c)^K < 0.05$. The number of ancestors of n samples at the time t is represented by a probability distribution, $An(t)$. Thus, the probability of observing only one kind of sequences in n samples becomes:

$$\mathrm{Pr(only\ human\ sequences\ observed)} = \Sigma(\mathrm{Pr}(An(t) - K) \times (1 - c)^K),$$

where K vary from 1 to n. For a population of constant size over time, $\mathrm{Pr}(An(t) = K)$ has been derived in Tavare (1984). We estimated the number of ancestors of n samples at time t as the expected value of $An(t)$, $E(An(t))$, according to this model and calculate the probability of observing only human sequences for different values of c.

SUPPORTING INFORMATION

Determination of the mtDNA Sequence of Vi-80 from Vindija, Croatia

The entire hypervariable region I sequence was determined from this specimen using amplifications and clones given in Figure S1. Its sequence is identical to the sequence previously determined from individual Vi-75 from Vindija (Krings et al. 2000). We could exclude cross-contamination from the old extract to this bone because different primers were used and some of the fragments of mtDNA amplified from Vi-80 were longer than those used to determine the sequence of Vi-75. Morphological analyses do not exclude that these two fragmentary bones (Vi-75 and Vi-80) may come from a single individual. Carbon-14 accelerator mass spectrometry dating, conducted in the Angstrom Laboratory (Uppsala University, Sweden), yielded a date for Vi-80 of 38,310 ± 2,130 BP (before present). Since Vi-75 has been previously dated to over 42,000 BP (Krings et al. 2000), the possibility exists that the dates overlap since 42,000 BP is within two standard deviations of the Vi-80 date. Therefore, the bone labeled Vi-80 that yields the new mtDNA sequence could either be (i) a fragment of the same skeleton (individual) that was already successfully extracted, (ii) a bone from another individual maternally related to the first individual amplified, or (iii) another unrelated individual having by chance the same mtDNA sequence, which is not unlikely given the apparently low mtDNA diversity of Neandertals (Krings et al. 2000; Schmitz et al. 2002).

Figure S1. The DNA Sequences of the Clones Used to Reconstruct the Sequence of the Mitochondrial Hypervariable Region I from the Bone Vi-80

Found at DOI: 10.1371/journal.pbio.0020057.sg001 (30 KB PDF).

Figure S2. Expected Number of Ancestors $E(An(t))$ of n Individuals under a Model of Constant Population Size of Ne = 10,000

The number of ancestors of n individuals (x axis) is estimated at 20,000, 25,000, and 30,000 years ago. For example, 150 humans living today have approximately seven ancestors 20,000 years ago.

Found at DOI: 10.1371/journal.pbio.0020057.sg002 (56 KB PDF).

Figure S3. Probability of Different Levels of Admixture

Probability of observing only modern human mtDNA sequences in both five early human remains and the current mtDNA gene pool given different proportion of Neandertal contribution c (x axis) under a model of constant population size (see text; Materials and Methods). For example, the probability of observing only human mtDNA sequences given a Neandertal contribution of 25% or more is smaller than 0.05 (dotted line).

Found at DOI: 10.1371/journal.pbio.0020057.sg003 (42 KB PDF).

Table S1. Results of the Amino Acid Analyses of 40 Human and 24 Neandertal Remains

The bones were analyzed by high performance liquid chromatography for their amino acid content (see Materials and Methods). The extent of racemization of aspartic acid (D-/L-Asp), the ratio of glycine to aspartic acid (Gly/Asp), and the total amount of the eight amino acid analyzed (ppm) are given for each specimen. Zero indicates values below detection level. The five human and four Neandertal specimens from which DNA extraction were performed are displayed in green.

Found at DOI: 10.1371/journal.pbio.0020057.st001 (54 KB PDF).

ACKNOWLEDGMENTS

We are indebted to J.-J. Hublin, M. Nordborg, M. Przeworski, M. Stoneking, and L. Vigilant for helpful discussions and comments; to the many persons and institutions that allowed access to fossils; and to the Max Planck Gesellschaft and the Deutsche Forschungsgemein-schaft for financial support.

Conflicts of interest. The authors have declared that no conflicts of interest exist.

Author contributions. DS and SP conceived and designed the experiments. DS, MH, and GP performed the experiments. DS, GP, and SP analyzed the data. AL, MC, MT-N, MP, and PM contributed reagents/materials/analysis tools. DS, AL, and SP wrote the paper.

REFERENCES

Abbott A (2003) Anthropologists cast doubt on human DNA evidence. Nature 423: 468.

Adcock GJ, Dennis ES, Easteal S, Huttley GA, Jermiin LS, et al. (2001) Mitochondrial DNA sequences in ancient Australians: Implications for modern human origins. Proc Natl Acad Sci U S A 98: 537-542.

Anderson S, Bankier AT, Barrell BG, de Bruijn MH, Coulson AR, et al. (1981) Sequence and organization of the human mitochondrial genome. Nature 290: 457-465.

Cann RL, Stoneking M, Wilson AC (1987) Mitochondrial DNA and human evolution. Nature 325: 31-36.

Caramelli D, Lalueza-Fox C, Vernesi C, Lari M, Casoli A, et al. (2003) Evidence for a genetic discontinuity between Neandertals and 24,000-year-old anatomically modern Europeans. Proc Natl Acad Sci U S A 100: 6593-6597.

Duarte C, Mauricio J, Pettitt PB, Souto P, Trinkaus E, et al. (1999) The early Upper Paleolithic human skeleton from the Abrigo do Lagar Velho (Portugal) and modern human emergence in Iberia. Proc Natl Acad Sci U S A 96: 7604-7609.

Enflo P, Hawks K, Wolpoff M (2001) A simple reason why Neanderthal ancestry can be consistent with current DNA information. Am J Phys Anthropol 114: 62.

Frayer DW (1986) Cranial variation at Mladeic and the relationship between Mousterian and Upper Paleolithic hominids. Anthropos 23: 243-256.

Frayer DW (1992) Evolution at the European edge: Neanderthal and Upper Paleolithic relationships. Prehist Europeenne 2: 9-69.

Hawks JD, Wolpoff MH (2001) The accretion model of Neandertal evolution. Evol Int J Org Evol 55: 1474-1485.

Hofreiter M, Jaenicke V, Serre D, von Haeseler A, Paabo S (2001a) DNA sequences from multiple amplifications reveal artifacts induced by cytosine deamination in ancient DNA. Nucleic Acids Res 29: 4793-4799.

Hofreiter M, Serre D, Poinar HN, Kuch M, Paabo S (2001b) Ancient DNA. Nat Rev Genet 2: 353-359.

Ingman M, Kaessmann H, Paabo S, Gyllensten U (2000) Mitochondrial genome variation and the origin of modern humans. Nature 408: 708-713.

Knight A (2003) The phylogenetic relationship of Neandertal and modern human mitochondrial DNAs based on informative nucleotide sites. J Hum Evol 44: 627-632.

Krings M, Stone A, Schmitz RW, Krainitzki H, Stoneking M, et al. (1997) Neandertal DNA sequences and the origin of modern humans. Cell 90: 1930.

Krings M, Capelli C, Tschentscher F, Geisert H, Meyer S, et al. (2000) A view of Neandertal genetic diversity. Nat Genet 26: 144-146.

Nordborg M (1998) On the probability of Neanderthal ancestry. Am J Hum Genet 63: 1237-1240.

Ovchinnikov IV, Gotherstrom A, Romanova GP, Kharitonov VM, Liden K, et al. (2000) Molecular analysis of Neanderthal DNA from the northern Caucasus. Nature 404: 490-493.

Poinar HN, Htoss M, Bada JL, Paabo S (1996) Amino acid racemization and the preservation of ancient DNA. Science 272: 864-866.

Relethford JH (1999) Models, predictions, and the fossil record of modern human origins. Evol Anthropol 8: 7-10.

Schmitz RW, Serre D, Bonani G, Feine S, Hillgruber F, et al. (2002) The Neandertal type site revisited: Interdisciplinary investigations of skeletal remains from the Neander Valley, Germany. Proc Natl Acad Sci U S A 99: 13342-13347.

Smith FH (1984) Fossil hominids from the Upper Pleistocene of Central Europe and the origin of modern Europeans. In: Spencer F, editor. The origins of modern humans: A world survey of the fossil evidence. New York: Alan R. Liss. pp. 137-210.

Stringer C (2002) Modern human origins: Progress and prospects. Philos Trans R Soc Lond B Biol Sci 357: 563-579.

Stringer CB, Andrews P (1988) Genetic and fossil evidence for the origin of modern humans. Science 239: 1263-1268.

Tavare S (1984) Line-of-descent and genealogical processes, and their applications in population genetics models. Theor Popul Biol 26: 119-164.

Trinkaus E (2001) The Neandertal paradox. In: Finlayson C, editor. Neanderthals and modern humans in late Pleistocene Eurasia. Gibraltar: The Gibraltar Museum. pp. 73-74.

Underhill PA, Shen P, Lin AA, Jin L, Passarino G, et al. (2000) Y chromosome sequence variation and the history of human populations. Nat Genet 26: 358-361.

Wall J (2000) Detecting ancient admixture in humans using sequence polymorphism data. Genetics 154: 1271-1279.

Wandeler P, Smith S, Morin PA, Pettifor RA, Funk SM (2003) Patterns of nuclear DNA degeneration over time: A case study in historic teeth samples. Mol Ecol 12: 1087-1093.

Weidenreich F (1943) The "Neanderthal man" and the ancestors of "Homo sapiens." Am Anthropologist 45: 39-48.

Wolpoff MH (1999) Paleoanthropology. Boston: McGraw-Hill. 936 p.

Wolpoff M, Wu X, Thorne AG (1984) Modern Homo sapiens origins: A general theory of hominid evolution involving the fossil evidence from East Asia. In: Spencer F, editor. The origins of modern humans: A world survey of the fossil evidence. New York: Alan R. Liss. pp. 411-483.

Wolpoff MH, Hawks J, Caspari R (2000) Multiregional, not multiple origins. Am J Phys Anthropol 112: 129-136.

█ Neanderthal anatomical features are examined, and concluded to result in large part from their evolutionary history, their adaptation to the environmental conditions peculiar to glacial Eurasia, and the high activity levels inherent in their rigorous way of life.

24. The Meaning of Neandertal Skeletal Morphology

By Timothy D. Weaver[1]

Since the discovery of Neandertals in 1856 at the Kleine Feldhofer Grotte in the Neander Valley near Düsseldorf, Germany (1), deciphering the meaning of Neandertal skeletal morphology has fascinated scientists and the public alike. According to some early proposals, Neandertal skeletons were simply pathological modern human skeletons, but as more fossils accumulated with a consistent set of morphological features these explanations became untenable (2, 3). Although pathology cannot explain Neandertal skeletal morphology in general, pathological lesions, particularly healed traumatic injuries, are frequent on Neandertal skeletons (4).

Current evidence suggests that Neandertals last shared a common ancestor with modern humans >350,000 years ago (5–7), and fossils that are certainly classified as Neandertals are present in the fossil record by ≈130,000 years ago (8, 9) and persist until <35,000 years ago (10, 11). Separate Neandertal and modern human lineages perhaps emerged when geographic barriers produced by climate fluctuations isolated Neandertal populations in Europe from modern human populations further south (8, 12). Although Neandertals originated in Europe they later extended their geographic range into western and central Asia, ranging as far south as Israel and perhaps as far east as southern Siberia (8, 13).

Timothy D. Weaver, "The Meaning of Neandertal Skeletal Morphology," *PNAS*, vol. 106, no. 38, pp. 16028–16033. Copyright © 2009 by National Academy of Sciences. Reprinted with permission.

My purpose is to present current views on the meaning of Neandertal skeletal morphology. Instead of a giving comprehensive review, I concentrate on aspects of Neandertal cranial and post-cranial morphology that have been studied extensively using a variety of different approaches. I begin by outlining a procedure for distinguishing among competing hypotheses for fossil morphology.

DISTINGUISHING AMONG COMPETING EXPLANATIONS

The morphology of fossil skeletons, like any aspect of the phenotype, is the product of genetic influences, environmental influences, and often interactions between the two (14). Genetic influences on skeletal morphology are ultimately the result of the adaptive (i.e., natural selection) or neutral (i.e., mutation, gene flow, genetic drift) evolutionary forces that have shaped allele frequencies in a population or species over multiple generations. There are many possible environmental influences on the phenotype (14), but dietary, locomotor, or manipulative behaviors that shape skeletal form through the mechanical loading patterns they produce over the lifetime of an individual are of particular interest to investigations of ancient skeletons (15). Therefore, the task of deciphering the meaning of Neandertal skeletal morphology can be encapsulated as finding ways to infer the evolutionary and lifetime behavioral causes of Neandertal skeletal features. This task is not straightforward, and, even when it is possible to determine whether genetic or environmental influences are primarily responsible for variation among individuals, populations, or species for a particular skeletal trait, it is still necessary to decide among competing evolutionary or lifetime behavioral explanations. With this in mind, I outline a procedure for going from a description of fossil morphology to its meaning.

Lifetime Behavior vs. Evolution

Traits produced by lifetime behaviors should typically be found on the skeletons of adults, possibly older subadults, but not the skeletons of very young individuals. Individuals so young that they have not yet done certain behaviors would not be expected to show traits that result from the mechanical loading produced by actually doing a behavior. This argument is certainly relevant to the foraging, manipulative, or mobility activities that have been proposed to explain certain Neandertal traits (16, 17). Therefore, if a trait is present on the skeletons of young Neandertals, it must either have an evolutionary explanation (i.e., be due to genetic differences shaped by natural selection or neutral evolutionary forces) or result from environmental influences unrelated to adult behaviors. An improved understanding of development often cannot help with distinguishing among possible evolutionary explanations, because neutral evolutionary forces or different natural selective pressures can act through similar developmental shifts (18), but it can help with deciding whether an evolutionary explanation is warranted or not.

Controlled experiments on laboratory animals are another way to distinguish between lifetime behavioral and evolutionary explanations for morphology (19, 20). Because it is possible in the laboratory to control many variables other than the ones of interest, the results of laboratory experiments can often be interpreted unambiguously. However, it is important to be cautious when extending laboratory results outside the realm of the experiment. It is well known that the sources of variation within and between groups and for different sets of groups can be quite different (21). This means, for example, that variation in a feature could be mostly due to environmental effects for the laboratory animals within the context of the experiment, but genetic effects could be responsible for variation in the feature between different groups of the same species or between different species. The central issue is that, although interpretation of the experimental results is straightforward, determining their applicability to understanding extinct species, such as Neandertals, is more difficult.

Single Features vs. Complexes of Features.

If features vary together because of genetic, developmental, or functional links, then explaining one of them may be sufficient to explain them all. Ideally, we would like to be able to estimate the covariance among features directly from fossil specimens, but a much larger and less fragmentary Neandertal sample would be necessary to robustly estimate covariance patterns. Even so, arguments that 2 features form a complex would be weakened by finding fossil specimens that have one of the features but not the other. However, consistently finding a set of

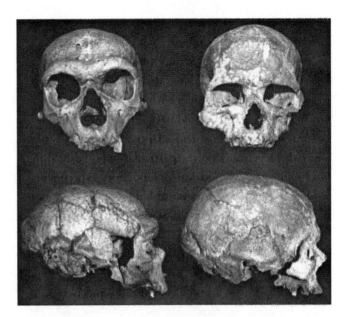

Fig. 1. Neandertal and modern human cranial differences. On the left is a Neandertal (La Chapelleaux-Saints). On the right is a modern human (Cro-Magnon 1). Anterior (above) and lateral (below) views. Photos courtesy of Chris Stringer and the Musée de l'Homme (Paris).

features together does not demonstrate that they all have the same explanation, because individuals of a species will share features simply due to shared ancestry, even if the features are genetically, developmentally, and functionally unlinked.

An alternative to directly estimating covariance patterns from fossils is to study extant species, with the implicit assumption that they have similar covariance patterns to the fossil species of interest. Covariance patterns are similar across human populations (22), and although there are some important differences, African apes and humans have broadly similar covariance patterns (23– 25). The sum suggests that it is reasonable to assume that Neandertals would have had similar covariance patterns to humans, at least for most features. Most important for evolutionary explanations is the within-group additive genetic covariance matrix, which can often be approximated by the within-group phenotypic covariance matrix (26, 27). Within-group additive genetic covariance is what constrains the response to natural selection or the direction of change by genetic drift (28). Within-individual covariance patterns (fluctuating asymmetry) can give insights into the covariance caused by developmental interactions (29). Analyses that combine among- and within-group variation within a species may identify covariance patterns that are not readily apparent from analyses of individual groups (30), but these associations should be interpreted cautiously, because they could be due to population history or phylogeny rather than genetic, developmental, or functional links.

Evolutionary Explanations

If an evolutionary explanation is warranted, the final step is to distinguish among possible hypotheses. One approach is to investigate whether there is an empirical relationship between the morphological feature of interest and a potential selective factor (e.g., temperature, humidity, locomotor behavior, etc.) in one or more extant species. If so, then perhaps the same relationship explains patterns of variation for the feature in the fossil record. This approach implicitly assumes that whatever factors lead to a relation-ship in the extant species are also important for the extinct species, and consequently, is most robust when similar relationships are found for multiple populations or species.

A second approach is to evaluate whether the form of the feature, or complex of features, observed in fossil specimens is consistent with its purported function. This approach does not attempt to directly model how natural selection would have acted; it simply evaluates the internal consistency of an adaptive hypothesis. An internally consistent adaptive hypothesis is not necessarily correct, but an inconsistent one can be rejected. Depending on the particular hypothesis, different approaches can be taken to assess consistency, but biomechanical modeling or laboratory experiments are often used (31).

Third, it is sometimes possible to distinguish among different evolutionary explanations by explicitly modeling evolutionary forces with quantitative and population genetics (18, 32). This modeling can be used to evaluate the importance of genetic drift vs. natural selection or the fit of different selective hypotheses with observed data. A strength this approach is that the dynamics of the evolutionary process are quantitatively incorporated into the testing of hypotheses (33). This additional level of quantification requires hypotheses to be specified more precisely, which can sometimes be difficult, but, in principle, it allows for more rigorous tests.

Finally, the patterning of traits in the fossil record can be used to evaluate competing evolutionary explanations. The value of this final approach and the previous one would increase substantially if we knew more about how evolutionary forces typically act over hundreds to thousands of generations.

NEANDERTAL CRANIAL MORPHOLOGY

Numerous metric and nonmetric features typically distinguish the crania and mandibles of Neandertals from those of modern humans (30, 34 –38) (Fig. 1, Table 1). Table 1 lists both uniquely derived (autapomorphic) and primitive (symplesiomorphic) features, because both need to be explained. The appearance of derived features in the fossil record can point to the action of directional natural selection or genetic drift, and the retention of primitive features can indicate stabilizing natural selection.

Lifetime Behavior vs. Evolution

Many distinctive Neandertal cranial features are present on the skeletons of very young individuals, suggesting that they are not the result of mechanical loading patterns produced by lifetime behaviors. Of particular interest are the features present on 2 well-preserved neonatal skeletons from Mezmaiskaya, Russian Federation and Le Moustier, France. The Neandertal features found on the Mezmaiskaya specimen include an overall cranial shape similar to that of other Neandertals, an elongated foramen magnum, a projecting midface, an inferiorly positioned posterior semicircular canal, and an inferiorly positioned mandibular condyle (39, 40). Those on Le Moustier 2 include the absence of an infraorbital concavity and nasal bones shaped like those of adult Neandertals (41). The slightly older Amud 7 skeleton from Israel also shows Neandertal cranial features, including the absence of a mental eminence, an oval foramen magnum, and an enlarged medial ptery-goid tubercle (42). The general impression from these skeletons of very young Neandertals, along with studies of older subadults (43), is that most Neandertal cranial features are present very early in development and, consequently, appear to warrant evolutionary rather than lifetime behavioral explanations. It should be pointed out, however, that most studies of subadult Neandertals have tended to focus on the Neandertal features that are present rather than providing a

Table 1. Selected Neandertal cranial features

ANATOMICAL REGION	FEATURES
Cranial vault	Receding frontal squama
	Long, low braincase, sometimes with a posteriorly bulging occipital ("bun")
	Globular ("en-bombe") braincase when viewed from behind
	Occipital torus with a suprainiac fossa above it
Cranial base	Fairly unflexed ectobasicranium
	Large juxtamastoid eminence and relatively small mastoid process
	Tubercle on mastoid process adjacent to the external auditory meatus
	Anteroposteriorly elongated foramen magnum
Acoustic cavities	Large lateral, small anterior, and small and inferiorly positioned posterior semicircular canal
Facial skeleton	Pronounced, double-arched supraorbital torus
	Projecting midface
	Minimally angled zygomatic bone
	Absence of infraorbital concavity and canine fossa
	Wide, tall nasal aperture
	Wide, projecting nasal bridge
	Depressed nasal floor
Mandible	Retromolar space
	Inferiorly positioned and laterally expanded condyle
	Asymmetric sigmoid notch
	Large coronoid process
	Horizontal-oval mandibular foramen
	Large medial pterygoid tubercle
	Absence of mental eminence

systematic assessment of the percentages of present vs. absent features, which may give the impression that young Neandertals look more like adult Neandertals than they actually do.

Although many cranial differences between Neandertals and modern humans are likely due to different allele frequencies at loci underlying cranial form, there is some experimental evidence that lifetime behavior differences, specifically which foods are eaten, can influence cranial form. For example, Lieberman and colleagues (20) performed laboratory experiments on rock hyraxes to investigate the effects of food processing on cranial growth and form. The maxillary molars of rock hyraxes are positioned directly be-neath or behind the orbits as in humans, which may make them more appropriate models for human mechanical loading patterns than more prognathic nonhuman primates (20). The hyraxes were divided into 2 groups of 4 animals each. One group was fed cooked food, whereas the other was fed raw/dry food. The animals raised on cooked food showed ≈10% less growth for some facial dimensions, suggesting that diet, and perhaps other behaviors, may influence facial size (20). These results are intriguing, but unless the animals in the 2 treatment groups were specifically selected to be siblings, they could reflect genetic differences between treatment groups rather than diet. Al-though differences in diet do not appear to explain most cranial differences between Neandertals and contemporaneous modern humans, they could explain why the crania of Pleistocene modern humans tend to be more robust than those of Holocene humans (19, 20).

Single Features vs. Complexes of Features

On the one hand, studies of extant species have consistently demonstrated substantial integration of cranial features (31). On the other hand, the fossil record shows a certain degree of independence for the cranial features typically found in Neandertals. For example, European fossils >130,000 years old exhibit some but not all Neandertal features (8), which is not the expected pattern if all Neandertal features were part of an integrated package. This point is illustrated nicely with specimens from the Sima de los Huesos, Spain. Fossils from this site have prognathic midfaces like Neandertals and some of the associated morphological features, but they lack cranial base traits such as the mastoid tubercle or a large juxtamastoid eminence coupled with a relatively small mastoid process (44). They also lack some cranial vault traits, such as a globular shape when viewed from behind, but display others, such as an incipient suprainiac fossa (44).

Evolutionary Explanations

Three main evolutionary explanations have been proposed for Neandertal cranial morphology: adaptation to cold climates, adaptation to anterior dental loading, or genetic drift. The cold-climate hypothesis is based on the observation that the geographic range of Neandertals was centered quite far north in Europe, and except for brief warm periods, global climates were substantially cooler when Neandertals were evolving than they are today. Neandertals clearly experienced fairly cold temperatures, but this does not require that their cranial features are adaptations to these climatic conditions. Most climatic hypotheses for Neandertal cranial form focus on the nasal region and how other facial features may result from adaptations in this region (30, 36, 45, 46).

Studies by Franciscus (36) of internal nasal dimensions and Holton and Franciscus (30) of external ones fail to support adaptation to cold climates as the primary explanation for Neandertal facial morphology. The depressed nasal floors often found in Neandertals are most common in recent humans from subSaharan Africa (36). Likewise, wide nasal apertures, which characterize Neandertals, are most frequently found in equatorial recent humans (30). Al-though the Neandertal nasal region, in general, does not appear to be an adaptation to cold climates, the narrow superior internal nasal dimensions, tall nasal apertures, and project-ing nasal bridges of Neandertals could be, because these features are typically found in high-latitude recent humans (30). If Neandertals were adapting to the cold similarly to present-day humans, then climatic adaptation is an unlikely explanation for their cranial form.

Neandertals tend to have more worn anterior teeth than posterior ones, and their anterior teeth show a high incidence of enamel chipping, microfractures, and microstriations on the labial surfaces. Taken together, these signatures of anterior tooth use suggest that Neandertals were using their mouths like a vise. The anterior dental loading hypothesis extends this idea by proposing that Neandertal facial form, and perhaps other cranial features, are adaptations to dissipate the high mechanical loads produced by this behavior (47–52). Because Neandertal facial features appear early in development, they cannot be direct mechanical responses to anterior dental loading. They would have to be adaptations produced by natural selection after the species consistently performed this behavior for multiple generations.

One problem with the anterior dental loading hypothesis is that biomechanical modeling suggests that Neandertals were not able to produce particularly high bite forces (53, 54). Neandertal cranial form cannot be adapted to resisting high bite forces if Neandertals were incapable of producing them in the first place. O'Connor and colleagues (54) showed that, although Neandertals would have been able to produce fairly high bite forces in absolute magnitude, their bite forces would not have been unusually large for the size of their crania. Additionally, if efficiency is quantified as the ratio of bite force to muscle force, Neandertals were actually less efficient than many modern humans (54).

Table 2. Selected Neandertal postcranial features

ANATOMICAL REGION	FEATURES
General	Wide bodies with short extremities, particularly the distal limb segments
	Long bones tend to have bowed shafts and thick cortical bone
	Postcranial bones tend to be robust with rugose muscle attachments
Axial skeleton	Horizontal lower cervical spinous processes
	Robust, rounded rib shafts
Upper extremity	Long clavicle
	Wide scapula with narrow glenoid fossa and dorsal axillary sulcus
	Humerus with wide olecranon fossa and narrow surrounding dorsodistal pillars
	Ulna with high and long olecranon process and anteriorly oriented trochlear notch
	Radius with medially directed tuberosity and long neck
	Trapezium with flat first metacarpal facet
	Hamate with large hamulus
	Third metacarpal with short styloid process
	Subequal proximal and distal thumb phalanges
	Large hand distal phalangeal tubercles
Lower extremity	Wide pelvis with long, thin superior pubic ramus
	Femur with large articulations, rounded midshaft lacking a pilaster, and low neck-shaft angle
	Tibia with projecting tuberosity and absence of diaphyseal concavities
	Relatively symmetrical medial and lateral patellar facets
	Large foot distal phalangeal tubercles

Neandertal and modern human populations seem to have became isolated from each other >350,000 years ago (5–7). When this occurred, Neandertals and modern humans would have diverged from each other even in the absence of natural selection through the random fluctuations in allele frequencies that happen in all real populations (i.e., populations that are not infinite in size). This process of genetic drift could explain Neandertal cranial features. My colleagues and I (18) tested this hypothesis using predictions from quantitative and population genetics with a sample of 37 cranial measurements collected on 20 Neandertal specimens and 2,524 recent humans, and we were unable to reject it with multiple statistical tests. Subsequently, calibrated on the rate of cranial divergence among recent human populations, we estimated that Neandertals and modern humans diverged ≈311,000 years ago or ≈435,000 years ago, depending on assumptions about within-group variation (7). These split dates match quite closely with those derived from ancient Neandertal and extant human DNA sequences, which is the expected result if genetic drift were responsible for the cranial divergence.

Additional support for the genetic drift hypothesis comes from the fossil record. Neandertal features do not appear all at once. In fact, they seem to gradually accumulate over a period of >300,000 years (8). A similar pattern may characterize the appearance of modern human features (55), but the dating and more fragmentary nature of the African fossil record allows for other interpretations. This "accretion" of Neandertal features is exactly the expected pattern if genetic drift were responsible, and it seems less compatible with existing adaptive hypotheses such as climatic adaptation or anterior dental loading.

NEANDERTAL POSTCRANIAL MORPHOLOGY

The postcranial anatomy of Neandertals, like their cranial anatomy, distinguishes them from modern humans (34, 38, 56– 59) (Table 2). As with Table 1 for cranial features, Table 2 includes both primitive and derived postcranial features.

Lifetime Behavior vs. Evolution

At least some Neandertal postcranial features are present on Neandertal fossils from individuals <1 year of age. For example, Mezmaiskaya has a femoral diaphysis that is long relative to the tibial diaphysis, bowed long bones, a long superior pubic ramus of the pelvis, a medially directed radial tuberosity, and a fairly robust skeleton (39, 40). Additionally, Amud 7 has a long clavicle (60), and the Kiik-Koba 2 individual from the Crimea, thought to be ≈3–7 months old, has an incipient scapular dorsal axillary sulcus (61) and an opponens pollicis flange on the first metacarpal (56). However, some Neandertal postcranial features only appear later in development, including the thinness of the superior pubic ramus (62) and thick long-bone cortices (60, 63).

Numerous studies of laboratory animals, human growth series, and biomechanical models indicate that long bone cortical thickness reflects, at least in part, mechanical loading produced by locomotion and other behaviors (15, 64). These results are consistent across a variety of studies, making it likely that mechanical loading history explains a significant portion of the variation in cortical bone thickness between Neandertals and modern humans, but it is possible that at least some differences are due to genetic influences.

Single Features or Complexes of Features

One of the foremost postcranial contrasts between Neandertals and early modern humans is in body proportions. Specifically, Neandertals have a wide pelvis, short limbs relative to trunk height, and short distal limb segments, whereas early modern humans have narrower bodies with relatively longer limbs (45, 57, 58, 65–69). These contrasts in body proportions have lead multiple researchers to propose that other postcranial differences between Neandertals and modern humans are simply secondary consequences of differences in body proportions. If this proposal is correct, an explanation for Neandertal body proportions could account for many other postcranial features as well. There are few fossil individuals that preserve a large fraction of their postcranial skeleton, so, unlike the situation with cranial features, covariance patterns among postcranial features are difficult to investigate directly with the fossil record. Consequently, I focus on studies of covariance patterns based primarily on recent human samples.

Churchill (70) investigated whether upper body features typically found in Neandertals could be explained as secondary consequences of upper body size, chest shape, and robusticity. He found fairly weak correlations between upper body variables. Although a model of upper body integration fit the data better than one with no integration, the integration model explained less than half of the variance in upper body morphology. Based on these results, Churchill (70) concluded that it was unlikely that an overarching causal factor, such as body proportions, could explain Neandertal upper body morphology. This interpretation is reasonable, but it is important to note that only a fraction of the unexplained variance is likely to be the result of lifetime behavioral or evolutionary causes. Some proportion of phenotypic variance will always be due to genetic variation among individuals, microenvironmental variation, random developmental perturbations, and measurement error (14). If the variance due to these factors were to be partitioned out, the percentage of the remaining variance explained by the integration model might be quite high.

In a study of the entire postcranial skeleton, Pearson (69) found that articular size and long bone shaft thickness relative to bone length is closely related to body pro-portions. Focusing more narrowly on the hip region, I (71) found that a wide pelvis relative to femur length was associated with femora with large articulations, thick and round midshafts shafts, and low neck-shaft angles. Neandertals typically have large articulations, thick shafts, and femora with round midshafts and low neck-shaft angles, so based on the results of these 2 studies, it is plausible that many Neandertal postcranial features are best explained as secondary consequences of their body proportions. Furthermore, a wide pelvis coupled with the maintenance of a transversely oval outlet of the birth canal may explain additional Neandertal pelvic features, including why both sexes have similar superior pubic ramus lengths (72).

Evolutionary and Lifetime Behavioral Explanations

Two main evolutionary explanations have been proposed for Neandertal postcranial morphology: adaptation to cold climates or activity patterns (either lifetime behavioral response or evolutionary adaptation). In recent humans (65–67), as in other endothermic species (73, 74), body proportions like those of Neandertals are characteristic of individuals with ancestry in cold climates. Individuals with ancestry in warm climates, in contrast, tend to have similar body proportions to the earliest modern humans (68). These robust empirical patterns suggest that Neandertal body proportions, and the covarying features discussed in the previous section, reflect adaptation to the cold climates of Pleistocene Eurasia.

The climate hypothesis is further supported by laboratory experiments. For example, Tilkens and colleagues (75) showed that human subjects with long legs relative to body mass had higher resting metabolic rates than individuals with relatively shorter limbs when sitting in an ≈22°C room wearing shorts and a T-shirt. These experiments demonstrate that individuals with "warm adapted" body proportions need to expend more energy to prevent their body temperatures from dropping due to heat loss.

It could be argued that the early *Homo* pelvis from Gona, Ethiopia refutes the climate hypothesis, because it may demonstrate that a wide pelvis was the primitive condition for the genus *Homo* (76). However, showing that a morphological feature is primitive for a taxonomic group does not explain why this feature persists in some descendant taxa and not others. Even if a wide pelvis was unrelated to climate in early *Homo*, climate adaptation is still the best explanation for why Neandertals maintained a wide pelvis, early modern humans living closer to the equator evolved a narrow pelvis, and recent humans who migrated to cold climates regained a wide pelvis.

Although climatic adaptation may explain Neandertal body proportions and other morphological features of their postcranium, activity patterns could be responsible for at least some postcranial features, because, as discussed above, numerous studies indicate that long bone cortical thickness reflects mechanical loading from locomotion and other behaviors. As with the cranium, activity levels may also explain why Pleistocene modern humans tend to have more robust postcrania than Holocene humans (15, 58).

CONCLUSIONS

Deciphering the meaning of Neandertal skeletal morphology is a complex endeavor that starts with determining whether a morphological feature is best considered to result from lifetime behaviors or, alternatively, from alleles passed from parents to offspring that were previously shaped by evolutionary forces. It continues with investigations of whether a feature is best explained in isolation or as part of a complex of features. It concludes with evaluating competing hypotheses using empirical studies of extant species, tests of form vs. function, modeling based on quantitative and population genetics, and documenting the patterning of features in the fossil record.

Currently, the best explanation for many Neandertal cranial features is divergence by genetic drift that began when Neandertal and modern human populations became isolated from each other >350,000 years ago. This explanation is supported by modeling based on quantitative and population genetics and the "accretional" appearance of Neandertal features in the fossil record. Neandertal body proportions, and likely other postcranial features, appear to be adaptations, or secondary consequences of adaptations, to the typically cold climates of Pleistocene Eurasia. However, for both the cranium and the postcranium, changes in diet or activity patterns may explain some features, and in particular, could underlie why Neandertals and Pleistocene modern humans are more robust than Holocene humans.

ACKNOWLEDGMENTS

I thank Richard Klein and David Stopak for inviting me to contribute to the special feature on "Out of Africa: Modern Human Origins"; Chris Stringer and the Musée de l'Homme (Paris) for the photos for Fig. 1; and Jean-Jacques Hublin, Teresa Steele and 2 anonymous reviewers for helpful feedback.

1. Schaaffhausen H (1857) Brief communication (Translated from German). *Verhandlungen des Naturhistorischen Vereins der Preussischen Rheinlande und Westfalens* 14:50–52.

2. Stringer CB, Gamble C (1993) *In Search of the Nean-derthals: Solving the Puzzle of Human Origins* (Thames and Hudson, New York).

3. Trinkaus E, Shipman P (1992) *The Neandertals: Of Skeletons, Scientists, and Scandal* (Random House, New York).

4. Berger T, Trinkaus E (1995) Patterns of trauma among the Neandertals. *J Archaeol Sci* 22:841–852.

5. Stringer CB, Hublin J-J (1999) New age estimates for the Swanscombe hominid, and their significance for human evolution. *J Hum Evol* 37:873–877.

6. Noonan JP, et al. (2006) Sequencing and analysis of Neanderthal genomic DNA. *Science* 314:1113–1118.

7. Weaver TD, Roseman CC, Stringer CB (2008) Close correspondence between quantitative- and molecular-genetic divergence times for Neandertals and modern humans. *Proc Natl Acad Sci USA* 105:4645–4649.

8. Hublin J-J (1998) In *Neandertals and Modern Humans in Western Asia*, eds Akazawa T, Aoki K, Bar-Yosef O (Plenum, New York), pp 295–310.

9. Rink WJ, Schwarcz HP, Smith FH, Radovcic J (1995) ESR ages for Krapina hominids. *Nature* 378:24.

10. Hublin J-J, Barroso Ruiz C, Medina Lara P, Fontugne M, Reyss J-L (1995) The Mousterian site of Zafarraya (Andalucia, Spain): Dating and implications on the Palaeolithic peopling processes of Western Europe. *Comptes Rendus de l'Academie des Sciences Paris* 321:931–937.

11. Higham T, Bronk Ramsey C, Karavanic I, Smith FH, Trinkaus E (2006) Revised direct radiocarbon dating of the Vindija G_1 Upper Paleolithic Neandertals. *Proc Natl Acad Sci USA* 103:553–557.

12. Howell FC (1952) Pleistocene glacial ecology and the evolution of "classic Neandertal man." *Southwestern J Anthropol* 8:377–410.

13. Krause J, et al. (2007) Neanderthals in central Asia and Siberia. *Nature* 449:902–904.

14. Lynch M, Walsh B (1998) *Genetics and Analysis of Quantitative Traits* (Sinauer, Sutherland, MA).

15. Ruff CB (2000) In *Biological Anthropology of the Human Skeleton*, eds Katzenberg MA, Saunders SR (Wiley-Liss, New York), 2nd Ed, pp 71–102.

16. Trinkaus E (1997) Appendicular robusticity and the paleobiology of modern human emergence. *Proc Natl Acad Sci USA* 94:13367–13373.

17. Schmitt D, Churchill SE, Hylander WL (2003) Experimental evidence concerning spear use in Neandertals and early modern humans. *J Archaeol Sci* 30:103–114.

18. Weaver TD, Roseman CC, Stringer CB (2007) Were Neandertal and modern human cranial differences produced by natural selection or genetic drift? *J Hum Evol* 53:135–145.

19. Lieberman DE (1996) How and why humans grow thin skulls: Experimental evidence for sytemic cortical robusticity. *Am J Phys Anthropol* 101:217–236.

20. Lieberman DE, Krovitz GE, Yates FW, Devlin M, St. Claire M (2004) Effects of food processing on masticatory strain and craniofacial growth in a retrognathic face. *J Hum Evol* 46:655– 677.

21. Feldman M, Lewontin RC (1975) The heritability hangup. *Science* 190:1163–1168.

22. Gonzáles-José R, Van der Molen S, Gonzales-Perez E, Hernandez M (2004) Patterns of phenotypic covariation and correlation in modern humans as viewed from morphological integration. *Am J Phys Anthropol* 123:69 –77.

23. Ackermann RR (2005) Ontogenetic integration of the hominoid face. *J Hum Evol* 48:175–197.

24. Polanski JM, Franciscus RG (2006) Patterns of craniofacial integration in extant Homo, Pan, and Gorilla. *Am J Phys Anthropol* 131:38–49.

25. Ackermann RR (2009) Morphological integration and the interpretation of fossil hominin diversity. *Evol Biol* 36:149–156.

26. Cheverud JM (1988) A comparison of genetic and phenotypic correlations. *Evolution* 42:958–968.

27. Roff DA (1996) The evolution of genetic correlations: An analysis of patterns. *Evolution* 50:1392–1403.

28. Lande R (1979) Quantitative genetic analysis of multivariate evolution, applied to brain:body size allometry. *Evolution* 33:402–416.

29. Klingenberg CP, Badyaev AV, Sowry SM, Beckwith NJ (2001) Inferring developmental modularity from morphological integration: Analysis of individual variation and asymmetry in bumblebee wings. *Am Nat* 157:11–23.

30. Holton NE, Franciscus RG (2008) The paradox of a wide nasal aperture in cold-adapted Neandertals: A causal assessment. *J Hum Evol* 55:942–951.

31. Lieberman DE (2008) Speculations about the selective basis for modern human craniofacial form. *Evol An-thropol* 17:55–68.

32. Ackermann RR, Cheverud JM (2004) Detecting genetic drift versus selection in human evolution. *Proc Natl Acad Sci USA* 101:17946–17951.

33. Roseman CC, Weaver TD (2007) Molecules versus morphology? Not for the human cranium. *Bioessays* 29:1185–1188.

34. Franciscus RG (2002) *Encyclopedia of Evolution*, ed Pagel M (Oxford Univ Press, Oxford), pp 493–497.

35. Rak Y, Ginzburg A, Geffen E (2002) Does Homo nean-derthalensis play a role in modern human ancestry? The mandibular evidence. *Am J Phys Anthropol* 119:199–204.

36. Franciscus RG (2003) Internal nasal floor configuration in Homo with special reference to the evolution of Neandertal facial form. *J Hum Evol* 44:701–729.

37. Spoor F, Hublin J-J, Braun M, Zonneveld F (2003) The bony labyrinth of Neanderthals. *J Hum Evol* 44:141–165.

38. Trinkaus E (2006) Modern human versus Neandertal evolutionary distinctiveness. *Curr Anthropol* 47:597–620.

39. Golovanova LV, Hoffecker JF, Kharitonov VM, Romanova G (1999) Mezmaiskaya Cave: A Neanderthal occupation in the northern Caucasus. *Curr Anthropol* 40:77–86.

40. Ponce de León M, et al. (2008) Neanderthal brain size at birth provides insights into the evolution of human life history. *Proc Natl Acad Sci USA* 105:13764–13768.

41. Maureille B (2002) A lost Neanderthal neonate found. *Nature* 419:33–34.

42. Rak Y, Kimbel WH, Hovers E (1994) A Neandertal infant from Amud Cave, Israel. *J Hum Evol* 26:313–324.

43. Ponce de León MS, Zollikofer CPE (2001) Neanderthal cranial ontogeny and its implications for late hominid diversity. *Nature* 412:534–538.

44. Arsuaga JL, Martínez I, Gracia A, Lorenzo C (1997) The Sima de los Huesos crania (Sierra de Atapuerca, Spain). A comparative study. *J Hum Evol* 33:219–281.

45. Coon CS (1962) *The Origin of Races* (Alfred A. Knopf, New York).

46. Sergi S (1958) In *Hundert Jahr Neanderthaler*, ed von Koenigswald GHR (Kemink en Zoon, Utrecht), pp 38–51.

47. Brace CL (1964) The fate of the "classic" Neanderthals: A consideration of hominid catastrophism. *Curr Anthropol* 5:3–43.

48. Demes B (1987) Another look at an old face: Biomechanics of the Neandertal facial skeleton reconsidered. *J Hum Evol* 16:297–303.

49. Rak Y (1986) The Neanderthal: A new look at an old face. *J Hum Evol* 15:151–164.

50. Smith FH, Paquette SP (1989) In *The Emergence of Modern Humans: Biocultural Adaptations in the Later Pleistocene*, ed Trinkaus E (Cambridge Univ Press, Cambridge, UK), pp 181–210.

51. Spencer MA, Demes B (1993) Biomechanical analysis of masticatory system configuration in Neandertals and Inuits. *Am J Phys Anthropol* 91:1–20.

52. Trinkaus E (1987) The Neandertal face: Evolutionary and functional perspectives on a recent hominid face. *J Hum Evol* 16:429–443.

53. Antón SC (1994) In *Integrative Paths to the Past: Paleoanthropological Advances in Honor of F. Clark Howell*, eds Corruccini RS, Ciochon RL (Prentice Hall, Englewood Cliffs, NJ), pp 677–695.

54. O'Connor CF, Franciscus RG, Holton NE (2005) Bite force production capability and efficiency in Neandertals and modern humans. *Am J Phys Anthropol* 127:129–151.

55. Bräuer G (2008) The origin of modern anatomy: By speciation or intraspecific evolution? *Evol Anthropol* 17:22–37.

56. Trinkaus E (1983) In *The Mousterian Legacy: Human Biocultural Change in the Upper Pleistocene*, ed Trinkaus E (British Archaeological Reports International, Oxford), Vol 164, pp 165–200.

57. Holliday TW (1997) Postcranial evidence of cold adaptation in European Neandertals. *Am J Phys Anthropol* 104:245–258.

58. Pearson OM (2000) Postcranial remains and the origins of modern humans. *Evol Anthropol* 9:229 –247.

59. Yokley TR, Churchill SE (2006) Archaic and modern human distal humeral morphology. *J Hum Evol* 51:603–616.

60. Odwak H (2000) Long bone robusticity and claviculohumeral proportions of the Amud 7 Neandertal baby. *Am J Phys Anthropol* 30 (Suppl):241.

61. Trinkaus E (2008) Kiik-Koba and Neandertal axillary border ontogeny. *Anthropol Sci* 116:231–236.

62. Tompkins RL, Trinkaus E (1987) La Ferrassie 6 and the development of Neandertal pubic morphology. *Am J Phys Anthropol* 73:233–239.

63. Cowgill LW, Trinkaus E, Zeder MA (2007) Shanidar 10: A Middle Paleolithic immature distal lower limb from Shanidar Cave, Iraqi Kurdistan. *J Hum Evol* 53:213–223.

64. Carter DR, Beaupré GS (2001) *Skeletal Function and Form: Mechanobiology of Skeletal Development, Aging, and Regeneration* (Cambridge Univ Press, Cambridge, UK).

65. Trinkaus E (1981) In *Aspects of human evolution, Symposia of the society for the study of human biology*, ed Stringer CB (Taylor and Francis, London), Vol 21, pp 187–224.

66. Ruff CB (1994) Morphological adaptation to climate in modern and fossil hominids. *Yearbook Phys Anthropol* 37:65–107.

67. Holliday TW (1997) Body proportions in Late Pleistocene Europe and modern human origins. *J Hum Evol* 32:423–447.

68. Holliday TW (2000) Evolution at the crossroads: Modern human emergence in Western Asia. *Am Anthropol* 102:54–68.

69. Pearson OM (2000) Activity, climate, and postcranial robusticity. *Curr Anthropol* 41:569–607.

70. Churchill SE (1996) Particulate versus integrated evolution of the upper body in Late Pleistocene humans: A test of two models. *Am J Phys Anthropol* 100:559–583.

71. Weaver TD (2003) The shape of the Neandertal femur is primarily the consequence of a hyperpolar body form. *Proc Natl Acad Sci USA* 100(12):6926–6929.

72. Weaver TD, Hublin J-J (2009) Neandertal birth canal shape and the evolution of human childbirth. *Proc Natl Acad Sci USA* 106:8151–8156.

73. Ashton KG, Tracy MC, de Queiroz A (2000) Is Bergmann's rule valid for mammals? *Am Nat* 156:390–415.

74. Freckleton RP, Harvey PH, Pagel M (2003) Bergmann's rule and body size in mammals. *Am Nat* 161:821–825.

75. Tilkens MJ, Wall-Scheffler CM, Weaver TD, Steudel-Numbers K (2007) The effects of body proportions on thermoregulation: An experimental assessment of Allen's rule. *J Hum Evol* 53:286–291.

76. Simpson SW, et al. (2008) A female Homo erectus pelvis from Gona, Ethiopia. *Science* 322:1089–1092.

The stable isotope ratios of C and N in animal bone reflect the diet of the animal when it was alive. Collagen recovered from a sample of Neanderthal bone from Vindji Cave, Croatia, was found to contain sufficient organic material for isotopic analysis. Its isotopic content is compared with that found in bone of other animals of the same age and with known diet living in the same geographic region at approximately the same time, giving insight into the ability of Neanderthals to obtain meat, as well into as their other dietary preferences.

25. Neanderthal Diet at Vindija and Neanderthal Predation

The Evidence from Stable Isotopes

By Michael P. Richards, Paul B. Pettitt, Erik Trinkaus, Fred H. Smith, Maja Paunovic, and Ivor Karavanic

Reconstructions of European Neanderthal subsistence strat-egies have overwhelmingly focused on the specialized hunting and scavenging of herbivores as the predominant method of obtaining food (1–6). These reconstructions are based principally on the analysis of the abundantly preserved faunal remains, supplemented by artifactual evidence of lithic and wood hunting apparatuses, as well as on the relative importance of the faunal biomass in the environments that European Neanderthals occupied during later oxygen isotope stage 5 and especially oxygen isotope stages 4 and 3 of the Late Pleistocene. Understanding Neanderthal diet has implications for understanding Neanderthal land use, social organization, and behavioral complexity. Yet despite the abundant evidence for successful hunting techniques across Neanderthal Eurasia, faunal remains can indicate only hunting or scavenging episodes; they cannot tell us about the predominant foods in the diet over the long term.

By contrast, the measurement of the ratios of the stable isotopes of carbon and nitrogen in mammal bone collagen provides an indication of aspects of diet over the last few years of life (7–9). This stable isotope evidence can therefore provide us with *direct* information on Neanderthal diet. This method has been applied to Neanderthal remains from the sites of Marillac, France (10), and Scladina Cave, Belgium (11).

Michael P. Richards et al., "Neanderthal Diet at Vindija and Neanderthal Predation: The Evidence from Stable Isotopes," *PNAS*, vol. 97, no. 13, pp. 7663–7666. Copyright © 2000 by National Academy of Sciences. Reprinted with permission.

These studies, focusing particularly on their high δ^{15}N values, indicated that the Neanderthals measured occupied the top trophic level, obtaining nearly all of their dietary protein from animal sources. In the context of this finding, we undertook stable isotope analyses of the two late Neanderthal specimens from Vindija Cave, in the Hrvatsko Zagorje of northern Croatia [Vi -207 and Vi-208 (12)], and of the fauna with which they were stratigraphically associated.

Vindija Neanderthal and Faunal Specimens. Recently, the Vi-207 and Vi-208 Neanderthal specimens, as well as various other archeological materials from level G1 of Vindija Cave, Croatia, were submitted for accelerator mass spectrometer radiocarbon dating at the Oxford Radiocarbon Accelerator Unit, University of Oxford (13). The two Neanderthal specimens were dated to 29,080 ± 400 years before present (B.P.) (OxA-8296, Vi-207) and 28,020 ± 360 years B.P. (OxA-8295, Vi-208), making them the youngest directly dated Neanderthal specimens in Europe (13). Because the radiocarbon sample preparation process includes assessments of stable isotopes, in part to control for potential contamination, this analysis also yielded stable isotope profiles for these late archaic humans. Combined with similar data obtained from faunal remains from level G_1 and the older level G_3 of Vindija Cave, this provides a means of assessing the dietary profiles of these Neanderthals.

Stable Isotope Analyses. Mammal bone collagen δ^{13}C and δ^{15}N values reflect the δ^{13}C and δ^{15}N values of dietary protein (14). They furnish a long-term record of diet, giving the average δ^{13}C and δ^{15}N values of all of the protein consumed over the last years of the measured individual's life. δ^{13}C values can be used to discriminate between terrestrial and marine dietary protein in humans and other mammals (15, 16). In addition, because of the canopy effect, species that live in forest environments can have δ^{13}C values that are more negative than species that live in open environments (17). δ^{15}N values are, on average, 2–4‰ higher than the average δ^{15}N value of the protein consumed (18). Therefore, δ^{15}N values can be used to determine the trophic level of the protein consumed. By measuring the δ^{13}C and δ^{15}N values of various fauna in a paleo-ecosystem, it is possible to reconstruct the trophic level relationships within that ecosystem. Therefore, by comparing the δ^{13}C and δ^{15}N values of omnivores such as hominids with the values of herbivores and carnivores from the same ecosystem, it is possible to determine whether those omnivores were obtaining dietary protein from plant or animal sources.

Vindija Neanderthal and Faunal Isotope Values. Collagen was extracted from the two Neanderthal specimens from level G_1 of Vindija Cave and from various faunal remains from level G_1 and the older level G_3 according to standard collagen extraction procedures; the Neanderthal specimens were extracted according to the methods outlined in Law and Hedges (19), and the faunal specimens were extracted according to the procedure outlined in Richards and Hedges (16). The collagen extracts varied in quality, and only those samples that had acceptable collagen attributes were used. These attributes are based on values determined by DeNiro (20) and Ambrose (21) and used by the majority of stable isotope researchers and radiocarbon dating labs. The acceptable values are a C:N ratio between 2.9 and 3.6, "percent collagen" >1%, and %C and %N in the extracted collagen of >13% for carbon and >5% for nitrogen. These collagen attributes allow us to identify and exclude collagen that is heavily degraded or contaminated. This is in contrast to stable isotope measurements of bioapatite in bone mineral and enamel, where no such criteria exist. The stable isotope values and various collagen attributes are given in Table 1; based on these, we are confident that the collagen δ^{13}C and δ^{15}N values reported here are robust and reflect the organisms' original collagen δ^{13}C and δ^{15}N values. The Neanderthal samples were measured at the Oxford Radiocarbon Accelerator Unit, and the

Table 1. Bone collagen $\delta^{13}C$ and $\delta^{15}N$ values of Neanderthals and associated fauna from Vindija Cave, Croatia

SAMPLE	SPECIES	LEVEL	$\delta^{13}C$	$\delta^{15}N$	C:N	% COLL.	% C	% N
Vi-207	Neanderthal	G_1	−19.5	10.1	3.2	6.5	37.1	13.5
Vi-208	Neanderthal	G_1	−20.5	10.8	3.6	4.2	36.1	11.7
V1	Bos/Bison spp.	G_3	−20.4	5.3	3.2	11.4	18.8	6.8
V3	Cervid	G_1	−20.3	5.2	3.2	16.1	20.4	7.4
V4	Ursus spelaeus	G_3	−21.1	1.3	3.3	29.1	14.4	5.1
V5	Ursus spelaeus	G_1	−20.7	1.5	3.3	12.6	18.8	6.7

$\delta^{13}C$ values are measured relative to the Vienna Pee Dee Belemnite standard, and $\delta^{15}N$ values are measured relative to the ambient inhalable reservoir standard. "% Coll." is the mass of freeze-dried "collagen" produced as a percentage of the starting total bone mass. % C and % N are the percent amounts of carbon and nitrogen measured in the mass spectrometer compared with the starting mass of extracted collagen. Measurement errors on the $\delta^{13}C$ values are ±0.3‰; errors on the $\delta^{15}N$ values are ±0.4‰.

faunal samples were measured at the Stable Isotope Laboratory, Research Laboratory for Archaeology and the History of Art, University of Oxford.

We used the ecosystem approach and compared the omni-vores of interest, in this case the Neanderthals, with the isotope values of temporally and geographically associated fauna. Un-fortunately, it was possible to extract collagen from only a few of the faunal samples taken from Vindija. A particular problem was our inability to extract collagen from our carnivore samples. For this reason, we have supplemented the Vindija faunal sample with data from the slightly later (≈23,000–26,000 B.P.) sites of Dolní Věstonice II and Milovice in the Czech Republic (22). In addition, we have contributed a single herbivore sample from the site of Brno-Francouzská, which dates within this time range (23).

There are fluctuations in faunal $\delta^{15}N$ values through time that are correlated with climate changes (24, 25). For example, Richards et al. (26) observed faunal $\delta^{15}N$ values dated to ≈12,000 years B.P. from Gough's Cave, U.K. that were ≈2‰ lower than the $\delta^{15}N$ values of similar species from the Holocene. Therefore, comparing isotope values between sites, especially sites of dif-ferent ages, could be problematic. However, by employing fauna that are as geographically and temporally as close to our samples as possible, we should be providing an appropriate comparative framework for the Vindija Neanderthal samples. Moreover, the relative distribution, especially of $\delta^{15}N$ values, for the species included in this pooled sample is similar to the distributions derived for various faunal species from single sites (10, 11).

Fauna. The Bos/Bison and cervid samples from Vindija (Table 1) have herbivore $\delta^{13}C$ and $\delta^{15}N$ values that are within the ranges observed for European Holocene specimens (25, 27) . The $\delta^{13}C$ values are more indicative of open-ranging species (≈200‰), rather than forest-dwelling species (≈220‰), but ranges of variation in Late Pleistocene Bos/Bison $\delta^{13}C$ values (24) as well as the hilly terrain in the vicinity of Vindija Cave make it difficult to assess which of these bovine genera is most likely represented. The cave bear samples are interesting from a paleobiological, rather than an anthropological, perspective as they have very low $\delta^{15}N$ values. Similarly low Ursus spelaeus $\delta^{15}N$ values have been observed for samples from Slovenia (28), France (29), and Belgium (30). The low U. spelaeus values probably reflect a high degree of herbivory (31); they may also be a result of their unusual metabolism related to hibernation (32), although the hibernation model has been disputed (30).

Neanderthals. The Neanderthal samples from Vindija have high $\delta^{15}N$ values, which indicate that the overwhelming majority of their dietary protein was from animal, rather than plant, sources (Table 1, Fig. 1). The associated $\delta^{13}C$ values indicate the exploitation of more open-ranging herbivores, despite

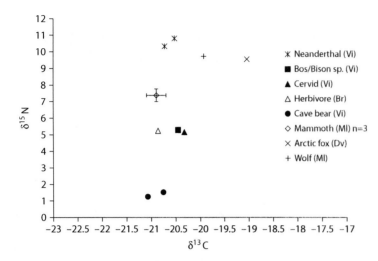

Fig. 1. Bone collagen δ^{13}C and δ^{15}N values of Neanderthals and associated fauna from Vindija Cave, Croatia (Vi), dated to ≈28,500 years B.P. Included is a single faunal value from the site of Brno-Francouzská (Br), Czech Republic (≈24,000 years B.P.). Also plotted are faunal values from Ambrose (22) from ≈22,000–26,000 years B.P. sites in the Czech Republic: Dolní Věstonice II (Dv) and Milovice (Ml).

the hilly terrain of the Hrvatsko Zagorje. The Neanderthal values are close to the later carnivore isotope values from Dolní Věstonice II and Milovice (22), as well as those of earlier carnivores from Marillac and Scladina (10, 11), indicating that these Neander-thals had diets similar to nonhuman carnivores.

The insufficient associated faunal samples make it impossible to identify which herbivore species were preferentially being consumed by the Neanderthals. The mammoth δ^{15}N values from Milovice are intriguing, as they are higher than the other herbivores. This pattern of higher mammoth values has been observed previously (30, 33, 34) and may relate to mammoths targeting specific plant species, whereas other herbivores con-sume a wider range of species. The higher mammoth δ^{15}N values may be of relevance here, as the Neanderthal δ^{15}N values could make sense if their main dietary protein source was mammoths rather than the other faunal species. However, archeological evidence for Neanderthal exploitation of proboscideans is extremely rare, and a broader series of fauna needs to be analyzed before the spectrum of predated herbivores can be evaluated through stable isotope analysis.

Our findings concerning the diet of the Vindija Neanderthals are remarkably similar to those observed by Bocherens and colleagues for other European Neanderthals (10, 11). They obtained similar δ^{13}C and δ^{15}N values for two Neanderthals from the site of Marillac dated to ≈40,000–45,000 years B.P. and for a Neanderthal specimen from Scladina Cave, Belgium, which is earlier, dated to between 80,000 and 130,000 years B.P. (Table 2). Moreover, the high δ^{15}N for the Marillac Neanderthal remains are most closely approached by the values for *Canis lupus* and *Crocuta crocuta* from that site (10), whereas the earlier Neanderthal δ^{15}N value from Scladina is most closely approached in that site's faunal assemblage by *Panthera spelaea* and secondarily by slightly lower values for *Crocuta crocuta* and *Canis lupus* (11). For these five Neanderthal specimens, therefore, we have stable isotope data indicating that geographically and chronologically dispersed Neanderthals consistently behaved as top-level carnivores.

Neanderthals as Predators. Neanderthal subsistence strategies were varied in space and time, with carcass utilization patterns varying on intersite and interspecies levels (4, 35). The role of hunting versus scavenging in meat acquisition by Middle Paleolithic humans has been debated particularly over the last two decades (3, 36, 37), and from this discussion it has become clear that the Neanderthals were capable of, and frequently engaged in, predation on mammals.

In particular, taphonomic analyses of a number of Middle Paleolithic, Neanderthal-associated mammalian faunal assemblages in recent years have concluded that focused and selective hunting strategies resulting in high meat utility acquisition were carried out by these late archaic humans in areas of Europe and the Near East as dispersed as France (Bau de l'Aubesier, La Borde, Canalettes, Coudoulous, Mauran, Le Portel), Germany (Salzgitter Lebenstedt, Wallertheim), Italy (Grotta Breuil), Croatia (Krapina), Iran (Kobeh), Israel

Table 2. Isotope values of Neanderthals from Marillac, France (10), and Scladina, Belgium (11)

SITE	SAMPLE	SITE AGE	$\delta^{13}C$	$\delta^{13}N$
Marillac	Layer 9	40,000–45,000 BP	−20.2	9.3
Marillac	Layer 10	40,000–45,000 BP	−19.1	11.6
Scladina Cave	SC18800	80,000–130,000 BP	−19.9	10.9

(Kebara), and Russia (Il'skaja) (1–3, 6, 35, 38–44). These interpretations are based principally on mortality profiles and/or distributions of skeletal part frequencies of the prey species being processed, combined with direct evidence of human carcass processing with lithic tools. In the former, prime age-dominated assemblages are usually taken to indicate selective and active predation by these hominids. In the latter, a proximal limb element-dominated assemblage or a preserved skeletal distribution representative of anatomical frequencies, as opposed to a head and foot-dominated assemblage, are generally taken to indicate primary carcass access and hence active predation.

However, not only do a significant number of these assemblages not meet both criteria for active predation on the part of the Neanderthals, it is increasingly apparent that a variety of factors can contribute to the mortality and skeletal element distributions documented in archeological faunal assemblages. These factors include prey population demographic dynamics, nonhuman predator prey selection patterns, carcass consumption patterns by both humans and other carnivores, human carcass element transport variation, and postdepositional processes acting differentially on skeletal elements. Moreover, it remains unclear how representative of overall Neanderthal diet such episodes are. Consequently, current taphonomic analyses of these and other archeological faunal assemblages do not always permit assessment of the degrees to which the assemblages were accumulated through active predation versus scavenging.

Neanderthal predation has also been supported by the evidence for spears (stone-tipped and wooden) among both the Neanderthals and their Middle Pleistocene European predecessors (45–49), combined with rare examples of such weapons in the remains of apparent prey animals [e.g., the wooden spear in the ribs of an *Elephas* skeleton at Lehringen, Germany, and the Levallois point embedded an *Equus* cervical vertebra from Umm el Tlel in Syria (45, 50)]. In addition, indirect measures of Neanderthal subsistence such as the Levallois point to core frequencies have been used to suggest that the Neanderthals were highly predatory in the Near East (ref. 51; but see refs. 52 and 53), despite the absence of evidence for the kind of projectile weaponry seen in the Upper Paleolithic that would increase the mechanical efficiency and safety of hunting or for the patterned variance in extractive technologies widely seen in Upper Paleolithic and more recent hunter–gatherer toolkits (54).

This inference of active predation on the part of the Neanderthals is further supported by their anatomical distribution of trauma, which suggests proximate encounters with large animals (55) of the kind necessitated by their predominantly heavy available weaponry (45, 47, 48, 56). Yet, their pattern of trauma does not permit distinctions between injuries sustained during hunting versus those suffered in competition with other carni-vores for carcasses or space.

Consequently, although several lines of evidence support active mammalian predation by the Neanderthals and contradict the previous models of the Neanderthals acquiring their animal protein principally through scavenging, the archeological data nonetheless remain frequently ambiguous as to the extent to which these late archaic humans were the primary predators of the mammals whose remains they processed. The consistent stable isotope data indicating their position as top-level carnivores provides insight into this issue.

There are no true mammalian scavengers, as all are omnivores (ursids and canids) and/or actively hunt (hyenas) (57). This is because the search time for scavenging relative to the return is too expensive for terrestrial homeothermic vertebrates, and most predators actively defend their kills, thereby increasing risk to any potential terrestrial scavenger (57). If the Neanderthals were obtaining their animal protein principally through scavenging, they would have had to obtain most of their food from plants, as a reliable food source, and only supplemented this with scavenged animal products. Even though the isotope data cannot distinguish the species or even the sizes of the animals consumed, they clearly show that animal products were the overwhelming source of protein in European Neanderthal diets and that protein from plants was insignificant. It is therefore likely that scavenging, although undoubtedly practiced on an opportunistic basis by these European Neanderthals, must have been distinctly secondary to predation.

SUMMARY AND CONCLUSIONS

Isotope analyses of two Neanderthals and associated fauna from Vindija Cave, Croatia, have indicated that the bulk of their dietary protein came from animal sources. Comparison with faunal remains from this and other sites of similar age indicates that the Vindija Neanderthal isotope values were similar to those of other carnivores. These results are very close to the results for earlier Late Pleistocene Neanderthals from France and Belgium.

Therefore, the emerging picture of the European Neanderthal diet indicates that although physiologically they were presumably omnivores, they behaved as carnivores, with animal protein being the main source of dietary protein. This finding is in agreement with the indirect archeological evidence and strongly points to the Neanderthals having been active predators.

We thank H. Bocherens, F. B. Marshall, and M. C. Stiner for helpful comments. The collection and analysis of the Vindija hominid samples was supported by the L. S. B. Leakey Foundation, by the Wenner–Gren Foundation, and by the Prehistoric Society of the United Kingdom. The analysis of the Vindija faunal samples was supported the Natural Environment Research Council (U.K.) and the Social Sciences and Humanities Research Council of Canada.

REFERENCES

1. Jaubert, J., Lorblanchet, M., Laville, H., Slott-Moller, R., Turq, A. & Brugal, J-P. (1990) *Les Chasseurs d'Aurochs de La Borde: Un Site du Paléolithique Moyen (Livernon, Lot)* (Maison des Sciences de l'Homme, Paris).

2. Farizy, C., David, F. & Jaubert, J. (1994) *Hommes et Bisons du Paléolithique Moyen á Mauran (Haute-Garonne)* (Centre National de la Recherche Scientifique, Paris).

3. Stiner, M. C. (1994) *Honor Among Thieves: A Zooarchaeological Study of Neandertal Ecology* (Princeton Univ. Press, Princeton).

4. Mellars, P. (1996) *The Neanderthal Legacy* (Princeton Univ. Press, Princeton).

5. Gamble, C. (1999) *The Palaeolithic Societies of Europe* (Cambridge Univ. Press, Cambridge).

6. Gardeisen, A. (1999) *J. Archaeol. Sci.* **26,** 1145–1158.

7. Ambrose, S. H. (1993) in *Investigations of Ancient Human Tissue: Chemical Analyses in Anthropology,* ed. Sandford, M. K. (Gordon & Breach, Langhorne, PA), pp. 59–130.

8. Schwarcz, H. & Schoeninger, M. (1991) *Yearb. Phys. Anthropol.* **34,** 283–321.

9. Bocherens, H. (1999) *Bull. Mém. Soc. Anthropol. Paris* **ns 11,** 261–287.

10. Fizet, M., Mariotti, A., Bocherens, H., Lange-Badré, B., Vandermeersch, B., Borel, J. & Bellon, G. (1995) *J. Archaeol. Sci.* **22,** 67–79.

11. Bocherens, H., Billiou, D., Mariotti, A., Patou-Mathias, M., Otte, M., Bonjean, & Toussaint, M. (1999) *J. Archaeol. Sci.* **26,** 599–607.

12. Wolpoff, M. H., Smith, F. H., Malez, M., Radovčić, J. & Rukavina, D. (1981) *Am. J. Phys. Anthropol.* **54,** 499–545.

13. Smith, F. H., Trinkaus, E., Pettitt, P. B., Karavanić, I. & Paunović, M. (1999) *Proc. Natl. Acad. Sci. USA* **96,** 12281–12286.

14. Ambrose S. H. & Norr, L. (1993) in *Prehistoric Human Bone: Archaeology at the Molecular Level*, eds. Lambert, J. & Grupe, G. (Springer, New York), pp. 1–37.

15. Schoeninger, M. DeNiro, M. & Tauber, H. (1983) *Science* **220,** 1381–1383.

16. Richards, M. P. & Hedges, R. E. M. (1999) *J. Archaeol. Sci.* **26,** 717–722.

17. van der Merwe, N. J. & Medina, E. (1991) *J. Archaeol. Sci.* **18,** 249–259.

18. Schoeninger, M. & DeNiro, M. (1984) *Geochim. Cosmochim. Acta* **48,** 625–639.

19. Law, I. A. & Hedges, R. E. M. (1989) *Radiocarbon* **31,** 247–254.

20. DeNiro, M. J. (1985) *Nature (London)* **317,** 806–809.

21. Ambrose, S. H. (1990) *J. Archaeol. Sci.* **17,** 431–451.

22. Ambrose, S. H. (1998) in *Neandertals and Modern Humans in Western Asia*, eds. Akazawa, T., Aoki, K. & Bar-Yosef, O. (Plenum, New York), pp. 277–289.

23. Pettitt, P. B. & Trinkaus, E. (2000) *Anthropologie (Brno)*, in press.

24. Iacumin, P., Bocherens, H., Delgado Huertas, A., Mariotti, A. & Longinelli, A. (1997) *Earth Planet. Sci. Lett.* **148,** 349–357.

25. Richards, M. P. (1998) D. Phil. thesis (Univ. of Oxford, Oxford).

26. Richards, M. P., Jacobi, R., Currant, A., Stringer, C. & Hedges, R. E. M. (2000) *Archaeol. Sci.* **27,** 1–3.

27. Bocherens, H., Fizet, M., Mariotti, A., Lange-Badré, B., Vandermeersch, B., Borel, J. P. & Bellon, G. (1991) *J. Hum. Evol.* **20,** 481–492.

28. Lidén, K. & Angerbjörn, A. (1999) *Proc. R. Soc. London Ser. B* **266,** 1779–1783.

29. Bocherens, H., Fizet, M., Mariotti, A., Gangloff, R. A. & Burns, J. A. (1994) *Hist. Biol.* **7,** 187–202.

30. Bocherens, H., Billiou, D., Patou-Mathis, M., Bonjean, D., Otte, M. & Mariotti, (1997) *Quat. Res.* **48,** 370–380.

31. Kurtén, B. (1958) *Acta Zool. Fennica* **95,** 1–59.

32. Nelson, D. E., Angerbjörn, A., Lidén, K. & Turk, I. (1998) *Oecologia* **116,** 177–181.

33. Bocherens, H., Fizet, M. & Mariotti, A. (1994) *Palaeogeogr. Palaeoclimatol. Palaeoecol.* **107,** 213–225.

34. Bocherens, H., Pacaud, G., Lazarev, P. & Mariotti, A. (1996) *Palaeogeogr. Palaeoclimatol. Palaeoecol.* **126,** 31–44.

35. Gaudzinski, S. (1999) in *The Middle Palaeolithic Occupation of Europe*, eds. Roebroeks, W. & Gamble, C. (Univ. of Leiden Publishers & European Science Foundation, Leiden, The Netherlands), pp. 215–233.

36. Binford, L. R. (1985) *J. Anthropol. Archaeol.* **4,** 292–327.

37. Chase, P. G. (1989) in *The Human Revolution*, eds. Mellars, P. A. & Stringer, C. B. (Princeton Univ. Press, Princeton), pp. 321–327.

38. Gaudzinski, S. (1996) *Proc. Prehist. Soc.* **62,** 19–40.

39. Patou-Mathis, M. (1993) in *L'abri des Canalettes: Un habitat moustérien sur les grands Causses (Nant, Aveyron)*, ed. Meignen, L. (Centre National de la Recherche Scientifique, Paris), pp. 199–237.

40. Fernandez, P., Faure, M., Guérin, C. & Lebel, S. (1998) in *Économie Préhistorique: Les Comportements de Subsistence au Paléolithique* (Éditions de l'Association pour la Promotion et la Diffusion des Connaissances Archéologiques, Sophia Antipolis, France), pp. 309–323.

41. Speth, J. & Tchernov, E. (1998) in *Neandertals and Modern Humans in Western Asia*, eds. Akazawa, T., Aoki, K. & Bar-Yosef, O. (Plenum, New York), pp. 223–239.

42. Marean, C. W. & Kim, S. Y. (1998) *Curr. Anthropol.* **39,** S79–S113.

43. Miracle, P. (2000) *The Krapina Fauna: Catalog and Zooarchaeology of the Faunal Remains* (Hrvatski Priodoslovni Muzej, Zagreb, Croatia).

44. Gaudzinski, S. & Roebroeks, W. (2000) *J. Hum. Evol.* **38,** 497–521.

45. Jacob-Friesen, K. H. (1956) *Jahrb. Röm.-German. Zentralmuseums Mainz.* **3,** 1–22.

46. Oakley, K. P., Andrews, P., Keeley, L. H. & Clark, J. D. (1977) *Proc. Prehist. Soc.* **43,** 13–30.

47. Beyries, S. (1987) in *La Main et l'Outil: Manches et Emmanchements Préhistoriques*, ed. Stordeur, D. (Travaux de la Maison de l'Orient, Lyon, France), pp. 55–64.

48. Shea, J. J. (1988) *J. Field Archaeol.* **15,** 441–450.

49. Thieme, H. (1997) *Nature (London)* **385,** 807–810.

50. Boëda, E., Geneste, J. M., Griggo, C., Mercier, N., Muhesen, S., Reyss, J. L., Taha, A. & Valladas, H. (1999) *Antiquity* **73,** 394–402.

51. Shea, J. J. (1998) *Curr. Anthropol.* **39,** S45–S78.

52. Churchill, S. E. (1998) *Curr. Anthropol.* **39,** S61–S62.

53. Kuhn, S. L. (1998) *Curr. Anthropol.* **39,** S66–S67.

54. Kuhn, S. L. (1995) *Mousterian Lithic Technology: An Ecological Perspective* (Princeton Univ. Press, Princeton).

55. Berger, T. D. & Trinkaus, E. (1995) *J. Archaeol. Sci.* **22,** 841–852.

56. Churchill, S. E. (1993) *Archeol. Pap. Am. Anthropol. Assoc.* **4,** 11–24.

57. Houston, D. C. (1979) in *Serengeti: Dynamics of an Ecosystem*, eds. Sinclair, R. E. & Norton-Griffiths, M. (Univ. of Chicago Press, Chicago), pp. 263–286.

Study Questions

1. How are Neanderthal skulls different from those of modern people, and what are the reasons for these differences?

2. How are Neanderthal postcranial bones different from those of modern people, and what are the reasons for these differences?

3. What is the evolutionary relationship of modern humans to Neanderthals?

4. What was the likely diet of Neanderthals, and how do we know?

5. What peculiar Neanderthal practice is shown by examining their front teeth?

SECTION VIII

EARLY *HOMO SAPIENS*

The anatomies of early *Homo sapiens* from different parts of the world are compared with each other and with those of earlier hominins, and the likely evolutionary history of *Homo sapiens* is described.

26. Homo Sapiens

By Chris Stringer

S pecies to which modern humans belong. In the nineteenth century and the earlier years of the twentieth, it was common for workers who studied newly discovered fossil hominids to erect new species or even genus names for virtually every new find, even where the specimen was clearly closely related to previous finds. Thus, some years after the Neanderthal skeleton was discovered in 1856, it was made the type of a new species of the genus *Homo* called *Homo neanderthalensis*, and this practice was repeated by some workers for various other Neanderthal finds, such as those from Spy ("*Homo spyensis*"), Le Moustier ("*Homo transprimigenius mousteriensis*"), and La Chapelle-aux-Saints ("*Homo chapel-lensis*"). Similarly, the Broken Hill cranium was assigned to "*Homo rhodesiensis*" and later to "*Cyphanthropus rhodesiensis*," the Skhūl remains to "*Palaeanthropus palestinus*," and the Steinheim skull to "*Homo steinheimensis*."

During the period 1943–1964, however, a number of influential papers reexamined the basic concepts of hominid classification from the perspectives of more general paleontology and the developing field of population genetics. It was argued that, as living *Homo sapiens* represented a single polytypic species, so did fossil humans at any one time level in the past. Particularly important to these discussions was the status of the Zhoukoudian (China) remains (then commonly attributed to *Sinanthropus pekinensis*), and the Mount

Carmel (Israel: Skhūl and Tabūn) remains (then commonly attributed to a single nonmodern population). The German anatomist F. Weidenreich, who described the Zhoukoudian fossils, actually regarded them as representing only a distinct race of early humans, despite his persistent use of a separate generic name for the material. This led several workers to suggest that the Zhoukoudian remains, in fact, represented merely a subspecies of an early human species, *Homo erectus*. T. McCown and A. Keith's interpretation of the Mount Carmel fossils as representing a highly variable single population led them to suggest that the taxonomic boundary between Neanderthals and modern *H. sapiens* had been broken down. The Mount Carmel "population" could be interpreted as a group close to the common ancestry of Neanderthals and modern humans, or a group in the process of evolving from a Neanderthal to a modern morphology, or even a hybrid population between two (closely related) forms.

Thus, reassessments of the fossil material suggested that no more than a single hominid species had existed at any one time in the Pleistocene and that *H. erectus* (including such geographical variants as "Java Man" and "Peking Man") and *H. sapiens* (including such variants as Neanderthals and modern humans) were polytypic species. This viewpoint was formalized by B. Campbell in the 1960s, when he proposed that *H. sapiens* Linnaeus 1758 should be subdivided into the following living or fossil subspecies: *sapiens* (modern humans), *neanderthalensis, steinheimensis, rhodesiensis,* and *soloensis* (for the Ngandong remains). This scheme was widely adopted after 1964, and a number of previous and new fossil discoveries have been incorporated into it under one or other subspecific categories. Subsequently, it has become common to differentiate the anatomically modern form of *H. sapiens* (*Homo sapiens sapiens*) from the other forms of the species by the additional epithets *modern* or *archaic Homo sapiens*. Thus, "archaic *Homo sapiens*" includes Middle or Late Pleistocene hominids that are distinct from, but supposedly closely related to, modern humans.

MODERN *HOMO SAPIENS*

Anatomically modern *H. sapiens* can be characterized by a number of anatomical features found in all living human populations. Many of these features are related to an overall gracility of the skeleton compared with archaic humans. Although living *H. sapiens* around the world display a remarkable variation in stature, physique, and weight (much of which can be attributed to environmental adaptations and nutritional factors), most modern humans are quite large bodied but have slenderly constructed bones and a less heavy musculature than was the case among archaic humans. This may well be an indication of the extent to which sophisticated behaviors found in all living humans have taken the selective weight off the skeleton (almost literally) through an emphasis on economy of effort rather than high activity and muscle power as the basic behavioral adaptation of the species.

Compared with archaic humans, modern *H. sapiens* have large brains (also found in Neanderthals), with an average volume exceeding 1,300 ml (but varying somewhat according to sex and body size). To house this large brain, there is a highly distinctive and derived cranial shape in modern humans. The vault is relatively short (front to back) and high, with a domed forehead and well-arched (rather than flattened) parietal. The base of the skull is narrow, as is the occipital bone. The occipital itself is rounded in profile, lacking the transverse torus and heavy neck musculature of many archaic forms, as well as the distinctive torus shape and suprainiac fossa found in Neanderthals. As in late Neanderthals, the skull walls of modern humans are relatively thin, and this lack of robusticity is also reflected in the small or nonexistent browridge and the gracile face and jaws with small teeth. The mandible itself is not thickened and has a bony chin on its outside, even in young individuals. The degree of flatness of the face and the shape of the nose vary in

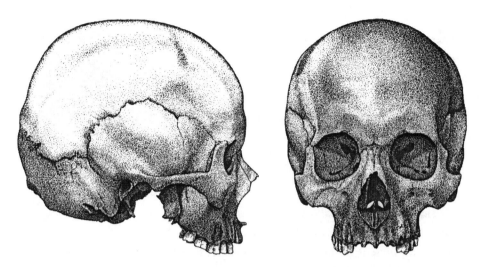

Side and front views of a modern human cranium from Egypt. Scale is 1 cm.

different populations, but in none of them is there the voluminous and projecting nasal region found in Neanderthals.

The whole skeleton of modern *H. sapiens* is slenderly built with thin-walls to the limb bones and only moderate muscularity. The scapula (shoulder blade) has less muscle attachment on the back edge; the pelvis is not robustly constructed, and it lacks the extended pubic ramus found in Neanderthals. There are also distinctive features of growth and development in modern humans compared with our closest primate relatives, since humans have a long period of childhood growth and dependency, mature later, and complete

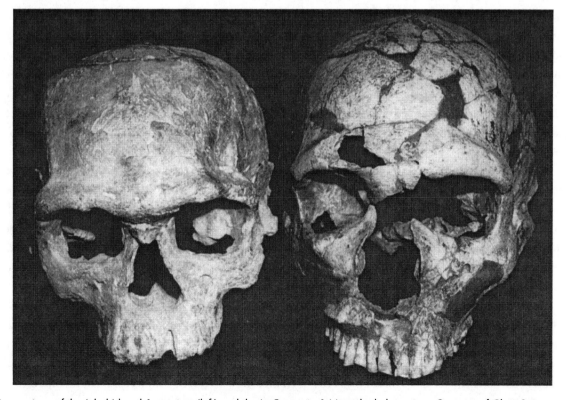

Comparison of the Jebel Irhoud 1 cranium (left) and the La Ferrassie 1 Neanderthal cranium. Courtesy of Chris Stringer.

growth much later than the apes. In addition, the life span of humans is such that there is often a long period of postreproductive survival, which is undocumented in the apes. The slow development of humans and the presence of postreproductive survival into old age may both be linked to the importance of intergenerational transmission of cultural information. Thus, old individuals may be provisioned, since they have a wealth of experience useful to younger, less experienced individuals. Similarly, the slow development of children allows them ample time to develop linguistic skills, which are of use in absorbing the complexities of the culture into which they have been born. Although this developmental pattern is found in all living human populations, there is little evidence (but much speculation) about when this distinctive pattern emerged.

Traditionally, it was believed that the human pattern of slow development was present in early hominids, such as the australopiths, *Homo habilis*, and *H. erectus*. However, new techniques of determining more accurately the age at death of fossil remains of young individuals have suggested that the modern human growth pattern was not present in these early hominids. If this is so, the modern *H. sapiens* pattern may have originated quite recently, and its presence or absence in the Neanderthals is a topic of both speculation and research.

ORIGIN OF MODERN *HOMO SAPIENS*

Two extreme models have been proposed to account for the origin of modern people, with some workers adopting various intermediate positions. One extreme view (multiregional evolution) postulates that modern humans evolved locally in different parts of the world from already distinct archaic ancestors. This model of local continuity is sometimes termed the *Neanderthal-phase model*, since it envisages hominids of comparable evolutionary grade to the European Neanderthals giving rise to local descendant modern populations by parallel or polyphyletic evolution. Thus, in Europe, a direct unilinear evolutionary sequence might exist between the oldest European populations, represented by the Mauer (Germany) mandible, and modern Europeans via such intermediates as the Neanderthals and Cro-Magnons. Similarly, in China, the Lantian and Zhoukoudian *H. erectus* specimens could represent ancient ancestors for modern Asian peoples via such intermediates as the Maba, Jinniu shan, and Dali material. And in Indonesia, Javanese *H. erectus* fossils could represent populations that eventually gave rise to modern Australasian peoples via such intermediates as the Ngandong (Solo) and Kow Swamp fossils. In the *center-and-edge model*, the great variation found in recent and Pleistocene Australians is explained as a result of local evolution (from Indonesian *H. erectus*) combined with migration or gene flow from the Asian mainland (e.g., as represented by the Mungo fossils).

In the model of multiregional evolution, "racial" variation is very ancient, with "local" features traceable between ancient and modern populations over periods longer than 0.5 Myr. Variants of this model allow for significant gene flow to have occurred between the local lineages, so that speciation did not occur and so that the spread of the fundamentally similar anatomy of all modern peoples can be explained. In fact, some proponents of multiregional evolution have proposed that the taxon name *H. sapiens* should be extended to the whole human clade after the cladogenetic split from *H. habilis* (thus sinking *Homo ergaster* and *H. erectus*, as well as all later hominids, into *H. sapiens*).

In contrast to the local-continuity model, the *single-origin*, or *Noah's Ark*, *model* proposes that all modern humans derived from a single fairly recent common ancestral population. From this model, it follows that population movement or expansion, rather than local evolution, was the primary determinant of the spread of modern human characteristics during the last 50 Ka. As such, local racial features evolved *after* the anatomical features that are shared by all living *H. sapiens*, whereas, in the local continuity model, racial or local features were much more ancient. The geographical location of such a source population for all living humans is still uncertain, but most proponents of single-origin models favor Africa as the critical area, with a minority case also presented for Southwest or Southeast Asia. The evidence for the earliest occurrence of anatomically modern fossils in these areas is discussed elsewhere (see ARCHAIC MODERNS), but there is support for the model that is independent of the fossil evidence from considerations of modern human skeletal variation and recently published genetic analyses. Different human populations show a fundamental similarity in anatomy, and it is difficult to believe that such a large number of characters in common could have evolved independently under very different environmental or cultural conditions in various parts of the world. Those features that distinguish modern humans from one another are relatively minor and could easily have been superimposed on a fundamentally modern anatomy inherited from a recent common ancestor. The genetic data that support a recent African origin for all modern *H. sapiens* come from many different kinds of analyses.

The most probable scenario has an African origin for modern morphological and genetic variation, probably during the African Middle Stone Age (MSA), which lasted from ca. 150 to 40 Ka. Ancestral populations probably resembled such specimens as Eliye Springs (Kenya) or Omo Kibish 2 (Ethiopia), while fossils approaching the modern condition in more respects occur at Guomde (Kenya), Ngaloba (Tanzania), Florisbad (South Africa), and Jebel Irhoud (Morocco). Specimens within the modern anatomical range can be recognized from such African sites as Klasies River Mouth, Border Cave, and Omo Kibish 1, all of which are likely to be older than 50 Ka, with actual or claimed MSA associations. The extent to which modern behavioral patterns were already present in MSA populations is still unclear, with some workers suggesting that there was a precocious appearance of "Upper Paleolithic" aspects in some MSA industries, while others argue that such changes do not occur until the end of the MSA. So it is also still uncertain whether there was a linkage or a decoupling between the morphological and behavioral changes that heralded the advent of modern *H. sapiens* in Africa.

Following an early Late Pleistocene establishment of modern features in Africa (and perhaps also Southwest Asia), the modern anatomical pattern probably first radiated by population expansion, migration, or gene flow from North Africa, through Southwest Asia, to eastern Asia and Australia. Modern humans may also have been present in Ukraine (Starosel'e) and eastern Europe (Krapina A and Bacho Kiro?) by 40 Ka and were probably widespread in Europe by 35 Ka, judging by the appearance of Aurignacian industries as far west as Spain and France by that time.

In all cases in which a hominid association with the Aurignacian is unequivocal, that hominid is always anatomically modern *H. sapiens*, and the European populations of these early-modern people are collectively known as *Cro-Magnons*. The term was formerly considered to be virtually synonymous with the term *Upper Paleolithic humans*, covering the period from ca. 35 to 10 Ka in Europe, but the discovery of a genuine Neanderthal associated with the early Upper Paleolithic Chatelperronian industry at Saint-Césaire (France) necessitates a revision of this usage. The term *Cro-Magnon* has come to cover a wide range of fossil material associated with different "cultures," such as the Aurignacian, the Gravettian, the Solutrean, and the Magdalenian, and the extent to which it is legitimate to group this range of material is debatable.

While no one doubts that the Cro-Magnons do represent anatomically modern humans, they were undoubtedly distinct in a number of respects from modern Europeans. In some of these aspects, it is possible to see retained primitive characters, such as relatively large teeth and brows, but attempts to recognize these aspects as specifically retained from ancestral Neanderthals are generally unconvincing, and, in some respects, it is the Neanderthals who seem more derived in their characters. For example, the body proportions of the early Cro-Magnons were quite distinct from those of Neanderthals, since the lower portions of their arms and legs were elongated compared with the upper parts, whereas in the Neanderthals the lower portions were relatively shortened. In modern humans, this elongation is a pattern characteristic

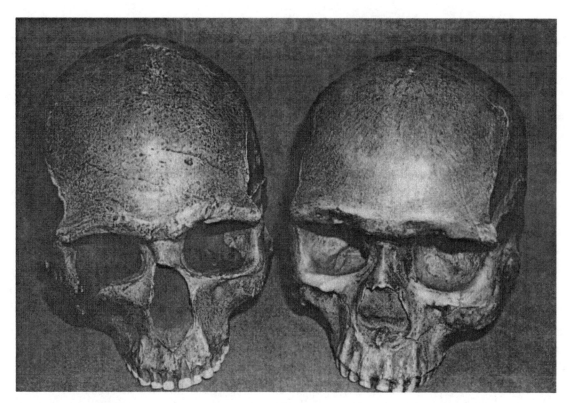

Two early modern human crania, each dated ca. 25 Ka: Předmosti 3 (left) from the Czech Republic, and Zhoukoudian Upper Cave 101 from China. Courtesy of Chris Stringer.

of warm-adapted populations, and this physique may be an early Cro-Magnon retention from African ancestors. Similar retentions may be observed in certain indices of facial shape (such as in possessing a shorter, flatter, and relatively broader face, with low orbits and short nose), and these features were present in Middle and early Late Pleistocene African specimens but not in Neanderthals.

Another feature that distinguished Neanderthals and early Cro-Magnons was the lower pelvic width/stature ratio of the latter, despite their overall similarity in estimated average body weight, probably comparable with that of modern Europeans. Cro-Magnon stature probably averaged more than 180 cm in males and ca. 167 cm in females, a significant increase over typical European Neanderthals (males ca. 167 cm and females ca. 160 cm). This tall, slender physique of the Cro-Magnons certainly more closely resembled that of the Levantine Skhūl and Qafzeh specimens than that of the Neanderthals, since average stature in the European and Israeli early moderns was virtually identical. There is uncertainty about the ancestral African pattern, but the little evidence that exists (e.g., Broken Hill, KNM-ER 999) suggests that it was more similar to that found in Eurasian early-modern, rather than Neanderthal, skeletons.

However, certain early Cro-Magnon specimens from eastern Europe do not fit so neatly into this distinct Neanderthal/Cro-Magnon dichotomy. These include Předmosti 3, a specimen with some Neanderthal-like features in facial shape. This arguably indicates the possibility that some gene flow did occur between late Neanderthal and early-modern humans in Europe during a probable period of coexistence between about 40 and 30 Ka, and a possible hybrid fossil between the two groups has even been claimed from the site of Hahnöfersand (Germany). This specimen is dated at ca. 33 Ka by radiocarbon but can be interpreted in a variety of ways. If such hybridization did occur, it appears to have been on a limited scale, and even then there is no certainty that such hybrids gave rise to later Europeans.

MODERN *HOMO SAPIENS* FOSSILS FROM OUTSIDE EUROPE

Early-modern fossils have been discovered in Africa and Southwest Asia, but those so far discussed probably all date to more than 35 Ka. Unfortunately, there is a dearth of Late Pleistocene human material from many of these areas, with the notable exception of the large North African collections from such sites as Afalou and Taforalt. What material there is suggests that, even at the end of the Pleistocene, there were still rather robust modern humans represented at such sites as Iwo Eleru (Nigeria), East Turkana (Kenya), and Springbok Flats and Boskop (South Africa). The Ishango skeletal material from eastern Zaire, recently redated to ca. 25 Ka, reflects a very robust but long-limbed population with some traits apparently linking them to modern Nilotic peoples. At the same time, there were other populations that already closely resembled the modern Khoisan (Bushman) peoples of southern Africa.

From the slender evidence available from central Asia, certain populations of the Late Pleistocene seem to have been physically and culturally related to those of the European Upper Paleolithic. Farther east, however, there is evidence of populations that may be related to modern aboriginal populations of eastern Asia and the Americas. Several partial skeletons from the Upper Cave at Zhoukoudian (China) may have represented a population close to the ancestry of Native Americans or Ainu (unfortunately, these specimens were lost at the same time as the main Zhoukoudian collection of *H. erectus* fossils). An isolated skull from Liujiang (China) and partial skeletons from Minatogawa (Japan) seem more similar in facial form to modern "Mongoloids" of Asia, suggesting that such "racial" differences were evolving by 20 Ka.

In Southeast Asia, there is possible evidence from the cave site of Niah (Borneo) that modern humans were present there by 40 ka, but this date needs further independent confirmation. Farther south, there is archaeological evidence that modern humans may have reached Australasia by 50 Ka, but the nature of the original colonists, and whether they represented a single population or multiple migrations from different source areas, is still unclear. The Mungo skeletons from southeastern Australia are dated at 34–24 Ka, and

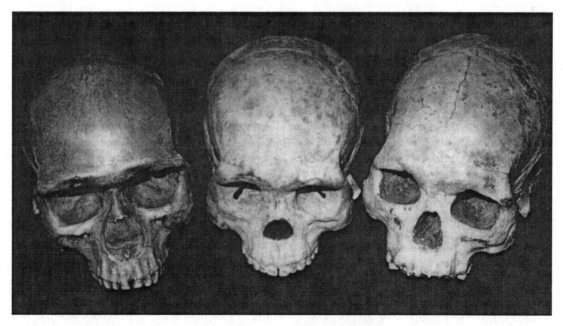

Three early modern human crania from eastern localities. From left: Zhoukoudian Upper Cave 101 and Liujang (both China); Keilor, Australia. Courtesy of Chris Stringer.

the most complete specimens (1 and 3) seem remarkably gracile by the standards of many early-modern humans from elsewhere in the world, or even in comparison with some populations today. The contrast is all the more marked because southeastern Australia was populated by much more robust peoples at the end of the Pleistocene, as represented by the Cohuna and Kow Swamp samples (now, unfortunately, reburied). Publications concerning this latter group have tended to emphasize the robusticity of some of the specimens, which is evident, but the sample also includes Mungo-like cranial and postcranial material.

One scenario postulates that two founder populations originally entered Australia, the first derived from Indonesian ancestors (such as Javanese *H. erectus* and the Ngandong material) and represented by the Kow Swamp, Cohuna, and Talgai specimens, while the other migrated into the region from the Asian mainland, as represented by the Mungo and Keilor fossils. These two groups coexisted through the later Pleistocene and eventually gave rise to modern Australian Aboriginal populations by hybridization. It is also possible to propose that there was only *one* founding population from either Indonesia or farther afield and that much variation was created within Australia as the huge unpopulated continent became colonized. This variation may also have been compounded by pathological factors and the practice of head binding, which was certainly responsible for some of the peculiarities in cranial shape among the Kow Swamp sample. What is probably the most archaic-looking specimen from Australia, however, might also be the most ancient, providing possible evidence of an Indonesian origin for at least some Pleistocene Australians. This skull (WLH 50) is still not published in detail, but if it can be accurately dated it could throw further light on the mysterious origins of modern *H. sapiens* in Australia. It is very large and angular, with a broad base, its cranial proportions are modern and its great cranial thickness may be due to pathology, rather than a link with Indonesian *H. erectus*.

See also Archaic Homo sapiens; Archaic Moderns; Border Cave; Cro-Magnon; Florisbad; Ishango; Jebel Irhoud; Kabwe; Kibish; Klasies River Mouth; Kow Swamp; Lagar Velho; Lake Mungo; Modern Human Origins; Neanderthals; Ngandong (Solo); Niah; Zhoukoudian. [C.B.S.]

FURTHER READINGS

Howells, W.W. (1976) Explaining modern man: Evolutionists versus migrationists. J. Hum. Evol. 5:477–495.
Kimbel, W.H., and Martin, L.B. eds. (1993) Species, Species Concepts, and Primate Evolution. New York: Plenum.
Kimbel, W.H., and Rak, Y. (1993) The importance of species taxa in Paleoanthropology and an argument for the phylogenetic concept of the species category. In W.H. Kimbel and L.B. Martin (eds.): Species, Species Concepts, and Primate Evolution. New York: Plenum, pp. 461–485.
Smith, F.H., and Spencer, F. eds. (1984) The Origins of Modern Humans. New York: Liss.
Tattersall, I. (1986) Species recognition in human paleontology. J. Hum. Evol. 15:165–175.
Tattersall, I. (1992) Species concepts and species identification in human evolution. J. Hum. Evol. 22:341–349.
Turner, A. (1986) Species, speciation, and human evolution. Hum. Evol. 1:419–430.

HOMOLOGY

Features of organisms that, by virtue of position, structure, or function, seem to be comparable are held to be homologous. In evolutionary theory, homologies are organismic attributes derived from a single ancestral condition. Thus, homologies may consist of very similar attributes (the eyes of all vertebrates) or very different ones (hair of mammals, feathers of birds, scales of reptiles). The term *homology* is usually contrasted with *analogy* (= *convergence*), in which attributes appear to be similar but have separate evolutionary origins (the wings of birds, bats, and pterosaurs are homologous as vertebrate forelimbs but analogous as wings; the wings of insects are only analogous with the wings of any vertebrate). By saying that certain features are homologous as structures of a given group, it is implied that the features so described are derived from the earlier structure in the ancestor of the broader group.

Evolution necessarily produces a complex nesting of adaptations (modified structures); these are homologies. In the reconstruction of evolutionary (phylogenetic) history, taxa (groups of species) are defined and recognized on the basis of features held in common, thus possibly derived from a single ancestral condition as homologies. Such restricted sets of homologous features are *synapomorphies*. Homology is a more general term (hair is a synapomorphy linking all mammals; hair is homologous with the dermal structures–feathers and scales–of birds and reptiles, respectively).

See also Adaptation(s); Cladistics; Evolution; Phylogeny. [N.E.]

FURTHER READINGS

Eldredge, N., and Cracraft, J. (1980) Phylogenetic Patterns and the Evolutionary Process. New York: Columbia University Press.

The author synthesizes anatomical, genetic, and archaeological evidence to reconstruct events at the origin of *Homo sapiens* and its subsequent expansion out of Africa. In this paper the author remains ambivalent about the precise time, place, and mechanisms involved in the origin of modern human anatomy and behavior.

27. Modern Human Origins

Progress and Prospects

By Chris Stringer

1. INTRODUCTION

Over the past ten years, one topic has dominated palaeo-anthropological debate—the origin of 'modern' humans. While it is generally agreed that Africa was the evolutionary homeland of Pliocene hominins (such as *Australopithecus*) and the earliest humans (members of the genus *Homo*), was it also the sole place of origin of our own species, *Homo sapiens*, during the Pleistocene (1.8–0.012 Myr ago) (see figure 1)? Originally centred on the fossil record, the debate has more recently drawn on archaeological and genetic data. The latter have become increasingly significant, and now even include DNA from Neanderthal fossils. Yet, despite the growth of such data, and the availability of increasingly sophisticated methods of analysis, there is still a perception in some quarters that the debate about modern human origins is sterile and as far from resolution as ever. In this review, I wish to discuss the impact of recent discoveries and analyses, and give my own perspective on the current debate, as well as discussing possible future progress. I hope to show that there are rich and stimulating differences of opinion and approach, even within the polarized factions that have grown up during the current vigorous debate, and that further exciting developments are imminent.

As discussed later, there is no agreement about the number of human species that have existed during the Pleistocene. For some workers there may have been only one—*H. sapiens* (e.g. Hawks *et al.* 2000*a*)—while for others, there may have been at least eight (e.g. Tattersall & Schwartz 2000). My preference lies between these extremes, and for the rest of this paper I will recognize and use four species names: *H. erectus*, its probable descendant *H. heidelbergensis*, and two probable descendant species of *H. heidelbergensis*: *H. neanderthalensis* and *H. sapiens*.

First, I will concentrate on the fossil records of Africa and western Eurasia. In order to discuss these in a consistent fashion, I am going to use the following morphologically based terms: '*Recent H. sapiens*' are members of the clade containing all living *H. sapiens* and their closest past relatives, inclusive of the last morphological common ancestor of the whole group. '*Archaic H. sapiens*' are members of the stem group (Smith 1994) of *H. sapiens*, more closely related to recent *H. sapiens* than are any members of the sister clade to *H. sapiens*, *H. neanderthalensis*, or the last common ancestor of *H. sapiens* and *H. neanderthalensis* which, in my view, is represented by the species *H. heidelbergensis*. *Homo sapiens* thus consists of the combination of the crown group of recent *H. sapiens* and the stem group of archaic *H. sapiens*. It should be noted that my usage of 'archaic *H. sapiens*' is distinct from, and more restricted than, others that may include Neanderthal or early Middle Pleistocene fossils from Europe and Africa. *Homo neanderthalensis* forms the sister clade to *H. sapiens*, and may be divided in a comparable fashion into 'late *H. neanderthalensis*' and 'archaic *H. neanderthalensis*'. The more primitive *H. heidelbergensis* represents the putative Middle Pleistocene ancestral species for the *H. sapiens* and *H. neanderthalensis* clades, and is used here for both Eurasian and African fossils.

The growing body of archaeological, morphological and genetic evidence concerning modern human origins is still generally assessed against two contrasting models known as 'Recent African Origin' (also called 'Out of Africa', 'African Replacement', or simply 'Replacement' model) and 'Multiregional Evolution' (also sometimes called 'Regional Continuity'). However, as Aiello (1993) discussed, there are two other models of modern human evolution that also merit consideration (figure 2). One ('Hybridization and Replacement') can be viewed as a variant of Recent African Origin, while the other ('Assimilation') combines elements of Recent African Origin and Multiregional Evolution. Aiello summarized them as follows (my editing [ ]):

1. [*Recent African Origin*] argues that modern humans first arose in Africa about 100 000 years ago and spread from there throughout the world.... Indigenous premodern populations in other areas of the world were replaced by the migrating populations with little, if any, hybridization between the groups [figure 2*a*].

2. *The (African) Hybridization and Replacement Model* is similar to the above, but allows for a greater or lesser extent of hybridization between the migrating population and the indigenous premodern populations... [figure 2*b*; Bräuer 1992].

3. *The Assimilation Model* also accepts an African origin for modern humans. However, it differs from the previous models in denying replacement, or population migration, as a major factor in the appearance of modern human.... Rather, this model emphasizes the importance of gene flow, admixture, changing selection pressures, and resulting directional morphological change [figure 2*c*].

4. [*Multiregional Evolution*] differs from the previous three in denying a recent African origin for modern humans.... It emphasizes the role of both genetic continuity over time and gene flow between contemporaneous populations in arguing that modern humans arose not only in Africa but also in Europe and Asia from their Middle Pleistocene forebears [figure 2*d*].

5. I discussed the development of Recent African Origin models in Stringer (1994). From 1980 to 1986, early Recent African Origin proposals argued that modern humans evolved in Africa about 100 thousand years (kyr) ago, spread to Western Asia by about 45 kyr, and to Europe by about 35 kyr. However, uncertainties about the records from the Far East and Australasia led to greater caution about events there, and a reluctance to propose a global model. Some early Recent African Origin formulations were implicitly punctuational, with the assumption of a relatively late evolution of a package of 'modern' morphological and behavioural features, and their subsequent rapid spread from Africa. This package included, morphologically, a high and midsagittally rounded cranial vault, a mental eminence and a lightly built skeleton, and behaviourally, the presence of blade tools, symbolism and (inferred) complex language. At this stage total replacement models, in which it was argued that archaic populations living outside Africa had become completely extinct, were rarely articulated due to the lack of relevant fossil evidence from many regions and time periods. Thus, the distinction between models 1 and 2 was not made in early presentations of Recent African Origin models.

From 1986 two significant developments began to force modification of the original models. The first was the development and application of new dating techniques that could reach beyond the range of conventional radiocarbon dating (*ca.*

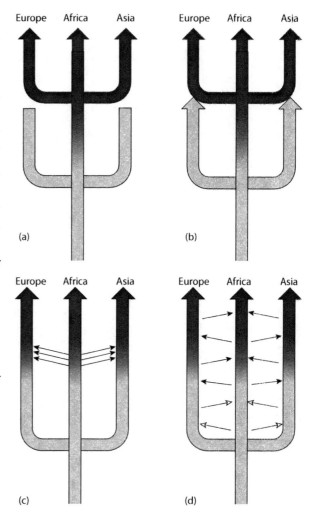

Figure 1. This comparison of late Pleistocene crania from Liujiang, China (a) and Fish Hoek, South Africa (b) highlights a central issue in modern human origins research. The cranium from Liujiang is seen by some workers as a link between archaic and recent Chinese populations, yet this visual comparison conforms with metrical analyses in showing its close resemblance to an African fossil from over 10 000 km away. Does such a resemblance reflect the late Pleistocene dispersal of a shared 'modern' morphology, or gene flow between different regions? Scale bar, 50 mm.

40 kyr), in particular, luminescence applied to burnt stone tools, and electron spin resonance applied to fossil mammal tooth enamel (Taylor & Aitken 1997). These applications made their greatest impact on the dating of Neanderthal and early modern human burial sites in Israel, although they have also affected reconstructions of events elsewhere (Grün & Stringer 1991; Stringer 2001*a*). The second development was the increasing impact of genetic data on the debate, leading to greater polarization and a hardening of some Recent African Origin proposals in the direction of complete replacement (model 1, above). Pioneering genetic work on the reconstruction of early human evolution had been conducted by researchers such as Cavalli-Sforza & Bodmer (1971) and Nei & Roychoudhury (1982), but it was not until the late 1980s that clearer resolution started to become possible using genetic systems such as betaglobins (e.g. Wainscoat *et al.* 1986) and, in particular, mitochondrial DNA (mtDNA; e.g. Cann *et al.* 1987).

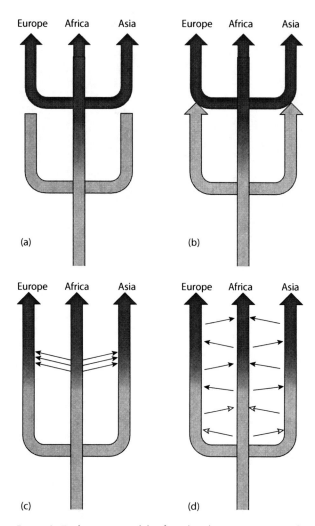

Figure 2. Evolutionary models of modern human origins (modified from Aiello 1993). (a) Recent African Origin; (b) (African) Hybridization and Replacement Model; (c) Assimilation Model; (d) Multiregional Evolution.

The Assimilation Model (3, above) arose through integration of the emerging evidence for an important African role in modern human origins with multiregional views. It was developed by Smith (1992), who was originally a multiregionalist. Other multiregionalists also modified their position, although less explicitly. Aspects of the original Multiregional Model (4, above) can be found in Thorne & Wolpoff (1992, p. 83), where it is summarized as follows: 'Human evolution happened everywhere because every area was always part of the whole'. It was argued that each inhabited area showed a continuous anatomic sequence leading to modern humans, and those outside Africa showed no special African influence.

By 1997, Wolpoff and some colleagues had in many respects shifted to a position close to that of the Assimilation Model (Wolpoff & Caspari 1997). Because this shift was not explicit, I have distinguished it from the original Multiregional Model by the designation 'Multiregional 2' (Stringer 2001*b*). Multiregional 2 argues that an African influence predominated throughout Pleistocene human evolution because of larger population size, while populations outside Africa were more vulnerable to bottle-necking and extinctions. Thus, modern populations would mainly have African-derived genes and African-derived morphological characters, although these were predominantly acquired through gene flow, rather than via rapid replacement. It is argued that modern genes and characters accumulated over the entire Pleistocene within a genetic exchange network dominated by Africa (Hawks *et al.* 2000*a*).

There is now more than enough fossil evidence to demonstrate that most of the characters claimed to link archaic and recent populations in the same areas under multiregional evolution are either retained plesiomorphies or are not homologous (e.g. Stringer 1992; Lahr 1996). Neither the distinctive characteristics of the species *H. sapiens*, nor those of its modern regional variants, were present in the earlier Pleistocene, and this is supported by the absence of such characters even in Middle Pleistocene fossil samples that, on morphological grounds, may represent ancestors of Neanderthals and recent humans (see below). As is also discussed below, the estimated date for the mitochondrial last common ancestor of Neanderthals and recent humans is between 317 and 741 kyr, and this range of dates would appear to set another maximum age for the appearance of recent characters that were not already present in the common ancestor with Neanderthals. The original version of Multiregional Evolution thus appears no longer tenable, even to its previous adherents, while the data just discussed appear sufficient to falsify the aspects of Multiregional 2 that really distinguish it from the Assimilation Model (i.e. stipulation of the entire Pleistocene time-scale for the establishment of novel *H. sapiens* characters rather than a later Pleistocene one). Moreover, despite the careful arguments of Relethford (1999), the level of gene flow required to spread the ubiquitous modern morphology under Multiregional 2 would appear incompatible with the claimed parallel long-term maintenance of regional features in small peripheral populations.

All of the remaining models focus on the central importance of Africa in modern human origins during the later Pleistocene, while differing over the mechanisms by which modern characters spread from the continent and the relative importance of any extra-African genetic input. Therefore, in the rest of this article I will concentrate on the following aspects of the Middle–Upper Pleistocene fossil evidence: the origin of *H. neanderthalensis* and *H. sapiens*; the early African record of *H. sapiens*; the western Eurasian record of *H. neanderthalensis* and *H. sapiens*; and the later Pleistocene records of eastern Asia and Australasia (see figure 3). I will then discuss the relevance of recent genetic data and, finally, review recent and possible future developments in this research area, including a discussion of the concept of modernity.

2. THE ORIGIN OF *H. NEANDERTHALENSIS* AND *H. SAPIENS*

The European fossil human record of the Middle to Late Pleistocene has grown appreciably during the past decade, especially with the discovery of large skeletal samples from the Sierra de Atapuerca (Spain). This locality has produced important earlier (Gran Dolina—GD) and later (Sima de los Huesos—SH) fossil samples. The early component, dated at *ca.* 800 kyr, has been claimed to represent a new species ('*H. antecessor*'; Bermú-dez de Castro *et al.* 1997) that was the last common ancestor of *H. neanderthalensis* and *H. sapiens*. It is argued that this species gave rise to *H. heidelbergensis* in Europe, which in turn evolved into *H. neanderthalensis*. A parallel African descendant lineage of '*H. antecessor*' gave rise to *H. sapiens*. However, while I recognize the distinctiveness of the '*H. antecessor*' material, I am cautious about its taxonomic status, and in particular about the phylogenetic significance placed on the 'modern' morphology of the infraorbital region of the immature individual ATD6-69. The adult form of this fossil may be represented by the approximately contemporaneous Ceprano cranium (Manzi *et al.* 2001), and if so, this shows much less similarity to *H. sapiens*. In addition, there is enough variation in the infraorbital region of African and European hominins from the Middle Pleistocene to warrant caution about the taxonomic value of this character. In my view (cf. Manzi *et al.* 2001), the '*H. antecessor*' material and Ceprano may represent a transitional form between *H. erectus* and *H. heidelbergensis*. Thus, for the moment, I still prefer to group early Middle Pleistocene European (e.g. Arago, Petralona and Mauer) and African (e.g. Bodo, Broken Hill and Salé) material in *H. heidelbergensis* as representing the common ancestral species for *H. neanderthalensis* and *H. sapiens*. This usage is very comparable to that of Right-mire (1998).

The Middle Pleistocene European sequence shows an accretional (mosaic and gradual) appearance of Neanderthal characters (Hublin 1998; Stringer 1998*b*), but I would argue that this process only becomes marked towards the end of the Middle Pleistocene, making a clade origination with '*H. antecessor*' some 500 000 years earlier less probable. However, the apparent gradual nature of Neanderthal evolution does make recognition of the species/clade origin difficult. This is an important question, because if *H. neanderthalensis* is our sister group, then its origin also marks the origin of our own clade (Stringer & Hublin 1999). The inference of an early origin would imply that *H. sapiens* clade characters should be present in African fossils right through the Middle Pleistocene, but I would argue that these are not recognizable in fossils such as Bodo, Broken Hill and Salé, only appearing in the late Middle Pleistocene.

An alternative model of Neanderthal and recent human origins is that of Foley & Lahr (1997), who have hypothesized an even later divergence between Neanderthals and *H. sapiens*, *ca.* 250 kyr, linking this with the development of prepared core or levallois (Mode 3; Clark 1968, and table 1) technology in the 'Mode 3 Hypothesis'. In turn, they relate this archaeological innovation to the African species '*H. helmei*', based on the Florisbad cranium (now directly dated to *ca.* 260 kyr; Grün *et al.* 1996). In their view, '*H. helmei*' evolved from *H. heidelbergensis* in Africa and then dispersed to give rise to Neanderthals in Eurasia, and modern humans in Africa. '*H. helmei*' carried the newly derived Mode 3 technology with it during its late Middle Pleistocene dispersal. For Lahr and Foley (Foley & Lahr 1997; Lahr & Foley 1998), '*H. helmei*' is represented by African fossils such as Florisbad and Jebel Irhoud, perhaps ultimately ancestral to *H. sapiens*, and European fossils such as Atapuerca SH and Ehringsdorf, ancestral to the Neanderthals. Their use of '*H. helmei*' hence differs from mine (e.g. Stringer 1996) when I argued that this species might lie within the modern clade, as an evolutionary intermediate between *H. heidelbergensis* and *H. sapiens*.

While I appreciate the rationale behind the Mode 3 hypothesis, I do not consider it provides a realistic model for the origins of *H neanderthalensis* and *H. sapiens*. First, Neanderthal characteristics were already evolving in Europe prior to the hypothesized appearance and dispersal of '*H. helmei*', e.g. in the Swanscombe specimen, dated to *ca.* 400 kyr (Stringer & Hublin 1999). Second, African specimens such as Florisbad and Jebel Irhoud make unparsimonious ancestors for the Neanderthals, since not only do they post-date the appearance of Neanderthal clade characters in Europe, but they appear to lack Nean-derthal morphological characteristics that might be expected in a common ancestor. A large cranial capacity is cited by Lahr and Foley (Foley & Lahr 1997; Lahr & Foley 1998), but this is highly variable in Middle Pleistocene fossils and is more evident in the European fossils that might be assigned to '*H. helmei*', such as Atapuerca SH4 and Ehringsdorf calvaria 9, than in African examples.

Usage of Mode 3 technology as an ancestral 'taxo-nomic' characteristic is also problematic, in my opinion. This is partly because technologies might transfer between distinct populations or even different species, as has been hypothesized for the spread of Upper Palaeolithic elements in Europe (see below), but also because the time and place of origin of prepared core techniques are currently unknown. These apparently existed in Europe and Africa (Roebroeks & Gamble 1999; McBrearty & Brooks 2000) by Oxygen Isotope Stage 9 (OIS 9 *ca.* 325 kyr ago), but it is unclear in which area, or areas, they originated. Their origin may have

Table 1. Time relationships of technological categories in western Eurasia and sub-Saharan Africa. (The earliest archaeological record extends beyond 1.8 Myr in Africa. The alternative 'Mode' nomenclature was introduced by Clark (1968).)

AGE (KYR)	STRATIGRAPHIC	WESTERN EURASIA	AFRICA
12	—	—	
		Upper Palaeolithic	Later Stone Age
		(Mode 4)	
	Upper Pleistocene	—	—
		Middle Palaeolithic	Middle Stone Age
		(Mode 3)	
130	—	—	
	Middle Pleistocene		
790	—	Lower Palaeolithic	Early Stone Age
	Lower Pleistocene	(Modes 1–2)	
1800	—		

been African, as Lahr and Foley (Foley & Lahr 1997; Lahr & Foley 1998) propose, European or Asian, or the concept might even have been developed independently in different regions. But if Mode 3 technology does identify the ancestor of *H. neanderthalensis*, this was already present in Europe during OIS 9.

Thus, I question the evidence not only for an early Middle Pleistocene origin for the Neanderthal and modern human clades, based on '*H. antecessor*' as the last common ancestor, but also for a late Middle Pleistocene divergence implied by the Mode 3 hypothesis. Instead, I believe that *H. heidelbergensis*, present in the Middle Pleistocene of both Europe and Africa, represents the probable common ancestral species for *H. neanderthalensis* and *H. sapiens* in the later Middle Pleistocene. In principle, recognizing the origin of either descendant species (*H. neanderthalensis* or *H. sapiens*) would indicate the time of origin of our own species. Neanderthal mitochondrial DNA has been used to estimate a Neanderthal/*H. sapiens* clade separation at *ca.* 600 kyr (see below), and this in turn has been used to support the view of a deep separation time for the Neanderthal–modern clades, as suggested by the '*H. antecessor*' material. However, using the analogy of recent human diversification, a rather different conclusion can be reached. This is because genetic differentiation inevitably precedes population and specific differentiation. It is probable that *H. sapiens* has been diverging genetically for some 150 kyr, and yet we are unquestionably still a single species. Thus, for a period of time, mtDNA differences must have been accumulating *within* a Middle Pleistocene species (?*H. heidelbergensis*) prior to cladogenesis. Hence, an estimated mtDNA coalescent date of *ca.* 600 kyr in fact provides a *maximum* age for any specific separation of *H. neanderthalensis* and *H. sapiens*.

This also raises the question of the evolution of morphological characteristics, and again analogy with recent *H. sapiens* is useful. If human evolution was continuing to take its Pleistocene course, present human populations in, say, Africa, Europe or Australia might eventually form new species. Looked at from a perspective half a million years in the future, it would be possible to detect genetic or morphological apomorphies characterizing the nascent species *within* present-day populations, i.e. recent geographic variants of *H. sapiens* would contain clade features of the future distinct species. This illustrates a fundamental point that apomorphies characterizing new species must necessarily originate within previously existing species. Therefore, the fact that some fossils attributed to *H. heidelbergensis* (such as Mauer and Petralona) display apomorphies characteristic of *H. neanderthalensis* does not necessarily require their attribution to the Neanderthal clade, contrary to some arguments (e.g. those of Arsuaga *et al.* 1997; Bermúdez de Castro *et al.* 1997). As an example, metrical and morphological studies instead suggest that variation between the European Petralona cranium and the African Broken Hill cranium is comparable to the differences found today between geographically distinct populations of *H. sapiens* (Seidler *et al.* 1997). I would argue that *H. heidelbergensis* was a geographically widespread and diverse species that gave rise to *H. neanderthalensis* in Eurasia, and *H. sapiens* in Africa (cf. Rightmire 1998).

Finally, what might have driven the cladogenesis that culminated in *H. neanderthalensis* and *H. sapiens*? The ancestral, geographically dispersed populations would have been repeatedly bottlenecked as glacial–interglacial cycles intensified during the Middle Pleistocene. They would inevitably have diverged genetically and morphologically with the heightened effectiveness, during climatic changes, of biogeographic barriers such as an enlarged Caspian Sea and the cold, arid uplands of the Anatolian–Iranian plateaux. Possible gene exchange between eastern Europe and the Levant would thus have been regularly disrupted or prevented. Surviving populations in the, at times, arid Levant would also have been increasingly genetically isolated from those south of the Sahara. Thus, in my view, regional characters began to develop and accumulate in *H. heidelbergensis*, including idiosyncratic 'Neanderthal' cranial features found in European material from Arago, Petralona and Swanscombe, as well as those that might be related to climatic adaptation (e.g. comparing the tibia from Boxgrove with that from Broken Hill; Stringer *et al.* (1998)). While I would argue that the Atapuerca SH material represents archaic *H. neanderthalensis*, I recognize that it can equally be regarded as a late and derived form of the ancestral species *H. heidelbergensis*.

3. THE AFRICAN RECORD

The pattern of human evolution in Africa remains less well understood than that of Europe, but the developing picture suggests that there are parallels between the two continents. Twenty-five years ago the prevailing view, based mainly on radiocarbon dating, was that although the earliest humans may have originated in Africa, subsequent human development lagged behind that of Europe. Thus, the earliest technological stage, the Lower Palaeolithic, was believed to have continued in Africa until *ca.* 50 kyr, whereas the subsequent Middle Stone Age may have only given way to the Later Stone Age at *ca.* 12 kyr, some 25 kyr later than the equivalent Middle–Upper Palaeolithic transition in Europe. The hominin sequence was thought to be comparably retarded, with the archaic Broken Hill cranium (Zambia) perhaps dated to 130 kyr, and the somewhat less archaic Florisbad (South Africa) specimen dated to *ca.* 40 kyr (Stringer 2001*a*).

The situation now is dramatically different. Argon–argon dating has shown that stone tool making began in Africa by at least 2.3 Myr, and the whole time-scale of the African Palaeolithic has been stretched back in time (Klein 1999). The Middle Stone Age is now believed to have begun by at least 250 kyr and the transition to the Later Stone Age began prior to 45 kyr (table 1). Thus, the African record can now be seen to be in concert with, or even in advance of, the record from Eurasia. The hominin record has been similarly reassessed. Biostratigraphic correlation suggests that the Broken Hill cranium (*H. heidelbergensis*) probably dates from at least 300 kyr (Klein 1999), while a combination of electron spin resonance dating on human tooth enamel and luminescence dating of sediments suggests that the Florisbad cranium—an archaic *H. sapiens*—actually dates from *ca.* 260 kyr rather than the former estimate of *ca.* 40 kyr (Grün *et al.* 1996).

Fossil specimens showing mosaic archaic–modern *H. sapiens* characters from Guomde (Kenya) and Singa (Sudan) are now dated by gamma rays, and a combination of electron spin resonance and uranium series, to at least 150 kyr (Bräuer *et al.* 1997) and 133 kyr (McDermott *et al.* 1996). *Homo sapiens* fossils such as Omo Kibish 1 (Ethiopia), Border Cave 1 (South Africa) and those from the Middle Stone Age levels of the Klasies River Mouth Caves (South Africa) are of comparable, or somewhat younger, age, although much of this material is fragmentary and difficult to date more precisely (Klein 1999). Overall, the picture of human evolution in Africa over the last 300 kyr can now be seen to parallel that of Europe. Both regions appear to show a mosaic and perhaps gradual transition from *H. heidelbergensis* to a more derived species: in Europe *H. neanderthalensis*, and in Africa *H. sapiens* (Bräuer *et al.* 1997; Rightmire 1998; Stringer 1998*b*).

If this model of gradual, regional, evolution can be applied to the African fossil record, an accretional mode of *H. sapiens* evolution would consequently be expected (Stringer 1998*b*). In which case, how can we recognize when identifiably 'modern' humans appear? So far, I have avoided further discussion of the term 'modern', but it will be necessary to discuss the use of this important but complex concept in detail later. However, the term is generally used to contrast the shared characteristics of recent humans (whether morphological, behavioural or cultural) with those of earlier (non-modern or archaic) humans. Unfortunately, there are no generally agreed definitions or diagnoses of the term as applied to the fossil or archaeological record. Moreover, acceptance of a gradualistic scenario for the origin of modernity means that diagnosing 'modernity' will be dependent on the particular criteria selected. In addition, in the case of morphology, while individual anatomical characters may be used to recognize which fossils belong to the *H. sapiens* clade, membership of this clade will not necessarily be synonymous with modernity as an assemblage, since this may have evolved long after the cladistic origin of *H. sapiens* (which, in my view, was at the *H. neanderthalensis–H. sapiens* cladogenetic event). Thus, fossils such as Florisbad, Singa, and even those from Skhul and Qafzeh, probably belong to *H. sapiens* cladistically, but do not necessarily represent 'modern' humans.

4. THE WESTERN EURASIAN RECORD

The Levant occupies a unique geographical position linking Africa and Eurasia, but its Middle Pleistocene hominin record is much poorer than that of adjoining regions. Only fragmentary specimens from sites such as Zuttiyeh and the lower levels of Tabun provide physical evidence of the Levantine human populations before *ca.* 130 kyr, but they are insufficient to provide much information about the nature of those populations (Klein 1999). Interpretations of the regional fossil record after this period have undergone some remarkable upheavals brought about by the application of new dating techniques. As late as 1985, it was believed by most workers that the pattern of population change in this area paralleled that of Europe, or rather preceded it by a small amount of time. Thus, Neanderthals at Israeli sites such as Tabun and Amud evolved into, or gave way to, early modern humans such as those known from Skhul and Qafzeh by *ca.* 40 kyr ago (e.g. Trinkaus 1984). For some workers technological and biological changes were inter-linked, leading to an evolution of modern humans in the region, and it was postulated that these early moderns could then have migrated into Europe, giving rise to the Cro-Magnons (the term used for Upper Palaeolithicasso-ciated *H. sapiens* in Europe). One of the first applications of the newer chronometric techniques (thermo-luminescence applied to burnt flint) seemed to reinforce this pattern, dating a recently discovered Neanderthal burial at Kebara in the anticipated time-range of *ca.* 60 kyr ago (Valladas *et al.* 1987).

Shortly afterwards, the first application was made to the site of the Qafzeh early modern material, giving a surprisingly old age estimate of *ca.* 90 kyr, more than twice the generally expected figure. Further applications of non-radiocarbon dating methods have amplified the pattern suggested by the age estimates for Qafzeh and Kebara (see reviews in Grün & Stringer 1991; Klein 1999). It seems probable that the early modern burials at Qafzeh and Skhul date from more than 90 kyr, and some may be as old as 130 kyr. The Neanderthal burials at Kebara and Amud date younger than this figure, in the range 50–60 kyr ago. As the intervening period approximates the transition from the supposedly predominantly interglacial stage 5 to predominantly glacial stage 4, this has led to a proposed scenario where Neanderthals only appeared in the Levant after the onset of glaciation further North (Akazawa *et al.* 1998).

In this context, it has been difficult to establish the age of the Tabun Neanderthal burial, for two different reasons. First, while age estimates for the stratigraphy at Tabun based on electron spin resonance and luminescence both considerably stretch the late Pleistocene time-scale previously proposed for the site into the Middle Pleistocene, the methods do not give compatible results. Luminescence estimates from burnt flint excavated from the rear of the cave are much older than electron spin resonance estimates from mammal teeth from correlated levels nearer the mouth of the cave (compare Grün *et al.* (1991) with Mercier *et al.* 1995). Second, the stratigraphic position of the Tabun burial cannot be established with certainty over 60 years after its excavation, giving further doubt about its actual age (Garrod & Bate 1937; Bar-Yosef & Callander 1999). Direct non-destructive gamma ray (uranium series) dating of the mandible and leg bones from this skeleton had suggested a surprisingly young age of less than 40 kyr (Schwarcz *et al.* 1998). However, the accuracy of this estimate was questioned (Millard & Pike 1999; Alperson *et al.* 2000) and direct electron spin resonance dating of a tooth enamel fragment from a molar on the mandible has now given a much older age estimate of *ca.* 120 kyr (Grün & Stringer 2000). Thus, the extent of

Neanderthal–early modern contemporaneity in the Levant over the period 90–130 kyr ago is still an open question, but given that the region lies in the potential overlap zone of range expansions of either the evolving African *H. sapiens* lineage or that of Eurasian Neanderthals, this was certainly probable (Stringer 1998*b*). Yet, after this time, the Neanderthals appear to have predominated in the region until *ca.* 45 kyr ago, when the development of new technology and behaviour by early modern humans may have fuelled major range expansions, heralding the eventual extinction of the Neanderthals.

Having discussed the beginning of the Neanderthal and modern human lineages and their presence in western Asia, I will now examine the fate of the Neanderthals. New luminescence and electron spin resonance dating, in concert with the accelerator radiocarbon technique (which requires much smaller samples of organic material than conventional methods), has generally confirmed previous views of the Middle/Upper Palaeolithic sequence, but with some additional complexity, especially in Europe. Upper Palaeolithic industries such as the Aurignacian, by inference associated with early modern humans, have been dated in parts of Eurasia (e.g. northern Spain and Hungary) by luminescence, electron spin resonance, uranium series or radiocarbon accelerator methods to *ca.* 40 kyr. Middle Palaeolithic (Mousterian) industries, actually or presumably associated with Neanderthals, start to disappear from some areas of Europe from about this time. However, both the old favoured models of rapid *in situ* evolution of Neanderthals into Cro-Magnons or a rapid replacement of Neanderthals by them can now be shown to be invalid. Late Neanderthal levels at French sites such as Le Moustier and Saint-Césaire have been dated in the range 35–40 kyr ago, while those at Arcy have been radiocarbon dated at *ca.* 32 kyr ago (Mellars 1999). These dates may well be compatible, given that radiocarbon dates at this period could underestimate calendar ages by several millennia (Stringer & Davies 2001). Moreover, Neanderthal fossils have now been dated at *ca.* 30 000 radiocarbon years in areas such as Southern Spain, Croatia and the Caucasus, and regions such as southern Iberia and the Crimea show a parallel persistence of Middle Palaeolithic industries (e.g. Hublin *et al.* 1995; Smith *et al.* 1999; Ovchinnikov *et al.* 2000). If these dates and associations are accurate, it appears that Neanderthals survived quite late in some regions, and had a potential coexistence with the Cro-Magnons of at least ten millennia.

The previous relatively clear picture of the Middle Palaeolithic/Neanderthal and Upper Palaeolithic/*H. sapiens* interface in Europe has also become cloudier since the identification of Neanderthal remains in Châtelperronian (early Upper Palaeolithic) levels at the French sites of Saint-Césaire and Arcy (Hublin *et al.* 1996). Moreover, there is an apparent association of Neanderthals with symbolic artefacts such as pendants at Arcy. Furthermore, it has been suggested that other industries with supposed Upper Palaeolithic affinities in central Europe (Szeletian) and Italy (Uluzzian) may also have been the handiwork of late Neanderthals (see reviews in d'Errico *et al.* 1998; Klein 1999). Thus, the Neanderthals appear to show some of the same technological and behavioural innovations as the Cro-Magnons. For some researchers (e.g. Klein 1999; Mellars 1999), this late pattern of regionalization in the Neanderthals reflects the final fragmentation of their formerly continent-wide range, while in contrast the wide distribution of the Aurignacian reflects the dispersal of early modern humans across much of Europe. Present dating evidence no longer clearly demonstrates a wave of advance of the Aurignacian, since its oldest mani-festations may be as ancient in northern Spain as in the east of the continent. The assumed external source for the Aurignacian and its manufacturers is also now unclear, and it remains possible that *H. sapiens* first arrived in the region with a pre-Aurignacian, even Middle Palaeolithic, technology. Such a precursor industry that might mark the appearance of early modern pioneers, although currently without diagnostic fossil material, is the Bohunician of eastern Europe, dated beyond 40 000 radiocarbon years (Stringer & Davies 2001).

Workers such as Zilhão and Trinkaus have proposed still greater complexity in the European picture (e.g. d'Errico *et al.* 1998; Duarte *et al.* 1999). To them, Middle–Upper Palaeolithic transitions are indicative of complex and changing population dynamics as incoming Cro-Magnons mixed and merged with native

Neanderthals over many millennia. In this scenario, the Neanderthals were arguably as culturally advanced as the Cro-Magnons, and were simply absorbed into a growing Cro-Magnon gene pool. It is even claimed that a hybrid child has been discovered at Lagar Velho in Portugal, dated to *ca.* 25 000 radiocarbon years (Duarte *et al.* 1999), but this claim remains unresolved until more detailed studies have been published. Whatever the outcome of that particular proposal (and I still consider that this may represent an unusually stocky modern human child), the impact of new dates and discoveries in Europe shows that the whole gamut of population interactions between the last Neanderthals and the first Cro-Magnons could, and perhaps did, occur, ranging from conflict to possible interbreeding. Nevertheless, the outcome of these processes was the extinction of the Neanderthals after a long period of survival in the challenging and unstable climates of Pleistocene Europe. MtDNA studies, discussed later, suggest that the genes of the earliest Cro-Magnons are not necessarily well represented in recent Europeans, because of intervening replacement or bottlenecking (Richards & Macaulay 2000). Therefore, any small Neanderthal genetic component 30 kyr ago could easily have been subsequently lost.

5. THE LATER PLEISTOCENE RECORDS OF EAST ASIA AND AUSTRALASIA

Homo erectus was present in both China and Indonesia prior to 1 Myr ago (Culotta 1995; Klein 1999). The largest sample of Chinese material of this species, from the Zhoukoudian Lower Cave, is now dated at *ca.* 400–500 kyr by uranium series and electron spin resonance, and comparable southern Chinese material from Hexian is of similar, or somewhat younger, age (Grün *et al.* 1997, 1998). Other Middle Pleistocene fossils are indicative of morphological and perhaps, specific diversity, but limited knowledge of them has prevented their integration into the wider fossil record. Relatively complete, but heavily distorted, cranial material from the site of Yunxian (Etler 1996) may exhibit variation away from the standard *H. erectus* pattern towards that of *H. heidelbergensis*, while a partial cranium from Nanjing, still not described in detail, even appears reminiscent of Neanderthals in nasal, although not maxillary, morphology (C. Stringer, personal observation). These populations were apparently succeeded by more derived humans formerly attributed to 'archaic *H. sapiens*', represented by fossils from sites such as Jinniushan and Dali, and dated to *ca.* 250–300 kyr ago (Etler 1996; Yin *et al.* 2001). Their affinities are still unclear, with some workers (e.g. Etler 1996) seeing them as descended from local *H. erectus* antecedents, others (e.g. C. Stringer; Lahr 1996; Rightmire 1998) regarding them as possible eastern representatives of *H. heidelbergensis*. The isolated Narmada calvaria from India (Klein 1999) may also represent such a population (figure 3). Fragmentary early late Pleistocene fossils (*ca.* 100 kyr) from Chinese sites such as Xujiayo and Maba may record further local evolution, with Maba showing possible affinity to western Eurasian Neanderthals. However, the arrival of *H. sapiens* in the region is still poorly dated and poorly understood. That arrival must precede the modern human fossils known from the Upper Cave (Shandingdong) at Zhoukoudian, dated by radiocarbon on associated fauna to between 12 and 30 kyr ago, and might even extend back beyond 70 kyr if the Liujiang skeleton (figure 1) is of that age (Shen & Wang 2001). On the basis of cranial data, neither these specimens nor the late Pleistocene Minatogawa material from Japan seem very closely related to recent populations in the region (Brown 1999; Stringer 1999), and may provide evidence of early diversity that is either now lost or survives in the form of aboriginal iso-lates such as the Ainu of Hokkaido and the Andamanese Islanders.

In Indonesia, several *H. erectus* fossils have been indirectly dated to *ca.* 1.7 Myr ago using argon–argon dating on volcanic sediments (Klein 1999), although some workers doubt that the fossils have been correctly associated with the dated rocks (Culotta 1995). Other *H. erectus* fossils are dated by combinations of argon–argon, palaeo-magnetics and biostratigraphy to between 500 kyr and 1.2 Myr ago (Klein 1999). The Ngandong and Sambung-macan fossils have been even more controversially dated to less than 50 kyr by electron spin resonance and uranium series on associated fauna, implying a survival of *H. erectus* in Indonesia as late as Neanderthals survived in Eurasia (Swisher *et al.* 1996). Other workers have argued that these dates must be underestimates (Grün & Thorne 1997), but further uranium series determinations, including direct measurements on the fossils, do support these dates (Falgue`res *et al.* 2001). The date of arrival of modern humans in the region is still uncertain, but given the evidence from Australia discussed below it must lie before 60 kyr. Known fossils such as Wajak (Java) and Niah (Sarawak) remain poorly dated, but may derive from the late Pleistocene.

Exactly when humans first arrived in Australia has been unclear until recently. Sites such as Malakunanja II, Nawalabila and Devil's Lair appear to contain artefacts or evidence of human–faunal interaction dating from at least 50 kyr, based on luminescence or minimum-age radiocarbon dates (Roberts *et al.* 1990, 1994; Turney *et al.* 2001). However, in none of these sites were associated human remains preserved, thus leaving the nature of the first Australians uncertain. Two different views have pre-dominated in recent debate about the peopling of Australia. For some workers, there were two original colonizations of the continent (Thorne & Wolpoff 1992; Frayer *et al.* 1993). An early colonization, originating from the archaic people of Java (here regarded as *H. erectus*, although regarded as early *H. sapiens* by some of the last group of authors) introduced a robust population at, perhaps, 50 kyr ago. This colonization event was supposedly represented by the Willandra Lakes human fossil known as WLH-50 (Willandra Lakes Human-50), and by sub-sequent populations sampled at sites such as Kow Swamp, Cohuna and Coobol Creek. A second colonization, pur-portedly derived from China, arrived via an eastern route and brought the more gracile people known from the Mungo fossils at *ca.* 30 kyr ago and sampled at later sites such as Keilor and King Island. Under this dual origin hypothesis, present day Australian Aboriginal variation is the result of Holocene hybridization between these robust and gracile peoples. A second, contrasting, view saw the robust and gracile peoples as parts of a single morphologically variable population. Their differences probably developed within Australia following a single colonization event, with recent Aborigines representing the end product of this process (Pardoe 1991; Brown 1992).

Recently, the Mungo 3 burial has been redated using a combination of the techniques of gamma ray uranium series dating on skull fragments, electron spin resonance on a piece of tooth enamel, uranium series on attached sediment, and optically stimulated luminescence applied to the sands containing the burial (Thorne *et al.* 1999). The dates obtained are 62 ± 6 kyr, approximately double the ages originally estimated from radiocarbon (Bowler & Thorne 1976). By correlation, these new age estimates may also apply to the Mungo 1 cremated individual found nearby. There has been critical debate about the accuracy of these new determinations (Grün *et al.* 2000), although even critics appear to accept that Mungo 1 and 3 are older than previously thought.

If these new dates for Mungo 1 and 3 are indeed accurate, they imply that gracile people were the first inhabitants of Australia. This is because, in a related study, skull fragments of the supposedly more archaic fossil WLH-50 were dated by the gamma ray method, giving a preliminary age estimate of only *ca.* 14 kyr (Simpson & Grün 1998). Thus this specimen, and the other robust fossils so far dated (Brown 1992), all apparently post-dated the last glacial maximum *ca.* 20 kyr ago. The sequence of morphologies supports a model of diversification within Australia, not derivation from separate ancestors. Otherwise, one would have to postulate the movement of 'gracile' people through Indonesia into Australia by 60 kyr ago, without replacement or interaction with existing 'robust' people, and then the arrival of surviving 'robust' people from Indonesia, who managed to disperse through Australia without significant intermixture with existing 'gracile' inhabitants.

Additionally, the description of the robust crania as archaic and *H. erectus*-like (e.g. Thorne & Wolpoff 1992; Frayer *et al.* 1993) has been challenged by several workers who instead argue that their distinctive features can be related to large size, artificial deformation, or pathology (Brown 1992; Lahr 1996; Stringer 1998*a*; Antón & Weinstein 1999). Nevertheless, continued attempts have been made to demonstrate regional continuity between the WLH-50 calvaria and archaic Indonesian predecessors (Hawks *et al.* 2000*b*), but these have been idiosyncratic in the scoring of morphological characters (cf. Lahr 1996) and failed to control for the confounding effect of size in metrical comparisons (cf. Stringer 1998*a*).

Overall, it seems probable that a modern human dispersal had reached Australia, via boats, by *ca.* 65 kyr ago. This may have been the endpoint of a long-term coastal expansion from Africa (Stringer 2000), but until more is known of the late Pleistocene populations of southern Asia, this will remain unclear. The relationship of the first Australians to later inhabitants of the continent is still uncertain. Late Pleistocene morphological diversity may well have been accentuated by the severity of the last glacial maximum, leading to isolation and the forcing of mor-phological change in some Australian populations. If archaic populations such as those known from Ngandong *did* survive into the late Pleistocene, an analogous situation to that in Europe might have obtained, raising the possibility of gene flow with dispersing *H. sapiens* (cf. Hawks *et al.* 2000*b*). Given previously discussed data from Europe and China, it is also possible that the genes of the first human colonizers are poorly represented in the aboriginal people of today because of extinctions, bottlenecking, or because later population expansions have largely over-printed their traces, physically, genetically and linguistically.

6. GENETIC DATA

Genetic data have assumed an increasing importance in reconstructions of recent human evolution over the past 15 years. Earlier studies had to work with population frequencies of genetic markers, the products of the genetic code (e.g. blood groups, proteins). By combining data from populations, attempts were made to reconstruct the genetic history of humans (Cavalli-Sforza & Bodmer 1971; Nei & Roychoudhury 1982). The advent of techniques that revealed individual molecular sequence data allowed phylogenetic trees or genealogies of specific genes or DNA segments to also be constructed. Two pioneering papers published in *Nature* in 1986 and 1987 illustrate, respectively, population-based and phylogenetic approaches using DNA markers called RFLPs (Restriction Fragmentation Length Polymorphisms). Using the former approach, Wainscoat *et al.* (1986) studied polymorphisms close to the beta-globin gene, and showed by genetic distance analyses that African populations were quite distinct from non-African ones. The following year, Cann *et al.* (1987) published their paper giving a genealogy of 134 mitochondrial DNA 'types' constructed from restriction maps of 148 people from different regions. The genealogy was used to reconstruct increasingly ancient hypothetical ancestors, culminating in one female, most parsimoniously located in Africa. More-over, using a mtDNA divergence rate calculated from studies of other organisms, it was estimated that this hypothetical female ancestor lived *ca.* 200 kyr ago. These conclusions were extremely controversial, and were subjected to critical scrutiny concerning the samples, methods and calibration used (Templeton 1993). Although it is now evident that Cann *et al.* (1987) were premature in the confidence with which they presented their results, much more extensive analyses (e.g. Ingman *et al.* 2000) have shown that they were fundamentally correct in their conclusions.

In the past ten years, with the development and application of PCR techniques, a wealth of sequenced data has been made available from autosomal (biparentally inherited) DNA, Y-chromosome DNA (inherited through males) and mitochondrial DNA (inherited through females).These data have been used to compare the DNA of human populations in ever greater detail (Tishkoff *et al.* 2000; Kayser *et al.* 2001), to estimate coalescent (last common ancestral) dates for various gene systems (Ingman *et al.* 2000), to reconstruct ancient demographic patterns (e.g. Rogers 2001), and to develop phylogeographic studies to map ancient dispersal events (e.g. Richards & Macaulay 2000; Underhill *et al.* 2001). While most of these data support a recent African origin for recent humans and their genetic diversity (e.g. Jorde *et al.* 2000; Ke *et al.* 2001), others may not (Zhao *et al.* 2000). Although the data are growing in power and resolution, analyses cannot yet resolve the precise time and place of our origins, nor establish whether there was only one or perhaps several significant dispersals of *H. sapiens* from Africa during the later Pleistocene.

Some genetic data, in the form of mtDNA, are now available from Neanderthal fossils (Krings *et al.* 2000) and these suggest a separation time of their lineage from that leading to recent humans of *ca.* 600 kyr (Krings *et al.* 2000; Ovchinnikov *et al.* 2000; figure 4). As explained earlier, such estimates necessarily provide *maximum* ages for evolutionary separation, since any population and species separations would inevitably post-date the first mitochondrial divergence by an unknown amount of time. But they are consistent with fossil evidence of an effective separation date of the *H. neanderthalensis* and *H. sapiens* lineages at *ca.* 300 kyr and also with subsequent genetic divergence among recent humans beginning less than 200 kyr ago (Stringer 1998*b*). Both the morphological data and the limited amount of fossil DNA available suggest that Neanderthal–recent human differences were of the order of two or three times that found within recent humans. But even in this case, where genetic and morphological differences are clear, the data can be used to support a placing of Neanderthals and recent humans in either the same or different species, given the recency of common ancestry.

There have also been recent claims for the recovery of ancient DNA from Australian fossils. Adcock *et al.* (2001) reported that 10 out of 12 specimens tested from Willandra Lakes and Kow Swamp had yielded mitochondrial sequences. One of these, from Mungo 3, was claimed to form an outgroup with a previously reported mitochon-drial nuclear insert, distinct from the other fossils and from recent human sequences. Adcock *et al.* (2001) claimed, moreover, that the distinctiveness of the Mungo 3 sequence undermined genetic support for a recent African origin. In an accompanying commentary, Relethford (2001) used the results to support alternative multi-regional interpretations, and to question previous interpretations of Neanderthal DNA. However, Cooper *et al.* (2001) in turn criticized various aspects of the work. First, they observed that the claimed recovery rate for the Australian ancient DNA was exceptional compared with results from elsewhere, and that standard experimental protocols had not been employed, suggesting the possibility of contamination. Second, they reanalysed the data, using a larger number of recent Australian and African sequences, and demonstrated that the Mungo 3 sequence did not now form an outgroup to recent human mtDNA in the most parsimonious phylogeny. Third, they observed that even the original published phylogeny presented no serious challenge to Recent African Origin. Australian fossils classed by multiregionalists as 'robust' and 'gracile', purportedly derived from archaic Indonesian and Chinese ances-tors respectively, grouped with the recent human sequences from regions such as Europe and Africa, while Mungo 3 was more closely related to all these than it was to the Neanderthal sequences used as an outgroup.

7. NEW APPROACHES TO MODERN HUMAN ORIGINS RESEARCH

In these concluding sections, I would like to draw together aspects of this review and also look at new approaches to some remaining problems. In my opinion, variants of one of the polar extremes in the debate about modern human origins discussed at the beginning of this paper—Multiregional Evolution—have been falsified, and the fundamental mode of modern human origins can be assumed to be that of a recent African origin. But until we have better records of late Pleistocene events in human history from regions such as China and Australia, we will continue to depend on genetic data to inform us whether a strict Recent African Origin model is likely to be adequate, rather than a variant incorporating a greater and more gradual (assimilation) or a lesser and more rapid (hybridization) degree of gene flow with contemporary populations outside Africa. However, even the strict Recent African Origin model has undergone considerable recent development in the Multiple Dispersals model of Lahr and Foley (1994, 1998), and this will be discussed next.

The Multiple Dispersals model proposes that significant recent human population subdivisions developed within Africa, and that there may then have been multiple dispersals of already differentiated populations from there, perhaps using different routes. This model has concentrated attention on the African fossil record of the late Middle Pleistocene. Other researchers recognized the high variation in these samples, but accepted that ancestors of recent humans were probably represented amongst them (Hublin 1993; Bräuer *et al.* 1997; Rightmire 1998; Stringer 1998*b*). Lahr & Foley (1994, 1998) have taken this further in arguing that they might represent subdivided and distinct populations, with some or many not representing ancestors for recent *H. sapiens*. Following a bottleneck during OIS 6 (*ca.* 150 kyr), one African population recovered and spread into the Levant during OIS 5 (*ca.* 125 kyr), as represented by the Skhul-Qafzeh fossils. However, in the Multiple Dispersals model, these Lev-antine pioneers went extinct around the onset of OIS 4 (*ca.* 70 kyr). Surviving Africans, meanwhile, became divided into subgroups that were to form the ancestors of both African and non-African populations. A subsequent Middle Palaeolithic-associated dispersal occurred via Arabia and southern Asia, eventually reaching Australia, while later dispersals took the ancestors of recent European, Asian and Oriental people out of Africa following the development of Later Stone Age–Upper Palaeolithic technologies. Other workers have raised the possibility of separate early dispersals to Australia, but Lahr & Foley (1994, 1998) proposed a specific coastal route for this via the Straits of Hormuz (Bab el Mandeb). Subsequently, Stringer (2000), using new evidence of Middle Stone Age littoral adaptations, argued that coastal expansion around the Red Sea basin could have facilitated a range expansion of modern humans towards Australasia without necessarily using the Straits of Hormuz. By focusing attention on the development of diversity within Africa, the Multiple Dispersals model has provided fruitful hypotheses for testing from fossil, behavioural and genetic data.

A number of taxonomic issues in modern human origins remain unresolved. However, new ways of comparing past human taxic diversity with that of recent primates are being developed, and new techniques of investigation are adding further data from the expanding fossil record. One of the most serious remaining areas of uncertainty and confusion in studies of modern human origins is the question of species recognition. Some workers (e.g. Tattersall & Schwartz 2000) argue that many distinct morphological groups in the fossil record warrant specific recognition, with the existence of at least eight such species of the genus *Homo* supported during the last two million years. Others (e.g. Thorne & Wolpoff 1992) argue that only one species warrants recognition over that period—*H. sapiens*. An additional complication is that different species concepts may become confused—for example, some multiregionalists have applied biological species concepts to the fossil record in an attempt to show that *H. neanderthalensis* and *H. sapiens* must have been conspecific. However, even if we accept controversial claims for the existence of supposed Neanderthal–modern hybrids (e.g. Duarte *et al.* 1999), it is well known that many closely related mammal species (including primates) can hybridize, and may even produce fertile offspring. However, if this is not a widespread or reproductively successful behaviour, it may have little or no impact on the populations that constitute the core of the different species or on future generations. The limited genetic data on Neanderthal–recent relationships show that Neanderthals and recent *H. sapiens* represent distinct but nevertheless closely related lineages, but are ambiguous about whether these samples represent different species. Thus, in fossils, morphological criteria necessarily remain the mode of species recognition, but recent research is providing better testing of the assumptions involved.

Harvati (2001) used differences in temporal bone morphology between common chimpanzees and specifically distinct bonobos to compare the level of difference between Neanderthals and recent *H. sapiens*. She concluded that Neanderthal–recent differences in the temporal bone were at least as great as those between the two chimpanzee species. As she recognized, this result was based on only one cranial area, and further tests were required before reaching more definitive conclusions. In a similar study based on cranial measurements, Schillaci & Froehlich (2001) compared the level of differentiation of fossil (Upper Palaeolithic) *H. sapiens* and Neanderthals with that calculated between species of macaques that are known to hybridize, or not to hybridize. Again, the degree of difference between the fossil human cranial samples exceeded that found between the recent primate species. Thus, both these studies supported the distinctiveness of *H. neanderthalensis*. Apart from more cranial studies, it would be valuable to extend this approach to comparisons of mandibular morphology and metrics (e.g. extending the data of Humphrey *et al.* (1999)) and of dental morphology (see discussion of the work of Bailey (2000) below).

In recent years, traditional osteometric methods of recording the size and shape of fossil bones and teeth have been complemented and increasingly superseded by techniques that capture such information digitally through digitizing or scanning (Harvati 2001). The medical technology of Computed Tomography (CT) has been particularly successful in extending such work into anatomical structures that are either difficult to measure through traditional techniques (e.g. external and internal frontal bone shape: Bookstein *et al.* (1999)) or are otherwise inaccessible (e.g. inner ear bone shape: Hublin *et al.* (1996)). The techniques of geometric morphometrics are now being used to investigate both ontogeny and phylogeny (e.g. Ponce de Leo´n & Zollikofer 2001). Much wider and more detailed comparisons of fossil and recent samples will undoubtedly have major impacts on future taxonomic and phylogenetic research on modern human origins.

Dental morphological variation provides an alternative and still rather neglected approach to reconstructing human population histories, despite the pioneering work of researchers such as Turner (1992) and K. and T. Hanihara (Hanihara 1992). Turner's 'Out of Asia' scenario for recent human evolution was based on phenetic distance analyses and assumptions of relatively constant rates of dental evolution. It postulated that the 'Sundadont' aboriginal peoples of Southeast Asia were closest to the original modern human dental pattern and that this indicated the original source area for *H. sapiens*. However, this approach was unable to account for the relatively close phenetic distance between Australian and African dental patterns, and no attempt was made to test the hypothesis by the use of fossil data as an outgroup. These limitations were remedied in the work of Stringer *et al.* (1997), Irish (1998) and Tyrell & Chamberlain (1998), who found that the use of either a Neanderthal or archaic African outgroup supported a sub-Saharan, not Asian, root for recent human dental dendrograms or cladograms. Figure 5 shows the first two factors of a principal components analysis from the data of Stringer *et al.* (1997), with the inclusion of the Krapina Neanderthal sample as an out-group. It is evident that if the Krapina dental sample is a representative outgroup, then European and East Asian ('Sinodont') samples appear derived, 'Sundadont' samples are rather average for recent humans (as Turner and the Haniharas have reported), while Australian and sub-Saharan African samples are relatively plesiomorphous. The dental ancestor for recent humans thus probably combined characters most commonly found today in sub-Saharan Africans and Australians. Shields (1998), using a different dataset derived from digitized dental radio-graphs, also concluded that Australians displayed the most plesiomorphous morphology of non-African populations, while 'Mongoloid' and Native American samples were more derived. Thus, it appears that in both dental and morphological/metrical characters the 'Mongoloid' cranial form is very derived. Bailey (2000) has extended dental morphological studies to a wider range of fossils, including those of the western Eurasian Upper and Middle Palaeolithic. She concluded that Eurasian Neanderthals were similar to each other but quite distinct from other fossil, and recent, human samples. Both the Skhul–Qafzeh and Upper Palaeolithic groups showed recent affinities, with the former closer to sub-Saharan Africans, the latter to Europeans and North Africans.

8. PROBLEMS WITH THE CONCEPT OF 'MODERNITY'

The fundamental problem of diagnosing ancient examples of 'modern' humans, morphologically and behaviourally, nevertheless persists because there is no agreement on how this should be carried out. In the past, I favoured the use of recent skeletal variation to diagnose whether a fossil could be termed 'modern' (Stringer 1994). It is now apparent that recent skeletal variation is smaller than that recognized for *H. sapiens* in even the late Pleistocene, and members of the *H. sapiens* clade in the African late Middle to early Late Pleistocene were much more distinct and diverse (Howells 1989; Stringer 1992; Lahr 1996). While there seems little doubt that Aurignacian and Gravettian-associated humans from 25–35 kyr ago in Europe share enough morphological and behavioural features with recent populations to warrant the application of the term 'modern', problems arise as we move further back in time. The samples from Skhul and Qafzeh in Israel appear to represent a primitive form of *H. sapiens* (Trinkaus 1984; Vandermeersch 1989; Stringer 1992; Lahr 1996) but reassessments of their morphology, and that of samples from sites such as Klasies River Mouth, Omo Kibish, Singa, Ngaloba, Jebel Irhoud and Guomde (e.g. Lahr 1996; Trinkaus 1997; Pearson 2000) show mosaic evolutionary patterns. This means that a morphological definition of modernity based on recent samples will be problematic when applied further back in time.

A further problem with the use of recent samples to assess fossils is that current 'regionality' appears to have evolved quite recently. In both China and Europe it may only really have developed during the last 20 kyr (e.g. Stringer 1992; Lahr 1996; Brown 1999). Is this a reflection of a relatively late colonization of these regions by modern humans compared with Africa and Australia, or is it reflecting the impact of the last glacial maximum *ca.* 20 kyr ago, purging the earliest colonizers and followed by recolonization with the actual ancestors of today's inhabitants? While the combination of a morphological and metrical approach by Lahr (1996) undermined classic multiregional claims for the long-term persistence of regional characters, her studies did confirm the individuality of Australians in some respects. She argued that concepts of *H. sapiens* should not just be based on recent representatives, as in several aspects such as reduced size and robusticity we represent a restricted and atypical sample of the species as it was even in the late Pleistocene.

If, as suggested earlier, the characteristic morphology of modern humans evolved in a gradual, mosaic fashion, what of modern human behaviour? The concept of a 'Human Revolution', demarcating a punctuational origin of a package of recent human behaviours, such as complex language, symbolism and specialized technologies, has been central to much archaeological debate over the past ten years (Klein 2000). Originally focused on apparent contrasts between the Middle and Upper Palaeolithic records in Europe, this concept has now been extended to the Middle to Later Stone Age transition in Africa (table 1). It is argued that the major changes in human behavioural evolution occurred there by *ca.* 50 kyr (possibly related to mutations that enhanced brain function, leading to changes in cognition or language; Klein 2000). In turn, this led to the successful expansion of modern humans and now-modern behaviour beyond Africa, and the replacement of the remaining archaic populations. Thus morphological and behavioural evolution were decoupled, since 'morphological modernity' may have evolved before 'behavioural modernity'. This pattern is counterintuitive for those who argue that behavioural change lay behind the transformation of the archaic skeletal pattern into that of modern humans. However, it is based on the fact that, despite their morphological 'modernity', fossil samples from sites such as Klasies River Mouth and Skhul or Qafzeh are associated with Middle Palaeolithic artefacts, comparable with those made by Neanderthals, and apparently lack other aspects of 'modern' behaviour. The contrast between their morphology and their inferred behaviour is sufficient for Klein (2000) to employ the term 'near-modern' for them, implying that they represent an evolutionary stage where modern anatomy was evolving *prior* to truly modern behaviour.

Workers such as Lahr & Foley (1998) and McBrearty & Brooks (2000) have instead argued that previous views of modern behavioural origins display a Eurocentric bias and a failure to appreciate the depth and breadth of an African Middle Stone Age record that precedes the supposed 'Human Revolution' by at least 100 kyr. In this view, 'modern' features, such as advanced technologies, increased geographic range, specialized hunting, aquatic resource exploitation, long distance trade and the symbolic use of pigments, occur across a broad spectrum of Middle Stone Age industries. This suggests a gradual assembly of the package of modern human behaviours in Africa during the late Middle–early Late Pleistocene, and its later export to the rest of the World. Thus the origin of our species, behaviourally and morphologically, was linked with the appearance of Middle Stone Age technology, dated in many parts of Africa to more than 250 kyr ago.

It is thus debatable whether African Middle Stone Age humans really lacked 'modern' behaviour. Moreover, the Middle Palaeolithic associated Skhul–Qafzeh samples display morphological signs of behavioural change (Churchill 2001) as well as burials that apparently display evidence of 'modern' symbolic behaviour in the form of grave goods. There are also more remote indications that the dispersal of modern humans was not dependent on the appearance of the Later Stone Age/Upper Palaeolithic, and that symbolic behaviour existed before their development. As discussed earlier, there is growing evidence that Australia was colonized prior to 50 kyr ago and prior to the technological changes characterizing Mode 4 industries. Not only would this have required the development of maritime adaptations, but if the earliest Mungo fossils are representative of the first colonizers, these people were also engaging in complex behaviours such as burial with red ochre, and cremation.

In my opinion it is still too early to definitively determine when and where 'modern' morphology and behaviour developed, especially when these concepts are apparently so fluid. In my view, Africa was the ultimate source of the basic elements of both our anatomy and our behaviour. But it has also become evident that some claimed unique attributes of recent human behaviours were present even during the Middle Pleistocene outside Africa, for example, the evidence for systematic hunting of large mammals from sites such as Boxgrove and Schöningen, and the carefully crafted wooden javelins from the latter site (Dennell 1997; Stringer *et al.* 1998). Additionally, the debate about Neanderthal, and specifically Châtelperronian, capabilities highlights the issue of potential versus performance. d'Errico *et al.* (1998) have argued that Neanderthals were developing 'modern' symbolic behaviour independently of a *H. sapiens* morphology, thus producing a contrasting decoupling of modern anatomy and behaviour from that envisaged by Klein (2000). Others (e.g. Mellars 1999) argue that Neanderthals were developing complex behaviours only through contact with dispersing modern humans, not independently of them. The question of whether behavioural innovations arose regularly and independently in different populations in human prehistory (but were often lost during population crises or extinctions), or they spread widely by diffusion or dispersals, even between distinct populations and even species, remains unresolved.

While the temperate–cold climates of western Eurasia may well have influenced the evolution of the Neanderthals (e.g. Holliday 1997), it is still unclear what drove the evolution of *H. sapiens* in Africa. The large habitable area of that continent, combined with dramatic changes in precipitation and vegetation, might have forced evolutionary change through isolation and adaptation. As discussed earlier, there is also growing evidence for the precocious appearance during the Middle Stone Age of aspects of modern human behaviour such as symbolism. It may well be that the predominance of Africa was fundamentally a question of its larger geographical and human population size (Relethford & Jorde 1999), giving greater opportunities for innovations to both develop and be conserved (Shennan 2001), rather than the result of a unique evolutionary pathway, perhaps based on mutations affecting cognition (Klein 2000). The rapidity and repetition of late Pleistocene climatic oscillations outside Africa may well have continually disrupted long-term adaptation by its human populations, while Africa perhaps had shallower resource gradients (Foley 1989), greater chances of isolation and endemism (Lahr & Foley 1998), or encouragement of 'variability selection' responses to its environmental fluctuations (Potts 1998). While the admittedly limited evidence does seem to point to a gradual assembly of recent human morphology and behaviour in Africa during the period from 300 to 100 kyr ago, rather than major punctuational events, genetic data are ambivalent on this question. Several genetic datasets suggest that there was at least one major population bottleneck during this time-period (Jorde *et al.* 2000; Ingman *et al.* 2000; Takahata *et al.* 2001), with effective population size reduced to only a few thousand individuals. Such population crashes might indeed have produced saltational changes in morphology and behaviour within what must have been a diverse early *H. sapiens* clade. However, other evidence of the conservation of older (?African) population sub-divisions suggests that there cannot have been severe, localized bottlenecks, as these could not have conserved earlier geographical substructuring (e.g. Tishkoff *et al.* 2000; Watkins *et al.* 2001).

9. CONCLUDING REMARKS ON MODERN HUMAN ORIGINS

It seems to me that the ideas discussed, whether ultimately supported or falsified, are important for the way that they highlight difficulties inherent in any absolute concept of 'modernity', behavioural or morphological. Yet, such concepts are critical to the reconstruction of our origins. Was 'modernity' a package that had a unique African origin in one time, place and population or was it a composite whose elements appeared at different times and places, and were then gradually assembled to assume the form we recognize today? While I argue that variants of the Multiregional Model have lost their validity when applied globally, could there have been an African-based multiregional model where 'modern' behaviours, morphologies and genes coalesced from different parts of that continent during the Middle Pleistocene? If so, we will need, yet again, to account for the unique importance of Africa in human evolution. Foley & Lahr (1997) argued that the contrasting geographies of Eurasia and Africa would have favoured latitudinal expansions and contractions in Eurasia but longitudinal ones in Africa. Consequently, both a larger population size and geography would have facilitated dispersal from Africa, but not in the reverse direction. However, much more evidence from the African late Middle Pleistocene archaeological, palaeontological and palaeoenvironmental records will be required to test such ideas. The burgeoning genetic data from present and, to a lesser extent, past populations will continue to illuminate events in human prehistory. These will feed into new models of modern human origins and dispersal. It also seems likely that many questions concerning the origins of the peoples of eastern Asia, Australasia, the Americas and even Europe will only be fully answerable when Asia yields up a later Pleistocene record to compare with that already recovered from Europe and beginning to be recovered from parts of Africa. Only then will we be in a position to finally establish whether all the most significant events in the early history of *H. sapiens* occurred in Africa and whether, as evidence is now suggesting, the main morphological and behavioural components that characterize our species had already developed there by 100 kyr ago.

Several relevant publications have appeared since the completion of this paper. These include:

Balter, M. 2002 What made humans modern? *Science* **295**, 1219–1225.

Barham, L. & Robson-Brown, K. (eds) 2001 *Human roots: Africa and Asia in the Middle Pleistocene*. Bristol: Western Academic and Specialist Press.

Templeton, A. 2002 Out of Africa again and again. *Nature* 416, 45–50.

The author thanks many colleagues for access to fossils and data, collaboration, and friendly discussions, all of which have directly, or indirectly, contributed to this review paper. More specifically, the Photographic Unit of The Natural History Museum produced figure 1 and Philip Rye prepared figure 2. The author also thanks five reviewers for their considerable help in improving this paper.

REFERENCES

Adcock, G., Dennis, E., Easteal, S., Huttley, G., Jermiin, L., Peacock, W. & Thorne, A. 2001 Mitochondrial DNA sequences in ancient Australians: implications for modern human origins. *Proc. Natl Acad. Sci. USA* **98**, 537–542.

Aiello, L. 1993 The fossil evidence for modern human origins in Africa; a revised view. *Am. Anthropol.* **95**, 73–96.

Akazawa, T. Aoki, K. & Bar-Yosef, O. (eds) 1998 *Neandertals and modern humans in Western Asia*. New York: Plenum.

Alperson, N., Barzilai, O., Dag, D., Hartman, G. & Matskevich, Z. 2000 The age and context of the Tabun 1 skeleton: a reply to Schwarcz *et al. J. Hum. Evol.* **38**, 849–853.

Antón, S. & Weinstein, K. 1999 Artificial cranial deformation and fossil Australians revisited. *J. Hum. Evol.* **36**, 195–209.

Arsuaga, J. L., Bermúdez de Castro, J. M. & Carbonell, E. (eds) 1997 The Sima de los Huesos hominid site. *J. Hum. Evol.* **33**, 105–421.

Bailey, S. 2000 Dental morphological affinities among late Pleistocene and Recent humans. *Dent. Anthropol.* **14**, 1–8.

Bar-Yosef, O. & Callander, J. 1999 The woman from Tabun: Garrod's doubts in historical perspective. *J. Hum. Evol.* **37**, 879–885.

Bermúdez de Castro, J. M., Arsuaga, J., Carbonell, E., Rosas, A., Martinez, I. & Mosquera, M. 1997 A hominid from the lower Pleistocene of Atapuerca, Spain: possible ancestor to Neandertals and modern humans. *Science* **276**, 1392–1395.

Bookstein, F. (and 12 others) 1999 Comparing frontal cranial profiles in archaic and modern *Homo* by morphometric analysis. *Anat. Rec.* **257,** 1–9.

Bowler, J. & Thorne, A. 1976 Human remains from Lake Mungo: discovery and excavation of Lake Mungo III. In *The origin of the Australians* (ed. R. Kirk & A. Thorne), pp. 127–138. Canberra: Australian Institute of Aboriginal Studies.

Bräuer, G. 1992 Africa's place in the evolution of *Homo sapiens*. In *Continuity or replacement? Controversies in* Homo sapiens *evolution* (ed. G. Bräuer & F. Smith), pp. 83–98. Rotterdam, The Netherlands: Balkema.

Bräuer, G., Yokoyama, Y., Falguères, C. & Mbua, E. 1997 Modern human origins backdated. *Nature* **386**, 337–338.

Brown, P. 1992 Recent human evolution in East Asia and Australasia. *Phil. Trans. R. Soc. Lond.* B **337**, 235–242.

Brown, P. 1999 The first modern East Asians? Another look at Upper Cave 101, Liujiang and Minatogawa 1. In *Interdisciplinary perspectives on the origins of the Japanese* (ed. K. Omoto), pp. 105–131. Kyoto, Japan: International Research Center for Japanese Studies.

Cann, R., Stoneking, M. & Wilson, A. 1987 Mitochondrial DNA and human evolution. *Nature* **325**, 31–36.

Cavalli-Sforza, L. & Bodmer, W. 1971 *The genetics of human populations*. San Francisco, CA: Freeman.

Churchill, S. 2001 Hand morphology, manipulation, and tool use in Neandertals and early modern humans of the Near East. *Proc. Natl Acad. Sci. USA* **98**, 2953–2955.

Clark, J. G. 1968 *World prehistory: a new outline*. Cambridge University Press.

Cooper, A., Rambaut, A., Macaulay, V., Willerslev, E., Hansen, A. & Stringer, C. 2001 Human origins and ancient human DNA. *Science* **292**, 1655–1656.

Culotta, E. 1995 Asian hominids grow older. *Science* **270**, 1116–1117.

Dennell, R. 1997 The world's oldest spears. *Nature* **385**, 767–768.

d'Errico, F., Zilhão, J., Julien, M., Baffier, D. & Pelegrin, J. 1998 Neanderthal acculturation in Western Europe? A critical review of the evidence and its interpretation. *Curr. Anthropol.* **39**, S1–S44.

Duarte, C., Maurício, J., Pettitt, P. B., Souto, P., Trinkaus, E., van der Plicht, H. & Zilhão, J. 1999 The early Upper Paleolithic human skeleton from the Abrigo do Lagar Velho (Portugal) and modern human emergence in Iberia. *Proc. Natl Acad. Sci. USA* **96**, 7604–7609.

Etler, D. 1996 The fossil evidence for human evolution in Asia. *A. Rev. Anthropol.* **25**, 275–301.

Falguères, C., Sémah, F., Saleki, H., Yokoyama, Y., Jacob, T., Fontugne, M. & Féraud, G. 2001 Advancements in the dating of Solo Man. In *XIVth Congr. Union Int. des Sciences Préhistoriques et Protohistoriques* (*UISPP*), Liège, 2–8 September 2001. Session 16.1 Abstract C15.

Foley, R. 1989 The ecological conditions of speciation: a comparative approach to the origins of anatomically-modern humans. In *The human revolution: behavioural and biological perspectives in the origins of modern humans* (ed. P. Mellars & C. Stringer), pp. 298–318. Edinburgh University Press.

Foley, R. & Lahr, M. 1997 Mode 3 technologies and the evolution of modern humans. *Camb. Archaeol. J.* **7**, 3–36.

Frayer, D., Wolpoff, M., Smith, F., Thorne, A. & Pope, G. 1993 The fossil evidence for modern human origins. *Am. Anthropol.* **95**, 14–50.

Garrod, D. & Bate, D. 1937 . *The Stone Age of Mount Carmel*, vol. 1. Oxford University Press.

Grün, R. & Stringer, C. 1991 Electron spin resonance dating and the evolution of modern humans. *Archaeometry* **33**, 153–199.

Grün, R. & Stringer, C. 2000 Tabun revisited: revised ESR chronology and new ESR and U-series analyses of dental material from Tabun C1. *J. Hum. Evol.* **39**, 601–612.

Grün, R. & Thorne, A. 1997 Dating the Ngandong humans. *Science* **276**, 1575–1576.

Grün, R., Stringer, C. & Schwarcz, H. 1991 ESR dating of teeth from Garrod's Tabun cave collection. *J. Hum. Evol.* **20**, 231–248.

Grün, R., Brink, J., Spooner, N., Taylor, L., Stringer, C., Franciscus, R. & Murray, A. 1996 Direct dating of Florisbad hominid. *Nature* **382**, 500–501.

Grün, R., Huang, P. H., Wu, X., Stringer, C., Thorne, A. & McCulloch, M. 1997 ESR analysis of teeth from the palaeoanthropological site of Zhoukoudian, China. *J. Hum. Evol.* **32**, 83–91.

Grün, R., Huang, P.-H., Huang, W., McDermott, F., Stringer, C., Thorne, A. & Yan, G. 1998 ESR and U-series analyses of teeth from the palaeoanthropological site of Hexian, Anhui Province, China. *J. Hum. Evol.* **34**, 555–564.

Grün, R., Spooner, N. A., Thorne, A., Mortimer, G., Simpson, J. J., McCulloch, M. T., Taylor, L. & Curnoe, D. 2000 Age of the Lake Mungo 3 skeleton, reply to Bowler & Magee and to Gillespie & Roberts. *J. Hum. Evol.* **38**, 733–741.

Hanihara, T. 1992 Dental and cranial affinities among populations of East Asia and the Pacific: the basic populations in East Asia IV. *Am. J. Phys. Anthropol.* **88**, 163–182.

Harvati, K. 2001 Analysis of Neanderthal temporal bone morphology using geometric morphometrics. *Am. J. Phys. Anthropol.* **32**, 76–77.

Hawks, J., Hunley, K., Lee, S. & Wolpoff, M. 2000*a* Population bottlenecks and Pleistocene human evolution. *Mol. Biol. Evol.* **17**, 2–22.

Hawks, J., Oh, S., Hunley, K., Dobson, S., Cabana, G., Dayalu, P. & Wolpoff, M. 2000*b* An Australasian test of the recent African origin hypothesis using the WLH-50 calvarium. *J. Hum. Evol.* **39**, 1–22.

Holliday, T. 1997 Body proportions in Late Pleistocene Europe and modern human origins. *J. Hum. Evol.* **32**, 423–448.

Howells, W. W. 1989 Skull shapes and the map. In *Papers of the Peabody Museum, Harvard*, vol. 79.

Hublin, J.-J. 1993 Recent human evolution in northwestern Africa. In *The origin of modern humans and the impact of chronometric dating* (ed. M. Aitken, C. Stringer & P. Mellars), pp. 118–131. Princeton University Press.

Hublin, J.-J. 1998 Climatic changes, paleogeography, and the evolution of the Neandertals. In *Neandertals and modern humans in Western Asia* (ed. T. Akazawa, K. Aoki & O. Bar-Yosef), pp. 295–310. New York: Plenum.

Hublin, J.-J., Barroso Ruiz, C., Medina Lara, P., Fontugne, M. & Reyss, J.-L. 1995 The Mousterian site of Zafarraya (Andalucia, Spain): dating and implications on the Palaeo-lithic peopling processes of Western Europe. *Crit. Rev. Acad. Sci. Paris* IIa **321**, 931–937.

Hublin, J.-J., Spoor, F., Braun, M., Zonneveld, F. & Condemi, S. 1996 A late Neanderthal associated with Upper Palaeo-lithic artefacts. *Nature* **381**, 224–226.

Humphrey, L., Dean, M. C. & Stringer, C. B. 1999 Morpho-logical variation in great ape and modern human mandibles. *J. Anat.* **195**, 491–513.

Ingman, M., Kaessmann, H., Pääbo, S. & Gyllensten, U. 2000 Mitochondrial genome variation and the origin of modern humans. *Nature* **408**, 708–713.

Irish, J. 1998 Ancestral dental traits in recent sub-Saharan Africans and the origins of modern humans. *J. Hum. Evol.* **34**, 81–98.

Jorde, L., Watkins, W., Bamshad, M., Dixon, M., Ricker, C., Seielstad, M. & Batzer, M. 2000 The distribution of human genetic diversity: a comparison of mitochondrial, autosomal, and Y-chromosome data. *Am. J. Hum. Genet.* **66**, 979–988.

Kayser, M. (and 11 others) 2001 An extensive analysis of Y-chromosomal microsatellite haplotypes in globally dis-persed human populations. *Am. J. Hum. Genet.* **68**, 990–1018.

Ke, Y. (and 22 others) 2001 African origin of modern humans in East Asia: a tale of 12 000 Y chromosomes. *Science* **292**, 1151–1153.

Klein, R. 1999 *The human career.* University of Chicago Press.

Klein, R. 2000 Archeology and the evolution of human behavior. *Evol. Anthropol.* **9**, 17–36.

Krings, M., Capelli, C., Tschentscher, F., Geisert, H., Meyer, S., von Haeseler, A., Grossschmidt, K., Possnert, G., Paunovic, M. & Pääbo, S. 2000 A view of Neanderthal genetic diversity. *Nature Genet.* **26**, 144–146.

Lahr, M. 1996 *The evolution of modern human diversity: a study of cranial variation.* Cambridge University Press.

Lahr, M. & Foley, R. 1994 Multiple dispersals and modern human origins. *Evol. Anthropol.* **3**, 48–60.

Lahr, M. & Foley, R. 1998 Towards a theory of modern human origins: geography, demography, and diversity in recent human evolution. *Ybk Phys. Anthropol.* **41**, 137–176.

McBrearty, S. & Brooks, A. 2000 The revolution that wasn't: a new interpretation of the origin of modern human behavior. *J. Hum. Evol.* **39**, 453–563.

McDermott, F., Stringer, C., Grün, R., Williams, C. T., Din, V. & Hawkesworth, C. 1996 New Late-Pleistocene uranium–thorium and ESR dates for the Singa hominid (Sudan). *J. Hum. Evol.* **31**, 507–516.

Manzi, G., Mallegni, F. & Ascenzi, A. 2001 A cranium for the earliest Europeans: phylogenetic position of the hominid from Ceprano, Italy. *Proc. Natl Acad. Sci. USA* **98**, 10 011–10 016.

Mellars, P. 1999 The Neanderthal problem continued. *Curr. Anthropol.* **40**, 341–350.

Mercier, N., Valladas, H., Valladas, G., Reyss, J.-L., Jelinek, A., Meignen, L. & Joron, J.-L. 1995 TL dates of burnt flints from Jelinek's excavations at Tabun and their implications. *J. Archaeol. Sci.* **22**, 495–509.

Millard, A. & Pike, A. 1999 Uranium-series dating of the Tabun Neanderthal: a cautionary note. *J. Hum. Evol.* **36**, 581–585.

Nei, M. & Roychoudhury, A. 1982 Genetic relationship and evolution of human races. *Evol. Biol.* **14**, 1–59.

Ovchinnikov, I., Anders, G., Götherström, A., Romanova, G., Kharitonov, V., Lidén, K. & Goodwin, W. 2000 Molecular analysis of Neanderthal DNA from the northern Caucasus. *Nature* **404**, 490–493.

Pardoe, C. 1991 Competing paradigms and ancient human remains: the state of the discipline. *Archaeol. Oceania* **26**, 79–85.

Pearson, O. 2000 Postcranial remains and the origin of modern humans. *Evol. Anthropol.* **9**, 229–247.

Ponce de León, M. & Zollikofer, C. 2001 Neanderthal cranial ontogeny and its implications for late hominid diversity. *Nature* **412**, 534–538.

Potts, R. 1998 Environmental hypotheses of hominin evolution. *Ybk Phys. Anthropol.* **41**, 93–136.

Relethford, J. 1999 Models, predictions and the fossil record of modern human origins. *Evol. Anthropol.* **8**, 7–10.

Relethford, J. 2001 Ancient DNA and the origin of modern humans. *Proc. Natl Acad. Sci. USA* **98**, 390–391.

Relethford, J. & Jorde, L. 1999 Genetic evidence for larger African population size during recent human evolution. *Am. J. Phys. Anthropol.* **108**, 251–260.

Richards, M. & Macaulay, V. 2000 Genetic data and the colonization of Europe: genealogies and founders. In *Archaeogenetics* (ed. C. Renfrew & K. Boyle), pp. 139–151. Cambridge: McDonald Institute.

Rightmire, G. P. 1998 Human evolution in the Middle Pleistocene: the role of *Homo heidelbergensis*. *Evol. Anthropol.* **6**, 218–227.

Roberts, R., Jones, R. & Smith, M. 1990 Thermoluminescence dating of a 50 000 year old human occupation site in northern Australia. *Nature* **345**, 153–156.

Roberts, R., Jones, R., Spooner, N., Head, M., Murray, A. & Smith, M. 1994 The human colonization of Australia: optical dates of 53 000 and 60 000 years bracket human arrival at Deaf Adder Gorge, Northern Territory. *Quat. Sci. Rev. (Quat. Geochronol.)* **13**, 575–583.

Roebroeks, W. & Gamble, C. (eds) 1999 *The Middle Palaeolithic occupation of Europe*. University of Leiden.

Rogers, A. 2001 Order emerging from chaos in human evolutionary genetics. *Proc. Natl Acad. Sci. USA* **98**, 779–780.

Schillaci, M. & Froehlich, J. 2001 Nonhuman primate hybridisation and the taxonomic status of Neanderthals. *Am. J. Phys. Anthropol.* **115**, 157–166.

Schwarcz, H. P., Simpson, J. J. & Stringer, C. B. 1998 Neanderthal skeleton from Tabun: U-series data by gammaray spectrometry. *J. Hum. Evol.* **35**, 635–645.

Seidler, H., Falk, D., Stringer, C., Wilfing, H., Muller, G., zur Nedden, D., Weber, G., Recheis, W. & Arsuaga, J. L. 1997 A comparative study of stereolithographically modelled skulls of Petralona and Broken Hill: implications for future studies of middle Pleistocene hominid evolution. *J. Hum. Evol.* **33**, 691–703.

Shen, G. & Wang, W. 2001 Chronological evidence for early appearance of modern humans in southern China. *XIVth Congr. Union Int. des Sci. Préhistoriques et Protohistoriques (UISPP)*, Liège, 2–8 September 2001. Session 16.1 Abstract C8.

Shennan, S. 2001 Demography and cultural innovation: a model and its implications for the emergence of modern human culture. *Camb. Archaeol. J.* **11**, 5–16.

Shields, E. 1998 Australian aborigines represent the first branch from Eurasian antecedents: odontometric evidence. *J. Craniofac. Genet. Devl Biol.* **18**, 228–232.

Simpson, J. & Grün, R. 1998 Non-destructive gamma spectrometric U-series dating. *Quat. Sci. Rev. (Quat. Geochronol.)* **17**, 1009–1022.

Smith, A. 1994 *Systematics and the fossil record: documenting evolutionary patterns*. Oxford: Blackwell Scientific.

Smith, F. 1992 The role of continuity in modern human origins. In *Continuity or replacement? Controversies in* Homo sapiens *evolution* (ed. G. Bräuer & F. Smith), pp. 145–156. Rotterdam, The Netherlands: Balkema.

Smith, F., Trinkaus, E., Pettitt, P., Karavanić, I. & Paunović, M. 1999 Direct radiocarbon dates for Vindija G$_1$ and Velika Peć in late Pleistocene hominid remains. *Proc. Natl Acad. Sci. USA* **96**, 12 281–12 286.

Stringer, C. 1992 Reconstructing recent human evolution. *Phil. Trans. R. Soc. Lond.* B **337**, 217–224.

Stringer, C. 1994 Out of Africa—a personal history. In *Origins of anatomically modern humans* (ed. M. Nitecki & D. Nitecki), pp. 149–172. New York: Plenum.

Stringer, C. 1996 Current issues in modern human origins. In *Contemporary issues in human evolution* (ed. W. Meikle, F. C. Howell & N. Jablonski), *California Academy of Sciences Memoir* **21**, 115–134.

Stringer, C. 1998*a* A metrical study of the WLH-50 calvaria. *J. Hum. Evol.* **34**, 327–332.

Stringer, C. 1998*b* Chronological and biogeographic perspectives on later human evolution. In *Neandertals and modern humans in Western Asia* (ed. T. Akazawa, K. Aoki & O. Bar-Yosef), pp. 29–37. New York: Plenum.

Stringer, C. 1999 The origin of modern humans and their regional diversity. *Newslett. Interdisc. Stud. Origins Jpn. Peoples Cultures* **9**, 3–5.

Stringer, C. 2000 Coasting out of Africa. *Nature* **405**, 24–27. Stringer, C. 2001*a* Dating the origin of modern humans. In *The age of the Earth: from 4004 BC to AD 2002* (ed. C. Lewis & S. Knell), pp. 265–274. London: Geological Society.

Stringer, C. 2001*b* Modern human origins—distinguishing the models. *Afr. Archaeol. Rev.* **18**, 67–75.

Stringer, C. & Davies, W. 2001 Those elusive Neanderthals. *Nature* **413**, 791–792.

Stringer, C. & Hublin, J.-J. 1999 New age estimates for the Swanscombe hominid, and their significance for human evolution. *J. Hum. Evol.* **37**, 873–877.

Stringer, C., Humphrey, L. & Compton, T. 1997 Cladistic analysis of dental traits in recent humans using a fossil outgroup. *J. Hum. Evol.* **32**, 389–402.

Stringer, C., Trinkaus, E., Roberts, M., Parfitt, S. & Macphail, R. 1998 The Middle Pleistocene human tibia from Boxgrove. *J. Hum. Evol.* **34**, 509–547.

Swisher, C., Rink, W., Anton, S., Schwarcz, H., Curtis, G., Suprijo, A., Widiasmoro 1996 Latest *Homo erectus* of Java: potential contemporaneity with *Homo sapiens* in southeast Asia. *Science* **274**, 1870–1874.

Takahata, N., Lee, S.-H. & Satta, Y. 2001 Testing multiregionality of modern human origins. *Mol. Biol. Evol.* **18**, 172–183.

Tattersall, I. & Schwartz, J. 2000 *Extinct humans*. Boulder, CO: Westview Press.

Taylor, R. & Aitken, M. (eds) 1997 *Chronometric dating in archaeology*. New York: Plenum.

Templeton, A. R. 1993 The 'Eve' hypothesis: a genetic critique and reanalysis. *Am. Anthropol.* **95**, 51–72.

Thorne, A. & Wolpoff, M. 1992 The multiregional evolution of modern humans. *Sci. Am.* **266**, 76–83.

Thorne, A., Grün, R., Mortimer, G., Spooner, N., Simpson, J., Mcculloch, M., Taylor, L. & Curnoe, D. 1999 Australia's oldest human remains: age of the Lake Mungo 3 skeleton. *J. Hum. Evol.* **36**, 591–612.

Tishkoff, S. (and 11 others) 2000 STRP-Alu haplotype variation at PLAT locus. *Am. J. Hum. Genet.* **67**, 901–925.

Trinkaus, E. 1984 Western Asia. In *The origins of modern humans* (ed. F. Smith & F. Spencer), pp. 251–293. New York: Alan R. Liss.

Trinkaus, E. 1997 Appendicular robusticity and the paleobiology of modern human emergence. *Proc. Natl Acad. Sci. USA* **94**, 13 367–13 373.

Turner III, C. 1992 Microevolution of east Asian and European populations: a dental perspective. In *The evolution and dispersal of modern humans in Asia* (ed. T. Akazawa, K. Aoki & T. Kimura), pp. 415–438. Tokyo: Hokusen-Sha.

Turney, C. (and 11 others) 2001 Early human occupation at Devil's Lair, southwestern Australia 50 000 years ago. *Quat. Res.* **55**, 3–13.

Tyrell, A. & Chamberlain, A. 1998 Non-metric trait evidence for modern human affinities and the distinctiveness of Neanderthals. *J. Hum. Evol.* **34**, 549–554.

Underhill, P., Passarino, G., Lin, A., Shen, P., Lahr, M., Foley, R., Oefner, P. & Cavalli-Sforza, L. 2001 The phylogeography of Y chromosome binary haplotypes and the origins of modern human populations. *Ann. Hum. Genet.* **65**, 43–62.

Valladas, H., Joron, J., Valladas, G., Arensburg, B., Bar-Yosef, O., Belfer-Cohen, A., Goldberg, P., Laville, H., Meignen, L. & Rak, Y. 1987 Thermoluminescence dates for the Neanderthal burial site at Kebara in Israel. *Nature* **330**, 159–160.

Vandermeersch, B. 1989 The evolution of modern humans: recent evidence from southwest Asia. In *The human revolution: behavioural and biological perspectives in the origins of modern humans* (ed. P. Mellars & C. Stringer), pp. 155–164. Edinburgh University Press.

Wainscoat, J. (and 10 others) 1986 Evolutionary relationships of human populations from an analysis of nuclear DNA polymorphisms. *Nature* **319**, 491–493.

Watkins, W., Ricker, C., Bamshad, M., Carroll, M., Nguyen, S., Batzer, M., Harpending, H., Rogers, A. & Jorde, L. 2001 Patterns of ancestral human diversity: an analysis of *Alu*-insertion and restrictionsite polymorphisms. *Am. J. Hum. Genet.* **68**, 738–752.

Wolpoff, M. & Caspari, R. 1997 *Race and human evolution: a fatal attraction.* New York: Simon & Schuster.

Yin, G., Falguères, C., Shen, G. & Lu, Y. 2001 The age of Dali Man. *XIVth Congr. Union Int. des Sci. Préhistoriques et Protohistoriques (UISPP)*, Liège, 2–8 September 2001. Session 16.1 abstract C7.

Zhao, Z. (and 12 others) 2000 Worldwide DNA sequence variation in a 10-kilobase noncoding region on human chromosome 22. *Proc. Natl Acad. Sci. USA* **97**, 11 354–11 358.

There are different models to describe the behavior of early *Homo sapiens* and how it differed from earlier hominins and present-day humans. The debate centers on the date, the tempo, and the nature of behavioral change in early humans.

28. The Morning of the Modern Mind

Controversial discoveries suggest that the roots of our vaunted intellect run far deeper than is commonly believed

By Kate Wong

Capetown, South Africa—Christopher Henshilwood empties a tiny plastic bag and hands me a square of worn blue cardstock to which 19 snail shells no larger than kernels of corn have been affixed in three horizontal rows. To the casual onlooker, they might well appear unremarkable, a handful of discarded mollusk armor, dull and gray with age. In fact, they may be more precious than the glittering contents of any velvetlined Cartier case.

The shells, discovered in a cave called Blombos located 200 miles east of here, are perfectly matched in size, and each bears a hole in the same spot opposite the mouth, notes Henshilwood, an archaeologist at the University of Bergen in Norway. He believes they were collected and perforated by humans nearly 75,000 years ago to create a strand of lustrous, pearllike beads. If he is correct, these modest shells are humanity's crown jewels—the oldest unequivocal evidence of personal adornment to date and proof that our ancestors were thinking like us far earlier than is widely accepted.

Kate Wong, "The Morning of the Modern Mind," *Scientific American* vol. 292, no. 6, pp. 86–95. Copyright © 2005 by Scientific American. Reprinted with permission.

A BEHAVIORAL BIG BANG

By most accounts, the origin of anatomically modern *Homo sapiens* was a singularly African affair. In 2003 the unveiling of fossils found in Herto, Ethiopia, revealed that this emergence had occurred by 160,000 years ago. And this past February researchers announced that they had redated *H. sapiens* remains from another Ethiopian site, Omo Kibish, potentially pushing the origin of our species back to 195,000 years ago. Far less clear is when our kind became modern of mind. For the past two decades, the prevailing view has been that humanity underwent a behavioral revolution around 40,000 years ago. Scholars based this assessment primarily on the well-known cultural remains of Ice Age Europeans. In Europe, the relevant archaeological record is divided into the Middle Paleolithic (prior to around 40,000 years ago) and the Upper Paleolithic (from roughly 40,000 years ago onward), and the difference between the two could not be more striking. Middle Paleolithic people seem to have made mostly the same relatively simple stone tools humans had been producing for tens of thousands of years and not much else. The Upper Paleolithic, in contrast, ushered in a suite of sophisticated practices. Within a geologic blink of an eye, humans from the Rhône Valley to the Russian plain were producing advanced weaponry, forming long-distance trade networks, expressing themselves through art and music, and generally engaging in all manner of activities that archaeologists typically associate with modernity. It was, by all appearances, the ultimate Great Leap Forward.

Perhaps not coincidentally, it is during this Middle to Upper Paleolithic transition that humans of modern appearance had begun staking their claim on Europe, which until this point was strictly Neandertal territory. Although the identity of the makers of the earliest Upper Paleolithic artifacts is not known with certainty, because of a lack of human remains at the sites, they are traditionally assumed to have been anatomically modern *H. sapiens* rather than Neandertals. Some researchers have thus surmised that confrontation between the two populations awakened in the invaders a creative ability that had heretofore lain dormant.

Other specialists argue that the cultural explosion evident in Europe grew out of a shift that occurred somewhat earlier in Africa. Richard G. Klein of Stanford University, for one, contends that the abrupt change from the Middle to the Upper Paleolithic mirrors a transition that took place 5,000 to 10,000 years beforehand in Africa, where the comparative culture periods are termed the Middle and Later Stone Age. The impetus for this change, he theorizes, was not an encounter with another hominid type (for by this time in Africa, *H. sapiens* was free of competition with other human species) but rather a genetic mutation some 50,000 years ago that altered neural processes and thereby unleashed our fore-bears' powers of innovation.

Key evidence for this model, Klein says, comes from a site in central Kenya called Enkapune Ya Muto, the "twilight cave," that places the origin of the Later Stone Age at 45,000 to 50,000 years ago. There Stanley H. Ambrose of the University of Illinois and his team have uncovered obsidian knives, thumbnail-size scrapers and—most notably—tiny disk-shaped beads fashioned from ostrich eggshell in Later Stone Age levels dating back some 43,000 years. Strands of similar beads are still exchanged as gifts today among the !Kung San huntergatherers of Botswana. Ambrose posits that the ancient bead makers at Enkapune Ya Muto created them for the same reason: to foster good relationships with other groups as a hedge against hard times. If so, according to Klein, a genetically conferred ability to communicate through symbols—in concert with the cognitive prowess to conceive of better hunting technology and resource use—may have been what enabled our species finally, nearly 150,000 years after it originated, to set forth from its mother continent and conquer the world.

STONE AGE SOPHISTICATION

Symbolism. The invention of external storage of information—whether in jewelry, art, language or tools—was the watershed event in modern human behavioral evolution, according to Christopher Henshilwood of the University of Bergen in Norway. *Homo sapiens* probably had the hardware required for symbolic thought by the time the species arose, at least 195,000 years ago, hence the occasional early glimpses of it in the archaeological record. But only once symbolism became the basis for human behavioral organization—resulting in the formation of trade and alliance networks, for example—was its full potential realized.

Ecological disaster. Genetic data suggest that *H. sapiens* experienced a bottleneck some 70,000 years ago. Stanley H. Ambrose of the University of Illinois posits that it was the fallout from an eruption of Sumatra's Mount Toba at around that time that may have brought on a devastating six-year-long volcanic winter and subsequent 1,000-year ice age. Those individuals who cooperated and shared resources with one another—beyond their local group boundaries—were the best equipped to survive in the harsh environs and pass their genes along to the next generation. The extreme conditions favored a transition from the troop level of social organization to that of the tribe.

Projectile technology. The innovation of projectile weapons between 45,000 and 35,000 years ago allowed humans to kill large game—and other humans—from a safe distance. This, says John Shea of Stony Brook University, provided people with a strong incentive to cooperate, which would in turn have fostered the development of social networks through which information could be readily shared.

Population growth. Modern ways bubbled up and disappeared at different times and in different places until the population size reached critical mass. At that point, confrontation between groups and competition for resources sparked symbolic behavior and spurred technological innovation, contend researchers, including Alison Brooks of George Washington University and Sally McBrearty of the University of Connecticut. And with more people to pass on these traditions, they began to stick, rather than dying out with the last member of a group.

Brain mutation. A genetic mutation roughly 50,000 years ago had the lucky effect of rewiring the human brain such that it was capable of symbolic thought—including language—argues Richard G. Klein of Stanford University. Humans carrying this mutation had a considerable advantage over those who did not and quickly outcompeted and replaced them.

SEEDS OF CHANGE

Inrecentyears, however, a small but growing number of archaeologists have eschewed the big bang theories of the origin of culture in favor of a fundamentally different model. Proponents believe that there was no lag between body and brain. Rather, they contend, modern human behavior emerged over a long period in a process more aptly described as evolution than revolution. And some workers believe that cognitive modernity may have evolved in other species, such as the Neandertals, as well.

The notion that our species' peerless creativity might have primeval roots is not new. For years, scientists have known of a handful of objects that, taken at face vaue, suggest that humans were engaging in modern practices long before *H. sapiens* first painted a cave wall in France. They include three 400,000-year-old wooden throwing spears from Schöningen, Germany; a 233,000-year-old putative figurine from the site of Berekhat Ram in Israel; a 60,000-year-old piece of fl int incised with concentric arcs from Quneitra, Israel; two 100,000-year-old fragments of notched bone from South Africa's Klasies River Mouth Cave; and a polished plate of mam-moth tooth from Tata in Hungary, dated to between 50,000 and 100,000 years ago. Many archaeologists looked askance at these remains, however, noting that their age was uncertain or that their significance was unclear. Any sign of advanced intellect that did

---

Mapping Modernity

Humans who looked like us had evolved by 195,000 years ago, as evidenced by *Homo sapiens* fossils from the site of Omo Kibish in Ethiopia. But received archaeological wisdom holds that humans did not begin behaving like us until nearly 150,000 years later. That notion stems largely from cultural remains uncovered in Europe, where art, ritual, technological advances and other indications of modern thinking flowered spectacularly and suddenly after about 40,000 years ago, around the time that anatomically modern humans started colonizing Europe. Recent finds, including those from Blombos Cave in South Africa, are revealing that many sophisticated practices emerged long before 40,000 years ago at sites outside of Europe, suggesting that humans were our cognitive equals by the time they attained anatomical modernity, if not earlier. Indeed, the fact that at least some Neandertals appear to have thought symbolically raises the possibility that such capacities were present in the last common ancestor of Neandertals and *H. sapiens.* The map below shows the locations of the sites mentioned in the article.

---

seem legitimately ancient was explained away as a one-off accomplishment, the work of a genius among average Joes.

That position has become harder to defend in the face of the growing body of evidence in Africa that our forebears' mental metamorphosis began well before the start of the Later Stone Age. In a paper entitled "The Revolution That Wasn't: A New Interpretation of the Origin of Modern Human Behavior," published in the *Journal of Human Evolution* in 2000, Sally McBrearty of the University of Connecticut and Alison S. Brooks of George Washington University laid out their case. Many of the components of modern human behavior said to emerge in lockstep between 40,000 and 50,000 years ago, they argued, are visible tens of thousands of years earlier at Middle Stone Age locales. Moreover, they appear not as a package but piecemeal, at sites farflung in time and space.

At three sites in Katanda, Democratic Republic of the Congo, Brooks and John Yellen of the Smithsonian Institution have found elaborate barbed harpoons carved from bone that they say date to at least 80,000 years ago, which would place them firmly within the Middle Stone Age. These artifacts exhibit a level of sophistication comparable to that seen in 25,000-year-old harpoons from Europe, not only in terms of the complexity of the weapon design but the choice of raw material: the use of bone and ivory in tool manufacture was not thought to have occurred until the Later Stone Age and Upper Paleolithic. In addition, remains of giant Nile catfish have turned up with some of the Katanda harpoons, suggesting to the excavators that people were going there when the fish were spawning—the kind of seasonal mapping of resources previously thought to characterize only later humans.

Other Middle Stone Age sites, such as ≠ Gi (the "≠" denotes a click sound) in Botswana's Kalahari Desert, which is dated to 77,000 years ago, have yielded butchered animal remains that have put paid to another oftmade claim, namely, that these ancient people were not as competent at hunting as Later Stone Age folks. The residents at ≠ Gi appear to have regularly pursued such large and dangerous prey as zebra and Cape warthog. And Hilary J. Deacon of Stellenbosch University has suggested that at sites such as South Africa's Klasies River Mouth Cave humans more than 60,000 years ago were deliberately burning grassland to encourage the growth of nutritious tubers, which are known to germinate after exposure to fire.

Some discoveries hint that certain alleged aspects of behavioral modernity arose even before the genesis of *H. sapiens*. Last summer excavations by McBrearty's team at a site near Lake Baringo in Kenya turned up stone blades—once a hall-mark of the Upper Paleolithic material cultures—more than 510,000 years old.

At a nearby locality, in levels dated to at least 285,000 years ago, her team has uncovered vast quantities of red ochre (a form of iron ore) and grindstones for processing it, signaling to McBrearty that the Middle Stone Age people at Baringo were using the pigment for symbolic purposes—to decorate their bodies, for instance—just as many humans do today. (Baringo is not the only site to furnish startlingly ancient evidence of ochre processing—Twin Rivers Cave in Zambia has yielded similar material dating back to more than 200,000 years ago.) And 130,000-year-old tool assemblages from Mumba Rock Shelter in Tanzania include fl akes crafted from obsidian that came from a volcanic fl ow about 200 miles away—compelling evidence that the hominids who made the implements traded with other groups for the exotic raw material.

Critics, however, have dismissed these finds on the basis of uncertainties surrounding, in some cases, the dating and, in others, the intent of the makers. Ochre, for one, may have been used as mastic for attaching blades to wooden handles or as an antimicrobial agent for treating animal hides, skeptics note.

SMART FOR THEIR AGE

Itisagainst this backdrop of long-standing controversy that the discoveries at Blombos have come to light. Henshilwood discovered the archaeological deposits at Blombos Cave in 1991 while looking for much younger coastal hunter-gatherer sites to excavate for his Ph.D. Located near the town of Still Bay in South Africa's southern Cape, on a bluff overlooking the Indian Ocean, the cave contained few of the Holocene artifacts he was looking for but appeared rich in Middle Stone Age material. As such, it was beyond the scope of his research at the time. In 1997, however, he raised the money to return to Blombos to begin excavating in earnest. Since then, Henshilwood and his team have unearthed an astonishing assemblage of sophisticated tools and symbolic objects and in so doing have sketched a portrait of a long-ago people who thought like us.

From levels dated by several methods to 75,000 years ago have come an array of advanced implements, including 40 bone tools, several of which are finely worked awls, and hundreds of bifacial points made of silcrete and other difficult-to-shape stones, which the Blombos people could have used to hunt the antelopes and other game that roamed the area. Some of the points are just an inch long, suggesting that they may have been employed as projectiles. And the bones of various species of deep-sea fish—the oldest of which may be more than 130,000 years old—reveal that the Blombos people had the equipment required to harvest creatures in excess of 80 pounds from the ocean.

Hearths for cooking indicate that the cave was a living site, and teeth representing both adults and children reveal that a family group dwelled there. But there are so many of the stone points, and such a range in their quality, that Hen-shilwood wonders whether the occupants may have also had a workshop in the tiny cave, wherein masters taught young-sters how to make the tools.

They may have passed along other traditions as well. The most spectacular material to emerge from Blombos is that which demonstrates that its occupants thought symbolically. To date, the team has recovered one piece of incised bone, nine slabs of potentially engraved red ochre and dozens of the tiny beads—all from the same 75,000-year-old layers that yielded the tools. In addition, sediments that may date back to more than 130,000 years ago contain vast quantities of processed ochre, some in crayon form.

Scientists may never know exactly what meaning the enigmatic etchings held for their makers. But it is clear that they were important to them. Painstaking analyses of two of the engraved ochres, led by Francesco d'Errico of the University of Bordeaux in France, reveal that the rust-colored rocks were hand-ground on one side to produce a facet that was then etched repeatedly with a stone point. On the largest ochre, bold lines frame and divide the crosshatched design.

Bead manufacture was likewise laborintensive. Henshilwood believes the marine tick shells, which belong to the *Nassarius kraussianus* snail, were collected from either of two estuaries, located 12 miles from the cave, that still exist today. Writing in the January issue of the *Journal of Human Evolution,* Henshilwood, d'Errico and their colleagues report that experimental reconstruction of the process by which the shells were perforated indicates that the precocious jewelers used bone points to punch through the lip of the shell from the inside out—a technique that commonly broke the shells when attempted by team members. Once pierced, the beads appear to have been strung, as evidenced by the wear facets ringing the perforations, and traces of red ochre on the shells hint that they may have lain against skin painted with the pigment.

In the case for cognitive sophistication in the Middle Stone Age, "Blombos is the smoking gun," McBrearty declares. But Henshilwood has not convinced everyone of his interpretation. Doubts have come from Randall White of New York University, an expert on Upper Paleolithic body ornaments. He suspects that the perforations and apparent wear facets on the *Nassarius* shells are the result of natural processes, not human handiwork.

HERE TODAY, GONE TOMORROW

If read correctly, however, the remarkable discoveries at Blombos offer weighty evidence that at least one group of humans possessed a modern mind-set long before 50,000 years ago, which may in some ways make previous claims for early behavioral modernity easier to swallow. So, too, may recent finds from sites such as Diepkloof in South Africa's Western Cape, which has produced pieces of incised ostrich eggshell dated to around 60,000 years ago, and Loiyangalani in Tanzania, where workers have found ostrich eggshell beads estimated to be on the order of 70,000 years old.

Yet it remains the case that most Middle Stone Age sites show few or none of the traits researchers use to identify fully developed cognition in the archaeological record. Several other locales in South Africa, for example, have yielded the so-phisticated bifacial points but no evidence of symbolic behavior. Of course, absence of evidence is not evidence of absence, as prehistorians are fond of saying. It is possible the people who lived at these sites did make art and decorate their bodies, but only their stone implements have survived.

Perhaps the pattern evident thus far in the African record—that of ephemeral glimpses of cognitive modernity before the start of the Later Stone Age and ubiquitous indications of it after that—is just an artifact of preservational bias or the relatively small number of African sites excavated so far. Then again, maybe these fits and starts are exactly what archaeologists should expect to see if anatomically modern *H. sapiens* possessed the capacity for modern human behavior from the get-go but tapped that potential only when it provided an advantage, as many gradualists believe.

The circumstances most likely to elicit advanced cultural behaviors, McBrearty and others hypothesize, were those related to increased population size. The presence of more people put more pressure on resources, forcing our ancestors to devise cleverer ways to obtain food and materials for toolmaking, she submits. More people also raised the chances of encounters among groups. Beads, body paint and even stylized tool manufacture may have functioned as indicators of an individual's membership and status in a clan, which would have been especially important when laying claim to resources in short supply. Symbolic objects may have also served as a social lubricant during stressful times, as has been argued for the beads from Enkapune Ya Muto.

"You have to make good with groups around you because that's how you're going to get partners," Henshilwood observes. "If a gift exchange system is going on, that's how you're maintaining good relations."

Indeed, gift giving may explain why some of the tools at Blombos are so aesthetically refined. A beautiful tool is not going to be a better weapon, he remarks, it is going to function as a symbolic artifact, a keeper of the peace.

Conversely, when the population dwindled, these advanced practices subsided—perhaps because the people who engaged in them died out or because in the absence of competition they simply did not pay off and were therefore forgotten. The Tasmanians provide a recent example of this relationship: when Europeans arrived in the region in the 17th century, they encountered a people whose material culture was simpler than even those of the Middle Paleolithic, consisting of little more than basic stone fl ake tools. Indeed, from an archaeological standpoint, these remains would have failed nearly all tests of modernity that are commonly applied to prehistoric sites. Yet the record shows that several thousand years ago, the Tasmanians possessed a much more complex tool kit, one that included bone tools, fishing nets, and bows and arrows. It seems that early Tasmanians had all the latest gadgetry before rising sea levels cut the island off from the mainland 10,000 years ago but lost the technology over the course of their small group's separation from the much larger Aboriginal Australian population.

This might be why South African sites between 60,000 and 30,000 years old so rarely seem to bear the modern signature: demographic reconstructions suggest that the human population in Africa crashed around 60,000 years ago because of a precipitous drop in temperature. Inferring capacity from what people produced is inherently problematic, White observes. Medieval folks doubtless had the brainpower to go to the moon, he notes. Just because they did not does not mean they were not our cognitive equals. "At any given moment," White refl ects, "people don't fulfill their entire potential."

SYMBOL-MINDED

The debate over when, where and how our ancestors became cognitively modern is complicated by the fact that experts disagree over what constitutes modern human behavior in the first place. In the strictest sense, the term encompasses every facet of culture evident today—from agriculture to the iPod. To winnow the definition into something more useful to archaeologists, many workers employ the list of behavioral traits that distinguish the Middle and Upper Paleolithic in Europe. Others use the material cultures of modern and recent hunter-gatherers as a guide. Ultimately, whether or not a set of remains is deemed evidence of modernity can hinge on the preferred definition of the evaluator.

Taking that into consideration, some experts instead advocate focusing on the origin and evolution of arguably the most important characteristic of modern human societies: symbolically organized behavior, including language. "The ability to store symbols externally, outside of the human brain, is the key to everything we do today," Henshilwood asserts. A symbol-based system of communication might not be a perfect proxy for behavioral modernity in the archaeological record, as the Tasmanian example illustrates, but at least researchers seem to accept it as a defining aspect of the human mind as we know it, if not *the* defining aspect.

It remains to be seen just how far back in time symbolic culture arose. And discoveries outside of Africa and Europe are helping to fl esh out the story. Controversial evidence from the rock shelters of Malakunanja II and Nauwalabila I in Australia's Northern Territory, for instance, suggests that people had arrived there by 60,000 years ago. To reach the island continent, emigrants traveling from southeastern Asia would have to have built sturdy watercraft and navigated a minimum of 50 miles of open water, depending on the sea level. Scholars mostly agree that any human capable of managing this feat must have been fully modern. And in Israel's Qafzeh Cave, Erella Hovers of the Hebrew University of Jerusalem and her team have recovered dozens of pieces of red ochre near 92,000-year-old graves of *H. sapiens*. They believe the lumps of pigment were heated in hearths to achieve a specific hue of scarlet and then used in funerary rituals.

Other finds raise the question of whether symbolism is unique to anatomically modern humans. Neandertal sites commonly contain evidence of systematic ochre processing, and toward the end of their reign in Europe, in the early Upper Paleolithic, Neandertals apparently developed their own cultural tradition of manufacturing body ornaments, as evidenced by the discovery of pierced teeth and other objects at sites such as Quinçay and the Grotte du Renne at Arcysur-Cure in France [see "Who Were the Neandertals?" by Kate Wong; SCIENTIFIC AMERICAN, April 2000]. They also interred their dead. The symbolic nature of this behavior in their case is debated because the burials lack grave goods. But this past April at the annual meeting of the Paleoanthropology Society, Jill Cook of the British Museum reported that digital microscopy of remains from Krapina Rock Shelter in Croatia bolsters the hypothesis that Neandertals were cleaning the bones of the deceased, possibly in a kind of mortuary ritual, as opposed to defleshing them for food.

Perhaps the ability to think symbolically evolved independently in Neandertals and anatomically modern *H. sapiens*. Or maybe it arose before the two groups set off on separate evolutionary trajectories, in a primeval common ancestor. "I can't prove it, but I bet [*Homo*] *heidelbergensis* [a hominid that lived as much as 400,000 years ago] was capable of this," White speculates.

For his part, Henshilwood is betting that the dawn of symbol-driven thinking lies in the Middle Stone Age. As this article was going to press, he and his team were undertaking their ninth field season at Blombos. By the end of that period they will have sifted through a third of the cave's 75,000-year-old deposits, leaving the rest to future archaeologists with as yet unforeseen advances in excavation and dating techniques. "We don't really need to go further in these levels at Blombos," Henshilwood says. "We need to find other sites now that date to this time period." He is confident that they will succeed in that endeavor, having already identified a number of very promising locales in the coastal De Hoop Nature Reserve, about 30 miles west of Blombos.

Sitting in the courtyard of the African Heritage Research Institute pondering the dainty snail shells in my hand, I consider what they might have represented to the Blombos people. In some ways, it is difficult to imagine our ancient ancestors setting aside basic concerns of food, water, predators and shelter to make such baubles. But later, perusing a Cape Town jeweler's offerings—from cross pendants cast in gold to diamond engagement rings—it is harder still to conceive of *Homo sapiens* behaving any other way. The trinkets may have changed somewhat since 75,000 years ago, but the all-important messages they encode are probably still the same.

Kate Wong is editorial director of Scientific American.com

According to the authors, the origin of agriculture resulted in pronounced changes in diet and activity patterns that have been greatly amplified in modern industrial societies. The "mismatch" between human dietary needs and the food actually consumed, together with reduced activity levels, may explain the prevalence of many chronic diseases in western society.

29. Origins and Evolution of the Western Diet

Health Implications for the 21st Century[1,2]

By Loren Cordain, S. Boyd Eaton, Anthony Sebastian, Neil Mann, Staffan Lindeberg, Bruce A. Watkins, James H. O'Keefe, and Janette Brand-Miller

EVOLUTIONARY DISCORDANCE

Evolution acting through natural selection represents an ongoing interaction between a species' genome and its environment over the course of multiple generations. Genetic traits may be positively or negatively selected relative to their concordance or discordance with environmental selective pressures (1). When the environment remains relatively constant, stabilizing selection tends to maintain genetic traits that represent the optimal average for a population (2). When environmental conditions permanently change, evolutionary discordance arises between a species' genome and its environment, and stabilizing selection is replaced by directional selection, moving the average population genome to a new set point (1, 2). Initially, when permanent environmental changes occur in a population, individuals bearing the previous average status quo genome experience evolutionary discordance (2, 3). In the affected genotype, this evolutionary discordance manifests itself phenotypically as disease, increased morbidity and mortality, and reduced reproductive success (1–3).

Loren Cordain et al., "Origins and Evolution of the Western Diet: Health Implications for the 21st Century," *American Journal of Clinical Nutrition*, vol. 81, pp. 341–354. Copyright © 2005 by American Society for Clinical Nutrition. Reprinted with permission.

Similar to all species, contemporary humans are genetically adapted to the environment of their ancestors—that is, to the environment that their ancestors survived in and that consequently conditioned their genetic makeup (1–3). There is growing awareness that the profound environmental changes (eg, in diet and other lifestyle conditions) that began with the introduction of agriculture and animal husbandry ≈10, 000 y ago occurred too recently on an evolutionary time scale for the human genome to adapt (2–5). In conjunction with this discordance between our ancient, genetically determined biology and the nutritional, cultural, and activity patterns in contemporary Western populations, many of the so-called diseases of civilization have emerged (2–12).

CHRONIC DISEASE INCIDENCE

In the United States, chronic illnesses and health problems either wholly or partially attributable to diet represent by far the most serious threat to public health. Sixty-five percent of adults aged 20 y in the United States are either overweight or obese (13), and the estimated number of deaths ascribable to obesity is 280,184 per year (14). More than 64 million Americans have one or more types of cardiovascular disease (CVD), which represents the leading cause of mortality (38.5% of all deaths) in the United States (15). Fifty million Americans are hypertensive; 11 million have type 2 diabetes, and 37 million adults maintain high-risk total cholesterol concentrations (>240 mg/dL) (15). In post-menopausal women aged ≥50 y, 7.2% have osteoporosis and 39.6% have osteopenia (16). Osteoporotic hip fractures are associated with a 20% excess mortality in the year after fracture (17). Cancer is the second leading cause of death (25% of all deaths) in the United States, and an estimated one-third of all cancer deaths are due to nutritional factors, including obesity (18).

HOMININ DIETARY CHARACTERISTICS

In the 5–7 million-year period since the evolutionary emergence of hominins (bipedal primates within the taxonomic tribe hominini; note that the newer term *hominin* supplants the previous term, *hominid*) ≥20 species may have existed (**Figure 1**) (19). Similar to historically studied hunter-gatherers (20, 21), there would have been no single universal diet consumed by all extinct hominin species. Rather, diets would have varied by geographic locale, climate, and specific ecologic niche. However, there are universal characteristics of preagricultural hominin diets that are useful in understanding how the current Western diet may predispose modern populations to chronic disease. In-creasingly, clinical trials and interventions that use dietary treatments with nutritional characteristics similar to those found in preindustrial and preagricultural diets have confirmed the beneficial health consequences predicted by the template of evolutionary discordance theory.

NUTRITIONAL CHARACTERISTICS OF PRE- AND POSTAGRICULTURAL DIETS

Before the development of agriculture and animal husbandry hominin dietary choices would have been necessarily limited to minimally processed, wild plant and animal foods. With the initial domestication of plants and animals, the original nutrient characteristics of these formerly wild foods changed, subtly at first

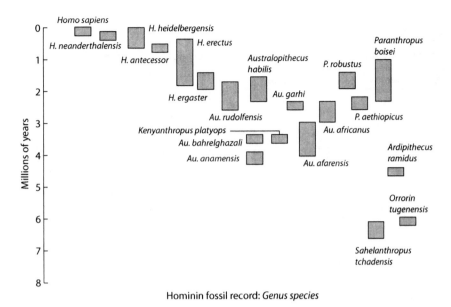

Figure 1. The hominin fossil record. Species are indicated with the dates of the earliest and latest fossil record. Adapted from Wood (19).

but more rapidly with advancing technology after the Industrial Revolution. Furthermore, with the advent of agriculture, novel foods were introduced as staples for which the hominin genome had little evolutionary experience. More importantly, food-processing procedures were developed, particularly following the Industrial Revolution, which allowed for quantitative and qualitative food and nutrient combinations that had not previously been encountered over the course of hominin evolution.

In contrasting pre- and postagricultural diets, it is important to consider not only the nutrient qualities and types of foods that likely would have been consumed by preagricultural hominins but to also recognize the types of foods and their nutrient qualities that could not have been regularly consumed before the development of agriculture, industrialization, and advanced technology. Food types that would have generally been unavailable to preagricultural hominins are listed in **Table 1** (22–24). Although dairy products, cereals, refined sugars, refined vegetable oils, and alcohol make up 72.1% of the total daily energy consumed by all people in the United States, these types of foods would have contributed little or none of the energy in the typical preagricultural hominin diet (20). Additionally, mixtures of foods listed in Table 1 make up the ubiquitous processed foods (eg, cookies, cake, bakery foods, breakfast cereals, bagels, rolls, muffins, crackers, chips, snack foods, pizza, soft drinks, candy, ice cream, condiments, and salad dressings) that dominate the typical US diet.

Dairy Foods

Hominins, like all mammals, would have consumed the milk of their own species during the suckling period. However, after weaning, the consumption of milk and milk products of other mammals would have been nearly impossible before the domestication of livestock because of the inherent difficulties in capturing and milking wild mammals. Although sheep were domesticated by ≈11, 000 before present (BP) (25) and goats and cows by ≈10, 000 BP (26, 27), early direct chemical evidence for dairying dates to 6100 to 5500 BP from residues of dairy fats found on pottery in Britain (28). Taken together, these data indicate that dairy foods, on an evolutionary time scale (Figure 1), are relative newcomers to the hominin diet.

Table 1. Food and food types found in Western diets generally unavailable to preagricultural hominins[1]

FOOD OR FOOD GROUP	VALUE
Dairy products	% of energy[2]
Whole milk	1.6
Low-fat milk	2.1
Cheese	3.2
Butter	1.1
Other	2.6
Total	10.6
Cereal grains	
Whole grains	3.5
Refined grains	20.4
Total	23.9
Refined sugars	
Sucrose	8.0
High-fructose corn syrup	7.8
Glucose	2.6
Syrups	0.1
Other	0.1
Total	18.6
Refined vegetable oils	
Salad, cooking oils	8.8
Shortening	6.6
Margarine	2.2
Total	17.6
Alcohol	1.4
Total energy	72.1
Added salt, as sodium chloride	9.6[3]

[1]Data adapted from references 22–24.
[2]In the US diet.
[3]Salt from processed foods, table salt use, and cooking; in g/d.

Cereals

Because wild cereal grains are usually small, difficult to harvest, and minimally digestible without processing (grinding) and cooking, the appearance of stone processing tools in the fossil record represents a reliable indication of when and where cultures systematically began to include cereal grains in their diet (7). Ground stone mortars, bowls, and cup holes first appeared in the Upper Paleolithic (from 40 000 y ago to 12 000 y ago) (29), whereas the regular exploitation of cereal grains by any world-wide huntergatherer group arose with the emergence of the Natufian culture in the Levant ≈13 000 BP (30). Domestication of emmer and einkorn wheat by the descendants of the Natufians heralded the beginnings of early agriculture and occurred by 10–11 000 BP from strains of wild wheat localized to southeastern Turkey (31). During the ensuing Holocene (10 000 y ago until the present), cereal grains were rarely consumed as year round staples by most worldwide hunter-gatherers (32, 33), except by certain groups living in arid and marginal environments (32, 34). Hence, as was the case with dairy foods, before the Epi-Paleolithic (10 000–11 000 y ago) and Neolithic (10 000 to 5500 y ago) periods, there was little or no previous evolutionary experience for cereal grain consumption throughout hominin evolution.

In Table 1, it is shown that 85.3% of the cereals consumed in the current US diet are highly processed refined grains. Preceding the Industrial Revolution, all cereals were ground with the use of stone milling tools, and unless the flour was sieved, it contained the entire contents of the cereal grain, including the germ, bran, and endosperm (35). With the invention of mechanized steel roller mills and automated sifting devices in the latter part of the 19th century (35), the nutritional characteristics of milled grain changed significantly because the germ and bran were removed in the milling process, leaving flour comprised mainly of endosperm of uniformly small particulate size (35, 36). Accordingly, the widespread consumption of highly refined grain flours of uniformly small particulate size represents a recent secular phenomenon dating to the past 150–200 y (35).

Refined Sugars

The per capita consumption of all refined sugars in the United States in 2000 was 69.1 kg, whereas in 1970 it was 55.5 kg (24). This secular trend for increased sugar consumption in the United States in the past 30 y reflects a much larger worldwide trend that has occurred in Western nations since the beginning of the Industrial Revolution some 200 y ago (37). The per capita refined sucrose consumption in England steadily rose from 6.8 kg in 1815 to 54.5 kg in 1970 (38), as shown in **Figure 2**. Similar trends in refined sucrose consumption have been reported during the Industrial Era for the Netherlands, Sweden, Norway, Denmark, and the United States (39).

The first evidence of crystalline sucrose production appears about 500 BC in northern India (37). Before this time, honey would have represented one of the few concentrated sugars to which hominins would have had access. Although honey likely was a favored food by all hominin species,

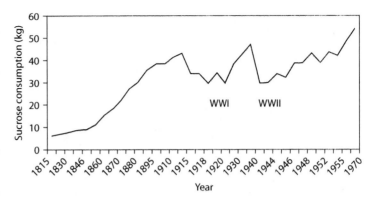

Figure 2. Per capita consumption of sucrose in England from 1815 to 1970. WWI, World War I; WWII, World War II. Adapted from Cleave (38).

seasonal availability would have restricted regular access. Studies of contemporary hunter-gatherers show that gathered honey represented a relatively minor dietary component over the course of a year, despite high intakes in some groups during short periods of availability. In the Anbarra Aborigines of northern Australia, average honey consumption over four 1-mo periods, chosen to be representative of the various seasons, was 2 kg per person per year (40). In the Ache Indians of Paraguay, honey represented 3.0% of the average total daily energy intake over 1580 consumer days (41). Consequently, current population-wide intakes of refined sugars in Westernized societies represent quantities with no precedent during hominin evolution.

In the past 30 y, qualitative features of refined sugar consumption have changed concurrently with the quantitative changes. With the advent of chromatographic fructose enrichment technology in the late 1970s, it became economically feasible to manufacture high-fructose corn syrup (HFCS) in mass quantity (42). The rapid and striking increase in HFCS use that has occurred in the US food supply since its introduction in the 1970s is indicated in **Figure 3**. HFCS is available in 2 main forms, HFCS 42 and HFCS 55, both of which are liquid mixtures of fructose and glucose (42% fructose and 53% glucose and 55% fructose and 42% glucose, respectively) (42). Increases in HFCS occurred simultaneously, whereas sucrose consumption declined (Figure 3). On digestion, sucrose is hydrolyzed in the gut into its 2 equal molecular moieties of glucose and fructose. Consequently, the total per capita fructose consumption (fructose from HFCS and fructose from the digestion of sucrose) increased from 23.1 kg in 1970 to 28.9 kg in 2000. As was the case with sucrose, current Western dietary intakes of fructose could not have occurred on a population-wide basis before industrialization and the introduction of the food-processing industry.

Refined Vegetable Oils

In the United States, during the 90-y period from 1909 to 1999, a striking increase in the use of vegetable oils occurred (**Figure 4**). Specifically, per capita consumption of salad and cooking oils increased 130%, shortening consumption increased 136%, and margarine consumption increased 410% (22). These trends occurred elsewhere in the world and were made possible by the industrialization and mechanization of the oil-seed industry (43). To produce vegetable oils from oil-bearing seeds, 3 procedures can be used: *1*) rendering and pressing, *2*) expeller pressing, and *3*) solvent extraction (43). Oils made from walnuts, almonds, olives, sesame seeds, and flax seeds likely were first produced via the rendering and pressing process between 5000 and 6000 y ago. However, except for olive oil, most early use of oils seems to have been for nonfood purposes such as illumination, lubrication, and medicine (43).

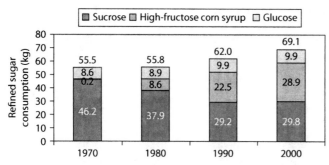

Figure 3. Per capita consumption of refined sugars in the United States from 1970 to 2000. Adapted from the US Department of Agriculture (24).

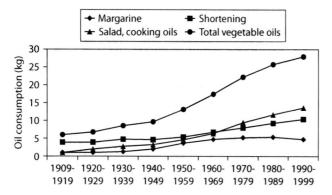

Figure 4. Per capita consumption of vegetable oils in the United States from 1909–1919 to 1990–1999. Adapted from Gerrior and Bente (22).

The industrial advent of mechanically driven steel expellers and hexane extraction processes allowed for greater world-wide vegetable oil productivity, whereas new purification procedures permitted exploitation of nontraditionally consumed oils, such as cottonseed (43). New manufacturing procedures allowed vegetable oils to take on atypical structural characteristics. Margarine and shortening are produced by solidifying or partially solidifying vegetable oils via hydrogenation, a process first developed in 1897 (44). The hydrogenation process produces novel *trans* fatty acid isomers (*trans* elaidic acid in particular) that rarely, if ever, are found in conventional human foodstuffs (44). Consequently, the large-scale addition of refined vegetable oils to the world's food supply after the Industrial Revolution significantly altered both quantitative and qualitative aspects of fat intake.

Alcohol

In contrast with dairy products, cereal grains, refined sugars, and oils, alcohol consumption in the typical US diet represents a relatively minor contribution (1.4%) to the total energy consumed. The earliest evidence for wine drinking from domesticated vines comes from a pottery jar dated 7400–7100 y BP from the Zagros Mountains in northern Iran (45), whereas the earliest archaeologic indication of the brewing of beer and beer consumption dates to the late fourth millennium BC from the Godin site in southern Kurdistan in Iran (46). The incorporation of distilled alcoholic beverages into the human diet came much later. During the period from ≈800 to 1300 AD, various populations in Europe, the Near East, and China learned to distill alcoholic beverages (47).

The fermentation process that produces wine takes place naturally and, without doubt, must have occurred countless times before humans learned to control the process. As grapes reach their peak of ripeness in the fall, they may swell in size and burst, thereby allowing the sugars in the juice to be exposed to yeasts growing on the skins and to produce carbon dioxide and ethanol (48). Because of seasonal fluctuations in fruit availability and the limited liquid storage capacity of hunter-gatherers, it is likely that fermented fruit drinks, such as wine, would have made an insignificant or nonexistent contribution to total energy in hominin diets before the Neolithic (49).

Salt

The total quantity of salt included in the typical US diet amounts to 9.6 g/d (Table 1). About 75% of the daily salt intake in Western populations is derived from salt added to processed foods by manufacturers;

15% comes from discretionary sources (ie, cooking and table salt use), and the remainder (10%) occurs naturally in basic foodstuffs (50). Hence, 90% of the salt in the typical US diet comes from manufactured salt that is added to the food supply.

The systematic mining, manufacture, and transportation of salt have their origin in the Neolithic Period. The earliest salt use is argued to have taken place on Lake Yuncheng in the Northern Province of Shanxi, China, by 6000 BC (51). In Europe the earliest evidence of salt exploitation comes from salt mines at Cardona, Spain, dating to 6200–5600 BP (52). It is likely that Paleolithic (the old stone age which began 2.6 million years ago and ended 10 000–12 000 y ago) or Holocene (10 000 y ago to the present) hunter-gatherers living in coastal areas may have dipped food in seawater or used dried seawater salt in a manner similar to nearly all Polynesian societies at the time of European contact (53). However, the inland living Maori of New Zealand lost the salt habit (53), and the most recently studied inland hunter-gatherers add no or little salt to their food on a daily basis (54). Furthermore, there is no evidence that Paleolithic people undertook salt extraction or took interest in inland salt deposits (55). Collectively, this evidence suggests that the high salt consumption (≈10 g/d) in Western societies has minimal or no evolutionary precedent in hominin species before the Neolithic period.

Fatty domestic meats

Before the Neolithic period, all animal foods consumed by hominins were derived from wild animals. The absolute quantity of fat in wild mammals is dependent on the species body mass–larger mammals generally maintain greater body fat percentages by weight than do smaller animals (21, 56). Additionally, body fat percentages in wild mammals typically vary by age and sex and also seasonally in a cyclic waxing and waning manner with changing availability of food sources and the photoperiod (**Figure 5**) (57, 58). Hence, maximal or peak body fat percentages in wild mammals are maintained only for a few months during the course of a year, even for mammals residing at tropical and southern latitudes (59). In mammals, storage of excess food energy as fat occurs primarily as triacylglycerols in subcutaneous and abdominal fat depots. The dominant (>50% fat energy) fatty acids in the fat storage depots (adipocytes) of wild mammals are saturated fatty acids (SFAs), whereas the dominant fatty acids in muscle and all other organ tissues are polyunsaturated fatty acids (PUFAs) and monounsaturated fatty acids (MUFAs) (11). Because subcutaneous and abdominal body fat stores are depleted during most of the year in wild animals, PUFAs and MUFAs ordinarily constitute most of the total carcass fat (11). MUFAs and PUFAs are the dominant fats in the edible carcass of caribou for all 12 mo of the year, as illustrated in **Figure 6** (11, 60–65). Because of the seasonal cyclic depletion of SFAs and enrichment of PUFAs and MUFAs, a year-round dietary intake

of high amounts of SFAs would have not been possible for preagricultural hominins preying on wild mammals. Even with selective butchering by hominins, in which much of the lean muscle meat is discarded, MUFAs and PUFAs constitute the greatest percentage (>50% of energy as fat) of edible fatty acids in the carcass of wild mammals throughout most of the year (Figure 6).

Beginning with the advent of animal husbandry, it became feasible to prevent or attenuate the seasonal decline in body fat

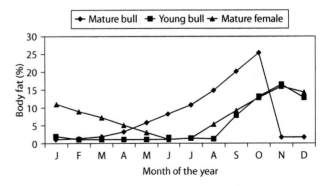

Figure 5. Seasonal fluctuations in percentage body fat in caribou. Adapted from Spiess (57).

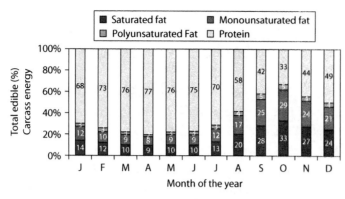

Figure 6. Seasonal variation in mean percentage body fat for mature male, immature male, and mature female caribou (57). Total body fat and total body protein, as a percentage of energy, were calculated from the respective mean values by weight by using the cubic regression equations developed by Cordain et al (20). The edible carcass mass was calculated by subtracting the mass of the bones (minus marrow), hide, hooves, antlers, blood, urine, and gastrointestinal contents from the total live weight. The mass of the edible organs and tissues were calculated from the allometric relation between body mass and organ and tissue mass (60–63). Edible carcass fatty acid composition was calculated by multiplying tissue and organ mass by fatty acid composition (% mass) in these tissues from values for caribou or similar ruminant species (11, 64, 65).

(and hence in SFAs) by provisioning domesticated animals with stored plant foods. Furthermore, it became possible to consistently slaughter the animal at peak body fat percentage. Neolithic advances in food-processing procedures allowed for the storage of concentrated sources of animal SFAs (cheese, butter, tallow, and salted fatty meats) for later consumption throughout the year.

Technologic developments of the early and mid 19th century—such as the steam engine, mechanical reaper, and railroads—allowed for increased grain harvests and efficient transport of both grain and cattle, which in turn spawned the practice of feeding grain (corn primarily) to cattle sequestered in feedlots (66). In the United States before 1850, virtually all cattle were free range or pasture fed and were typically slaughtered at 4–5 y of age (66). By about 1885, the science of rapidly fattening cattle in feedlots had advanced to the point that it was possible to produce a 545-kg steer ready for slaughter in 24 mo and that exhibited "marbled meat" (66). Wild animals and free-range or pasturefed cattle rarely display this trait (11). Marbled meat results from excessive triacylglycerol accumulation in muscle interfascicular adipocytes. Such meat has a greatly increased SFA content, a lower proportion of n –3 fatty acids, and more n –6 fatty acids (11, 65).

Modern feedlot operations involving as many as 100 000 cattle emerged in the 1950s and have developed to the point that a characteristically obese (30% body fat) (67) 545-kg pound steer can be brought to slaughter in 14 mo (68). Although 99% of all the beef consumed in the United States is now produced from grainfed, feedlot cattle (69), virtually no beef was produced in this manner as recently as 200 y ago (66). Accordingly, cattle meat (muscle tissue) with a high absolute SFA content, low n –3 fatty acid content, and high n –6 fatty acid content represents a recent component of human diets (11).

HEALTH RAMIFICATIONS OF FOODS IN THE NEOLITHIC AND INDUSTRIAL ERAS

The novel foods (dairy products, cereals, refined cereals, refined sugars, refined vegetable oils, fatty meats, salt, and combinations of these foods) introduced as staples during the Neolithic and Industrial Eras fundamentally altered several key nutritional characteristics of ancestral hominin diets and ultimately had far-reaching effects on health and well-being. As these foods gradually displaced the minimally processed wild plant and animal foods in hunter-gatherer diets, they adversely affected the following dietary indicators 1) glycemic load, 2), fatty acid composition, 3) macronutrient composition, 4) micro-nutrient density, 5) acid-base balance, 6) sodium-potassium ratio, and 7) fiber content.

Glycemic Load

The glycemic index, originally developed in 1981, is a relative comparison of the blood glucose raising potential of various foods or combination of foods based on equal amounts of carbohydrate in the food (70). In 1997, the concept of glycemic load (glycemic index x the carbohydrate content per serving size) was introduced to assess blood glucose raising potential of a food based on both the quality and quantity of dietary carbohydrate (71). **Table 2** shows that refined grain and sugar products nearly always maintain much higher glycemic loads than unprocessed fruits and vegetables. Unrefined wild plant foods like those available to contemporary hunter-gatherers typically exhibit low glycemic indices (73).

Acute elevations in blood glucose concentrations, along with increases in hormones secreted from the gut, stimulate pancreatic insulin secretion causing an acute rise in blood insulin concentrations. Consumption of mixed meals containing protein and fat combined with carbohydrate may lower the total glycemic and insulinemic response of the carbohydrate food alone (74). Nevertheless, it is established that repeated consumption of high glycemic index, mixed meals results in higher mean 24 h blood glucose and insulin concentrations when compared with low glycemic index, mixed meals of identical caloric content (75, 76).

Within the past 20 y, substantial evidence has accumulated showing that long term consumption of high glycemic load carbohydrates can adversely affect metabolism and health (71, 77, 78). Specifically, chronic hyperglycemia and hyperinsulinemia induced by high glycemic load carbohydrates may elicit a number of hormonal and physiologic changes that promote insulin resistance (71, 77, 78). Chronic hyperinsulinemia represents the primary metabolic defect in the metabolic syndrome (79). Diseases of insulin resistance are frequently referred to as "diseases of civilization" (5, 78, 79) and include: obesity, coronary heart disease (CHD), type 2 diabetes, hypertension, and dyslipidemia [elevated serum triacylgycerols, smalldense, LDL cholesterol and reduced HDL cholesterol]. It is likely that the metabolic syndrome may extend to other chronic illnesses and conditions that are widely prevalent in Western societies, including: myopia (80), acne (81), gout (79), polycystic ovary syndrome, epithelial cell cancers (breast, colon, and prostate), male vertex balding, skin tags and acanthosis nigricans (78). Diseases of insulin resistance are rare or absent in hunter-gatherer and other less westernized societies living and eating in their traditional manner (5, 21, 82, 83).

In addition to high-glycemic-load carbohydrates, other elements of Neolithic and Industrial Era foods may contribute to the insulin resistance underlying metabolic syndrome diseases. Milk, yogurt, and ice cream, despite having relatively low glycemic loads (Table 2), are highly insulinotropic, with insulin indexes comparable with white bread (84). Fructose maintains a low glycemic index of 23 and a low glycemic load, but paradoxically it is routinely used to induce insulin resistance in laboratory rodents at high (35–65% of energy) dietary concentrations (85, 86). Diets containing lower concentrations (20% of energy) of fructose worsened insulin sensitivity in hyperinsulinemic men (87); more recently it was shown that fructose infusions in healthy men and women induce insulin resistance (88). Dietary fructose may contribute to insulin resistance via its unique ability among all sugars to cause a shift in balance from oxidation to esterification of serum nonesterified free fatty acids (89, 90).

In the typical US diet, sugars with a high glycemic load (HFCS 42, HFCS 55, sucrose, glucose, honey, and syrups) now supply 18.6% of total energy, whereas refined cereal grains with a high glycemic load supplies 20.4% of energy (Table 1). Hence, $\geq$39% of the total energy in the typical US diet is supplied by foods that may promote the 4 proximate causes of insulin resistance: chronic and substantial elevations in plasma glucose (91, 92), insulin (93, 94), VLDL (95), and free fatty acid (96) concentrations. Although sugars and grains with a high glycemic load now represent a dominant element of the modern urban diet, these foods were rarely or never consumed by average citizens as recently as 200 y ago.

Table 2. Glycemic indexes and glycemic loads of various food groups[1]

	GLYCEMIC INDEX	GLYCEMIC LOAD[2]
Grain products		
Rice Krispies cereal[3]	82	72.0
Cornflakes[3,4]	81	70.1
Rice cakes[5]	78	63.6
Shredded wheat cereal[6]	75	62.0
Graham wafers[7]	74	56.8
Cheerios cereal[8]	74	54.2
Rye crisp bread[9]	64	52.6
Vanilla wafers[7]	77	49.7
Stoned Wheat thins[7]	67	41.9
Corn chips[10,11]	63	39.9
Muesli bar[12]	61	39.3
Bagel	72	38.4
Doughnuts	76	37.8
White bread	70	34.7
Whole-wheat bread	71	32.7
All-bran cereal[3,4]	42	32.5
Sugar, sweets		
Jelly beans	78	72.6
Lifesavers[13]	70	67.9
Table sugar (sucrose)	65	64.9
Mars bar[14,15]	65	40.4
Vegetables	85	21.4
Baked potato	61	14.8
Sweet potato	37	8.4
Yam	72	6.3
Rutabaga	64	6.3
Beets	47	4.7
Carrots		
Fruit		
Banana	52	11.9
Grapes	46	8.2
Kiwi fruit	53	7.5
Pineapple	59	7.3
Apple	38	5.8
Pear	38	5.7
Watermelon	72	5.2
Orange	42	5.0
Dairy foods		
Ice cream	61	14.4
Yogurt, low-fat	27	5.3
Skim milk	32	1.6
Whole milk	27	1.3

[1]Data adapted from reference 72.
[2]Glycemic load = glycemic index × carbohydrate content (in 100-g portions); the glycemic reference is glucose with a glycemic index of 100.
[3]Kellogg's Inc, London.
[4]Kellogg's Inc, Auckland, Australia and Battle Creek, MI.
[5]Rice Growers Co-op, Leeton, Australia.
[6]Nabisco Brands Ltd, Toronto.
[7]Christie Brown and Co, Toronto.
[8]General Mills Inc, Mississauga, Canada.
[9]Ryvita Company Ltd, Poole, United Kingdom.
[10]Smith's Snack Food Co, Adelaide, Australia.
[11]Old El Paso Foods Co, Mississauga, Canada.
[12]Uncle Toby's, North Ryde, Australia.
[13]Nestlé, Rhodes, Australia.
[14]Mars Confectionery, Ballarat, Australia.
[15]M & M Mars, Hackettstown, NJ.

Fatty Acid Composition

Chemically, fats are defined as acylglycerols—compounds in which a fatty acid molecule (acyl group) is linked to a glycerol molecule by an ester bond. Almost all dietary and storage fats are triacylglycerols, compounds in which 3 fatty acid molecules are bound to a single glycerol molecule. Fatty acids fall into 1 of 3 major categories: 1) SFAs, 2) MUFAs, and 3) PUFAs. Additionally, essential PUFAs occur in 2 biologically important families, the n–6 PUFAs and the n–3 PUFAs. Substantial evidence now indicates that to prevent the risk of chronic disease, the absolute amount of dietary fat is less important than is the type of fat (97). Beneficial health-promoting fats are MUFAs and some PUFAs, whereas most SFAs and *trans* fatty acids are detrimental when consumed in excessive quantities (97). Furthermore, the balance of dietary n–6 and n–3 PUFAs is integral in preventing the risk of chronic disease and promoting health (97–99).

The Western diet frequently contains excessive saturated and *trans* fatty acids and has too little n–3 PUFAs than n–6 PUFAs (97–99). High dietary intakes of SFAs and *trans* fatty acids increase the risk of CVD by elevating blood concentrations of total and LDL cholesterol (97, 100–102). n–3 PUFAs may reduce the risk of CVD via many mechanisms, including reductions in ventricular arrhythmias, blood clotting, serum triacyl-glycerol concentrations, growth of atherosclerotic plaques, and blood pressure (98). A 20% reduction in overall mortality and a 45% reduction in sudden death after 3.5 y were reported in subjects with preexisting CVD when given 850 mg n–3 fatty acids, either with or without vitamin E (103). Higher dietary intakes of n–3 fatty acids are also therapeutic in preventing or ameliorating many inflammatory and autoimmune diseases (99). Low- (22% energy) and high- (39% energy) fat diets that had identical ratios of PUFAs to SFAs, n–6 PUFAs to n–3 PUFAs, and MUFAs to total fat produced no significant differences in total or

LDL cholesterol after a 50-d trial (104). These data support the notion that fat quality is more important than fat quantity in regard to CVD risk.

Although much of the early work on the link between diet and CVD focused primarily on dietary fats and their effect on total and LDL-cholesterol concentrations, there are many other dietary elements that can operate synergistically to promote atherosclerosis. As was previously mentioned, carbohydrates with a high glycemic load encourage a proatherogenic blood profile by elevating triacylglycerols and small-dense LDLs, while reducing HDL cholesterol. Atherosclerosis is not just a "plumbing" problem involving excessive LDL cholesterol in the blood from excessive dietary SFAs, but also from chronic inflammation, which is essential in the formation of atherosclerotic plaques (105). A recent study suggested that the blood concentration of the inflammatory marker Creactive protein (CRP) is a stronger predictor of CVD than is LDL cholesterol (106). High-glycemic-load diets are associated with increased concentrations of CRP (107), as are low dietary intakes of n–3 PUFAs (108), and diets that encourage weight loss reduce CRP (109) concentrations. These studies indicate how multiple interrelated qualities of Western diets and recently introduced Neolithic and Industrial Era foods may drive a variety of mechanisms that promote the development of chronic diseases.

The 6 major sources of SFAs in the United States diet are fatty meats, baked goods, cheese, milk, margarine, and butter (110). Five of these 6 foods would not have been components of hominin diets before the advent of animal husbandry or the Industrial Revolution. Because of the inherently lean nature of wild animal tissues throughout most of the year (Figure 5) and the dominance of MUFAs and PUFAs, high dietary levels of SFAs on a year-round basis (Figure 6) could not have exerted adverse selective pressure on the hominin genome before the development of agriculture.

The advent of the oil-seed processing industry at the beginning of the 20th century significantly raised the total intake of vegetable fat (Figure 4), which directly increased the dietary level of n–6 PUFAs at the expense of a lowered level of n–3 PUFAs because of the inherently higher concentrations of n–6 PUFAs and lower concentrations of n–3 PUFAs in most vegetable oils (111). The trend toward a higher ratio of n–6 to n–3 PUFAs was exacerbated as meat from grain fed cattle and livestock became the norm in the US diet over the past 100 y (11, 66). In the current US diet, the ratio of n–6 to n–3 PUFAs has risen to 10:1 (112), whereas the ratio in hunter-gatherer diets predominant in wild animal foods (20, 21) has been estimated to be between 2:1 and 3:1 (11, 111).

The invention of the hydrogenation process in 1897 (44) allowed vegetable oils to become solidified and marketed as shortening or margarine and as foods containing hydrogenated vegetable oils. The hydrogenation process introduced a novel *trans* fatty acid (*trans* elaidic acid) into the human diet, which elevates blood cholesterol concentrations and leads to an increased risk of CVD (113). *trans* Fatty acids in the US diet are now estimated to constitute 7.4% of the total fatty acid intake (114).

Macronutrient Composition

In the present US diet, the percentage of total food energy derived from the 3 major macronutrients is as follows (23): carbohydrate (51.8%), fat (32.8%), and protein (15.4%). Current advice for reducing the risk of cardiovascular disease and other chronic diseases is to limit fat intake to 30% of total energy, to maintain protein at 15% of total energy, and to increase complex carbohydrates to 55–60% of total energy (115, 116). Both the current US macronutrient intakes and suggested healthful levels differ considerably from average levels obtained from ethnographic (20) and quantitative (21) studies of hunter gatherers in which dietary protein is characteristically elevated (19–35% of energy) at the expense of carbohydrate (22–40% of energy) (20, 21). Although the macronutrient compositions of hominin diets during the Paleolithic period cannot be directly determined, recent isotopic data from Neanderthal (117) and Upper Paleolithic European (118) skeletons support the notion that protein consumption may have been substantially higher than current values.

An increasing body of evidence indicates that high-protein diets may improve blood lipid profiles (119–123) and thereby lessen the risk of CVD. Wolfe and Giovannetti (121) have shown that the isocaloric substitution of protein (23% of energy) for carbohydrate in moderately hypercholesterolemic subjects resulted in significant decreases in total, LDL, and VLDL cholesterol and triacylglycerols and an increase in HDL cholesterol. Similar beneficial blood lipid changes have been observed in type 2 diabetic patients in conjunction with improvements in glucose and insulin metabolism (119, 120). Furthermore, high-protein diets have been shown to improve metabolic control in patients with type 2 diabetes (119, 120, 124). In obese women, hypocaloric, high-protein diets improved insulin sensitivity and prevented muscle loss, whereas hypocaloric, high-carbohydrate diets worsened insulin sensitivity and caused reductions in fat-free mass (125).

Epidemiologic evidence supports the clinical data, which shows a cardiovascular protective effect of dietary protein. Protein intake has been shown to be inversely related to CVD in a cohort of 80 082 women (126). Dietary protein is also inversely related to blood homocysteine concentration (127), an independent risk factor for CVD. Meat-eating populations have been shown to maintain lower plasma homocysteine concentrations than nonmeat eaters (128, 129). In numerous population studies, summarized by Obarzanek et al (130), higher blood pressure has been associated with lower intakes of protein. A 4-wk dietary intervention of hypertensive subjects showed that a high-protein diet (25% energy) was effective in significantly lowering blood pressure (131). Furthermore, many population studies have established that stroke mortality is inversely related to protein intake (132, 133).

Because protein has >3 times the thermic effect of either fat or carbohydrate (134) and because it has a greater satiety value than do fat or carbohydrate (134, 135), increased dietary protein may represent an effective weight-loss strategy for the overweight or obese. Recent clinical trials have shown that calorie-restricted, high-protein diets are more effective than are calorie-restricted, high-carbohydrate diets in promoting (136–138) and maintaining (139) weight loss in overweight subjects while producing less hunger and more satisfaction (140).

Micronutrient density

Refined sugars are essentially devoid of any vitamin or mineral (64). Accordingly, the consumption of refined sugar or foods containing refined sugar reduces the total vitamin and mineral (micronutrient) density of the diet by displacing more nutrientdense foods. A similar situation exists for refined vegetable oils, except that they contain 2 fat-soluble vitamins (vitamin E and vitamin K) (64). Because vegetable oils and refined sugars contribute ≥36.2% of the energy in a typical US diet (Table 1), the widespread consumption of these substances—or foods made with them—has considerable potential to influence the risk of vitamin and mineral deficiencies.

The vitamins and minerals most frequently lacking in the US diet are listed in **Table 3**. At least half the US population fails to meet the recommended dietary allowance (RDA) for vitamin B-6, vitamin A, magnesium, calcium, and zinc, and 33% of the population does not meet the RDA for folate. Adequate dietary intake of both folate and vitamin B-6 prevents the accumulation of homocysteine in the bloodstream. Elevated blood concentrations of homocysteine represent an independent risk factor for the development of CVD, stroke, and deep vein thrombosis (141, 142).

Table 3. Percentages of all individuals aged ≥2 y not meeting 100% of the 1989 US recommended dietary allowances[1]

NUTRIENT	VALUE
	%
Vitamin B-12	17.2
Niacin	25.9
Phosphorus	27.4
Riboflavin	30.0
Thiamine	30.2
Folate	33.2
Vitamin C	37.5
Iron	39.1
Vitamin B-6	53.6
Vitamin A	56.2
Magnesium	61.6
Calcium	65.1
Zinc	73.3

[1]Values are the 2-d average of data collected from 1994 to 1996 (23).

The nutrient density in various food groups for the 13 vitamins and minerals most frequently lacking in the US diet are contrasted in **Table 4** (64, 143, 144). Because whole grains and milk maintain the next to the lowest nutrient density rankings, displacement of fruit, vegetables, lean meats, and seafood by these 2 staple food groups lowers the overall micronutrient density in the diet. Wild plant foods known to be consumed by hunter-gatherers generally maintain higher micronutrient concentrations than do their domesticated counterparts (4, 145), as does the muscle meat of wild animals (64). Consequently, the Neolithic introduction of dairy foods and cereal grains as staples would have caused the average micronutrient content of the diet to decline. This situation worsened as cereal milling techniques developed in the Industrial era allowed for the production of bread flour devoid of the more nutrientdense bran and germ (35). The displacement of more nutrientdense foods (eg, fruit, vegetables, lean meats, and seafood) by less-dense foods (refined sugars, grains, vegetable oils, and dairy products)

Table 4. Mean nutrient density of various foods groups (418-kJ samples)[1]

	WHOLE GRAINS (N = 8)	WHOLE MILK (N = 1)	FRUIT (N = 20)	VEGETABLES (N = 18)	SEAFOOD (N = 20)	LEAN MEATS (N = 4)	NUTS AND SEEDS (N = 10)
Vitamin B-12 (μg)	0.00 [4]	0.58 [5]	0.00 [4]	0.00 [4]	7.42 [7]	0.63 [6]	0.00 [4]
Vitamin B-3 (mg)	1.12 [4]	0.14 [1]	0.89 [3]	2.73 [5]	3.19 [6]	4.73 [7]	0.35 [2]
Phosphorus (mg)	90 [3]	152 [5]	33 [1]	157 [6]	219 [7]	151 [4]	80 [2]
Riboflavin (mg)	0.05 [2]	0.26 [6]	0.09 [3]	0.33 [7]	0.09 [4]	0.14 [5]	0.04 [1]
Thiamine (mg)	0.12 [5]	0.06 [1]	0.11 [3]	0.26 [7]	0.08 [2]	0.18 [6]	0.12 [4]
Folate (μg)	10.3 [4]	8.1 [2]	25.0 [6]	208.3 [7]	10.8 [3]	3.8 [1]	11.0 [5]
Vitamin C (mg)	1.53 [3]	74.2 [5]	221.3 [7]	93.6 [6]	1.9 [4]	0.1 [1]	0.4 [2]
Iron (mg)	0.90 [4]	0.08 [1]	0.69 [2]	2.59 [7]	2.07 [6]	1.10 [5]	0.86 [3]
Vitamin B-6 (mg)	0.09 [3]	0.07 [1]	0.20 [5]	0.42 [7]	0.19 [4]	0.32 [6]	0.08 [2]
Vitamin A (RE)	2 [2]	50 [5]	94 [6]	687 [7]	32 [4]	1 [1]	2 [3]
Magnesium (mg)	32.6 [4]	21.9 [2]	24.6 [3]	54.5 [7]	36.1 [6]	18.0 [1]	35.8 [5]
Calcium (mg)	7.6 [2]	194.3 [7]	43.0 [4]	116.8 [6]	43.1 [5]	6.1 [1]	17.5 [3]
Zinc (mg)	0.67 [4]	0.62 [3]	0.25 [1]	1.04 [5]	7.6 [7]	1.9 [6]	0.6 [2]
Sum rank score	44	44	48	81	65	50	38

[1]Food types within food groups are based on the most commonly consumed foods in the US diet (135, 136). Values in brackets represent relative ranking (7 highest; 1 lowest). The micronutrient concentrations for each food group were derived from reference 64. RE, retinol equivalents.

and the subsequent decline in dietary vitamin and mineral density has far reaching health implications—consequences that not only promote the development of vitamin- deficiency diseases but also numerous infectious and chronic diseases (7).

Acid-Base Balance

After digestion, absorption, and metabolism, nearly all foods release either acid or bicarbonate (base) into the systemic circulation (146, 147). As shown in **Table 5**, fish, meat, poultry, eggs, shellfish, cheese, milk, and cereal grains are net acid producing, whereas fresh fruit, vegetables, tubers, roots, and nuts are net base producing. Legumes yield near-zero mean acid values, which reflects an overlapping distribution from slightly net acid producing to slightly net base producing. Not shown in Table 5 are energy-dense, nutrient-poor foods such as separated fats and refined sugars that contribute neither to the acid nor the base load. Additionally, salt is net acid producing because of the chloride ion (146).

The typical Western diet yields a net acid load estimated to be 50 mEq/d (148). As a result, healthy adults consuming the standard US diet sustain a chronic, low-grade pathogenic metabolic acidosis that worsens with age as kidney function declines (146, 149). Virtually all preagricultural diets were net base yielding because of the absence of cereals and energy-dense, nutrient-poor foods—foods that were introduced during the Neolithic and Industrial Eras and that displaced base-yielding fruit and vegetables (147). Consequently, a net base-producing diet was the norm throughout most of hominin evolution (147). The known health benefits of a net base-yielding diet include preventing and treating osteoporosis (150, 151), age-related muscle

Table 5. Potential net acid (or base) loads of 17 food groups[1]

	NET ACID LOAD[2]	NET ACID LOAD[2]	POTASSIUM	PROTEIN	PROTEIN
	mEq/418 kJ	*mEq/10 460 kJ*	*mEq/418 kJ*	*g/418 kJ*	*g/100 mEq potassium*
Acid-producing foods					
Fish (*n* = 8)	14.6	398	8.1	16.8	207
Meat (*n* = 3)	12.4	342	7.6	18.4	242
Poultry (*n* = 2)	7.8	227	4.7	13.4	287
Egg (*n* = 1)	7.3	215	2.4	8.3	339
Shellfish (*n* = 3)	7.3	215	18.4	18.0	159
Cheese (*n* = 9)	3.3	115	0.8	7.1	982
Milk (*n* = 4)	1.3	64	6.4	5.7	90
Cereal grains (*n* = 7)	1.1	60	2.6	3.2	153
Near-neutral foods					
Legumes (*n* = 6)	−0.4	24	12.6	10.6	100
Base-producing foods					
Nut (*n* = 6)	−1.1	6	3.8	2.5	86
Fresh fruit (*n* = 11)	−5.2	−98	9.4	1.6	16
Tuber (*n* = 2)	−5.4	−102	11.8	2.2	18
Mushroom (*n* = 1)	−11.2	−247	62.3	25.7	41
Root (*n* = 5)	−17.1	−395	34.3	6.8	21
Vegetable fruit (*n* = 1)	−17.5	−404	35.5	5.6	15
Leafy greens (*n* = 6)	−23.4	−553	43.5	10.0	24
Plant stalks (*n* = 1)	−24.9	−590	54.8	4.6	8

[1]Daily net acid load per 10 460-kJ hypothetical diet, for which a single food group is solely consumed; 32.9 mEq/d was added to baseline to account for diet-independent organic acid production. For example, the total net endogenous acid production for a 10 460-kJ diet of cereal grains = (1.1 mEq) ×(10 460 kJ/418 kJ) + 32.9 mEq = 60.4 mEq/d.

[2]Calculations were made with the use of previously described procedures (148). Positive and negative values represent acid-producing and base-producing equivalents, respectively.

wasting (152), calcium kidney stones (153, 154), hypertension (155, 156), and exercise-induced asthma (157) and slow the progression of age- and disease-related chronic renal insufficiency (158).

Sodium-Potassium Ratio

The average sodium content (3271 mg/d) of the typical US diet is substantially higher than its potassium content (2620 mg/d) (23). Three dietary factors are primarily responsible for the dietary ratio of sodium to potassium, which is >1.0. First, 90% of the sodium in Western diets comes from manufactured salt (sodium chloride); hence, the sodium content of naturally occurring foods in the average US diet ($\approx$330 mg) is quite low. Second, vegetable oils and refined sugars, which are essentially devoid of potassium, constitute 36% of the total food energy. The inclusion of these 2 foods into the diet displaces other foods with higher potassium concentrations and thereby reduces the total dietary potassium content. Third, the displacement of vegetables and fruit by whole grains and milk products may further reduce the potassium intake because potassium concentrations in vegetables are 4 and 12 times those in milk and whole grains, respectively, whereas in fruit the potassium concentration is 2 and 5 times that in milk and whole grains (64). Taken together, the addition of manufactured salt to the food supply and the displacement of traditional potassium-rich foods by foods introduced during the Neolithic and Industrial periods caused a 400% decline in the potassium intake while simultaneously initiating a 400% increase in sodium ingestion (4, 12, 159).

The inversion of potassium and sodium concentrations in hominin diets had no evolutionary precedent and now plays an integral role in eliciting and contributing to numerous diseases of civilization. Diets low in potassium and high in sodium may partially or directly underlie or exacerbate a variety of maladies and chronic illnesses, including hypertension, stroke, kidney stones, osteoporosis, gastrointestinal tract cancers, asthma, exercise-induced asthma, insomnia, air sickness, high-altitude sickness, and Meniere's Syndrome (ear ringing) (160–170).

Fiber Content

The fiber content (15.1 g/d) (23) of the typical US diet is considerably lower than recommended values (25–30 g) (116). Refined sugars, vegetable oils, dairy products, and alcohol are devoid of fiber and constitute an average of 48.2% of the energy in the typical US diet (Table 1). Furthermore, fiber-depleted, refined grains represent 85% of the grains consumed in the United States (Table 1), and because refined grains contain 400% less fiber than do whole grains (by energy), they further dilute the total dietary fiber intake. Fresh fruit typically contains twice the amount of fiber in whole grains, and nonstarchy vegetables contain almost 8 times the amount of fiber in whole grains on an energy basis (64). Fruit and vegetables known to be consumed by hunter-gatherers also maintain considerably more fiber than do their domestic counterparts (145). Contemporary diets devoid of cereal grains, dairy products, refined oils and sugars, and processed foods have been shown to contain significantly more fiber (42.5 g/d) than either current or recommended values (159).

Once again, the displacement of fiber-rich plant foods by novel dietary staples, introduced during the Neolithic and Industrial periods, was instrumental in changing the diets that our species had traditionally consumed—a diet that would have almost always been high in fiber. Soluble fibers (those found primarily in fruit and vegetables) modestly reduce total and LDL-cholesterol concentrations beyond those achieved by a diet low in saturated fat and fiber, by slowing gastric emptying, may reduce the appetite and help to control caloric intake (171). Diets low in dietary fiber may underlie or exacerbate constipation, appendicitis, hemorrhoids, deep vein thrombosis, varicose veins, diverticulitis, hiatal hernia, and gastro-esophageal reflux (172).

SUMMARY

In the United States and most Western countries, diet-related chronic diseases represent the single largest cause of morbidity and mortality. These diseases are epidemic in contemporary Westernized populations and typically afflict 50–65% of the adult population, yet they are rare or nonexistent in hunter-gatherers and other less Westernized people. Although both scientists and lay people alike may frequently identify a single dietary element as the cause of chronic disease (e.g., saturated fat causes heart disease and salt causes high blood pressure), evidence gleaned over the past 3 decades now indicates that virtually all so-called diseases of civilization have multifactorial dietary elements that underlie their etiology, along with other environmental agents and genetic susceptibility. Coronary heart disease, for instance, does not arise simply from excessive saturated fat in the diet but rather from a complex interaction of multiple nutritional factors directly linked to the excessive consumption of novel Neolithic and Industrial era foods (dairy products, cereals, refined cereals, refined sugars, refined vegetable oils, fatty meats, salt, and combinations of these foods). These foods, in turn, adversely influence proximate nutritional factors, which universally underlie or exacerbate virtually all chronic diseases of civilization: *1)* glycemic load, *2)* fatty acid composition, *3)* macronutrient composition, *4)* micronutrient density, *5)* acid-base balance, *6)* sodium-potassium ratio, and *7)* fiber content. However, the ultimate factor underlying diseases of civilization is the collision of our ancient genome with the new conditions of life in affluent nations, including the nutritional qualities of recently introduced foods.

LC, SBE, and SL conceived the article and wrote much of the evolutionary, historical, and background perspective. AS edited the health ramification section on acid-base balance and on the sodium-potassium ratio. BAW and NM edited the health ramification section on fatty acid composition. JHO edited and reviewed all sections concerning the health ramifications of CVD and the metabolic syndrome. JBM reviewed the section of the article on glycemic index and fiber. None of the authors had a financial interest or professional or personal affiliation that compromised the scientific integrity of this work.

REFERENCES

1. Gould SJ. The structure of evolutionary theory. Cambridge, MA: Harvard University Press, 2002.
2. Boaz NT. Evolving health: the origins of illness and how the modern world is making us sick. New York: Wiley & Sons, Inc, 2002.
3. Nesse RM, Williams GC. Why we get sick. The new science of Darwinian medicine. New York: Times Books, 1994.
4. Eaton SB, Konner MJ. Paleolithic nutrition. A consideration of its nature and current implications. N Engl J Med 1985;312:283–9.
5. Eaton SB, Konner M, Shostak M. Stone agers in the fast lane: chronic degenerative diseases in evolutionary perspective. Am J Med 1988;84:739–49.
6. Cordain L, Gotshall RW, Eaton SB. Physical activity, energy expenditure and fitness: an evolutionary perspective. Int J Sports Med 1998; 19:328–35.
7. Cordain L. Cereal grains: humanity's double edged sword. World Rev Nutr Diet 1999;84:19–73.

8. Cohen MN. Health and the rise of civilization. London: Yale University Press, 1989.

9. Abrams HL. The relevance of Paleolithic diet in determining contemporary nutritional needs. J Appl Nutr 1979;31:43–59.

10. Truswell AS. Diet and nutrition of hunter-gatherers. In: Health and disease in tribal societies. New York: Elsevier; 1977:213–21.

11. Cordain L, Watkins BA, Florant GL, Kehler M, Rogers L, Li Y. Fatty acid analysis of wild ruminant tissues: evolutionary implications for reducing dietrelated chronic disease. Eur J Clin Nutr 2002;56:181–91.

12. Frassetto L, Morris RC Jr, Sellmeyer DE, Todd K, Sebastian A. Diet, evolution and aging—the pathophysiologic effects of the post-agricultural inversion of the potassium-to-sodium and base-to-chloride ratios in the human diet. Eur J Nutr 2001;40:200–13.

13. Hedley AA, Ogden CL, Johnson CL, Carroll MD, Curtin LR, Flegal KN. Prevalence of overweight and obesity among US children, adolescents, and adults, 1999–2002. JAMA 2004;291:2847–50.

14. Allison DB, Fontaine KR, Manson JE, Stevens J, VanItallie TB. Annual deaths attributable to obesity in the United States. JAMA 1999; 282:1530–8.

15. American Heart Association. Heart and stroke statistics—2004 update. Dallas: American Heart Association, 2003.

16. Siris ES, Miller PD, Barrett-Connor E, et al. Identification and fracture outcomes of undiagnosed low bone mineral density in postmenopausal women. Results from the National Osteoporosis Risk Assessment. JAMA 2001;286:2815–22.

17. National Osteoporosis Foundation. Osteoporosis: review of the evidence for prevention, diagnosis, and treatment and cost-effectiveness analysis. Osteoporos Int 1998;8(suppl):S1–88.

18. American Cancer Society. Cancer facts & figures 2004. Atlanta: American Cancer Society, 2004.

19. Wood B. Palaeoanthropology: hominid revelations from Chad. Nature 2002;418:133–5.

20. Cordain L, Brand Miller J, Eaton SB, Mann N, Holt SHA, Speth JD. Plant to animal subsistence ratios and macronutrient energy estimations in world wide hunter-gatherer diets. Am J Clin Nutr 2000;71:682–92.

21. Cordain L, Eaton SB, Brand Miller J, Mann N, Hill K. The paradoxical nature of hunter-gatherer diets: meat based, yet non-atherogenic. Eur J Clin Nutr 2002;56(suppl):S42–52.

22. Gerrior S, Bente L. Nutrient content of the U.S. food supply, 1909–99: a summary report. Washington, DC: US Department of Agriculture, Center for Nutrition Policy and Promotion, 2002. (Home Economics report no. 55.)

23. US Department of Agriculture, Agricultural Research Service. Data tables: results from USDA's 1994-96 Continuing Survey of Food In-takes by Individuals and 1994–96 Diet and Health Knowledge Survey. ARS Food Surveys Research Group, 1997. Internet: (available under "Releases"): http://www.barc.usda.gov/bhnrc/foodsurvey/home.htm (accessed 11 May 2004).

24. US Department of Agriculture, Economic Research Service. Food Consumption (per capita) data system, sugars/sweeteners. 2002. Internet: http://www.ers.usda.gov/Data/foodconsumption/datasystem.asp (accessed 11 May 2004).

25. Hiendleder S, Kaupe B, Wassmuth R, Janke A. Molecular analysis of wild and domestic sheep questions current nomenclature and provides evidence for domestication from two different subspecies. Proc R Soc Lond B 2002;269:893–904.

26. Luikart G, Gielly L, Excoffier L, Vigne J, Bouvet J, Taberlet P. Multiple maternal origins and weak phylogeographic structure in domestic goats. Proc Natl Acad Sci U S A 2001;98:5927–32.

27. Loftus RT, Ertugrul O, Harba AH, et al. A microsatellite survey of cattle from a centre of origin: the Near East. Mol Ecol 1999;8:2015–22.

28. Copley MS, Berstan R, Dudd SN, et al. Direct chemical evidence for widespread dairying in prehistoric Britain. Proc Natl Acad Sci U S A 2003;100:1524–9.

29. Wright K. The origins and development of ground stone assemblages in Late Pleistocene Southwest Asia. Paleorient 1991;17:19–45.

30. Bar-Yosef O. The Natufian culture in the Levant, threshold to the origins of agriculture. Evol Anthropol 1998;6:159–77.

31. Salami F, Ozkan H, Brandolini A, Schafer-Pregl R, Martin W. Genetics and geography of wild cereal domestication in the near east. Nat Rev Genet 2003;3:429–41.

32. Keeley LH. The use of plant foods among hunter-gatherers: a cross-cultural survey. In: Anderson PC, ed. Prehistoire de l'agriculture. Nou-velles approches experimentales et ethnographiques. (Prehistoric agriculture. New experimental approaches and ethnography.) Paris: National Center for Scientific Research, 1992:29–38 (in French).

33. Eaton SB. Humans, lipids and evolution. Lipids 1992;27:814–20.

34. Harlan JR. 1992. Wild grass seed harvesting and implications for domestication. In: Anderson PC, ed. Prehistoire de l'agriculture. Nouvelles approches experimentales et ethnographiques. Paris: National Center for Scientific Research, 1992;21–7.

35. Storck J, Teague WD. Flour for man's bread, a history of milling. Minneapolis: University of Minnesota Press, 1952.

36. Nelson JH. Wheat: its processing and utilization. Am J Clin Nutr 1985; 41:1070–6.

37. Galloway JH. 2000. Sugar. In: Kiple KF, Ornelas KC, eds. The Cambridge world history of food. Vol 1. Cambridge: Cambridge University Press, 2000:437–49.

38. Cleave TL. The saccharine disease. Bristol, United Kingdom: John Wright & Sons, Ltd, 1974;1974:6–27.

39. Ziegler E. Secular changes in the stature of adults and the secular trend of modern sugar consumption. Z Kinderheilkd 1967;99:146–66.

40. Meehan B. Shell bed to shell midden. Canberra, Australia: Australian Institute of Aboriginal Studies, 1982.

41. Hawkes K, Hill K, O'Connell JF. Why hunters gather: optimal foraging and the Ache of eastern Paraguay. Am Ethnologist 1982;9:379–98.

42. Hanover LM, White JS. Manufacturing, composition, and applications of fructose. Am J Clin Nutr 1993;58(suppl):724S–32S.

43. O'Keefe SF. 2000. An overview of oils and fats, with a special emphasis on olive oil. In: Kiple KF, Ornelas KC, eds. The Cambridge world history of food. Vol 1. Cambridge, United Kingdom: Cambridge University Press, 2000:375–97.

44. Emken EA. Nutrition and biochemistry of trans and positional fatty acid isomers in hydrogenated oils. Annu Rev Nutr 1984;4:339–76.

45. McGovern PE, Voigt MM, Glusker DL, Exner LJ. Neolithic resinated wine. Nature 1996;381:480–1.

46. Rudolph MH, McGovern PE, Badler VR. Chemical evidence for ancient beer. Nature 1992;360:24.

47. Comer J. Distilled beverages. In: Kiple KF, Ornelas KC, eds. The Cambridge world history of food. Vol 1. Cambridge, United Kingdom: Cambridge University Press, 2000:653–64.

48. Newman J. Wine. In: Kiple KF, Ornelas KC, eds. The Cambridge world history of food. Vol 1. Cambridge, United Kingdom: Cambridge University Press, 2000;730–7.

49. Eaton SB, Shostak M, Konner M. The paleolithic prescription. New York: Harper and Row Publishers, 1988.

50. James WP, Ralph A, Sanchez-Castillo CP. The dominance of salt in manufactured food in the sodium intake of affluent societies. Lancet 1987;1:426–9.

51. Kurlansky M. Salt: a world history. New York: Walker and Company, 2002.

52. Weller O. The earliest salt exploitation in Europe: a salt mountain in the Spanish Neolithic. Antiquity 2002;76:317–8.

53. Norton SA. Salt consumption in ancient Polynesia. Perspect Biol Med 1992;5:160–81.

54. Denton D. The hunger for salt. An anthropological, physiological and medical analysis. New York: Springer, 1984.

55. Brothwell D, Brothwell P. Food in antiquity: a survey of the diet of early peoples. New York: Frederick A Praeger Publishers, 1969.

56. Pitts CG, Bullard TR. Some interspecific aspects of body composition in mammals. In: Body composition in animals and man. Washington, DC: National Academy of Sciences, 1968:45–70. (Publication 1598.)

57. Spiess AE. Reindeer and caribou hunters: an archaeological study. New York: Academic Press, 1979.

58. Mercer JG. Regulation of appetite and body weight in seasonal mammals. Comp Biochem Physiol Part C 1998;119:295–303.

59. Shackleton CM, Granger JE. Bone marrow fat index and kidney-fat of several antelope species from Transkei. S Afr J Wildl Res 1989;19: 129–34.

60. Stahl WR. Organ weights in primates and other mammals. Science 1965;150:1039–42.

61. Calder WA. Size, function and life history. Cambridge, United Kingdom: Harvard University Press, 1984.

62. Meadows SD, Hakonson TE. Contributions of tissues to body mass in elk. J Wildl Manage 1982;46:838–41.

63. Hakonson TE, Whicker FW. The contribution of various tissues and organs to total body mass in mule deer. J Mammal 1971;52:628–30.

64. First Data Bank. Nutritionist V nutrition software, version 2.3. San Bruno, CA: First Data Bank, 2000.

65. Rule DC, Broughton KS, Shellito SM, Maiorano G. Comparison of muscle fatty acid profiles and cholesterol concentrations of bison, beef cattle, elk, and chicken. J Anim Sci 2002;80:1202–11.

66. Whitaker JW. Feedlot empire: beef cattle feeding in Illinois and Iowa, 1840–1900. Ames, IA: The Iowa State University Press, 1975.

67. Wells RS, Preston RL. Effects of repeated urea dilution measurement on feedlot performance and consistency of estimated body composition in steers of different breed types. J Anim Sci 1998;76:2799–804.

68. Pollan M. Power steer. New York Times Magazine. 2002. Internet: http://www.nytimes.com/2002/03/31/magazine/31BEEF.html (accessed 11 May 2004).

69. Kidwell B. All grass, no grain. Progressive Farmer Magazine, 8 October 2002: Internet: http://www.progressivefarmer.com/farmer/magazine/article/0,14730,355103,00.html (accessed May 11, 2004).

70. Jenkins DJ, Wolever TM, Taylor RH, et al. Glycemic index of foods: a physiological basis for carbohydrate exchange. Am J Clin Nutr 1981; 34:362–6.

71. Liu S, Willett WC. Dietary glycemic load and atherothrombotic risk. Curr Atheroscler Rep 2002;4:454–61.

72. Foster-Powell K, Holt SH, Brand-Miller JC. International table of glycemic index and glycemic load values: 2002. Am J Clin Nutr 2002; 76:5–56.

73. Thorburn AW, Brand JC, Truswell AS. Slowly digested and absorbed carbohydrate in traditional bushfoods: a protective factor against diabetes? Am J Clin Nutr 1987;45:98–106.

74. Wolever TM, Jenkins DJ. The use of the glycemic index in predicting the blood glucose response to mixed meals. Am J Clin Nutr 1986;43: 167–72.

75. Jenkins DJ, Wolever TM, Collier GR, et al. Metabolic effects of a low-glycemic diet. Am J Clin Nutr 1987;46:968–75.

76. Miller JC. Importance of glycemic index in diabetes. Am J Clin Nutr 1994;59(suppl):747S–52S.

77. Ludwig DS. The glycemic index: physiological mechanisms relating obesity, diabetes, and cardiovascular disease. JAMA 2002;287: 2414–23.

78. Cordain L, Eades MR, Eades MD. Hyperinsulinemic diseases of civilization: more than just syndrome X. Comp Biochem Physiol Part A 2003;136:95–112.

79. Reaven GM. Pathophysiology of insulin resistance in human disease. Physiol Rev 1995;75:473–86.

80. Cordain L, Eaton SB, Brand Miller J, Lindeberg S, Jensen C. An evolutionary analysis of the aetiology and pathogenesis of juvenile-onset myopia. Acta Opthalmol Scand 2002;80:125–35.

81. Cordain L, Lindeberg S, Hurtado M, Hill K, Eaton SB, Brand-Miller J. Acne vulgaris: a disease of western civilization. Arch Dermatol 2002; 138:1584–90.

82. Schaeffer O. When the Eskimo comes to town. Nutr Today 1971; 6:8–16.

83. Trowell HC. From normotension to hypertension in Kenyans and Ugandans 1928–1978. East Afr Med J 1980;57:167–73.

84. Ostman EM, Liljeberg Elmstahl HG, Bjorck IM. Inconsistency between glycemic and insulinemic responses to regular and fermented milk products. Am J Clin Nutr 2001;74:96–100.

85. Thorburn AW, Storlien LH, Jenkins AB, Khouri S, Kraegen EW. Fructose-induced in vivo insulin resistance and elevated plasma tri-glyceride levels in rats. Am J Clin Nutr 1989;49:1155–63.

86. Taghibiglou C, Carpentier A, Van Iderstine SC, et al. Mechanism of hepatic very low density lipoprotein over-production in insulin resistance. J Biol Chem 2000;275:8416–25.

87. Reiser S, Powell AS, Scholfield DJ, Panda P, Fields M, Canary JJ. Day-long glucose, insulin, and fructose responses of hyperinsulinemic and non-hyperinsulinemic men adapted to diets containing either fructose or high-amylose cornstarch. Am J Clin Nutr 1989;50:1008–14.

88. Dirlewanger M, Schneiter P, Jequier E, Tappy L. Effects of fructose on hepatic glucose metabolism in humans. Am J Physiol Endocrinol Metab 2000;279:E907–11.

89. Mayes PA. Intermediary metabolism of fructose. Am J Clin Nutr 1993;58 (suppl):754S–65S.

90. Elliott SS, Keim NL, Stern JS, Teff K, Havel PJ. Fructose, weight gain, and the insulin resistance syndrome. Am J Clin Nutr 2002;76:911–22.

91. Rossetti L, Giaccari A, DeFronzo RA. Glucose toxicity. Diabetes Care 1990;13:610–30.

92. McClain PA. Hexosamines as mediators of nutrient sensing and regulation in diabetes. J Diabetes Complications 2002;16:72–80.

93. Del Prato S, Leonetti F, Simonson DC, Sheehan P, Matsuda M, De-Fronzo RA. Effect of sustained physiologic hyperinsulinaemia and hyperglycaemia on insulin secretion and insulin sensitivity in man. Diabetologia 1994;37:1025–35.

94. Thomson MJ, Williams MG, Frost SC. Development of insulin resistance in 3T3–L1 adipocytes. J Biol Chem 1997;272:7759–64.

95. Zammit VA, Waterman IJ, Topping D, McKay G. Insulin stimulation of hepatic triacylglycerol secretion and the etiology of insulin resistance. J Nutr 2001;131:2074–7.

96. Boden G, Shulman GI. Free fatty acids in obesity and type 2 diabetes: defining their role in the development of insulin resistance and betacell dysfunction. Eur J Clin Invest 2002;32(suppl 3):14–23.

97. Institute of Medicine of the National Academies. Dietary fats: total fat and fatty acids. In: Dietary reference intakes for energy, carbohydrate, fiber, fat, fatty acids, cholesterol, protein, and amino acids (macronutrients). Washington, DC: The National Academy Press, 2002:335–432.

98. Kris-Etherton PM, Harris WS, Appel LJ. Fish consumption, fish oil, omega-3 fatty acids, and cardiovascular disease. Circulation 2002;106: 2747–57.

99. Simopoulos AP. Omega-3 fatty acids in inflammation and autoimmune disease. J Am Coll Nutr 2002;21:495–505.

100. Spady DK, Woollett LA, Dietschy JM. Regulation of plasma LDL-cholesterol levels by dietary cholesterol and fatty acids. Annu Rev Nutr 1993;13:355–81.

101. Mustad VA, Etherton TD, Cooper AD, et al. Reducing saturated fat intake is associated with increased levels of LDL receptors on mono-nuclear cells in healthy men and women. J Lipid Res 1997;38:459–68.

102. Stamler J, Daviglus ML, Garside DB, Dyer AR, Greenland P, Neaton JD. Relationship of baseline serum cholesterol levels in 3 large cohorts of younger men to long-term coronary, cardiovascular, and all-cause mortality and to longevity. JAMA 2000;19:284:311–8.

103. GISSI-Prevention Investigators. Dietary supplementation with n–3 polyunsaturated fatty acids and vitamin E after myocardial infarction: results of the GISSI-Prevenzione trial. Gruppo Italiano per lo Studio della Sopravvivenza nell'Infarto miocardico. Lancet 1999; 354:447–55.

104. Nelson GJ, Schmidt PC, Kelley DS. Low-fat diets do not lower plasma cholesterol levels in healthy men compared to high-fat diets with similar fatty acid composition at constant caloric intake. Lipids 1995;30: 969–76.

105. Rifai N, Ridker PM. Inflammatory markers and coronary heart disease. Curr Opin Lipidol 2002;13:383–9.

106. Ridker PM, Fifai N, Rose L, Buring JE, Cook NR. Comparison of Creactive protein and low-density lipoprotein cholesterol levels in the prediction of first cardiovascular events. N Engl J Med 2002; 347:1557–65.

107. Liu S, Manson JE, Buring JE, Stampfer MJ, Willett WC, Ridker PM. Relation between a diet with a high glycemic load and plasma concentrations of high-sensitivity Creactive protein in middle-aged women. Am J Clin Nutr 2002;75:492–8.

108. Madsen T, Skou HA, Hansen VE, et al. Creactive protein, dietary n–3 fatty acids, and the extent of coronary artery disease. Am J Cardiol 2001;88:1139–42.

109. Tchernof A, Nolan A, Sites CK, Ades PA, Poehlman ET. Weight loss reduces Creactive protein levels in obese postmenopausal women. Circulation 2002;105:564–9.

110. Subar AF, Krebs-Smith SM, Cook A, Kahle LL. Dietary sources of nutrients among US adults, 1989 to 1991. J Am Diet Assoc 1998;98: 537–47.

111. Cordain L. The paleo diet. New York: Wiley, Inc, 2002.

112. Kris-Etherton PM, Taylor DS, Yu-Poth S, et al. Polyunsaturated fatty acids in the food chain in the United States. Am J Clin Nutr 2000; 71(suppl):179S–88S.

113. Ascherio A, Hennekens CH, Buring JE, Master C, Stampfer MJ, Willett WC. Trans-fatty acids intake and risk of myocardial infarction. Circulation 1994;89:94–101.

114. Allison DB, Egan SK, Barraj LM, Caughman C, Infante M, Heimbach JT. Estimated intakes of trans fatty and other fatty acids in the US population. J Am Diet Assoc 1999;99:166–74.

115. US Department of Agriculture. The food guide pyramid. Center for Nutrition Policy and Promotion. 2000. Internet: http://www.pueblo.gsa.gov/cic_text/food/food-pyramid/main.htm (accessed 11 May 2004). (Home and Garden Bulletin 252.)

116. Krauss RM, Eckel RH, Howard B, et al. AHA dietary guidelines: revision 2000: a statement for healthcare professionals from the Nutrition Committee of the American Heart Association. Circulation 2000;102:2284–99.

117. Richards MP, Pettitt PB, Trinkaus E, Smith FH, Paunovic M, Karavanic. I. Neanderthal diet at Vindija and Neanderthal predation: the evidence from stable isotopes. Proc Natl Acad Sci U S A 2000;97: 7663–6.

118. Richards MP, Hedges RM. Focus: Gough's Cave and Sun Hole Cave human stable isotope values indicate a high animal protein diet in the British Upper Palaeolithic. J Archaeol Sci 2000;27:1–3.

119. O'Dea K. Marked improvement in carbohydrate and lipid metabolism in diabetic Australian Aborigines after temporary reversion to traditional lifestyle. Diabetes 1984;33:596–603.

120. O'Dea K, Traianedes K, Ireland P, et al. The effects of diet differing in fat, carbohydrate, and fiber on carbohydrate and lipid metabolism in type II diabetes. J Am Diet Assoc 1989;89:1076–86.

121. Wolfe BM, Giovannetti PM. Short term effects of substituting protein for carbohydrate in the diets of moderately hypercholesterolemic human subjects. Metabolism 1991;40:338–43.

122. Wolfe BM, Giovannetti PM. High protein diet complements resin therapy of familial hypercholesterolemia. Clin Invest Med 1992;15: 349–59.

123. Wolfe BM, Piche LA. Replacement of carbohydrate by protein in a conventional-fat diet reduces cholesterol and triglyceride concentrations in healthy normolipidemic subjects. Clin Invest Med 1999;22: 140–8.

124. Seino Y, Seino S, Ikeda M, Matsukura S, Imura H. Beneficial effects of high protein diet in treatment of mild diabetes. Hum Nutr Appl Nutr 1983;37 A(3):226–30.

125. Piatti PM, Monti F, Fermo I, et al. Hypocaloric high-protein diet improves glucose oxidation and spares lean body mass: comparison to hypocaloric high-carbohydrate diet. Metabolism 1994;43:1481–7.

126. Hu FB, Stampfer MJ, Manson JE, et al. Dietary protein and risk of ischemic heart disease in women. Am J Clin Nutr 1999;70:221–7.

127. Stolzenberg-Solomon RZ, Miller ER III, Maguire MG, Selhub J, Appel LJ. Association of dietary protein intake and coffee consumption with serum homocysteine concentrations in an older population. Am J Clin Nutr 1999;69:467–75.

128. Mann NJ, Li D, Sinclair AJ, et al. The effect of diet on plasma homo-cysteine concentrations in healthy male subjects. Eur J Clin Nutr 1999; 53:895–99.

129. Mezzano D, Munoz X, Martinez C, et al. Vegetarians and cardiovascular risk factors: hemostasis, inflammatory markers and plasma homocysteine. Thromb Haemost 1999;81:913–7.

130. Obarzanek E, Velletri PA, Cutler JA. Dietary protein and blood pressure. JAMA 1996;275:1598–603.

131. Burke V, Hodgson JM, Beilin LJ, Giangiulioi N, Rogers P, Puddey IB. Dietary protein and soluble fiber reduce ambulatory blood pressure in treated hypertensives. Hypertension 2001;38:821–6.

132. Klag MJ, Whelton PK. The decline in stroke mortality. An epidemiologic perspective. Ann Epidemiol 1993;3:571–5.

133. Kinjo Y, Beral V, Akiba S, et al. Possible protective effect of milk, meat and fish for cerebrovascular disease mortality in Japan. J Epidemiol 1999;9:268–74.

134. Crovetti R, Porrini M, Santangelo A, Testolin G. The influence of thermic effect of food on satiety. Eur J Clin Nutr 1998;52:482–8.

135. Stubbs RJ. Nutrition Society Medal Lecture. Appetite, feeding behaviour and energy balance in human subjects. Proc Nutr Soc 1998;57: 341–56.

136. Skov AR, Toubro S, Ronn B, Holm L, Astrup A. Randomized trial on protein vs carbohydrate in ad libitum fat reduced diet for the treatment of obesity. Int J Obes Relat Metab Disord 1999;23:528–36.

137. Baba NH, Sawaya S, Torbay N, Habbal Z, Azar S, Hashim SA. 1999. High protein vs high carbohydrate hypoenergetic diet for the treatment of obese hyperinsulinemic subjects. Int J Obes Relat Metab Disord 1999;23:1202–6.

138. Layman DK. The role of leucine in weight loss diets and glucose homeostasis J Nutr 2003;133:261S–7S.

139. Westerterp-Plantenga MS, Lejeune MP, Nijs I, van Ooijen M, Kovacs EM. High protein intake sustains weight maintenance after body weight loss in humans. Int J Obes Relat Metab Disord. 2004;28:57–64.

140. Johnston CS, Tjonn SL, Swan PD. High-protein, low-fat diets are effective for weight loss and favorably alter biomarkers in healthy adults. J Nutr 2004;134:586–91.

141. Wald DS, Law M, Morris JK. Homocysteine and cardiovascular disease: evidence on causality from a meta-analysis. BMJ 2002;325:1202–8.

142. Meleady R, Graham I. Plasma homocysteine as a cardiovascular risk factor: causal, consequential, or of no consequence? Nutr Rev 1999; 57:299–305.

143. Kurtzweil P. Nutritional info available for raw fruits, vegetables, fish. FDA Consumer Magazine. May 1993. US Health and Human Services, Food and Drug Administration, Rockville, MD. Internet: http://www.fda.gov/fdac/special/foodlabel/raw.html (accessed 11 May 2004).

144. US Department of Agriculture, Economic Research Service. 1999. America's eating habits: changes and consequences. Elizabeth Frazao, ed. Washington, DC. Internet: http://www.ers.usda.gov/publications/aib750/aib750app.pdf (accessed 11 May 2004). (Agriculture Information Bulletin No. 750.)

145. Brand-Miller JC, Holt SH. Australian aboriginal plant foods: a consideration of their nutritional composition and health implications. Nutr Res Rev 1998;11:5–23.

146. Frassetto LA, Todd KM, Morris RC, Sebastian A. Estimation of net endogenous noncarbonic acid production in humans from diet potassium and protein contents. Am J Clin Nutr 1998;68:576–83.

147. Sebastian A, Frassetto LA, Sellmeyer DE, Merriam RL, Morris RC. Estimation of the net acid load of the diet of ancestral preagricultural *Homo sapiens* and their hominid ancestors. Am J Clin Nutr 2002;76: 1308–16.

148. Lemann J. Relationship between urinary calcium and net acid excretion as determined by dietary protein and potassium: a review. Nephron 1999;81(suppl 1):18–25.

149. Frassetto L, Morris RC, Sebastian A. Effect of age on blood acid-base composition in adult humans: role of age-related renal functional decline. Am J Physiol 1996;271:1114–22.

150. Sebastian A, Harris ST, Ottaway JH, Todd KM, Morris RC Jr. Improved mineral balance and skeletal metabolism in post-menopausal women treated with potassium bicarbonate. N Engl J Med 1994;330: 1776–81.

151. Bushinsky DA. Metabolic alkalosis decreases bone calcium efflux by suppressing osteoclasts and stimulating osteoblasts. Am J Physiol 1996;271:F216–22.

152. Frassetto L, Morris RC Jr, Sebastian A. Potassium bicarbonate reduces urinary nitrogen excretion in postmenopausal women. J Clin Endocrinol Metab 1997;82:254–9.

153. Pak CY, Fuller C, Sakhaee K, Preminger GM, Britton F. Long-term treatment of calcium nephrolithiasis with potassium citrate. J Urol 1985;134:11–9.

154. Preminger GM, Sakhaee K, Skurla C, Pak CY. Prevention of recurrent calcium stone formation with potassium citrate therapy in patients with distal renal tubular acidosis. J Urol 1985;134:20–3.

155. Morris RC Jr, Sebastian A, Forman A, Tanaka M, Schmidlin O. Nor-motensive salt sensitivity: effects of race and dietary potassium. Hypertension 1999;33:18–23.

156. Sharma AM, Kribben A, Schattenfroh S, Cetto C, Distler A. Salt sensitivity in humans is associated with abnormal acid-base regulation. Hypertension 1990;16:407–13.

157. Mickleborough TD, Gotshall RW, Kluka EM, Miller CW, Cordain L. Dietary chloride as a possible determinant of the severity of exercise-induced asthma. Eur J Appl Physiol 2001;85:450–6.

158. Alpern RJ, Sakhaee S. The clinical spectrum of chronic metabolic acidosis: homeostatic mechanisms produce significant morbidity. Am J Kidney Dis 1997;29:291–302.

159. Cordain L. The nutritional characteristics of a contemporary diet based upon Paleolithic food groups. J Am Neutraceutical Assoc 2002;5:15–24.

160. Antonios TF, MacGregor GA. Salt—more adverse effects. Lancet 1996;348:250–1.

161. Massey LK, Whiting SJ. Dietary salt, urinary calcium, and kidney stone risk. Nutr Rev 1995;53:131–9.

162. Devine A, Criddle RA, Dick IM, Kerr DA, Prince RL. A longitudinal study of the effect of sodium and calcium intakes on regional bone density in postmenopausal women. Am J Clin Nutr 1995;62:740–5.

163. Gotshall RW, Mickleborough TD, Cordain L. Dietary salt restriction improves pulmonary function in exercise-induced asthma. Med Sci Sports Exerc 2000;32:1815–9.

164. Miller MM. Low sodium chloride intake in the treatment of insomnia and tension states. JAMA 1945;129:262–6.

165. Lindseth G, Lindseth PD. The relationship of diet to airsickness. Aviat Space Environ Med 1995;66:537–41.

166. Porcelli MJ, Gugelchuk GM. A trek to the top: a review of acute mountain sickness. J Am Osteopath Assoc 1995;95:718–20.

167. Thai-Van H, Bounaix MJ, Fraysse B. Meniere's disease: pathophysiology and treatment. Drugs 2001;61:1089–102.

168. Jansson B. Geographic cancer risk and intracellular potassium/sodium ratios. Cancer Detect Prev 1986;9:171–94.

169. Tuyns AJ. Salt and gastrointestinal cancer. Nutr Cancer 1988;11: 229–32.

170. Carey OJ, Locke C, Cookson JB. Effect of alterations of dietary sodium on the severity of asthma in men. Thorax 1993;48:714–8.

171. Anderson JW, Smith BM, Gustafson NJ. Health benefits and practical aspects of high-fiber diets. Am J Clin Nutr 1994;59(suppl):1242S–7S.

172. Trowell H. Dietary fiber: a paradigm. In: Trowell H, Burkitt D, Heaton K, Doll R, eds. Dietary fibre, fibre-depleted foods and disease. New York: Academic Press, 1985:1–20.

Study Questions

1. What distinguishes the skeletons of *Homo sapiens* from those of earlier hominins?

2. What is the pattern in the geographic distribution of *Homo sapiens* from its first appearance to its dispersal throughout the world?

3. What are the behavioral changes seen with the earliest *Homo sapiens*, and where and when did they first appear?

4. How do the diet and activity patterns of modern western people differ from those of our forager ancestors, and what are the health implications of these differences?

CPSIA information can be obtained at www.ICGtesting.com
Printed in the USA
LVOW11s0045130114

368818LV00006B/5/P